D1282382

Primer for White Folks

Primer for White Folks

EDITED BY

BUCKLIN MOON

Doubleday, Doran and Co., Inc.

GARDEN CITY, NEW YORK 1945

PRINTED IN THE UNITED STATES
AT
THE COUNTRY LIFE PRESS, GARDEN CITY, N. Y.
FIRST EDITION

For Bets

Acknowledgments

THANKS ARE DUE the following authors, agents, periodicals, and publishers for permission to reprint the selections indicated:

Accent—for "He Don't Plant Cotton," by J. F. Powers, with special permission from the author.

Will W. Alexander—for his article "Our Conflicting Racial Policies," from the January 1945 issue of *Harper's*.

Earl Brown—for his article "The Truth About the Detroit Riot," from the November 1943 issue of *Harper's*.

Common Ground—for "What Shall We Do About the South?" by Langston Hughes; "Democracy Is for the Unafraid," by Chester B. Himes; "The Flying Africans," by Kenneth Porter; and "The South Needs Help," by Thomas Sancton.

Curtis Brown, Ltd.—for "A Short Wait between Trains," from *A Short Wait between Trains,* by Robert McLaughlin, copyright, 1944, reprinted by permission of the author and *The New Yorker*.

Doubleday, Doran & Company, Inc.—for "Little White Girl," from *The Making of a Lady,* copyright, 1931, by Sara Haardt; and "The *Amistad* Mutiny," from *Willard Gibbs,* by Muriel Rukeyser, copyright, 1942.

Duell, Sloan & Pearce, Inc.—for "The People vs. Abe Lathan, Colored," from *Jackpot,* by Erskine Caldwell.

L. B. Fischer Publishing Corp.—for "Trouble Keeping Quiet," by Leonard Wallace Robinson, from *Cross Section,* edited by Edwin Seaver, with special permission from Mr. Robinson.

Fortune—for "The Negro's War," from the June 1942 issue, copyright, *Time,* Inc.

Margaret Halsey—for her article "Memorandum to Junior Hostesses."

Harcourt, Brace and Company, Inc.—for "White as Snow," from *The White Horses of Vienna,* by Kay Boyle, copyright, 1936, with permission from Ann Watkins, Inc.; and "Runagate Niggers," by William March, copyright, 1938, from *Trial Balance*.

Harper & Brothers—for "The Ethics of Living Jim Crow," from *Uncle Tom's Children,* copyright, 1937, by Richard Wright; and "Let My People Go," from *Let My People Go,* copyright, 1941, by Henrietta Buckmaster.

Hastings House—for "Slave No More," from *The Negro in Virginia,* by the Writer's Project of Virginia.

Alfred A. Knopf, Inc.—for "Slave on the Block," from *Ways of White Folks,* by Langston Hughes.

Little, Brown & Company—for "The Negro Problem: A Case History," from *Brothers Under the Skin,* by Carey McWilliams, special permission from Maxim Lieber.

Andrew Lytle—for his story "Mister McGregor," from the *Virginia Quarterly Review.*

The *New Republic*—for "The Negro: His Future in America," by the Editors of the *New Republic;* "The Revolt of the Evil Fairies," by Ted Poston, special permission from the author; and "Addressed to White Liberals," by Lillian Smith, special permission from the author.

The New Yorker—for "The Test," by Angelica Gibbs, copyright, 1940, The F-R. Publishing Corporation; "After You, My Dear Alphonse," by Shirley Jackson, copyright, 1943, The F-R. Publishing Corporation; and "The Touchin' Case of Mr. and Mrs. Massa," by St. Clair McKelway.

Opportunity—for "Color Trouble," by Harold Garfinkel; and "—Neber Said a Mumblin' Word," by Vernon Loggins.

Oxford University Press—for "African Culture," from *The Negro,* by W. E. B. DuBois.

PM—for "Report from England," by Roi Ottley, copyright, 1944, the Newspaper *PM,* Inc.

Public Affairs Committee, Inc.—for "The Races of Mankind," by Ruth Benedict and Gene Weltfish.

Simon and Schuster, Inc.—for "White on Black," from *Time the Present,* by Tess Slesinger.

University of North Carolina Press—for "Count Us In," by Sterling A. Brown, from *What the Negro Wants,* by Rayford W. Logan.

The Vanguard Press—for "For White Men Only," from *The Short Stories of James T. Farrell,* copyright, 1935, 1937, by Vanguard Press, Inc.

The Viking Press, Inc.—for "Arrangement in Black and White," from *The Portable Dorothy Parker,* copyright, 1930, 1944, by Dorothy Parker.

Robert C. Weaver—for his article, "The Negro Comes of Age in Industry," with special permission from the *Atlantic Monthly*.

The Estate of Wendell Willkie—for "Citizens of Negro Blood," by Wendell Willkie, with special permission from *Collier's*.

Robert C. Weaver—for his article, "The Negro Comes of Age in Industry," with special permission from the *Atlantic Monthly*.

The Estate of Wendell Willkie—for "Citizens of Negro Blood," by Wendell Willkie, with special permission from *Collier's*.

Preface

Primer for White Folks was conceived, not as a book for the expert in race relations, but rather for the average American who is disturbed by the rising racial tension which he feels around him and by the paradox of white and Negro relationships in a democracy waging a war of liberation and equality. In so far as space permits, it is an attempt to present a general picture of the Negro—his backgrounds, his relationship with whites, his everyday denial of first-class citizenship, and what he really wants in American life.

To do this it is necessary to shatter some of white America's most popular ideas about the Negro. Why such misconceptions sprung up is easily explained, for most of our race thinking over the last half century has been conditioned by the misguided theory that because the South had a larger colored population than the North, Southerners understood the Negro and knew best how to deal with him. Actually most white Southerners do not know the Negro, but only what the Negro feels the white South wants him to be. Thus, if we accept the role instead of flesh and blood, it is understandable how, over a period of years, a legend was born and became an integral part of our thinking, both North and South. Through the written word, the stage, and the radio we have so often seen the Negro presented as a stereotype that when he forsakes his role we no longer recognize him. He has ceased to be the Negro; he has become something else—a hoodlum, a communist, or an agitator—not only a danger to the white world but, in our minds, to his own as well. This book is an attempt to look beyond the stereotype and the legend.

The Emancipation Proclamation and the Thirteenth, Fourteenth, and Fifteenth Amendments to the Constitution, which were intended as a bill of rights for the Negro, have for some time been meaningless in the South and often in parts of the North as well. The gradualism which the white South promised would be a remedy has in no sense been a solution, for as the Negro has progressed through the years, so has the white South, and to speak of Negro gains alone is misleading. Today race relations in the South resemble an irresistible force rushing toward an immovable object. The white South boasts that it will fight, if necessary, to retain the status quo; the Negro, both North and South, is pledged to a program of action, and none of his leaders can caution him to abandon this strategy and still remain a leader. This is not the fault of the New Deal, the labor unions, agitators from the North, the Negro press, or this war. It has been growing for years, and our attempts to hold it back have only increased its tempo.

So, if the usual point of view of the South is absent from this book, the oversight is not without purpose, though many of the contributors are white Southerners. The South is slowly changing and there are forces at work in that region which furnish a rallying point for progressive action, channeling into one front what were formerly scattered islands of protest. Some Southerners are waging a continued fight against the poll tax, peonage, reaction, ignorance, and against the fear of race which has kept the white man in the South on a low plane because it was necessary to do so in order to keep the Negro one step lower. But they are still in the minority.

It is obvious that out of this war must come a new status for the Negro or what we are fighting for is mockery. Is there really a Negro problem or is it, as Lillian Smith recently suggested before the Herald Tribune Forum in New York City, actually a white problem? For eighty years we have tried to figure out why the Negro is a problem, yet after all our surveys, books, and research, there are no scientific findings to prove that he is one. Segregation is a costly experiment. We know what it has cost the Negro; it is time to figure out what it has cost us and how much longer we can afford the luxury.

I would like to add a word of appreciation to the many people who have helped me with invaluable suggestions in the selection of the material contained in this anthology. To John Woodburn, for several of the short stories in Part II, and to Sterling Brown, for the evenings we spent talking over the direction this project should take, I owe more than thanks. I am also deeply grateful to Henrietta Buckmaster, Tom Sancton, Dr. L. D. Reddick, curator of the Schomburg Collection at the 137th Street Branch of the New York Public Library, Arna Bontemps, librarian at Fisk University, Henry Lee Moon, and the many others who listened patiently and, when they had a chance, got a word in edgewise.

BUCKLIN MOON

March 20, 1945

Contents

Part I

HERITAGE

Part II

BLACK AND WHITE MORES

PART III

TODAY AND TOMORROW

Primer for White Folks

PART I

Heritage

AFRICAN CULTURE

W. E. B. DuBois

W. E. B. DuBois was born in Massachusetts, educated at Harvard, and until his recent retirement taught at Atlanta University. His better-known books include Dark Princess, Black Reconstruction, Black Folks: Then and Now, *and* Dusk at Dawn.

THAT Negro peoples were the beginners of civilization along the Ganges, the Euphrates, and the Nile seems proven. Early Babylon was founded by a Negroid race. Hammurabi's code, the most ancient known, says "Anna and Bel called me, Hammurabi the exalted prince, the worshiper of the gods; to cause justice to prevail in the land, to destroy the wicked, to prevent the strong from oppressing the weak, to go forth like the sun over the black-head race, to enlighten the land, and to further the welfare of the people." The Assyrians show a distinct Negroid strain, and early Egypt was predominantly Negro. These earliest of cultures were crude and primitive, but they represented the highest attainment of mankind after tens of thousands of years in unawakened savagery.

It has often been assumed that the Negro is physically inferior to other races and markedly distinguishable from them; modern science gives no authority for such an assumption. The supposed inferiority cannot rest on color,[1] for that is "due to the combined influences of a great num-

[1] "Some authors write that the Ethiopians paint the devil white, in disdain of our complexions."—Ludolf: *History of Ethiopia,* p. 72.

ber of factors of environment working through physiological processes," and "however marked the contrasts may be, there is no corresponding difference in anatomical structure discoverable."[2] So, too, difference in texture of hair is a matter of degree, not kind, and is caused by heat, moisture, exposure, and the like.

The bony skeleton presents no distinctly racial lines of variation. Prognathism "presents too many individual varieties to be taken as a distinctive character of race."[3] Difference in physical measurements does not show the Negro to be a more primitive evolutionary form. Comparative ethnology today affords "no support to the view which sees in the so-called lower races of mankind a transition stage from beast to man."[4]

Much has been made of the supposed smaller brain of the Negro race; but this is as yet on unproved assumption, based on the uncritical measurement of less than a thousand Negro brains as compared with eleven thousand or more European brains. Even if future measurements prove the average Negro brain lighter, the vast majority of Negro brain weights fall within the same limits as the whites; and finally, "neither size nor weight of the brain seems to be of importance" as an index of mental capacity. We may, therefore, say with Ratzel, "There is only one species of man. The variations are numerous, but do not go deep."[5]

To this we may add the word of the secretary of the First Races Congress: "We are, then, under the necessity of concluding that an impartial investigator would be inclined to look upon the various important peoples of the world as to all intents and purposes essentially equal in intellect, enterprise, morality, and physique."[6]

If these conclusions are true, we should expect to see in Africa the human drama play itself out much as in other lands, and such has actually been the fact. At the same time we must expect peculiarities arising from the physiography of the land—its climate, its rainfall, its deserts, and the peculiar inaccessibility of the coast.

Three principal zones of habitation appear: first, the steppes and deserts around the Sahara in the north and the Kalahari Desert in the south; secondly, the grassy highlands bordering the Great Lakes and connecting these two regions; thirdly, the forests and rivers of Central and West Africa. In the deserts are the nomads, and the Pygmies are

[2]Ripley: *Races of Europe*, pp. 58, 62.

[3]Denniker: *Races of Men*, p. 63.

[4]G. Finot: *Race Prejudice*. F. Herz: *Moderne Rassentheorien.*

[5]Ratzel: quoted in Spiller: *Inter-Racial Problems*, p. 31.

[6]Spiller: *Inter-Racial Problems*, p. 35.

in the forest fastnesses. Herdsmen and their cattle cover the steppes and highlands, save where the tsetse fly prevents. In the open forests and grassy highlands are the agriculturists.

Among the forest farmers the village is the center of life, while in the open steppes political life tends to spread into larger political units. Political integration is, however, hindered by an ease of internal communication almost as great as the difficulty of reaching outer worlds beyond the continent. The narrow Nile Valley alone presented physical barriers formidable enough to keep back the invading barbarians of the south, and even then with difficulty. Elsewhere communication was all too easy. For a while the Congo forests fended away the restless, but this only temporarily.

On the whole, Africa from the Sahara to the Cape offered no great physical barrier to the invader, and we continually have whirlwinds of invading hosts rushing now southward, now northward, from the interior to the coast and from the coast inland, and hurling their force against states, kingdoms, and cities. Some resisted for generations, some for centuries, some but a few years. It is, then, this sudden change and the fear of it that marks African culture, particularly in its political aspects, and which makes it so difficult to trace this changing past. Nevertheless beneath all change rests the strong substructure of custom, religion, industry, and art well worth the attention of students.

Starting with agriculture, we learn that "among all the great groups of the 'natural' races, the Negroes are the best and keenest tillers of the ground. A minority despise agriculture and breed cattle; many combine both occupations. Among the genuine tillers the whole life of the family is taken up in agriculture, and hence the months are by preference called after the operations which they demand. Constant clearings change forests to fields, and the ground is manured with the ashes of the burnt thicket. In the middle of the fields rise the light watchtowers, from which a watchman scares grain-eating birds and other thieves. An African cultivated landscape is incomplete without barns. The rapidity with which, when newly imported, the most various forms of cultivation spread in Africa says much for the attention which is devoted to this branch of economy. Industries, again, which may be called agricultural, like the preparation of meal from millet and other crops, also from cassava, the fabrication of fermented drinks from grain, or the manufacture of cotton, are widely known and sedulously fostered."[7]

Bücher reminds us of the deep impression made upon travelers when

[7]Ratzel: *History of Mankind,* II, 380 ff.

they sight suddenly the well-attended fields of the natives on emerging from the primeval forests. "In the more thickly populated parts of Africa these fields often stretch for many a mile, and the assiduous care of the Negro women shines in all the brighter light when we consider the insecurity of life, the constant feuds and pillages, in which no one knows whether he will in the end be able to harvest what he has sown. Livingstone gives somewhere a graphic description of the devastations wrought by slave hunts; the people were lying about slain, the dwellings were demolished; in the fields, however, the grain was ripening and there was none to harvest it."[8]

Sheep, goats, and chickens are domestic animals all over Africa, and Von Franzius considers Africa the home of the house cattle and the Negro as the original tamer. Northeastern Africa especially is noted for agriculture, cattle raising, and fruit culture. In the eastern Sudan, and among the great Bantu tribes extending from the Sudan down toward the south, cattle are evidences of wealth; one tribe, for instance, having so many oxen that each village had ten or twelve thousand head. Lenz (1884), Bouet-Williaumez (1848), Hecquard (1854), Bosman (1805), and Baker (1868) all bear witness to this, and Schweinfurth (1878) tells us of great cattle parks with two to three thousand head and of numerous agricultural and cattle-raising tribes. Von der Decken (1859–61) described the paradise of the dwellers about Kilimanjaro—the bananas, fruit, beans and peas, cattle raising with stall feed, the fertilizing of the fields, and irrigation. The Negroid Gallas have seven or eight cattle to each inhabitant. Livingstone bears witness to the busy cattle raising of the Bantus and Kaffirs. Hulub (1881) and Chapman (1868) tell of agriculture and fruit raising in South Africa. Shutt (1884) found the tribes in the southwestern basin of the Congo with sheep, swine, goats, and cattle. On this agricultural and cattle-raising economic foundation has arisen the organized industry of the artisan, the trader, and the manufacturer.

While the Pygmies, still living in the age of wood, make no iron or stone implements, they seem to know how to make bark cloth and fiber baskets and simple outfits for hunting and fishing. Among the Bushmen the art of making weapons and working in hides is quite common. The Hottentots are further advanced in the industrial arts, being well versed in the manufacture of clothing, weapons, and utensils. In the dressing of skins and furs, as well as in the plaiting of cords and the weaving of mats, we find evidences of their workmanship. In addition they are good workers in iron and copper, using the sheepskin bellows for this purpose.

[8] *Industrial Evolution*, p. 47.

The Ashantis of the Gold Coast know how to make "cotton fabrics, turn and glaze earthenware, forge iron, fabricate instruments and arms, embroider rugs and carpets, and set gold and precious stones."[9] Among the people of the banana zone we find rough basketwork, coarse pottery, grass cloth, and spoons made of wood and ivory. The people of the millet zone, because of uncertain agricultural resources, quite generally turn to manufacturing. Charcoal is prepared by the smiths, iron is smelted, and numerous implements are manufactured. Among them we find axes, hatchets, hoes, knives, nails, scythes, and other hardware. Cloaks, shoes, sandals, shields, and water and oil vessels are made from leather which the natives have dressed. Soap is manufactured in the Bautschi district, glass is made, formed, and colored by the people of Nupeland, and in almost every city cotton is spun and woven and dyed. Barth tells us that the weaving of cotton was known in the Sudan as early as the eleventh century. There is also extensive manufacture of woodenware, tools, implements, and utensils.

In describing particular tribes, Baker and Felkin tell of smiths of wonderful adroitness, goatskins prepared better than a European tanner could do, drinking cups and kegs of remarkable symmetry, and polished clay floors. Schweinfurth says, "The arrow and the spear heads are of the finest and most artistic work; their bristlelike barbs and points are baffling when one knows how few tools these smiths have." Excellent wood carving is found among the Bongo, Ovambo, and Makololo. Pottery and basketry and careful hut building distinguish many tribes. Cameron (1877) tells of villages so clean, with huts so artistic, that, save in book knowledge, the people occupied no low plane of civilization. The Mangbettu work both iron and copper. "The masterpieces of the Monbutto [Mangbettu] smiths are the fine chains worn as ornaments, and which in perfection of form and fineness compare well with our best steel chains." Shubotz in 1911 called the Mangbettu "a highly cultivated people" in architecture and handicraft. Barth found copper exported from Central Africa in competition with European copper at Kano.

Nor is the iron industry confined to the Sudan. About the Great Lakes and other parts of Central Africa it is widely distributed. Thornton says, "This iron industry proves that the East Africans stand by no means on so low a plane of culture as many travelers would have us think. It is unnecessary to be reminded what a people without instruction, and with the rudest tools to do such skilled work, could do if furnished with steel

[9]These and other references in this chapter are from Schneider: *Cultur-fähigkeit des Negers.*

tools." Arrows made east of Lake Nyanza were found to be nearly as good as the best Swedish iron in Birmingham. From Egypt to the Cape, Livingstone assures us that the mortar and pestle, the long-handled ax, the goatskin bellows, etc., have the same form, size, etc., pointing to a migration southwestward. Holub (1879), on the Zambesi, found fine workers in iron and bronze. The Bantu huts contain spoons, wooden dishes, milk pails, calabashes, hand mills, and axes.

Kaffirs and Zulus, in the extreme south, are good smiths, and the latter melt copper and tin together and draw wire from it, according to Kranz (1880). West of the Great Lakes, Stanley (1878) found wonderful examples of smithwork: figures worked out of brass and much work in copper. Cameron (1878) saw vases made near Lake Tanganyika which reminded him of the amphoræ in the Villa of Diomedes, Pompeii. Horn (1882) praises tribes here for iron and copper work. Livingstone (1871) passed thirty smelting houses in one journey, and Cameron came across bellows with valves, and tribes who used knives in eating. He found tribes which no Europeans had ever visited, who made ingots of copper in the form of the St. Andrew's cross, which circulated even to the coast. In the southern Congo basin iron and copper are worked; also wood and ivory carving and pottery making are pursued. In equatorial West Africa, Lenz and Du Chaillu (1861) found ironworkers with charcoal, and also carvers of bone and ivory. Near Cape Lopez, Hübbe-Schleiden found tribes making ivory needles inlaid with ebony, while the arms and dishes of the Osaka are found among many tribes even as far as the Atlantic Ocean. Wilson (1856) found natives in West Africa who could repair American watches.

Gold Coast Negroes make gold rings and chains, forming the metal into all kinds of forms. Soyaux says, "The works in relief which natives of Lower Guinea carve with their own knives out of ivory and hippopotamus teeth are really entitled to be called works of art, and many wooden figures of fetishes in the Ethnographical Museum of Berlin show some understanding of the proportions of the human body." Great Bassam is called by Hecquard the "Fatherland of Smiths." The Mandingo in the northwest are remarkable workers in iron, silver, and gold, we are told by Mungo Park (1800), while there is a mass of testimony as to the work in the northwest of Africa in gold, tin, weaving, and dyeing. Caille found the Negroes in Bambana manufacturing gunpowder (1824–28), and the Hausa make soap; so, too, Negroes in Uganda and other parts have made guns after seeing European models.

So marked has been the work of Negro artisans and traders in the manufacture and exchange of iron implements that a growing number of archeologists are disposed today to consider the Negro as the originator of the art of smelting iron. Gabriel de Mortillet (1883) declared Negroes the only iron users among primitive people. Some would, therefore, argue that the Negro learned it from other folk, but Andree declares that the Negro developed his own "Iron Kingdom." Schweinfurth, Von Luschan, Boaz, and others incline to the belief that the Negroes invented the smelting of iron and passed it on to the Egyptians and to modern Europe.

Boaz says, "It seems likely that at a time when the European was still satisfied with rude stone tools, the African had invented or adopted the art of smelting iron. Consider for a moment what this invention has meant for the advance of the human race. As long as the hammer, knife, saw, drill, the spade, and the hoe had to be chipped out of stone, or had to be made of shell or hard wood, effective industrial work was not impossible, but difficult. A great progress was made when copper found in large nuggets was hammered out into tools and later on shaped by melting, and when bronze was introduced; but the true advancement of industrial life did not begin until the hard iron was discovered. It seems not unlikely that the people who made the marvelous discovery of reducing iron ores by smelting were the African Negroes. Neither ancient Europe, nor ancient western Asia, nor ancient China knew iron, and everything points to its introduction from Africa. At the time of the great African discoveries toward the end of the past century, the trade of the blacksmith was found all over Africa, from north to south and from east to west. With his simple bellows and a charcoal fire he reduced the ore that is found in many parts of the continent and forged implements of great usefulness and beauty."[10]

Torday has argued recently, "I feel convinced by certain arguments that seem to prove to my satisfaction that we are indebted to the Negro for the very keystone of our modern civilization and that we owe him the discovery of iron. That iron could be discovered by accident in Africa seems beyond doubt: if this is so in other parts of the world, I am not competent to say. I will only remind you that Schweinfurth and Petherick record the fact that in the northern part of East Africa smelting furnaces are worked without artificial air current and, on the other hand, Stuhlmann and Kollmann found near Victoria Nyanza that the natives simply mixed powdered ore with charcoal and by introduction of air currents obtained the metal. These simple processes make it simple that iron

[10] Atlanta University Leaflet, No. 19.

should have been discovered in East or Central Africa. No bronze implements have ever been found in black Africa; had the Africans received iron from the Egyptians, bronze would have preceded this metal and all traces of it would not have disappeared. Black Africa was for a long time an exporter of iron, and even in the twelfth century exports to India and Java are recorded by Idrisi.

"It is difficult to imagine that Egypt should have obtained it from Europe, where the oldest find (in Hallstadt) cannot be of an earlier period than 800 B.C., or from Asia, where iron is not known before 1000 B.C., and where, in the times of Ashur Nazir Pal, it was still used concurrently with bronze, while iron beads have been only recently discovered by Messrs. G. A. Wainwright and Bushe Fox in a predynastic grave, and where a piece of this metal, possibly a tool, was found in the masonry of the great pyramid."[11]

The Negro is a born trader. Lenz says, "Our sharpest European merchants, even Jews and Armenians, can learn much of the cunning and trade of the Negroes." We know that the trade between Central Africa and Egypt was in the hands of Negroes for thousands of years, and in early days the cities of the Sudan and North Africa grew rich through Negro trade.

Leo Africanus, writing of Timbuktu in the sixteenth century, said, "It is a wonder to see what plentie of Merchandize is daily brought hither and how costly and sumptuous all things be. . . . Here are many shops of artificers and merchants and especially of such as weave linnen and cloth."

Long before cotton weaving was a British industry, West Africa and the Sudan were supplying a large part of the world with cotton cloth. Even today cities like Kuka on the west shore of Lake Chad and Sokota are manufacturing centers where cotton is spun and woven, skins tanned, implements and iron ornaments made.

"Travelers," says Bücher, "have often observed this tribal or local development of industrial technique. 'The native villages,' relates a Belgian observer of the Lower Congo, 'are often situated in groups. Their activities are based upon reciprocality, and they are to a certain extent the complements of one another. Each group has its more or less strongly defined specialty. One carries on fishing; another produces palm wine; a third devotes itself to trade and is broker for the others, supplying the community with all products from outside; another has reserved to itself

[11] *Journal of the Royal Anthropological Institute*, XLIII, 414, 415. Cf. also *The Crisis*, Vol. IX, p. 234.

work in iron and copper, making weapons for war and hunting, various utensils, etc. None may, however, pass beyond the sphere of its own specialty without exposing itself to the risk of being universally proscribed.' "

From the Loango coast, Bastian tells of a great number of centers for special products of domestic industry. "Loango excels in mats and fishing baskets, while the carving of elephants' tusks is specially followed in Chilungo. The so-called Mafooka hats with raised patterns are drawn chiefly from the bordering country of Kakongo and Mayyume. In Bakunya are made potter's wares, which are in great demand; in Basanza, excellent swords; in Basundi, especially beautiful ornamented copper rings; on the Congo, clever wood and tablet carvings; in Loango, ornamented clothes and intricately designed mats; in Mayumbe, clothing of finely woven mat work; in Kakongo, embroidered hats and also burnt-clay pitchers; and among the Bayakas and Mantetjes, stuffs of woven grass."[12]

A native Negro student tells of the development of trade among the Ashanti. "It was a part of the state system of Ashanti to encourage trade. The king once in every forty days, of the Adai custom, distributed among a number of chiefs various sums of gold dust with a charge to turn the same to good account. These chiefs then sent down to the coast caravans of tradesmen, some of whom would be their slaves, sometimes some two or three hundred strong, to barter ivory for European goods, or buy such goods with gold dust, which the king obtained from the royal alluvial workings. Down to 1873 a constant stream of Ashanti traders might be seen daily wending their way to the merchants of the coast and back again, yielding more certain wealth and prosperity to the merchants of the Gold Coast and Great Britain than may be expected for some time yet to come from the mining industry and railway development put together. The trade chiefs would, in due time, render a faithful account to the king's stewards, being allowed to retain a fair portion of the profit. In the king's household, too, he would have special men who directly traded for him. Important chiefs carried on the same system of trading with the coast as did the king. Thus every member of the state, from the king downward, took an active interest in the promotion of trade and in the keeping open of trade routes into the interior."[13]

The trade, thus encouraged and carried on in various parts of West Africa, reached wide areas. From the Fish River to Kuka, and from Lagos

[12]Bücher: *Industrial Revolution* (tr. by Wickett), pp. 57–58.

[13]Hayford: *Native Institutions*, pp. 95–96.

to Zanzibar, the markets have become great centers of trade, the leading implement to civilization. Permanent markets are found in places like Ujiji and Nyangwe, where everything can be bought and sold from earthenware to wives; from the one to three thousand traders flocked here.

"How like is the market traffic, with all its uproar and sound of human voices, to one of our own markets! There is the same rivalry in praising the goods, the violent, brisk movements, the expressive gesture, the inquiring, searching glance, the changing looks of depreciation or triumph, of apprehension, delight, approbation. So says Stanley. Trade customs are not everywhere alike. If when negotiating with the Bangalas of Angola you do not quickly give them what they want, they go away and do not come back. Then perhaps they try to get possession of the coveted object by means of theft. It is otherwise with the Songos and Kiokos, who let you deal with them in the usual way. To buy even a small article you must go to the market; people avoid trading anywhere else. If a man says to another, 'Sell me this hen' or 'that fruit,' the answer as a rule will be, 'Come to the market place.' The crowd gives confidence to individuals, and the inviolability of the visitor to the market, and of the market itself, looks like an idea of justice consecrated by long practice. Does not this remind us of the old Germanic 'market place'?"[14]

Turning now to Negro family and social life, we find, as among all primitive peoples, polygamy and marriage by actual or simulated purchase. Out of the family develops the typical African village organization, which is thus described in Ashanti by a native Gold Coast writer: "The headman, as his name implies, is the head of a village community, a ward in a township, or of a family. His position is important, inasmuch as he has directly to deal with the composite elements of the general bulk of the people.

"It is the duty of the head of a family to bring up the members thereof in the way they should go; and by 'family' you must understand the entire lineal descendants of a materfamilias, if I may coin a convenient phrase. It is expected of him by the state to bring up his charge in the knowledge of matters political and traditional. It is his work to train up his wards in the ways of loyalty and obedience to the powers that be. He is held responsible for the freaks of recalcitrant members of his family, and he is looked to to keep them within bounds and to insist upon conformity of their party with the customs, laws, and traditional observances of the community. In early times he could send off to

[14] Ratzel, II, 376.

exile by sale a troublesome relative who would not observe the laws of the community.

"It is a difficult task that he is set to, but in this matter he has all-powerful helpers in the female members of the family, who will be either the aunts, or the sisters, or the cousins, or the nieces of the headman; and as their interests are identical with his in every particular, the good women spontaneously train up their children to implicit obedience to the headman, whose rule in the family thus becomes a simple and an easy matter. 'The hand that rocks the cradle rules the world.' What a power for good in the native state system would the mothers of the Gold Coast and Ashanti become by judicious training upon native lines!

"The headman is par excellence the judge of his family or ward. Not only is he called upon to settle domestic squabbles, but frequently he sits judge over more serious matters arising between one member of the ward and another; and where he is a man of ability and influence, men from other wards bring him their disputes to settle. When he so settles disputes, he is entitled to a hearing fee, which, however, is not so much as would be payable in the regular court of the king or chief.

"The headman is naturally an important member of his company and often is a captain thereof. When he combines the two offices of headman and captain, he renders to the community a very important service. For in times of war, where the members of the ward would not serve cordially under a stranger, they would in all cases face any danger with their own kinsman as their leader. The headman is always succeeded by his uterine brother, cousin, or nephew—the line of succession, that is to say, following the customary law."[15]

We may contrast this picture with the more warlike Bantus of Southeast Africa. Each tribe lived by itself in a town with from five to fifteen thousand inhabitants, surrounded by gardens of millet, beans, and watermelon. Beyond these roamed their cattle, sheep, and goats. Their religion was ancestor worship with sacrifice to spirits and the dead, and some of the tribes made mummies of the corpses and clothed them for burial. They wove cloth of cotton and bark, they carved wood and built walls of unhewn stone. They had a standing military organization, and the tribes had their various totems, so that they were known as the Men of Iron, the Men of the Sun, the Men of the Serpents, Sons of the Corn Cleaners, and the like. Their system of common law was well conceived and there were organized tribunals of justice. In difficult cases precedents were sought and learned antiquaries consulted. At the age of fifteen or

[15]Hayford: *Native Institutions*, pp. 76 ff.

sixteen the boys were circumcised and formed into guilds. The land was owned by the tribe and apportioned to the chief by each family, and the main wealth of the tribe was in its cattle.

In general, among the African clans the idea of private property was but imperfectly developed and never included land. The main mass of visible wealth belonged to the family and clan rather than to the individual; only in the matter of weapons and ornaments was exclusive private ownership generally recognized.

The government, vested in fathers and chiefs, varied in different tribes from absolute despotisms to limited monarchies, almost republican. Viewing the Basuto National Assembly in South Africa, Lord Bryce recently wrote, "The resemblance to the primary assemblies of the early peoples of Europe is close enough to add another to the arguments which discredit the theory that there is any such thing as an Aryan type of institution."[16]

While women are sold into marriage throughout Africa, nevertheless their status is far removed from slavery. In the first place the tracing of relationships through the female line, which is all but universal in Africa, gives the mother great influence. Parental affection is very strong, and throughout Negro Africa the mother is the most influential councilor, even in cases of tyrants like Chaka or Mutesa.

"No mother can love more tenderly or be more deeply beloved than the Negro mother. Robin tells of a slave in Martinique who, with his savings, freed his mother instead of himself. 'Everywhere in Africa,' writes Mungo Park, 'I have noticed that no greater affront can be offered a Negro than insulting his mother. "Strike me," cried a Mandingo to his enemy, "but revile not my mother!" . . . The Herero swears "By my mother's tears!" . . . The Angola Negroes have a saying, "As a mist lingers on the swamps, so lingers the love of father and mother." ' "[17]

Black queens have often ruled African tribes. Among the Ba-Lolo, we are told, women take part in public assemblies where all-important questions are discussed. The system of educating children among such tribes as the Yoruba is worthy of emulation by many more civilized peoples.

Close knit with the family and social organization comes the religious life of the Negro. The religion of Africa is the universal animism or fetishism of primitive peoples, rising to polytheism and approaching monotheism chiefly, but not wholly, as a result of Christian and Islamic missions. Of fetishism there is much misapprehension. It is not mere

[16] *Impressions of South Africa,* 3d ed., p. 352.

[17] William Schneider.

senseless degredation. It is a philosophy of life. Among primitive Negroes there can be, as Miss Kingsley reminds us, no such divorce of religion from practical life as is common in civilized lands. Religion is life, and fetish an expression of the practical recognition of dominant forces in which the Negro lives. To him all the world is spirit. Miss Kingsley says, "If you want, for example, to understand the position of man in nature according to fetish, there is, as far as I know, no clearer statement of it made than is made by Goethe in his superb 'Prometheus.' "[18] Fetish is a severely logical way of accounting for the world in terms of good and malignant spirits.

"It is this power of being able logically to account for everything that is, I believe, at the back of the tremendous permanency of fetish in Africa, and the cause of many of the relapses into it by Africans converted to other religions; it is also the explanation of the fact that white men who live in the districts where death and danger are everyday affairs, under a grim pall of boredom, are liable to believe in fetish, though ashamed of so doing. For the African, whose mind has been soaked in fetish during his early and most impressionable years, the voice of fetish is almost irresistible when affliction comes to him."[19]

Ellis tells us of the spirit belief of the Ewe people, who believe that men and all nature have the indwelling "Kra," which is immortal; that the man himself after death may exist as a ghost, which is often conceived of as departed from the "Kra," a shadowy continuing of the man. Bryce, speaking of the Kaffirs of South Africa, says, "To the Kaffirs, as to the most savage races, the world was full of spirits—spirits of the rivers, the mountains, and the woods. Most important were the ghosts of the dead, who had power to injure or help the living, and who were, therefore, propitiated by offerings at stated periods, as well as on occasions when their aid was especially desired. This kind of worship, the worship once most generally diffused throughout the world, and which held its ground among the Greeks and Italians in the most flourishing period of ancient civilization, as it does in China and Japan today, was, and is, virtually the religion of the Kaffirs."[20]

African religion does not, however, stop with fetish, but, as in the case of other peoples, tends toward polytheism and monotheism. Among the Yoruba, for instance, Frobenius shows that religion and city-state go hand in hand.

[18]*West African Studies,* Chap. V.

[19]*Op. cit.*

[20]*Impressions of South Africa.*

"The first experienced glance will here detect the fact that this nation originally possessed a clear and definite organization so duly ordered and so logical that we but seldom meet with its like among all the peoples of the earth. And the basic idea of every clan's progeniture is a powerful God; the legitimate order in which the descendants of a particular clan unite in marriage to found new families, the essential origin of every new-born babe's descent in the founder of its race and its consideration as a part of the God in Chief; the security with which the newly wedded wife not only may, but should, minister to her own God in an unfamiliar home."[21]

The Yoruba have a legend of a dying divinity. "This people . . . give evidence of a generalized system; a theocratic scheme, a well-conceived perceptible organization, reared in rhythmically proportioned manner."

Miss Kingsley says, "The African has a great Over God."[22] Nassau, the missionary, declares, "After more than forty years' residence among these tribes, fluently using their language, conversant with their customs, dwelling intimately in their huts, associating with them in the various relations of teacher, pastor, friend, master, fellow traveler, and guest, and in my special office as missionary, searching after their religious thought (and therefore being allowed a deeper entrance into the arcana of their soul than would be accorded to a passing explorer), I am able unhesitatingly to say that among all the multitude of degraded ones with whom I have met, I have seen or heard of none whose religious thought was only a superstition.

"Standing in the village street, surrounded by a company whom their chief has courteously summoned at my request, when I say to him, 'I have come to speak to your people,' I do not need to begin by telling them that there is a God. Looking on that motley assemblage of villagers—the bold, gaunt cannibal with his armament of gun, spear, and dagger; the artisan with rude adze in hand, or hands soiled at the antique bellows of the village smithy; women who have hasted from their kitchen fire with hands white with the manioc dough or still grasping the partly scaled fish; and children checked in their play with tiny bow and arrow or startled from their dusty street pursuit of dog or goat—I have yet to be asked, 'Who is God?' "[23]

The basis of Egyptian religion was "of a purely Nigritian character,"[24]

[21]Frobenius: *Voice of Africa,* Vol. I.

[22]*West African Studies,* p. 107.

[23]Nassau: *Fetishism in West Africa,* p. 36.

[24]Encyclopædia Britannica, 9th ed., XX, 362.

and in its developed form Sudanese tribal gods were invoked and venerated by the priests. In Upper Egypt, near the confines of Ethiopia, paintings repeatedly represent black priests conferring on red Egyptian priests the instruments and symbols of priesthood. In the Sudan today Frobenius distinguishes four principal religions: first, earthly ancestor worship; next, the social cosmogony of the Atlantic races; third, the religion of the Bori, and fourth, Islam. The Bori religion spreads from Nubia as far as the Hausa, and from Lake Chad in the Niger as far as the Yoruba. It is the religion of possession and has been connected by some with Asiatic influences.

From without have come two great religious influences, Islam and Christianity. Islam came by conquest, trade, and proselytism. As a conqueror it reached Egypt in the seventh century and had by the end of the fourteenth century firm footing in the Egyptian Sudan. It overran the central Sudan by the close of the seventeenth century and at the beginning of the nineteenth century had swept over Senegambia and the whole valley of the Niger down to the Gulf of Guinea. On the east Islam approached as a trader in the eighth century; it spread into Somaliland and overran Nubia in the fourteenth century. Today Islam dominates Africa north of ten degrees north latitude and is strong between five and ten degrees north latitude. In the east it reaches below the Victoria Nyanza.

Christianity early entered Africa; indeed, as Mommsen says, "It was through Africa that Christianity became the religion of the world. Tertullian and Cyprian were from Carthage, Arnobius from Sicca Veneria, Lactantius and, probably in like manner, Minucius Felix, in spite of their Latin names, were natives of Africa, and not less so Augustine. In Africa the Church found its most zealous confessors of the faith and its most gifted defenders."[25]

The Africa referred to here, however, was not Negroland, but Africa above the desert, where Negro blood was represented in the ancient Mediterranean race and by intercourse across the desert. On the other hand Christianity was early represented in the valley of the Nile under "the most holy pope and patriarch of the great city of Alexandria and of all of the land of Egypt, of Jerusalem, the holy city, of Nubia, Abyssinia, and Pentapolis, and all the preaching of St. Mark." This patriarchate had a hundred bishoprics in the fourth century and included thousands of black Christians. Through it the Cross preceded the Crescent in some of the remotest parts of black Africa.

[25]*The African Provinces,* II, 345.

All these beginnings were gradually overthrown by Islam except among the Copts in Egypt, and in Abyssinia. The Portuguese in the sixteenth century began to replant the Christian religion and for a while had great success, both on the east and west coasts. Roman Catholic enterprise halted in the eighteenth century and the Protestants began. Today the west coast is studded with English and German missions, South Africa is largely Christian through French and English influence, and the region about the Great Lakes is becoming christianized. The Roman Catholics have lately increased their activities, and above all the Negroes of America have entered with their own churches and with the curiously significant "Ethiopian" movement.

Coming now to other spiritual aspects of African culture, we can speak at present only in a fragmentary way. Roughly speaking, Africa can be divided into two language zones: north of the fifth degree of north latitude is the zone of diversity, with at least a hundred groups of widely divergent languages; south of the line there is one minor language (Bushman-Hottentot), spoken by less than fifty thousand people, and elsewhere the predominant Bantu tongue with its various dialects, spoken by at least fifty million. The Bantu tongue, which thus rules all Central, West, and South Africa, is an agglutinative tongue which makes especial use of prefixes. The hundreds of Negro tongues or dialects in the north represent most probably the result of war and migration and the breaking up of ancient centers of culture. In Abyssinia and the great horn of East Africa the influence of Semitic tongues is noted. Despite much effort on the part of students, it has been impossible to show any Asiatic origin for the Egyptian language. As Sergi maintains, "everything favors an African origin."[26] The most brilliant suggestion of modern days links together the Egyptian of North Africa and the Hottentot and Bushmen tongues of South Africa.

Language was reduced to writing among the Egyptians and Ethiopians and to some extent elsewhere in Africa. Over one hundred manuscripts of Ethiopian and Ethiopic-Arabian literature are extant, including a version of the Bible and historical chronicles. The Arabic was used as the written tongue of the Sudan, and Negroland has given us in this tongue many chronicles and other works of black authors. The greatest of these, the *Epic of the Sudan* (*Tarikh-es-Soudan*), deserves to be placed among the classics of all literature. In other parts of Africa there was no written language, but there was, on the other hand, an unusual perfec-

[26] *Mediterranean Race,* p. 10.

tion of oral tradition through bards, and extraordinary efficiency in telegraphy by drum and horn.

The folklore and proverbs of the African tribes are exceedingly rich. Some of these have been made familiar to English writers through the work of "Uncle Remus." Others have been collected by Johnston, Ellis, and Theal.

A black bard of our own day has described the onslaught of the Matabili in poetry of singular force and beauty:

> They saw the clouds ascend from the plains:
> It was the smoke of burning towns.
> The confusion of the whirlwind
> Was in the heart of the great chief of the blue-colored cattle.
> The shout was raised,
> "They are friends!"
> But they shouted again,
> "They are foes!"
> Till their near approach proclaimed them Matabili.
> The men seized their arms,
> And rushed out as if to chase the antelope.
> The onset was as the voice of lightning,
> And their javelins as the shaking of the forest in the autumn storm.[27]

There can be no doubt of the Negro's deep and delicate sense of beauty in form, color, and sound. Soyaux says of African industry, "Whoever denies to them independent invention and individual taste in their work either shuts his eyes intentionally before perfectly evident facts, or lack of knowledge renders him an incompetent judge."[28] M. Rutot has told us how the Negro race brought art and sculpture to prehistoric Europe. The bones of the European Negroids are almost without exception found in company with drawings and sculpture in high and low relief; some of their sculptures, like the Wellendorff "Venus," are unusually well finished for primitive man. So, too, the painting and carving of the Bushmen and their forerunners in South Africa has drawn the admiration of students. The Negro has been prolific in the invention of musical instruments and has given a new and original music to the western world.

Schweinfurth, who has preserved for us much of the industrial art of the Negroes, speaks of their delight in the production of works of art for the embellishment and convenience of life. Frobenius expressed his

[27]Stowe: *Native Races*, etc., pp. 553–54.

[28]Quoted in Schneider.

astonishment at the originality of the African in the Yoruba temple which he visited. "The lofty veranda was divided from the passageway by fantastically carved and colored pillars. On the pillars were sculptured knights, men climbing trees, women, gods, and mythical beings. The dark chamber lying beyond showed a splendid red room with stone hatchets, wooden figures, cowry beads, and jars. The whole picture, the columns carved in colors in front of the colored altar, the old man sitting in the circle of those who reverenced him, the open scaffolding of ninety rafters, made a magnificent impression."[29]

The Germans have found, in Kamarun, towns built, castellated, and fortified in a manner that reminds one of the prehistoric cities of Crete. The buildings and fortifications of Zymbabwe have already been described and something has been said of the art of Benin, with its brass and bronze and ivory. All the work of Benin in bronze and brass was executed by casting, and by methods so complicated that it would be no easy task for a modern European craftsman to imitate them.

Perhaps no race has shown in its earlier development a more magnificent art impulse than the Negro, and the student must not forget how far Negro genius entered into the art in the valley of the Nile from Meroe and Nepata down to the great temples of Egypt.

Frobenius has recently directed the world's attention to art in West Africa. Quartz and granite he found treated with great dexterity. But more magnificent than the stone monument is the proof that at some remote era glass was made and molded in Yorubaland and that the people here were brilliant in the production of terra-cotta images. The great mass of potsherds, lumps of glass, heaps of slag, etc., "proves, at all events, that the glass industry flourished in this locality in ages past. It is plain that the glass beads found to have been so very common in Africa were not only not imported, but were actually manufactured in great quantities at home."

The terra-cotta pieces are "remains of another ancient and fine type of art" and were "eloquent of a symmetry, a vitality, a delicacy of form, and practically a reminiscence of the ancient Greeks." The antique bronze head Frobenius describes as "a head of marvelous beauty, wonderfully cast," and "almost equal in beauty and, at least, no less noble in form, and as ancient as the terra-cotta heads."[30]

In a park of monuments Frobenius saw the celebrated forge and hammer: a mighty mass of iron, like a falling drop in shape, and a block of

[29]Frobenius: *Voice of Africa,* Vol. I, Chap. XIV.

[30]Frobenius: *Voice of Africa,* Vol. I.

quartz fashioned like a drum. Frobenius thinks these were relics dating from past ages of culture, when the manipulation of quartz and granite was thoroughly understood and when iron manipulation gave evidence of a skill not met with today.

Even when we contemplate such revolting survivals of savagery as cannibalism we cannot jump too quickly at conclusions. Cannibalism is spread over many parts of Negro Africa, yet the very tribes who practice cannibalism show often other traits of industry and power. "These cannibal Bassonga were, according to the types we met with, one of those rare nations of the African interior which can be classed with the most esthetic and skilled, most discreet and intelligent of all those generally known to us as the so-called natural races. Before the Arabic and European invasion they did not dwell in 'hamlets,' but in towns with twenty or thirty thousand inhabitants, in towns whose highways were shaded by avenues of splendid palms planted at regular intervals and laid out with the symmetry of colonnades. Their pottery would be fertile in suggestion to every art craftsman in Europe. Their weapons of iron were so perfectly fashioned that no industrial art from abroad could improve upon their workmanship. The iron blades were cunningly ornamented with damascened copper, and the hilts artistically inlaid with the same metal. Moreover, they were most industrious and capable husbandmen, whose careful tillage of the suburbs made them able competitors of any gardener in Europe. Their sexual and parental relations evidenced an amount of tact and delicacy of feelings unsurpassed among ourselves, either in the simplicity of the country or the refinements of the town. Originally their political and municipal system was organized on the lines of a representative republic. True, it is on record that these well-governed towns often waged an internecine warfare; but in spite of this it had been their invariable custom from time immemorial, even in times of strife, to keep the trade routes open and to allow their own and foreign merchants to go their ways unharmed. And the commerce of these nations ebbed and flowed along a road of unknown age, running from Itimbiri to Batubenge, about six hundred miles in length. This highway was destroyed by the 'missionaries of civilization' from Arabia only toward the close of the eighteenth century. But even in my own time there were still smiths who knew the names of places along that wonderful trade route driven through the heart of the 'impenetrable forests of the Congo.' For every scrap of imported iron was carried over it."[31]

In disposition the Negro is among the most lovable of men. Practically

[31]Frobenius: *Voice of Africa,* I, 14–15.

all the great travelers who have spent any considerable time in Africa testify to this and pay deep tribute to the kindness with which they were received. One has but to remember the classic story of Mungo Park, the strong expressions of Livingstone, the words of Stanley and hundreds of others to realize this.

Ceremony and courtesy mark Negro life. Livingstone again and again reminds us of "true African dignity." "When Ilifian men or women salute each other, be it with a plain and easy curtsey (which is here the simplest form adopted), or kneeling down, or throwing oneself upon the ground, or kissing the dust with one's forehead, no matter which, there is yet a deliberateness, a majesty, a dignity, a devoted earnestness in the manner of its doing, which brings to light with every gesture, with every fold of clothing, the deep significance and essential import of every single action. Everyone may, without too greatly straining his attention, notice the very striking precision and weight with which the upper and lower native classes observe these niceties of intercourse."[32]

All this does not mean that the African Negro is not human with the all-too-well-known foibles of humanity. Primitive life among them is, after all, as bare and cruel as among primitive Germans or Chinese, but it is not more so, and the more we study the Negro the more we realize that we are dealing with a normal human stock which under reasonable conditions has developed and will develop in the same lines as other men. Why is it, then, that so much of misinformation and contempt is widespread concerning Africa and its people, not simply among the unthinking mass, but among men of education and knowledge?

One reason lies undoubtedly in the connotation of the term "Negro." In North America a Negro may be seven eighths white, since the term refers to any person of Negro descent. If we use the term in the same sense concerning the inhabitants of the rest of the world, we may say truthfully that Negroes have been among the leaders of civilization in every age of the world's history from ancient Babylon to modern America; that they have contributed wonderful gifts in art, industry, political organization, and religion, and that they are doing the same today in all parts of the world.

In sharp contrast to this usage, the term "Negro" in Africa has been more and more restricted until some scientists, late in the last century, declared that the great mass of the black and brown people of Africa were not Negroes at all, and that the "real" Negro dwells in a small space between the Niger and the Senegal. Ratzel says, "If we ask what

[32]Frobenius: *Voice of Africa,* I, 272.

justifies so narrow a limitation, we find that the hideous Negro type, which the fancy of observers once saw all over Africa, but which, as Livingstone says, is really to be seen only as a sign in front of tobacco shops, has on closer inspection evaporated from all parts of Africa, to settle no one knows how in just this region. If we understand that an extreme case may have been taken for the genuine and pure form, even so we do not comprehend the ground of its geographical limitation and location; for wherever dark, woolly-haired men dwell, this ugly type also crops up. We are here in the presence of a refinement of science which to an unprejudiced eye will hardly hold water."[33]

In this restricted sense the Negro has no history, culture, or ability, for the simple fact that such human beings as have history and evidence culture and ability are not Negroes! Between these two extreme definitions, with unconscious adroitness, the most extraordinary and contradictory conclusions have been reached.

Let it therefore be said, once for all, that racial inferiority is not the cause of anti-Negro prejudice. Boaz, the anthropologist, says, "An unbiased estimate of the anthropological evidence so far brought forward does not permit us to countenance the belief in a racial inferiority which would unfit an individual of the Negro race to take his part in modern civilization. We do not know of any demand made on the human body or mind in modern life that anatomical or ethnological evidence would prove to be beyond the powers of the Negro."[34]

"We have every reason to suppose that all races are capable, under proper guidance, of being fitted into the complex scheme of our modern civilization, and the policy of artificially excluding them from its benefits is as unjustifiable scientifically as it is ethically abhorrent."[35] What is, then, this so-called "instinctive" modern prejudice against black folk?

Lord Bryce says of the intermingling of blacks and whites in South America, "The ease with which the Spaniards have intermingled by marriage with the Indian tribes—and the Portuguese have done the like, not only with the Indians, but with the more physically dissimilar Negroes—shows that race repugnance is no such constant and permanent factor in human affairs as members of the Teutonic peoples are apt to assume. Instead of being, as we Teutons suppose, the rule in the matter, we are rather the exception, for in the ancient world there seems to have been little race repulsion."

[33]Ratzel: *History of Mankind,* II, 313.

[34]Atlanta University Publications, No. 11.

[35]Robert Lowie in the *New Review,* Sept. 1914.

In nearly every age and land men of Negro descent have distinguished themselves. In literature there is Terence in Rome, Nosseyeb and Antar in Arabia, Es-Sa'di in the Sudan, Pushkin in Russia, Dumas in France, Al Kanemi in Spain, Heredia in the West Indies, and Dunbar in the United States, not to mention the alleged Negro strain in Æsop and Robert Browning. As rulers and warriors we remember such Negroes as Queen Nefertari and Amenhotep III among many others in Egypt; Candace and Ergamenes in Ethiopia; Mansa Musa, Sonni Ali, and Mohammed Askia in the Sudan; Diaz in Brazil, Toussaint L'Ouverture in Haiti, Hannivalov in Russia, Sakanouye Tamuramaro in Japan, the elder Dumas in France, Calembe and Chaka among the Bantu, and Menelik, of Abyssinia; the numberless black leaders of India, and the mulatto strain of Alexander Hamilton. In music and art we recall Bridgewater, the friend of Beethoven, and the unexplained complexion of Beethoven's own father; Coleridge-Taylor in England, Tanner in America, Gomez in Spain; Ira Aldridge, the actor, and Johnson, Cook, and Burleigh, who are making the new American syncopated music. In the Church we know that Negro blood coursed in the veins of many of the Catholic African fathers, if not in certain of the popes; and there were in modern days Benoit of Palmero, St. Benedict, Bishop Crowther, the Mahdi who drove England from the Sudan, and Americans like Allen, Lot Carey, and Alexander Crummell. In science, discovery, and invention the Negroes claim Lislet Geoffroy of the French Academy, Latino and Amo, well known in European university circles; and in America the explorers Dorantes and Henson; Banneker, the almanac maker; Wood, the telephone improver; McCoy, inventor of modern lubrication; Matseliger, who revolutionized shoemaking. Here are names representing all degrees of genius and talent from the mediocre to the highest, but they are strong human testimony to the ability of this race.

We must, then, look for the origin of modern color prejudice not to physical or cultural causes, but to historic facts. And we shall find the answer in modern Negro slavery and the slave trade.

THE *AMISTAD* MUTINY

Muriel Rukeyser

One of the best of the younger poets, Muriel Rukeyser also has an outstanding biography to her credit, Willard Gibbs: American Genius. *"The* Amistad *Mutiny" is a chapter from that work.*

In the spring of 1839 a long, low, black schooner set sail from Havana with a cargo of assorted merchandise and fifty-three kidnaped Africans, its crew, and the two Spanish owners who had bought the slaves, against all the treaties then in existence.

The slave trade on the west coast of Africa was a thriving and universal business in February 1839, the most profitable business of the country. Everybody who could be was engaged in it. Extensive wars were being fought, and the captives taken in these tribal wars could be shipped down the streams and rivers to the slave ports or herded from the slopes through the low-lying rice fields. They would find their way to the slave factories on the Atlantic coast at last, whose depots were on islands in the rivers and lagoons. Towns made war for no other reason than to obtain slaves; in the peaceable villages many Africans were sold for their crimes and many for their debts. Black men captured other black men from these villages and brought them to the coast; no white man had yet been into the interior, and none dared be the first. But the slave traders on this coast were the educated men of Sierra Leone; they were trained at the slave depots, made their periodic trips inland, and became the principal dealers.

There was an island in the Gallinas River, the place called by the Spaniards Lomboko. A hundred years ago a large number of these natives were brought here and put on a boat sailing for Havana under the Portuguese flag.

They were confined on board the slaver according to the customs. Seated in a space three feet three inches high, they had scarcely room to sit or to lie down. There were a good many men in this chamber, but far more women and children. All the slaves were fastened in couples, chained tightly by the wrists and ankles with irons that left deep scars of laceration. They were kept like this day and night, sleeping twisted on the floor, and crouching by day between those decks, crowded to overflowing. They suffered every hour. They were given rice to eat, more than they could swallow, plenty of rice, but hardly anything to drink. They were ill; they wanted water; many men, women, and children died on that passage.

They were spared the last sudden horror of many of these slave ships running the long journey from Africa to the New World—the horror of being dragged above decks and flung all in irons overboard, at the sight of another ship, the dark chained bodies twirling down through the middle ocean. They were not hidden as many had been behind the coils of rope and under piles of cargo, as on one boat 240 people had been hidden, so that only the sight of a black leg gave away the presence of a villageful of Africans to the boarding party, come to search the ship.

For all of this suffering was illegal; it all ran counter to the laws and decrees and treaties among the countries of Europe and America. The robber chiefs of Africa, the Atlantic pirates, and the representatives of three continents were going against the decree of Spain of 1817. All slaves imported from Africa after 1820, according to that decree, were automatically declared free. In May 1818 the minister in Washington of the Spanish government, Don Onis, communicated to the government of the United States the treaty between Great Britain and Spain to that effect, and the agreement between Spain and the United States was revised in February 1819, after long negotiations between Don Onis and John Quincy Adams, then Secretary of State.

But the slave markets of Havana did a tremendous business. That pale, extensive city waited at the end of the long crossing for more slaves, its width sectioned off like a slaughterhouse into the teeming barracoons, fitted up exclusively for the housing and sale of lately landed Africans. And this new shipload, after their kidnaping and waiting in Sierra Leone, and the two-month crossing of the Middle Passage, landed by night at a small village near Havana. Their wounds were deep; they had been beaten and flogged, and some of them had had vinegar and gunpowder rubbed into their open flesh.

Cuba was beautiful. The aromatic island, with its rush of green, its rapid plants, the stoneworks of the harbor, after the long sea. But its coveted harbors were crowded with this traffic, and the masonry of the

Morro Castle hid behind them, according to a letter written to Adams in 1836, advocating Atlantic and Caribbean naval bases, "a mean and degraded people." But the brooks and the fields and the fortifications! "They were the most numerous fortifications in the Caribbean, and their people had the least energy for defending them." It was easy to see what value this "American Britain" had, this chain of islands: Summer Island, or Bermuda, was another, and naval officers were talking also to General Jackson about the misunderstood bars and shoals and islands of the sea, all the way from here to Charleston.

Africans did not see this land. It was like what they had left: the slave cages in the marshy, vivid green fields. Their village was like what they had left: huts like their huts in the glare of day, and the strong angular shadows of subtropical night. They stayed here for about ten days, until several white men arrived. Among these men was Ruiz, whom they learned to call by his Spanish nickname, Pipi. He looked them over, selected the ones he liked, and lined them up in the fierce sun. And then he went down the line making the traditional tests, feeling of them in every part, opening their mouths to see if their teeth were sound; the examination was carried to a degree of minuteness.

It was time to separate these terrible companions. Forty-nine of them had been bought by Señor Don José Ruiz, and four by Señor Don Pedro Montez, and these were taken from the others. When it was time to part at Havana, there was weeping among the women and children, and some of the men wept. Cinquez, a powerful young rice planter, a natural leader even on that journey, wept. He had been kidnaped from his home, where he left a wife and three children, and now this remnant, all taken from his country, were to be parted again. Another young planter, a short active man name Grabeau, did not weep—he felt it was not manly—but sat aside from the others, with Kimbo, older than most of the others, who had been a king's slave. They talked to each other for the last time of their friends and their country. At night the fifty-three were led through the narrow streets of Havana. The white walls stood out plain, slashed and sectioned by the deep black shadows: a thick crowded city, bigger than anything they had ever seen, far and lost from the thatch and fields of their country, where they had worshiped the spirits living in the cotton tree, the stream, and on the mountain.

They were put on board a long, low, black schooner when they reached Havana Harbor—a schooner already loaded and ready, swinging at anchor there, with the letters AMISTAD painted large on her. During that night they were kept in irons again—heavier irons than before, locked on their hands and feet and necks. During the day they were more mildly treated: some of them were freed of their chains, although the Spaniards took care never to free them all at once. They communicated with their new owner by signs, or through Antonio, the cabin boy, who was the only one on the ship who spoke both Spanish and the dialect they all had in common.

The *Amistad* was bound for Guanaja, the intermediate port for Principe, and the Spaniards held papers certifying that these were their slaves. But, down in the hold, the Africans did not understand why they should be on this new boat nor where they were being taken. When the mulatto cook, Selestino Ferrer, who was the slave of Captain Ramón Ferrer, came down with the cabin boy to feed them, they asked him their questions, through Antonio; they knew they were completely lost, they were very hungry, and the hot nights and days were made longer by thirst. There was much whipping, and their questions were not answered. On the fourth day out the cook and the cabin boy looked at each other when the questions were again repeated; then the cabin boy, Antonio, laughed and said that they were just sailing at the pleasure of the Spaniards, and, as for the Africans, *they* were to be cooked and eaten whenever the Spaniards got ready for them.

During the three days out from Havana, the wind had been ahead. On this fourth day and night it rained; a storm came up, and all hands were on deck, hard at work. Late in the evening mattresses were thrown down for them. Clouds covered the sky; the moon had not yet risen; it was very dark. All of the crew but the man at the helm were asleep by eleven o'clock. But the Africans, below deck, were not asleep; they were up and working at their chains and whispering in short tense phrases, passing on the information about the knives they had seen, the long knives used to cut sugar cane.

At three in the morning there was a noise in the forecastle.

None of the Spaniards ever knew how the thing began; but the freed Africans were among them, swinging their machetes. Ruiz picked up an oar and clubbed at the four men who had seized him, and then, up the deck, he heard his yell of "No! No!" followed by a boy's cry of murder. He heard the captain scream to Antonio to go below and get some bread. In the black and cloudy night it was very late to think of pacifying these men by throwing them scraps. Antonio rushed up, in time to see the captain struck across the face two or three times; the cook was struck oftener. Neither of them groaned before he died.

By now the rest of the Africans were unchained and pouring onto the deck, armed with machetes; and when the man at the wheel and the other hand saw this, they ran for the small canoe, lowered it, and escaped into the clouded sea. Montez ran up on deck, and they met him with knives; he defended himself with his own knife and a stick until he was slashed twice, on the head and on the arm. Then he ran for it, scurrying below and wrapping himself in a sail in his panic, trying to hide between two barrels. They came after him, as he burrowed farther in, trying frantically to work himself into a crevice of safety. They would have killed him, but another black man followed and ordered the first not to kill Montez but to bring him back on deck.

The decks were covered with blood. Ruiz was begging as he stood there, yelling not to be killed, calling that they spare the life of the old man, Montez. The Africans tied the two Spaniards together by the hands until they had had time to go down to the passengers' cabin and go through the trunks. Then they set to work. They had accomplished their purpose: they had their freedom, and they had killed the two great threats to their lives, the captain and the cook. They threw the bodies overboard and washed down the slippery deck. There were some who wanted the cabin boy killed. He was African by birth, but he had lived a long time in Cuba as the slave of the captain, whose name he used. The fact of his years in Cuba saved his life, for he was the only link of communication between the Africans and the Spaniards. Cinquez assumed responsibility here; he stopped in his inventory of the cargo and gave order that Antonio Ferrer was not to be killed, as he was needed for the rest of the voyage.

All night long the Africans washed the decks and went through the schooner they had captured. She was a fairly new ship, clipper-built in Baltimore only six years before, of 120 tons burden. The vessel and cargo were worth forty thousand dollars when they left Havana. The Africans had been bought at a price between twenty and thirty thousand dollars; and vessel and cargo had been insured in Havana, as under the captaincy of Ramón Ferrer.

With favorable winds, the *Amistad* should have made Principe in two days. The distance was only about one hundred leagues. But, when the winds are adverse, the short voyage sometimes takes as much as fifteen days.

The *Amistad* was not going on to Principe. All that the Africans knew was that they lived two moons due east. They gave the Spaniards their orders accordingly. Through Antonio, they ordered Ruiz and Montez to hold the course due east by the sun. Montez had been a sea captain before he went into business for himself at Principe. He was now about fifty years old, and although he had been given wounds in the night whose scars he would always carry, from this time on the Africans were friendly to him and promised that once they had reached the coast of Africa he would be permitted to find his way home.

After the floggings and starvation, the vinegar, chains, and terribly cramped quarters, it was sweet to have the freedom of the ship, the clothing that was among the cargo in place of the slave rags, and to know that the sea stretching so far and blue before them led home, to the African village with its palm trees, its round huts and cone-shaped thatch, the beads and blankets, pointed teeth and peace. But the Spaniards were trying to work out a very different plan.

Ruiz, who had been unconscious for most of the day after the uprising, began to recover from his head wound, and he and Montez plotted together at the wheel. A heavy gale was coming on, and in the clouds over the high seas the sun was covered. The Africans relied completely on the Spaniards for their knowledge of navigation; they were inland people, all of them, knowing the mountains of the interior, the fenced towns and rice fields, and now they faced an unknown sea; they steered by the sun, and the sun was hidden. The Spaniards had an idea.

They had started out six or seven leagues from land. Now they headed for open sea. During the next four days they boxed about in the Bahama Channel, and then the *Amistad* was steered for the island of St. Andrew, near New Providence. From here she went on to the Green Key, where they cast anchor. And again she headed out. During the day the Africans sailed eastward, eastward, toward home and full freedom, and threatened the lives of the Spaniards when the wind changed, they were so suspicious and dreaded so to be captured a second time. But at night, steering by the stars, Pedro Montez and José Ruiz headed north and west. And so the fabulous voyage continued, until ominous stories began to appear in Eastern newspapers, advising of the "long, low, black schooner," seen first at one point and then at another on an altogether different course, following no possible route that any observer could discover. By day east, by night northwest, the *Amistad* zigzagged up the Atlantic, within hail of other ships from time to time, casting anchor when water and supplies were needed, losing their anchor at New Providence. For sixty-three days they sailed, while ten of their number died, while the Spaniards hoped continually that they would fall in with some warship or be able to run into some port, and while the Africans looked continually for the coasts of home. Several times vessels drew up alongside, and they were boarded; once even an American schooner sent a party on board. That was on the eighteenth of August, 1839, and the stories of this phantom ship were already in the papers; but the American boat was friendly; it sold the *Amistad* a demijohn of water for a doubloon, and the Spaniards, locked up below, could not even shout until the American boat was out of sight. Two days later they were twenty-five miles from New York, and Pilot Boat No. 3 came alongside and gave them some apples. Now it was clear what the Spaniards' trick had done. It had taken them almost due north, to a strange country and a strange civilization, from Africa and the Spanish depots and the Spanish bright town of Havana up the Atlantic to Long Island.

The Africans knew they were not anywhere near home. When Pilot Boat No. 4 came up, it found them armed, refusing to allow anyone on board. The *Amistad* headed along the coast, and on the twenty-fourth it was off Montauk Point, the tip of Long Island, with its wiry sharp grasses, its sand dunes—the end of America. Here Cinquez ordered the ship steered for Montauk Light, whose tall freestone tower stood 250 feet above the beach, flashing its two lights—one blinking white, one shining steady and red over Shagwong Reef. Cinquez hoped he could go ashore here, but the tide drifted the boat up the bay, and it finally was anchored just off Culloden Point.

On the morning of the twenty-sixth, Cinquez and ten other men went ashore for water. The little houses on the Point looked strange to them, thick and thick-colored after the thatch and stucco. They were the little trim places of the lighthouse keeper and a few fishermen. The white dunes were brilliant in the late summer sunlight, and out on the bright water their ship was very black. The still beach was hot but windy—and quite still until a dog barked, and then, from a second house, another dog barked. From around the cove a straggling line of white men came to meet the Africans. The black men plowed through the soft sand. They were spots of brilliant and impressive color. The first man, Cinquez, the leader, was naked to the waist. He was about twenty-six years old, dark and powerful, erect and handsome, the symmetrical lines of his fine face curving in toward the eyes and mouth. He stood five feet eight, and that was tall for his race; he had already proved himself a match for any two men on the schooner; he had kept order during the long voyage; and now, as he stood on the beach in his white trousers, his white planter's hat, and with a brilliant and many-colored necklace against his naked chest, he commanded the respect of any man. Behind him were the wild colors of Spanish shawls, used as trousers; gauze and Canton crepe wound around the dark throats. One man had an ornate and beautiful bridle in his hand; one wore a linen cambric shirt with complicated embroidery worked across the bosom. They jingled doubloons in their hands. They were the strangest boatload that had ever landed at Montauk Point.

Cinquez pointed toward the dogs that ran beside the white men, held out some money, and the first sale was made: a couple of dogs bought at the rate of three doubloons each. But what they had come for was water. Cinquez sent three men up to one of the houses with the white patrol.

News traveled rapidly from house to house on the Point. Captain Green, who lived near the tip of the island, had read about the "long, low, black schooner" in the newspapers, and knew at once that the end of the riddle was here. Ever since early in August orders had been given, to the U.S.S. *Fulton* and to several revenue cutters, to chase the ship along its crazy maneuvering. Captain Green called together four or five of his friends and went down to the beach. There she was, the schooner, swinging at anchor just offshore, and eight or ten black men were now waiting on the beach for the rest of their party to return with water. As they saw this new group come toward them ominously over the dunes, marching through the stiff pale grass, they massed together in alarm, and Cinquez whistled sharply—the prearranged signal for the others to run back to the beach. Down from the house they came running, the red and pink silks flying behind them. Captain Green's men turned and fled. These blacks were unarmed, but the neighbors with the captain had thought to leave guns in the wagon standing on the shore road. When they came back, stepping gingerly, they held their rifles ready. The Africans waited together; and, seeing that the whites bore arms, the Africans sat down on the beach, and Cinquez waved his arm in a sign of peace and an invitation to talk. Captain Green sat on the sand, and his men gathered behind him, and there they held their parley, drawing crude pictures in the sand and making the hand signs by which men understand each other's simple basic fears and wishes, even when they have no words.

There were two questions the Africans first must have indicated. These were their two deepest dreads: Are there any slaves in this country? Are there any Spaniards? And when these two were answered, they were reassured and sat smiling and talking to one another in tones that anyone might have known were those of congratulation. They were safe; they were free; they were in a good country. But Captain Green destroyed their moment. He drew the clumsy, thick-lined drawing of a ship with his finger in the sand. Next to it he drew the heavy guns of a vessel of war. They knew by these signs that they were being pursued.

The parley on the beach lasted until late afternoon, four hours of slow exchange, by signal and drawing, until the Africans had turned over to Captain Green two guns, a knife, and a hat. Besides these tokens of peace and friendship, they had given their agreement to turn the schooner over to the captain, who was to take them to another part of the island, and from there to sail with them to Sierra Leone.

And then another vessel came in sight, slowly, from the straits between Montauk and Gardner's Point. It was the United States brig *Washington,* Lieutenant Gedney in command, which was making soundings. It had sighted the strange ship lying inshore, and, as it watched, the small boat was seen crossing from the shore to the ship and then back. Lieutenant Gedney had his career ahead of him, and he saw a prize in this black ship, riding so close to the beach. She looked like a pirate, he thought, as he squinted through the glass . . . and those people on the beach, with their carts and horses, and that boat crossing back and forth from land. He barked out his orders, and a boat was armed and dispatched with an officer.

As they rocked alongside the *Amistad,* riding in almost four fathoms of water, about three quarters of a mile off free New York State, she seemed to them like some Flying Dutchman of dream, a derelict, impossible ship. Her rigging and her sails were torn and hung in shrouds and bandages down to the deck. The sides of the hull were bright green below the water line, green and in motion, with the long, waving sea grass that covered them and covered the crusting of barnacles on the wood. The sailors from the *Washington* swarmed up the green sides of the *Amistad* and for the first time saw the deck.

Stacked and coiled across the ship were the piles of goods they had captured: rice, silk, firearms, raisins, vermicelli, cotton goods. Everything seemed to be heaped here: bread and thin, sick Africans, emaciated almost to the skeleton, books and mirrors, hardware, olives, saddles and holsters, luxuries and fruit and jars of olive oil. The twenty men left to guard the ship waited for the first hostile move of the boarding party; and over against the windlass three little girls between eight and thirteen laughed at the strangers, who were prying into the cabin and the hold, uncovering still more fruits and silk, the calico heaped high, the crepe, the pictures, the entire rich cargo of the *Amistad.*

They came to a long bundle wrapped in black bombazine, lying on the forward hatch, and pulled back the black. There was a naked corpse, the last of the ten who had died on the passage. Kon-no-ma, who was watching over the body, pulled back the shroud, frowning at the intruders; he was the most ferocious-looking of the Africans, short, with a large, round head, a diamond-shaped tattoo mark on his forehead, and filed teeth that projected past his lips. The men from the *Washington* stepped back, and one said to another, "Cannibal!" But there was no reason for fear. The Africans had given up their guns—and, besides, they were in a free country. They offered no resistance.

Cinquez' boatload rowed up and boarded, and the Africans crowded around him, talking and pointing. There was still no reason for anxiety. But in that minute the entire situation changed forever: a breathless sailor climbed up from the cabin, yelling something about two white men, and in a moment Ruiz and Montez were brought up from below. Ruiz, who spoke English, demanded protection and the arrest of everyone on board. Cinquez could see what was coming, even before the officer started his quick and formal statement of possession. He rushed to the rail, stood balanced for a second, and then cut a swift arc in the air. Once in the water, while everyone on deck rushed to the side, the downturned faces full of alarm and grief, he made a twisting motion, unbuckling the money belt around his waist. The doubloons—he had three hundred—sank, turning and seeming to darken and melt in the water. The faces watched, horrified; but he was already swimming back to the green side of the *Amistad*. They raised him, dripping, to the deck, and he gave himself up to the government of the United States.

The boat from the *Washington* rowed back with Ruiz, Montez, and Cinquez on it, leaving a guard mounted on the *Amistad*. Once on the *Washington,* however, Cinquez showed such distress that Lieutenant Gedney allowed him to return; the Africans clustered around him as he reached them, laughing and wildly happy. He spoke to them in words the Americans had never heard, but the Africans seemed so roused by what he said that the officer in command saw to it that Cinquez was led away by force. On the following day Cinquez signified by motions that if the sailors would take him aboard the *Amistad,* he would show them a handkerchief full of doubloons. They rowed him over once again; the irons, in which he had been manacled while he was on the *Washington,* were removed; he went below and made another speech to his own people. They were even more wildly excited than they had been the day before; when Cinquez looked at the white sailors who were with him, the Africans shouted and talked to each other with the same determination his voice carried. The sailors found this terrifying: the strange tongue, the looks, the Africans leaping in the crowded cabin—these black men who had already killed and gone through a fearful voyage for their freedom! There was no further indication concerning doubloons. They locked the irons on Cinquez again and took him back to the *Washington.* This time he said nothing, but he kept his eye steadily fixed on the long, low, black schooner.

Lieutenant Gedney had sent an express to the United States marshal at New Haven, and he in turn had given information to His Honor A. T. Judson, United States District Judge. He set sail that night for New London, and the *Amistad* followed. In the morning the two ships lay off the fort, and the gentlemen arrived to hold court on the deck of the *Washington,* a musket shot away from the schooner. The cutter *Experiment* took the newspapermen, who had arrived, on board the *Washington* for the judicial investigation, and the New London *Gazette* published a complete report at once, which was reprinted immediately up and down the East. It began:

We have just returned from a visit to the *Washington* and her prize, which are riding at anchor in the bay, near the fort. On board the former we saw and conversed with the two Spanish gentlemen, who were passengers on board the schooner, as well as owners of the negroes and most of the cargo. One of them, Jose Ruiz, is a very gentlemanly and intelligent young man, and speaks English fluently. He was the owner of most of the slaves and cargo, which he was conveying to his estate on the Island of Cuba. The other, Pedro Montez, is about fifty years of age, and is the owner of four of the slaves. He was formerly a ship master, and has navigated the vessel since her seizure by the blacks. Both of them, as may be naturally supposed, are most unfeignedly thankful for their deliverance. Jose Pedro is the most striking instance of complacency and unalloyed delight we have ever witnessed, and it is not strange, since only yesterday his sentence was pronounced by the chief of the bucaniers, and his death song chanted by the grim crew, who gathered with uplifted sabres around his devoted head, which, as well as his arms, bear the scars of several wounds inflicted at the time of the murder of the ill-fated captain and crew. He sat smoking his Havana on the deck, and to judge from the martyr-like serenity of his countenance, his emotions are such as rarely stir the heart of man. When Mr. Porter, the prize master, assured him of his safety, he threw his arms around his neck, while gushing tears coursing down his furrowed cheek, bespoke the overflowing transport of his soul. Every now and then he clasped his hands, and with uplifted eyes, gave thanks to "the Holy Virgin" who had led him out of his troubles. Senor Ruiz has given us two letters for his agents, Messrs. Shelton, Brothers & Co. of Boston, and Peter A. Harmony &

Co. of New York. It appears that the slaves, the greater portion of whom were his, were very much attached to him, and had determined after reaching the coast of Africa, to allow him to seek his home what way he could, while his poor companion was to be sacrificed.

After a description of the Africans on the *Amistad,* the reporter goes on:

> We were glad to leave this vessel, as the exhalations from her hold and deck, were like any thing but "gales wafted over the gardens of Gul."

And then to the point of the entire incident:

> There is a question for the laws of Admiralty to decide, whether captain Gedney and his fellow officers are entitled to prize or salvage money. To one or the other they are most surely entitled, and we hope they will get their just dues. Captain Gedney, when he first espied the Amistad, was running a line of sounding towards Montauk Point. He had heard nothing of this vessel being on the coast till after his arrival in this port.

The judicial investigation took place on the *Washington* on August 29, 1839. Complaints were lodged by Montez and Ruiz against Cinquez and the thirty-eight other Africans who were left alive, and the depositions of the two Spaniards were taken through interpreters. After they had gone to their cabins, the investigation adjourned to the schooner to inspect it and to allow Antonio, the cabin boy, to identify the Africans according to their roles in the mutiny. The examination proceeded exactly as if Ruiz and Montez had owned the *Amistad,* and as if Connecticut and New York had been passionate slave states. At the end of the investigation Ruiz and Montez caused a notice to be printed in all the city papers as a token of their thankfulness, and all the male Africans stood committed for trial before the next Circuit Court at Hartford. The three little girls and Antonio were held in one hundred dollars' bond apiece and, being unable to produce the money, were sent along with the rest on board a sloop.

In charge of Lieutenant Holcomb, of the *Washington,* and Colonel Pendleton, keeper of the prison to which they were being taken, they sailed up the Sound, and arrived in New Haven on Sunday morning, September 1, 1839.

Living in the county jail was not too different from living on the *Amistad*. The great wooden room in which most of them lived together was not unlike the hold of the ship. It was larger, lighter, cleaner. Here thirty-six of them were kept, and the rest were in three smaller chambers, the three little girls in one, the sick in another. They could be together, could talk together in their own tongue, which none of these strangers seemed to understand. And once a day they were taken out of their confinement for exercise.

There was nothing in the lives of the Africans to prepare them for that scene. The glare of Sierra Leone, the sharp glimpse of angled Havana, was what they knew; and this was intensely different, this New England autumn of a century ago.

This color that they saw, these flickering delicate elms, the wide sweep of the Green, the profound sky—nothing in the tropics, nothing on the sea, could have predicted this! But there was more; for past the avenues of feathers gleamed a whiteness never seen before, in soft round pillars rising as marble never seen before, a new and enchanting whiteness, fluted intricately, and rising to support great shapes that floated like white reefs over these pale and columned porches, whose steps rose up to them in the whiteness of astounding sand; and beyond this, a warm red never seen before, warm walls taller than they had dreamed, with shining squares, the gleaming windows in the warm brick. More feathers, feathery trees in double and triple arches, fell into green shadows, green brilliance, wherever they looked. And under these walked tall, pale men in black; and through all these crowds women passed, swathed at the shoulders and thighs, bound tight at the waist, in the most voluptuous bindings and cascade and swirl of clothes they yet had seen. This field, these temples, these oxcarts moving among such fantastically dressed white men and women, these deep wild bells sounding from the pinnacles of the white steeples—this was the softest, most luxurious, most surrealist scene possible to dream. Even the grass was softer here, the leaves cut and curled into softness. The smells of farm wagons, the fruit, the early fall vegetables, the oyster booths at the corner of the Green, mixed with the grass smells; and the rich shadows fell among this light more softly, more graciously, than shadows ever fell.

But, as far as the Africans were concerned, this was their prison yard and their time of day for exercise—these minutes when they were brought out on the Green, while a crowd of these swathed women and men in clothes like tubes, and children in little clothes like the men's, came and watched their acrobatics.

Some of the white men even came into the jail. Many were beginning to visit the prison rooms to stare, paying the admission price of twelve and a half cents; but some others arrived, making sounds at them, saying words not quite so strange as all the other words they had heard since the *Amistad* was boarded off Montauk. And then these gentlemen would turn to each other and talk for a long time.

In New York City, at a meeting of "a few friends of freedom," a committee was appointed to defend the Africans, and Lewis Tappan, Simeon S. Jocelyn, and Joshua Leavitt were now ready to receive donations, employ counsel, and act in any other ways as they saw fit for the conduct of the trial. The counsel that was engaged was Seth P. Staples and Theodore Sedgwick of New York, and, in New Haven, the rising and liberal lawyer, Roger S. Baldwin.

The main problem now was one of communication. The Africans spoke a language that was completely incomprehensible to anyone who had yet seen them; they were being tried, according to some, for a crime that included the worst, most anarchic list of separate crimes: mutiny, murder, theft of a ship on the high seas, abduction, piracy . . . but others, even while recognizing that the lack of speech might cover any sort of villainy, here saw these captives as people involved in a fight for their own freedom, against the strongest force possible: international business. For it was plain that, even at this early date, the Spanish government was going to make claims; the owners were demanding their rights; and Washington was rather ready to listen. By September 14 the papers were noting that the Spanish Minister had asked for the ship, the cargo, and the slaves, and would probably get them. Most of the press sneered at the abolitionists, saying that if they were really friendly to the blacks, they would leave them alone. The abolitionists gave them clothes, but the prisoners would not keep them on, said the mocking articles. In the election campaign the hostile newspapers poured out laughter, calling for Cinquez for President. But other newspapers answered, comparing democracy to the man's jackknife—he had had it for years, though it had had nine new blades and thirteen new handles. And now the Spanish Minister, the Chevalier de Argaiz, was making new claims. He was asking for a trial at Havana, where the slave trade was wide open and the whole thing could be railroaded through. One thing was on the side of a speedy trial, however. It was going to be held in Connecticut. Mr. Holabird, the United States District Attorney, and Ralph I. Ingersoll, already prominent in New Haven law, were counsel for the prosecution.

Abolitionist feeling was high in New England. Case after case in Connecticut alone had laid open the structure of the country, the structure, indeed, of the country's will and feeling and economic existence. Sixty years before, Lafayette had been horrified at the spectacle of black and white Revolutionary soldiers eating together at the same mess; and during these years the shape of the country was making itself plain. The South was farm country, breeding country, and it had become a breeding farm for slaves; annually Virginia was exporting forty thousand Negroes southward; and New England, which stood by, watching with a certain horror and making steady profits out of the end products of the cotton fields, had a shaky and equivocal position to maintain. The symptoms cropped up, in the small towns of New York and Massachusetts and Connecticut. All of the legalists involved in this new trial had been arguing one side of the slavery question in the courts for years, and the judge, Andrew Judson, had been prosecutor in the Prudence Crandall case, in 1833, which ended the persecution—her life had been threatened, her house attacked, her reputation smeared endlessly—of Prudence Crandall, a young schoolteacher who had admitted Negro children into her school at Canterbury.

The first trial, at Hartford, held on the habeas-corpus writ, served only to indicate how far-reaching the pressures were. A man named John Ferry, a native African, had been found in New York, who was able to speak freely with one or two of the prisoners and imperfectly with the others, being a member of the Gissi tribe. Communication had become the most important objective for the defense. The Africans had at first been committed for murder, but the Circuit Court decided that it could take no legal cognizance of an act on board a Spanish vessel. Gedney, as master of the ship that took the *Amistad,* then filed a libel on the vessel and cargo. This cargo included the prisoners, whom he claimed as salvage. Montez claimed the three little girls, Teme, Kagne, and Margru, who were listed in the passports which had been whipped up at Havana as Joana, Josepha, and Francisca. But District Attorney Holabird, in filing two claims for the United States, spoke for the split country. The first claim and libel was on behalf of the United States at the instance of the Spanish Minister, and called for the restoration of the Africans to the Spaniards. The second, also on behalf of the United States, claimed that the Africans were free persons, wrongfully brought into the country, and to be returned to their native land. The court was adjourned after the session on Saturday afternoon, September 21, and the Africans were sent back to the county house at New Haven.

The crowd gathering to watch them on the Green—the men in the long, black, tubed clothes, the swathed women—did not include one who could speak to them. In the courthouse John Ferry had shown the long papers under which they had marked their signs. But they had not yet been heard once. People had stared at them, pointing and laughing; strange, busy men had come into the jail and drawn pictures of them; plaster casts had been made for Mr. Fowler; and Mr. Fletcher, the phrenologist, was measuring their heads and jotting down notes on the number of inches from the root of the nose to the occipital protuberance over the top of the head, to determine their temperaments. It was not until the day after they returned from Hartford that a tall, thin man all in black, with strikingly deep-set eyes under a smooth bland forehead, its brown hair brushed in a wide swathe across—with lined and knotted cheeks, whose muscles of control tightened the jaw and mouth sternly together —came into the jail, walking in that day with his head down, in that stride they were to know well, brooding, remote, and careless. He came in, sat down among them, and with nods and thrustings of his fingers one after the other soon made them understand. He put out one finger and nodded and smiled at them. *"E-ta,"* said one of the Africans, in recognition, and one of the little girls repeated it like a lesson—*"e-ta,"* she said, and held up one finger. The tall clerical man wrote down the letters for it. And held up two fingers this time. Now several of them were answering, caught up in the game. *"Fe-le,"* they said; and for three fingers, *"sau-wa,"* and four, *"nai-ni,"* and so on, *"do-lu, we-ta, waw-fe-la, wai-ya-gba, ta-u,"* up to ten, *"pu."* The white man took his page of notes and smiled at them, another smile with the beginning of knowledge and promise in it.

He strode off, filled with this new possibility, striding across the Green that they had seen as soft and voluptuous, that he saw scarcely at all, lost in his plans.

"Good day, Professor Gibbs," said a bonneted, mittened woman as he passed without seeing her. He turned and spoke, courteously, but with a distance in his voice.

Josiah Willard Gibbs, professor of theology and sacred literature at Yale, had devoted his forty-nine years to religion, to the language of religion, and to the new comparative study of languages which German scholarship, in the early years of the century, was illuminating as a study of the nature of man expressed in his words, the sounds and the structure of their various grammars. Born in Salem, he was the third son of Henry Gibbs, a merchant who had been in the class of 1766 at Harvard and had then taught school at Rowley, at New Castle, N.H., and at Lynn, before he married Mercy Prescott of Salem and settled there. His father had died when he was four, and his mother had brought up the children, sending young Josiah to his uncle at New Haven—sending him to Yale rather than to Harvard, where the Gibbs family had always gone, and the Willards as well, as far back as Samuel Willard, acting president of the college from 1701 to 1707. Scholars and librarians, the family had handed down its qualities, unselfish scholarship, modesty, constitutional frailty, a single-minded pursuit of truth, in son after son. And the women they married were the rare intellectual women of early New England whose spirits reach out still from the old portraits—fine, tempered, and thin. A merchant like Henry Gibbs in this family was almost an aberration. It was possible, perhaps after many years of teaching. The tradition was one of withdrawal, of a canalized passion given mainly to scholarship, of a remoteness among which this visit to the jail was a thunderclap.

But this was a combining occasion, one of those events that bring a life into focus, summoning qualities that until such a moment seem remote from each other, alien and useless. It was the first and only moment in Josiah Gibbs's career that could call into play his religious belief in the value of the human being, his skill in language, and the reconstruction, as from fossils, of a grammar from the broken phrases set down in travel books, in the letters of missionaries, or on such a visit as he had just made —and the wish to affirm truth as he saw it that motivated a good section of the small faculty of Yale.

Walking home with his head down, almost looking behind him in the posture familiar to New Haven, he went from the college to Crown Street, where he lived in President Day's house, rented some time ago, with his wife—he had married when he was forty—the three small daughters, and the baby, his son and namesake who had just been born. He could be glad of his wife's understanding. For it was quite clear what he was to do. Communication—that was the problem here; and he held the key. Now he must find an interpreter. The abolitionists were eager for an adequate defense; his cousin, Roger Baldwin, would go to any length to give this trial its due, for it was now obvious that the deepest rights of the individual were concerned—and more, the deep rights of the inarticulate individual, the rights that must be fought for without the persuasion and argument that would move the Yankee mind. Tappan and Staples could be counted on to raise the money, at any sacrifice. But money and conviction were not enough without him. He, Gibbs, was the link. Communication was the link here.

Two days later he was on his way to New York. The port was the most likely place to find someone who could speak both Mendi, the dialect of the Africans, and English. The union stages left New Haven on Mondays at 3 A.M. and 11 A.M., and the early stage would take him through the morning darkness of Milford and Stratford to Bridgeport, from where the *Nimrod* and the *Fairfield* sailed for New York. For $1.75 the whole trip could be made, the hills rocking past the curtains of the stage-coach as the blackness lightened, and then the marvelous colored dawn over the farmland of the valley, just beginning to turn metal and red in mid-September; then the clang and hurry at the dock, as the bales and casks were loaded on the packet, with its decks like the floors of a ware-house, its machinery showing as the connecting rod and two tall black chimneys rose high above the wheelhouse, the whole thing standing high out of the water; and now the last comers rustling up the gangway; and the still blue hours on the Sound. The orchard lands and the drowned valleys slid by, and the turns of the river arrived—Hell's Gate, the Hog's Back, the Frying Pan; and at last the fenced-in island, behind its miles of masts and wooden piers, after the channels with their villas on the shore, the turf and trees, the lighthouse, the cheering inmates of the madhouse, and the jail. One could see from the deck as clear as water color the Dutch houses, almost brick by brick, see the gables and the little steps to the roofs and the shining weathercocks that gleamed in the bright air. The crowded streets, with their carts and omnibuses. The buildings and the flags and the bells. A sunny, vivid city under an Italian sky, moving slowly as the boat pushed among the river traffic, among all the red-and-black smokestacks of the ferries. And the New York sounds began, the puffing and churning of these boats, with their paddles, the clipped notes of the horses' hoofs as a carriage went by at the trot; until the last turn was made, and the slanting sails of the great packets at Sandy Hook began to fill the harbor. As he landed he could hear the street cries, "Ice," "Hot corn, *hot* corn," and he had the city before him, with a fantastic clue in his hand, the letters spelling out how the Africans had counted up to ten.

He made his way from ship to ship in the harbor, pausing to introduce himself and ask for a Negro boy who could understand his *"E-ta, fe-le, sau-wa,"* to be disappointed again and again. From the Battery, with the crickets chirping in the trees, he went farther uptown, to the elegant section of Waverley and Lafayette places, with their cream-painted brick houses, white lines in the seams, the section of parasols and coaches, as against the bowling saloons and oyster cellars and general wretchedness of the Five Points. Offal was thrown into the streets; wherever one turned pigs ran wild, great brown, black-blotched hogs shunting their snouts along the curbs, nudging the walkers, feasting in the gutters at City Hall.

From boat to boat he went, until at last, on the *Buzzard,* a British armed brig under Captain Fitzgerald, he found, among the Africans employed there, two who he thought would do, Charles Pratt and James Covey. The brig was lying in the harbor with a number of vessels seized by her on the coast of Africa for being engaged in the slave trade, and when Captain Fitzgerald was shown the request of the committee, he gave his permission that the two interpreters be brought to New Haven. James Covey was about twenty years old; he was born in the Mendi country, and his mother was Gissi. Covey had been kidnaped when he was very young and sold as a slave to the king of a neighboring tribe. He was used to plant the queen's rice fields for three years, at the end of which he was sold to a Portuguese and taken to Lomboko. He and about three hundred others were put on a slave ship to be sent to America; but, about four days out from Lomboko, the ship was captured by a British vessel, and Covey obtained his freedom in Sierra Leone, where he learned English at the Church Missionary Society. At the end of 1838 he enlisted as a sailor on the *Buzzard*. Pratt was a native Mendi and had been rescued from a slave ship about seven years before.

Gibbs and the two sailors started for New Haven at once.

There was "unspeakable joy" when they got to the jail. Professor Gibbs wrote to the committee about this meeting: "It would have done your heart good to witness the joy of the Africans at finding themselves able to converse with the men." And another witness added:

> We called with the interpreters at the prison this morning, just as the African captives were at breakfast. The Marshal objected to the entrance of the interpreters until the breakfast was over, but one of the captives coming to the door and finding a fellow countryman who could talk in their own language, took hold of him, and literally dragged him in. Such a scene ensued as you may better conceive than describe. Breakfast was forgotten, all crowded round the two men, and all talking as fast as possible. The children hugged one another with transport.

And now the trials began: a series of court session and newspaper debates, of international duplicity and intrigue on overlapping intrigue. The five sets of claims crossed a dozen ways: the Africans claimed freedom, charging Ruiz and Montez with assault, battery, and false imprisonment; Gedney (who had already earned prominence for supervising the dredging of the deep channel in New York Harbor which bears his name) claimed salvage on the vessel, the cargo, and the slaves; Captain Green and the Long Islanders who had met Cinquez at Montauk had filed a claim identical with Gedney's; the Spanish Minister, Calderón, and the new Minister, De Argaiz, claimed the boat and the Africans under the treaty of 1795, held that the trials should take place in Cuba, and objected that the effect of a "trial and execution" in Connecticut was not as good, and these Spanish demands were supported by a strong American proslavery press; and, finally, District Attorney Holabird claimed that the Africans should be held, according to the 1819 act, subject to the pleasure of the President. Acting according to the slavery interests, Holabird wrote to John Forsyth, the Secretary of State, asking whether the Federal government could deliver the Africans up to Spain *before* the court had actually sat. He inquired about possible treaty stipulations covering such an act. The Secretary of State knew there were no such stipulations, but he instructed Holabird to see that the court proceedings did not put the Africans out of the Federal jurisdiction; and he turned the letter over to the proslavery Attorney General, Felix Grundy, who could see no reason to investigate the possibilities and declared that they should be surrendered, together with the cargo, to persons designated by Calderón.

But President Van Buren, with all the sympathy in the world for the Spanish Minister, was unable to do this. There was no extradition treaty with Spain.

When the Circuit Court ruled that the *Amistad* had been found on the high seas and the Africans were not to be held for such a murder, De Argiz wrote another letter, denying the rights of the United States courts, and asked the President to send the Africans back to Cuba in a government boat. Van Buren, far from resenting this, sent an order to Lieutenants Gedney and Meade to stand ready to convey the Africans from New Haven. This order was sent *before* the court assembled at New Haven, on January 7, 1840.

At this trial the matter of the passports took on even greater weight. There was a distinction made in the terms for Africans newly landed in the New World, who were called *bozales,* and Africans landed before the prohibition of the slave trade in 1820, who were called *ladinos*. The mass passports made out for these "slaves" were by owner—one passport for forty-nine slaves belonging to J. Ruiz, and one for three slaves belonging to P. Montez (the three little girls; for the little boy, Kale, whom Montez later demanded, there was no passport at all), and in these documents the Africans are called *"cuerenta y nueva negros ladinos"* and *"tres negras ladinas."* Now, through the interpreters, it became possible to prove that the Africans had not been in Cuba and knew not a single word of

Spanish. The stories of their kidnaping and sale became known, as they told their history, living and dying in the New Haven jail. Six more had died since the beginning of their captivity, and had been buried. Local clergymen, including Leonard Bacon, had spoken at the funerals. At the funeral of Kaperi, prayers were offered in the room, and the substance of his friends' remarks was, "Kaperi is dead. His body is still, and will be laid in the ground. The soul of Kaperi is alive. It will never die. Our souls will never die. They will live after our bodies are dead and cold. The Bible tells us how our souls may go to the good place. You must learn to read the Bible. Pray to God, become good, and then when your bodies die, God will take your souls to the good place, and make you happy forever." And then, with a great number of the New Haven people, they walked in procession to the grave. A hymn was sung and read there, and Mr. Bacon offered a prayer.

The Africans were learning to read and write. They could say "Merica," when asked where they were. They could make simple conversation. But the shadow over their religious and linguistic education was their anxiety, according to their teachers, Professor Gibbs and the "young gentlemen connected with Yale College." They had uncertainty in respect to the future. They dreaded going back to Havana, and would interrupt their prayers, in the middle of *"O ga-wa-wa* [O great God], *bi-a-bi yan-din-go* [Thou art good], *bi-a-bi ha-ni gbe-le ba-te-ni* [Thou hast made all things]," to speak of this. When the nature of an oath was explained to them, and it was added that God would visit the man who violated an oath with His displeasure, they asked, "What will be done to the people of the United States if they send us back to Havana?"

In a contemporary account there is a description of the scene when they received the news of the decision of the District Court.

> They were assembled and seated in a commodious room—they knew that their case was pending—some of them had been called to testify in court—they were of course deeply anxious for the event. All being present and quiet, they were informed that the judge had decreed their return, not to Havana, but to their native land. They leaped from their seats, rushed across the room, threw themselves prostrate at the feet of those who brought them the glad tidings, while "thank you, thank you" was the expression of every tongue.
>
> The succeeding day Mr. Baldwin, one of their counsel, entered the jail. Cinquez was seated behind a table, and members of his class on either side of him. As Mr. B. approached, Cinquez was told that he pleaded his cause; said it would be wrong to send him to Havana. He dropped his book, rose

from his seat, seeming for a moment deliberating whether he should leap the table. Seeing this to be attended with difficulty, he reached forward, and seizing the extended hand of Mr. B. with a firm grasp, and looking him in the face, his own countenance beaming with the most grateful emotion, exclaimed, "We thank you, we bless you, this is all we can do for you."

During this icy winter the *Grampus* lay in New Haven Harbor. It had been sent up from the Brooklyn Navy Yard early in January, to the open dismay of most of New Haven, and a little later the anti-slavery group had stationed another schooner offshore, in the hope of running the Africans to Canada if any open attempt were made to ship them to Cuba or Spain. It was obvious that the verdict that they were freemen, not property—men who had fought to regain their lost freedom, not criminals—acquitted men, and not condemned slaves—it was obvious that any such verdict would not be allowed to stand. The case was appealed by order of the Secretary of State the moment the verdict was announced. The district attorney rushed a special messenger through the icy mud of the road to Washington, so that the President might correct a clerical error in his order to hold the Africans. Van Buren sent a flagrant message to the marshal—a message pandering at every point to the Spanish government, pandering in a manner so impossible for the Chief Executive of the United States that he was later forced to deny that it was his. But, with Justice Thompson on the bench, the decision of the District Court was affirmed *pro forma,* and the whole matter was left to the United States Supreme Court on appeal.

This was the end of April 1840. And now, with the addition of other members to the legal staff of the defense, the committee was prepared to go ahead without stint of time or money to the last appeal, before the Supreme Court. They needed a counsel whose argument would be brilliant and unquestioned in its honesty; they needed a defense that would set this case before history as a pivotal point in the climb towards freedom. They needed, not a lawyer, but an idealistic philosopher. The man they went to was John Quincy Adams.

He was ex-President, seventy-three years old, ill, tired, long ago defeated in a great and personal defeat. He was the "old man eloquent"; he was the President who had committed political suicide for the sake of science; and he had not been in a court for thirty-two years. He was one of the great peaks in democratic civilization, standing for law and human dignity, for science and faith. His standard was George Washington, and, as Brooks Adams says, "to him it was from the very outset clear that, if the democratic social system were capable of progression upward to a level at which it could hope to ameliorate the lot of men on earth, it must tend, at least, to produce an average which, if it did not attain to the eminent ability of the first President, might at least be capable of understanding and appreciating his moral altitude." He was at home in Quincy on October 27, 1840, when Ellis Loring and Lewis Tappan came to call, to enlist his sympathy in the case and to leave the two great scrapbooks of the *Amistad* captives—letters, press clippings, reports. As for his sympathy, that had been long ago enlisted. There was a sympathy in John Quincy Adams that must include these Africans. A year before, when he had had Loring's first letter about the case, just after the Hartford trial, he had begun to watch the developments; by that October he had been absorbed in their meaning; and only a few months ago he had offered a resolution in the House, calling on the President for papers concerning the *Amistad*.

He pushed back the two huge scrapbooks. He could not possibly take this case. He was old, he was infirm, he had been away from these lists too long. They argued with him; this was a matter of life and death, but that was the least argument; the case was critical, it touched his interests, causes in which he had spent a lifetime. He alone was equal to this. And after long demurring he pulled the scrapbooks across the table toward him. He would take the case. And he wrote in the diary which is only one of his monuments: "I implore the mercy of Almighty God so as to control my temper, to enlighten my soul, and to give me utterance, that I may prove myself in every respect equal to the task." And again, writing at night: "Oh, how shall I do justice to this case and to these men?"

Three weeks later, at five-thirty in the morning, he took the cars from Hartford to New Haven. At eight o'clock he arrived and went straight to the Tontine Hotel, the best in town, although the Quinnipiac was trying hard to equal it. He had a quiet breakfast there, and during breakfast Roger Baldwin called on him, talked for a while about the case, and invited him to his office to inspect the papers on the *Amistad* trials. They talked there for about two hours, and then Mr. Adams, with Baldwin, Marshal Wilcox, Deputy Pendleton, and a keeper, went through the rooms at the jail and met the Africans. He did not see the three little girls, who were in a separate chamber, but he met the men—of whom there were now thirty-two. They were sleeping double in crib beds, in a room thirty feet by twenty—"negro face, fleece, and form," he writes, "but varying in color from ebon black to dingy brown. 1 or 2 of them almost mulatto bright. Cinquez & Grabow, the 2 chief conspirators, have very remarkable countenances." They were put through their paces for him; while he listened politely, three of them took turns at reading part of a chapter in the English New Testament, "very indifferently." One boy writes, he noted. Mr. Ludlow was teaching them, but they learned slowly, huddled together as they were, with no one to talk to.

In lesser natures there is always the danger in an issue of this sort that a lack of impressiveness in the prisoners themselves may make a possible champion lose faith. The public expects its martyrs to be saints, and it is only the defender who puts the cause above the man, the fight for life above the individual life, who can be reconciled to the fact that he is a martyr and part of a cause, and not too much more. Adams was not only passionately devoted to the cause under which the *Amistad* Africans were defended, he was committed to a future in which its justification would be taken for granted. He was concerned with the future—a future living in one's own time, whose origins are to be seen in the flowing present, a future that must daily be found and helped clear. "Besides anticipating by nearly a hundred years some of the most enlightened measures of conservation," say the Beards, "Adams foresaw in a livid flash the doom of slavery in a social war." Repudiated by his country, conscious of failure at every step of his effort toward the country's enlightenment, he knew the depth of the contemporary antagonism—the cleft in the republic, the great split in which he acted a firm and frightful role, prophetic, integrated, and hostile to a planted majority.

By the thirtieth he was in Washington, where he spoke to Attorney General Gilpin about the case, urging him to submit to the President to have the case dismissed by consent, without argument. The Africans were obviously *bozales,* newly imported; that fact destroyed the last Spanish claim, which rested upon their passports. In the documents the term *ladino* had been willfully mistranslated as "sound." Early December was spent in going over the translations, particularly of Document No. 185—and on December 11, Gilpin's report came through. The President would not dismiss the case because of the Spanish Minister's claim. Adams records that he quarreled with Gilpin on the spot, and he writes on December 12, 1840, that he is preparing the case—

> with deep anguish of heart, and a painful search of means to defeat and expose the abominable conspiracy, Executive and Judicial, of this Government against the lives of those wretched men. How shall the facts be brought out? How shall it be possible to comment upon them with becoming temper—with calmness, with moderation, with firmness, with address, to avoid being silenced, and to escape the imminent danger of giving the

adversary the advantage in the argument by overheated zeal? Of all the dangers before me, that of losing my self-possession is the most formidable. I am yet unable to prepare the outline of the argument, which I must be ready to offer the second week in January. Let me not forget my duty.

December in Washington brought its bright sky and snow-chilled air, and the slush and mud for which the unfinished capital was notorious abroad. There were continual admissions and exasperations: the proof-reader confessed that the mistranslation was his fault; Adams, in going over the records, fumes against Gedney, raging for the lieutenant's having taken the men on the shore, without right, and the ship on the high seas, without right. He wished the whole thing were over; talking to the President, complaining about the difficulty and importance of correct printing, putting through the new license for the *Amistad*. In January, Gedney's sister-in-law arrived, pleading for the newly made captain. He was ill, she said, and not very sound in mind. Adams answered her stream of appeal with the assurance that he would have all due consideration for the condition of Captain Gedney. And when Baldwin came in three days later, Adams signed the brief and sighed over his diary, "I know not yet how to order my speech aright."

Francis Scott Key, the United States district attorney who wrote "The Star-Spangled Banner," came up to him, talking pessimistically about the case—this case for which Mr. Adams' heart was ready, while his unpreparedness more and more rankled in him. Key had argued the *Antelope* case, which was similar enough and which Adams knew he would have to review in his defense. Now document after document turned up—the chief clerk's letter saying he had been sorry to see "the rascally blacks fall into the hands of the abolitionists with whom Hartford is filled." The day after this came out into the open, a postponement was granted. Mr. Adams knew a momentary relief, but his suspense was too real. He was immediately involved with the British Minister, Henry Stephen Fox, who wished advice as to what he might do in case of a judgment against the *Amistad* captives. Adams advised him to write to the Secretary of State; and with the new date pushed ahead to February 16, and Baldwin's return to Connecticut until then, he plunged deep into the House debate, which was furious at the moment. These were desperate days for John Quincy Adams. Opposed by what were to him the most malignant forces of evil in the country, the reactionaries—the *popular* reactionaries—and by the slave oligarchy, he was fighting an isolated fight in the House, for free speech, for scientific innovations, for the civilized application of that education whose uncivilized use was creating the conflict now gathering its storm. The furious, brainless, heartless debate in the House could only be abandoned—he went back to read the old cases—he rose and went back to the House, to plunge into his savage feud with General Wise, attacking in this death struggle. In the meantime Fox had still had no answer to his letter. Time was growing short. Mr. Adams was deep in the demonic struggle in the House. He prayed. Praying for control, always more control, for he was swung from hell to hell in his passion, an immortal passion for America, for the mind of God in America, he raged against his "eccentric, wild, extravagant freaks of passion." Seeing this mind, this country, split, he remembered tragic Coriolanus and the Voices. He remembered the red and white roses in the Temple gardens. And soon the trial itself was on him, among all the reading, the books of the *Antelope* record piled high, the pathetic death of the servant Jeremy Leary and his funeral, the last postponement to the twenty-second ("I have yet to prepare a frame for my argument")—and now Baldwin begins, "sound and eloquent but exceedingly mild," carrying the legalistic burden in answer to Attorney General Gilpin. And on the twenty-third, with the hour rushing on him, he is still writing, "The very skeleton of my argument is not yet put together." But that night it breaks; he begins to come through; he finds his form; and on the morning of the twenty-fourth, the scene.

The great hall of the Court, and on the bench, under the carvings and panelings, the nine among whom Adams might have taken his place. He saw other faces, the judges of his day, dead, all dead—he was standing, as he knew and said, for the last time, before this court, with its new judges, scanning the double image of the Declaration hanging on the wall opposite. He began, with his inflamed left eye still giving him pain, old, shaken with his palsy—his hand off the eagle rest on which it lay in the House—ill with the rheumy affection from which he suffered. He was old, he was old, and his eyes watery, his voice shrill, and he trembled with emotion as he gathered himself together for one of the greatest denunciations offered against the entire government of the United States. For he laid open the craft and hypocrisy he saw leading up to "the death struggle now in continual operation between the spirit of liberty and the spirit of bondage on this continent of North America." In this great blast —"Justice!" he cried, "I stand before a Court of Justice. . . . I am obliged to take this ground, because, as I shall show, another Department of the Government of the United States has taken, with reference to this case, the ground of utter injustice, and these individuals for whom I appear, stand before this Court, awaiting their fate from its decision, under the array of the whole Executive power of this nation against them, in addition to that of a foreign nation."

He spoke of Shakespeare's Wolsey, and his virtue; of the Code Noir, the slave system, of the national sympathy with the slave traders of the barracoons, officially declared to be the prime motive of action of the government. He spoke of the demands of the Spanish Ambassador on the President, marking how the Secretary of State should have called on the Ambassador to name another instance where such a demand had been made by any other government on an independent government. "He should have told him, that such a demand was treating the President of the United States, not as the head of a nation, but as a constable, a catchpole. . . ." He breaks down the charge that the two Spaniards, Ruiz and Montez, were "victims of an intrigue." After their cruelty, he says, that killed men on their boat, men in New York advised with the lawyers—"fanatics, perhaps, I must call them, according to the general application of language, but if I were to speak my own language in my own estimate of their character, so far as concerns this case, and confining my remarks exclusively to this present case, I should pronounce them the FRIENDS OF HUMAN NATURE. . . ." This was to be done: human beings were to be saved from slavery and death. In a careful analysis of the legal factors, with an interruption caused by the death of Judge Barbour in the middle of the trial, Adams goes ahead with his passionate insistence on personal liberty. "Is it possible that a President of the United States should be ignorant that the right of personal liberty is individual? That the right to it of every one, is *his own*—JUS SUUM . . ." He rages in praise of the Africans, in the face of "such a scene of Liliputian trickery enacted by the rulers of a great, magnanimous, and Christian nation." As for Cinquez and Grabeau, they "are not slaves. Let them bear in future history the names of Harmodius and Aristogiton." He swings around, trembling, the old man, the eagle voice, pointing to the Declaration on the wall, speaking of the Official Journal which gives the war right of slavery—"Is that the principle on which these United States stand before the world?"

On March 8 the verdict was handed down. He wrote to Tappan and Baldwin that they had been confirmed. But he knew, he knew; and he wrote this in the diary, after the Africans went free:

I am yet to revise for publication my argument in the case of the Amistad Africans; and, in merely glancing over the slave-trade papers lent me by Mr. Fox, I find impulses of duty upon my own conscience which I cannot resist, while on the other hand are the magnitude, the danger, the insurmountable burden of labor to be encountered in the undertaking to touch upon the slave trade. No one else will undertake it; no one but a spirit unconquerable by man, woman, or fiend can undertake it but with the heart of martyrdom. The world, the flesh, and all the devils in hell are arrayed against any man who now in this North American Union shall dare to join the standard of Almighty God to put down the African slave trade; and what can I, upon the verge of my seventy-fourth birthday, with a shaking hand, a darkening eye, a drowsy brain, and with all my faculties dropping from me one by one, as the teeth are dropping from my head—what can I do for the cause of God and man, for the progress of human emancipation, for the suppression of the African slave trade? Yet my conscience presses me on; let me but die upon the breach.

And after the prison, the plaster casts, the phrenologists, the tales of their African homes, the trials and appeals and final acquittal, the green fields of Westville, the Bible, and the promise of return to Sierra Leone with the missionary society, Kinna—the young, the bright-countenanced, the good scholar—wrote to Professor Gibbs:

dear friend

I wish to write you a letter because you have been so kind to me and because you love Mendi people I think of you very often I shall pray for you Dear friend would you must pray for me If you love Jesus Christ and Christ will bless you and would you must come sometime to see Mendi people we must want to see you and I see you I am very Glad and Dear friend I pray for you My good love to your wife and all your family I love them very much I pray for them. . . .

LETTER TO THE EDITOR OF THE *TIMES*

Frances Ann Kemble

Fanny Kemble was a well-known English actress who came to America and married Pierce Butler, a Southern planter. This letter to the London Times, *giving her reaction to* Uncle Tom's Cabin, *is interesting because she had experienced at firsthand the life about which Harriet Beecher Stowe wrote.*

SIR,—As it is not to be supposed that you consciously afford the support of your great influence to misstatements, I request your attention to some remarks I wish to make on an article on a book called *"Uncle Tom's Cabin* as it is," contained in your paper of the eleventh. In treating Mrs. Harriet Beecher Stowe's work as an exaggerated picture of the evils of slavery, I beg to assure you that you do her serious injustice: of the merits of her book as a work of art I have no desire to speak; to its power as a most interesting and pathetic story, all England and America can bear witness; but of its truth and moderation as a representation of the slave system in the United States, I can testify with the experience of an eyewitness, having been a resident in the Southern states, and had opportunities of observation such as no one who has not lived on a slave estate can have. It is very true that in reviving the altogether exploded fashion of making the hero of her novel "the perfect monster that the world ne'er saw," Mrs. Stowe has laid herself open to fair criticism, and must expect to meet with it from the very opposite taste of the present day; but the ideal excellence of her principal character is no argument at all against the general accuracy of her statements with regard to the evils of slavery; everything else in her book is not only possible, but probable, and not only probable, but a very faithful representation of the existing facts: faithful, and not, as you accuse it of being, exaggerated; for, with the exception of the horrible catastrophe, the flogging to death of poor Tom, she has portrayed none of the most revolting instances of crime produced by the slave system, with which she might have darkened her picture, without detracting from its perfect truth. Even with respect to the incident of Tom's death, it must not be said that if such an event is possible, it is hardly probable; for this is unfortunately not true. It is not true that the value of the slave as property infallibly protects his life from the passions of his master. It is no new thing for a man's passions to blind him to his most obvious and immediate temporal interests, as well as to his higher and everlasting ones—in various parts of the world and stages of civilization, various human passions assume successive prominence, and become developed, to the partial exclusion or deadening of others. In savage existence, and those states of civilization least removed from it, the animal passions predominate. In highly cultivated modern society, where the complicated machinery of human existence is at once a perpetually renewed cause and effect of certain legal and moral restraints, which, in the shape of government and public opinion, protect the congregated lives and interests of men from the worst outrages of open violence, the natural selfishness of mankind assumes a different development, and the love of power, of pleasure, or of pelf, exhibits different phenomena from those elicited from a savage under the influence of the same passions. The channel in which the energy and activity of modern society inclines more and more to pour itself is the peaceful one of the pursuit of gain. This is pre-eminently the case with the two great commercial nations of the earth, England and America; and in either England or the Northern states of America, the prudential and practical views of life prevail so far that instances of men sacrificing their money interests at the instigation of rage, revenge, and hatred will certainly not abound. But the Southern slaveholders are a very different race of men from either Manchester manufacturers or Massachusetts merchants; they are a remnant of barbarism and feudalism, maintaining itself with infinite difficulty and danger by the side of the latest and most powerful development of commercial civilization.

The inhabitants of Baltimore, Richmond, Charleston, Savannah, and New Orleans, whose estates lie, like the suburban retreats of our city magnates, in the near neighborhood of their respective cities, are not now the people I refer to. They are softened and enlightened by many influences—the action of city life itself, where human sympathy and human respect, stimulated by neighborhood, produce salutary social restraint as well as less salutary social cowardice. They travel to the Northern states and to Europe, and Europe and the Northern states travel to them, and, in spite of themselves, their peculiar conditions receive modifications from foreign intercourse. The influence, too, of commercial enterprise, which in these latter days is becoming the agent of civilization all over the earth, affects even the uncommercial residents of the Southern cities, and, however cordially they may dislike or despise the mercantile tendencies of Atlantic Americans or transatlantic Englishmen, their frequent contact with them breaks down some of the barriers of difference between them, and humanizes the slaveholder of the great cities into some relation with the spirit of his own times and country. But these men are but a most inconsiderable portion of the slaveholding population of the South—a nation, for as such they should be spoken of, of men whose organization and temperament is that of the southern European; living under the influence of a climate at once enervating and exciting; scattered over trackless wildernesses of arid sand and pestilential swamp; intrenched within their own boundaries; surrounded by creatures absolutely subject to their despotic will; delivered over by hard necessity to the lowest excitements of drinking, gambling, and debauchery for sole recreation; independent of all opinion; ignorant of all progress; isolated from all society—it is impossible to conceive a more savage existence within the pale of any modern civilization.

The South Carolinian gentry have been fond of styling themselves the chivalry of the South, and perhaps might not badly represent, in their relations with their dependents, the nobility of France before the purifying hurricane of the Revolution swept the rights of the suzerain and the wrongs of the serf together into one bloody abyss. The planters of the interior of the Southern and Southwestern states, with their furious feuds and slaughterous combats, their stabbings and pistolings, their gross sensuality, brutal ignorance, and despotic cruelty, resemble the chivalry of France before the horrors of the Jacquerie admonished them that there was a limit even to the endurance of slaves. With such men as these, human life, even when it can be bought or sold in the market for so many dollars, is but little protected by considerations of interest from the effects of any violent passion. There is yet, however, another aspect of the question, which is, that it is sometimes clearly *not* the interest of the owner to prolong the life of his slaves; as in the case of inferior or superannuated laborers, or the very notorious instance in which some of the owners of sugar plantations stated that they found it better worth their while to *work off* (i.e., kill with labor) a certain proportion of their force, and replace them by new hands every seven years, than work them less severely and maintain them in diminished efficiency for an indefinite length of time. Here you will observe a precise estimate of the planter's material interest led to a result which you argue passion itself can never be so blind as to adopt. This was a deliberate economical calculation, openly avowed some years ago by a number of sugar planters in Louisiana. If, instead of accusing Mrs. Stowe of exaggeration, you had brought the same charge against the author of the *White Slave,* I should not have been surprised; for his book presents some of the most revolting instances of atrocity and crime that the miserable abuse of irresponsible power is capable of producing, and it is by no means written in the spirit of universal humanity which pervades Mrs. Stowe's volumes; but it is not liable to the charge of exaggeration any more than her less disgusting delineation. The scenes described in the *White Slave do* occur in the slave states of North America; and in two of the most appalling incidents of the book—the burning alive of the captured runaway, and the hanging without trial of the Vicksburg gamblers—the author of the *White Slave* has very simply related positive facts of notorious occurrence. To which he might have added, had he seen fit to do so, the instance of a slave who perished in the sea swamps, where he was left bound and naked, a prey to the torture inflicted upon him by the venomous musquito swarms. My purpose, however, in addressing you was not to enter into a disquisition on either of these publications; but I am not sorry to take this opportunity of bearing witness to the truth of Mrs. Stowe's admirable book, and I have seen what few Englishmen can see —the working of the system in the midst of it.

In reply to your "Dispassionate Observer," who went to the South professedly with the purpose of seeing and judging of the state of things for himself, let me tell you that, little as he may be disposed to believe it, his testimony is worth less than nothing; for it is morally impossible for any Englishman going into the Southern states, except as a *resident,* to know anything whatever of the real condition of the slave population. This was the case some years ago, as I experienced, and it is now likely to be more the case than ever; for the institution is not *yet* approved divine to the perceptions of Englishmen, and the Southerners are as anxious to hide its uglier features from any note-making observer from this side of the water as to present to his admiration and approval such as can by any possibility be made to wear the most distant approach to comeliness.

The gentry of the Southern states are pre-eminent in their own country for that species of manner which, contrasted with the breeding of the Northerners, would be emphatically pronounced "good" by Englishmen. Born to inhabit landed property, they are not inevitably made clerks and countinghouse men of, but inherit with their estates some of the invariable characteristics of an aristocracy. The shop is not their element; and the eager spirit of speculation and the sordid spirit of gain do not infect their whole existence, even to their very demeanor and appearance, as they too manifestly do those of a large proportion of the inhabitants of the Northern states. Good manners have an undue value for Englishmen, generally speaking; and whatever departs from their peculiar standard of breeding is apt to prejudice them, as whatever approaches it prepossesses them, far more than is reasonable. The Southerners are infinitely better bred men, according to English notions, than the men of the Northern states. The habit of command gives them a certain self-possession, the enjoyment of leisure a certain ease. Their temperament is impulsive and enthusiastic, and their manners have the grace and spirit which seldom belong to the deportment of a Northern people; but, upon more familiar acquaintance, the vices of the social system to which they belong will be found to have infected them with their own peculiar taint; and haughty, overbearing irritability, effeminate indolence, reckless extravagance, and a union of profligacy and cruelty, which is the immediate result of their irresponsible power over their dependents, are some of the less pleasing traits which acquaintance develops in a Southern character. In spite of all this, there is no manner of doubt that the "candid English observer" will, for the season of his sojourning among them, greatly prefer their intercourse to that of their Northern brethren. Moreover, without in the least suspecting it, he will be bribed insidiously and incessantly by the extreme desire and endeavor to please and prepossess him which the whole white population of the slave states will exhibit—as long as he goes only as a "candid observer," with a mind not *yet* made up upon the subject of slavery, and open to conviction as to its virtues. Every conciliating demonstration of courtesy and hospitable kindness will be extended to him, and, as I said before, if his observation is permitted (and it may even appear to be courted), it will be to a fairly bound, purified edition of the black book of slavery, in which, though the inherent viciousness of the whole story can not be suppressed, the coarser and more offensive passages will be carefully expunged. And now permit me to observe that the remarks of your traveler must derive much of their value from the scene of his inquiry. In Maryland, Kentucky, and Virginia, the outward aspect of slavery has ceased to wear its most deplorable features. The remaining vitality of the system no longer resides in the interests, but in the pride and prejudices of the planters. Their soil and climate are alike favorable to the labors of a white peasantry: the slave cultivation has had time to prove itself there the destructive pest which, in time, it will prove itself wherever it prevails. The vast estates and large fortunes that once maintained, and were maintained by, the serfdom of hundreds of Negroes, have dwindled in size and sunk in value, till the slaves have become so heavy a burden on the resources of the exhausted soil and impoverished owners of it that they are made themselves objects of traffic in order to ward off the ruin that their increase would otherwise entail. Thus the plantations of the Northern slave states now present to the traveler very few of the darker and more oppressive peculiarities of the system; and, provided he does not stray too near the precincts where the Negroes are sold, or come across gangs of them on their way to Georgia, Louisiana, or Alabama, he may, if he is a very superficial observer, conclude that the most prosperous slavery is not much worse than the most miserable freedom.

But of what value will be such conclusions applied to those numerous plantations where no white man ever sets foot without the express permission of the owner? Not estates lying close to Baltimore and Charleston, or even Lexington and Savannah, but remote and savage wildernesses like Legree's estate in *Uncle Tom,* like all the plantations in the interior of Tennessee and Alabama, like the cotton fields and rice swamps of the great muddy rivers of Louisiana and Georgia, like the dreary pine barrens and endless woody wastes of North Carolina. These, especially the islands, are like so many fortresses, approachable for "observers" only at the owners' will. On most of the rice plantations in these pestilential regions, no white man can pass the night at certain seasons of the year without running the risk of his life; and during the day the master and overseer are as much alone and irresponsible in their dominion over their black cattle as Robinson Crusoe was over his small family of animals on his desert habitation. Who, on such estates as these, shall witness to any act of tyranny or barbarity, however atrocious? No black man's testimony is allowed against a white, and who, on the dismal swampy rice grounds of the Savannah, or the sugar brakes of the Mississippi and its tributaries, or the upcountry cotton lands of the Ocmulgee, shall go to perform the task of candid observation and benevolent inquiry?

I passed some time on two such estates—plantations where the Negroes esteemed themselves well off, and, compared with the slaves on several of the neighboring properties, might very well consider themselves so; and I will, with your permission, contrast some of the items of my observation with those of the traveler whose report you find so satisfactory on the subject of the "consolations" of slavery.

And, first, for the attachment which he affirms to subsist between the slave and master. I do not deny that certain manifestations on the part of the slave may suggest the idea of such a feeling; but whether, upon better examination, it will be found to deserve the name, I very much doubt. In the first place, on some of the great Southern estates, the owners are habitual absentees, utterly unknown to their serfs, and enjoying the proceeds of their labor in residences as far remote as possible from the sands and swamps where their rice and cotton grow, and their slaves bow themselves under the eye of the white overseer and the lash of the black driver. Some of these Sybarites prefer living in Paris, that paradise of American republicans, some in the capitals of the Middle States of the Union, Philadelphia or New York.

The air of New England has a keen edge of liberty, which suits few Southern constitutions; and unkindly as abolition has found its native soil and native skies, that is its birthplace, and there it flourishes, in spite of all attempts to root it out and trample it down, and within any atmosphere poisoned by its influence no slaveholder can willingly draw breath. Some travel in Europe, and few, whose means permit the contrary, ever pass the entire year on their plantations. Great intervals of many years pass, and no master ever visits some of these properties: what species of attachment do you think the slave entertains for him? In other cases, the visits made will be of a few days in one of the winter months, the estate and its cultivators remaining for the rest of the year under the absolute control of the overseer, who, provided he contrives to get a good crop of rice or cotton into the market for his employers, is left to the arbitrary exercise of a will seldom uninfluenced for evil by the combined effects of the grossest ignorance and habitual intemperance. The temptation to the latter vice is almost irresistible to a white man in such a climate, and leading an existence of brutal isolation, among a parcel of human beings as like brutes as they can be made. But the owner who at these distant intervals of months or years revisits his estates is looked upon as a returning providence by the poor Negroes. They have no experience of his character to destroy their hopes in his goodness, and all possible and impossible ameliorations of their condition are anticipated from his advent—less work, more food, fewer stripes, and some of that consideration which the slave hopes may spring from his positive money value to his owner—a fallacious dependence, as I have already attempted to show, but one which, if it has not always predominating weight with the master, never can have any with the overseer, who has not even the feeling of regard for his own property to mitigate his absolutism over the slaves of another man.

There is a very powerful cause which makes the prosperity and well-being (as far as life is concerned) of most masters a subject of solicitude with their slaves. The only stability of their condition, such as it is, hangs upon it. If the owner of a plantation dies, his estates may fall into the market and his slaves be sold at public auction the next day; and whether this promises a better or threatens a worse condition, the slaves cannot know, and no human being cares. One thing it inevitably brings: the uprooting of all old associations, the disruption of all the ties of fellowship in misery, the tearing asunder of all relations of blood and affection, the sale into separate and far-distant districts of fathers, mothers, husbands, wives, and children. If the estate does not lie in the extreme South, there is the vague dread of being driven thither from Virginia to Georgia, from Carolina to Alabama, or Louisiana, a change which, for reasons I have shown above, implies the passing from a higher into a lower circle of the infernal pit of slavery.

I once heard a slave on the plantation of an absentee express the most lively distress at hearing that his master was ill. Before, however, I had recovered from my surprise at this warm "attachment" to a distant and all but unknown proprietor, the man added, "Massa die, what become of all him people?"

On my arrival on the plantation where I resided, I was hailed with the most extravagant demonstrations of delight, and all but lifted off my feet in the arms of people who had never seen me before, but who, knowing me to be connected with their owners, expected from me some of the multitudinous benefits which they always hope to derive from masters. These, until they come to reside among them, are always believed to be sources of beneficence and fountains of redress by the poor people, who have known no rule but the delegated tyranny of the overseer. In these expectations, however, they very soon find themselves cruelly mistaken. Of course, if the absentee planter has received a satisfactory income from his estate, he is inclined to be satisfied with the manager of it; and as subordination to the only white man among hundreds of blacks must be maintained at any and every cost, the overseer is justified and upheld in his whole administration. If the wretched slave ever dared to prefer a complaint of ill-usage the most atrocious, the law which refuses the testimony of a black against a white is not only the law of the land, but of every man's private dealings; and lying being one of the natural results of slavery, and a tendency to shirk compelled and unrequited labor another, the overseer stands on excellent vantage ground when he refers to these undoubted characteristics of the system, if called upon to rebut any charge of cruelty or injustice. But pray consider for a moment the probability of any such charge being preferred by a poor creature who has been for years left to the absolute disposal of this man, and who knows very well that in a few days, or months at farthest, the master will again depart, leaving him again for months, perhaps for years, utterly at the mercy of the man against whom he has dared to prefer a complaint. On the estates which I visited, the owners had been habitually absent, and the "attachment" of slaves to such masters as these, you will allow, can hardly come under the denomination of a strong personal feeling.

Your authority next states that the infirm and superannuated slaves no longer capable of ministering to their masters' luxuries, on the estate that he visited, were ending their lives among all the comforts of home, with kindred and friends around them, in a condition which he contrasts, at least by implication, very favorably with the workhouse, the last refuge provided by the social humanity of England for the pauper laborer when he has reached that term when "unregarded age is in corners thrown." On the plantation where I lived the infirmary was a large room, the walls of which were simply mud and laths; the floor, the soil itself, damp with perpetual drippings from the holes in the roof; and the open space which served for a window was protected only by a broken shutter, which, in order to exclude the cold, was drawn so near as almost to exclude the light at the same time. Upon this earthen floor, with nothing but its hard, damp surface beneath him, no covering but a tattered shirt and trowsers, and a few sticks under his head for a pillow, lay an old man of upward of seventy, dying. When I first looked at him I thought, by the glazed stare of his eyes and the flies that had gathered round his half-open mouth, that he was dead; but on stooping nearer, I perceived that the last faint struggle of life was still going on, but even while I bent over him it ceased; and so, like a worn-out hound, with no creature to comfort or relieve his last agony, with neither Christian solace or human succor near him, with neither wife, nor child, nor even friendly fellow being to lift his head from the knotty sticks on which he had rested it, or drive away the insects that buzzed round his lips and nostrils like those of a fallen beast, died this poor old slave, whose life had been exhausted in unrequited labor, the fruits of which had gone to pamper the pride and feed the luxury of those who knew and cared neither for his life or death, and to whom, if they had heard of the latter, it would have been a matter of absolute though small gain, the saving of a daily pittance of meal, which served to prolong a life no longer available to them.

I proceed to the next item in your observer's record. All children below the age of twelve were unemployed, he says, on the estate he visited: this is perhaps a questionable benefit, when, no process of mental cultivation being permitted, the only employment for the leisure thus allowed is that of rolling, like dogs or cats, in the sand and the sun. On all the plantations I visited, and on those where I resided, the infants in arms were committed to the care of these juvenile slaves, who were denominated nurses, and whose sole employment was what they call to "mind baby." The poor little Negro sucklings were cared for (I leave to your own judgment how efficiently or how tenderly) by these half-savage slips of slavery—carried by them to the fields where their mothers were working under the lash, to receive their needful nourishment, and then carried back again to the "settlement," or collection of Negro huts, where they wallowed unheeded in utter filth and neglect until the time again returned for their being carried to their mother's breast. Such was the employment of the children of eight or nine years old, and the only supervision exercised over either babies or "baby-minders" was that of the old woman left in charge of the infirmary, where she made her abode all day long, and bestowed such samples of her care and skill upon its inmates as I shall have occasion to mention presently. The practice of thus driving the mothers afield, even while their infants were still dependent upon them for their daily nourishment, is one of which the evil as well as the cruelty is abundantly apparent without comment. The next note of admiration elicited from your "impartial observer" is bestowed upon the fact that the domestic servants (i. e., house slaves) on the plantation he visited were *allowed* to live away from the owner's residence and to marry. But I never was on a Southern plantation, and I never heard of one, where any of the slaves were *allowed* to sleep under the same roof with their owner. With the exception of the women to whose care the children of the planter, if he had any, might be confided, and perhaps a little boy or girl slave, kept as a sort of pet animal, and allowed to pass the night on the floor of the sleeping apartment of some member of the family, the residence of *any* slaves belonging to a plantation night and day in their master's house, like Northern or European servants, is a thing I believe unknown throughout the Southern states. Of course I except the cities, and speak only of the estates, where the house servants are neither better housed or accommodated than the field hands. Their intolerably dirty habits and offensive persons would indeed render it a severe trial to any family accustomed to habits of decent cleanliness; and, moreover, considerations of safety, and that cautious vigilance which is a hard necessity of the planter's existence, in spite of the supposed attachment of his slaves, would never permit the near proximity, during the unprotected hours of the night, of those whose intimacy with the daily habits and knowledge of the nightly securities resorted to might prove terrible auxiliaries to any attack from without. The city guards, patrols, and night watches, together with their stringent rules about Negroes being abroad after night, and their well-fortified lockup houses for all detected without a pass, afford some security against these attached dependents; but on remote plantations, where the owner and his family and perhaps a white overseer are alone, surrounded by slaves and separated from all succor against them, they do not sleep under the white man's roof and, for politic reasons, pass the night away from their master's abode. The house servants have no other or better allowance of food than the field laborers, but have the advantage of eking it out by what is left from the master's table—if possible, with even less comfort in one respect, inasmuch as no time whatever is set apart for their meals, which they snatch at any hour and in any way that they can—generally, however, standing or squatting on their hams round the kitchen fire; the kitchen being a mere outhouse or barn with a fire in it. On the estate where I lived, as I have mentioned, they had no sleeping rooms in the house; but when their work was over, they retired like the rest to their hovels, the discomfort of which had to them all the additional disadvantage of comparison with their owner's mode of living. In all establishments whatever, of course some disparity exists between the accommodation of the drawing rooms and best bedrooms and the servants' kitchen and attics; but on a plantation it is no longer a matter of degree. The young women who performed the offices of waiting and house maids, and the lads who attended upon the service of their master's table where I lived, had neither table to feed at nor chair to sit down upon themselves; the "boys" lay all night on the hearth by the kitchen fire, and the women upon the usual slave's bed—a frame of rough boards, strewed with a little moss off the trees, with the addition perhaps of a tattered and filthy blanket. As for the so-called privilege of marrying—surely it is gross mockery to apply such a word to a bond which may be holy in God's sight, but which did not prevent the owner of a plantation where my observations were made from selling and buying men and their so-called wives and children into divided bondage, nor the white overseer from compelling the wife of one of the most excellent and exemplary of his master's slaves to live with him; nor the white wife of another overseer, in her husband's temporary absence from the estate, from barbarously flogging three *married* slaves within a month of their confinement, their condition being the result of the profligacy of the said overseer, and probably compelled by the very same lash by which it was punished. This is a very disgusting picture of married life on slave estates; but I have undertaken to reply to the statements of your informant, and I regret to be obliged to record the facts by which alone I can do so. "Work," continues your authority, "began at six in the morning; at nine an hour's rest was allowed for breakfast, and by two or three o'clock the day's work was done." Certainly this was a pattern plantation, and I can only lament that my experience lay amid such far less favorable circumstances. The Negroes among whom I lived went to the fields at daybreak, carrying with them their allowance of food, which toward noon, and not till then, they ate, cooking it over a fire which they kindled as best they could where they were working; their *second* meal in the day was at night, after their labor was over, having worked at the *very least* six hours without rest or refreshment since their noonday meal—properly so called, indeed, for it was meal and nothing else, or a preparation something thicker than porridge, which they call hominy. Perhaps the candid observer, whose report of the estate he visited appeared to you so consolatory, would think that this diet contrasted favorably with that of potato and buttermilk fed Irish laborers. But a more just comparison surely would be with the mode of living of the laboring population of the United States, the peasantry of Ohio, Pennsylvania, and Massachusetts, or indeed with the condition of those very potato and buttermilk fed Irishmen when they have exchanged their native soil for the fields of the Northern and Northwestern states, and when, as one of them once was heard to say, it was of no use writing home that he got meat three times a day, for nobody in Ireland would believe it. The next item in the list of commendation is the hospital, which your informant also visited, and of which he gives the following account: "It consisted of three separate wards, all clean and well ventilated: one was for lying-in women, who were invariably allowed a month's rest after their confinement." Permit me to place beside this picture that of a Southern infirmary, such as I saw it, and taken on the spot. In the first room that I entered I found only half of the windows, of which there were six, glazed; these were almost as much obscured with dirt as the other windowless ones were darkened by the dingy shutters which the shivering inmates had closed in order to protect themselves from the cold. In the enormous chimney glimmered the powerless embers of a few chips of wood, round which as many of the sick women as had strength to approach were cowering, some on wooden settles (there was not such a thing as a chair with a back in the whole establishment), most of them on the ground, excluding those who were too ill to rise; and these poor wretches lay prostrate on the earth, without bedstead, bed, mattress, or pillow, with no covering but the clothes they had on and some filthy rags of blanket in which they endeavored to wrap themselves as they lay literally strewing the floor, so that there was hardly room to pass between them. Here, in their hour of sickness and suffering, lay those whose health and strength had given way under unrequited labor—some of them, no later than the previous day, had been urged with the lash to their accustomed tasks—and their husbands, fathers, brothers, and sons were even at that hour sweating over the earth whose increase was to procure for others all the luxuries which health can enjoy, all the comforts which can alleviate sickness. Here lay women expecting every hour the terror and agonies of childbirth, others who had just brought their doomed offspring into the world, others who were groaning under the anguish and bitter disappointment of miscarriages—here lay some burning with fever, others chilled with cold and aching with rheumatism, upon the hard cold ground, the draughts and damp of the atmosphere increasing their sufferings, and dirt, noise, stench, and every aggravation of which sickness is capable combined in their condition. There had been among them one or two cases of prolonged and terribly hard labor; and the method adopted by the ignorant old Negress, who was the sole matron, midwife, nurse, physician, surgeon, and servant of the infirmary, to assist them in their extremity, was to tie a cloth tight round the throats of the agonized women, and by drawing it till she almost suffocated them she produced violent and spasmodic struggles, which she assured me she thought materially assisted the progress of the labor. This was one of the Southern infirmaries with which I was acquainted; and I beg to conclude this chapter of contrasts to your informant's consolatory views of slavery by assuring you once more very emphatically that they have been one and all drawn from estates where the slaves esteemed themselves well treated, were reputed generally to be so, and undoubtedly, as far as my observation went, were so, compared with those on several of the adjoining plantations.

With regard to the statement respecting the sums of money earned by industrious Negroes, there is no doubt that it is perfectly correct. I know of some slaves on a plantation in the extreme South who had received, at various times, large sums of money from a shopkeeper in the small town near their estate for the gray moss or lichen collected from the evergreen oaks of Carolina and Georgia, upon which it hangs in vast masses, and after some cleaning process becomes an excellent substitute for horsehair, for bed, chair, and sofa stuffing. On another estate, some of the slaves were expert boat makers, and had been allowed by their masters to retain the price (no inconsiderable one) for some that they had found time to manufacture after their day's labor was accomplished. These were undoubtedly privileges; but I confess it appears to me that the juster view of the matter would be this: if these men were industrious enough, out of their scanty leisure, to earn these sums of money, which a mere exercise of arbitrary will on the part of the master allowed them to keep, how much more of remuneration, of comfort, of improvement, physical and mental, might they not have achieved had the due price of their daily labor merely been paid to them? It seems to me that this is the mode of putting the case to Englishmen, and all who have not agreed to consider uncertain favor an equivalent for common justice in the dealings of man with man. As the slaves are well known to toil for years sometimes to amass the means of rescuing themselves from bondage, the fact of their being able and sometimes allowed to earn considerable sums of money is notorious. But now that I have answered one by one the instances you have produced, with others—I am sure as accurate, and I believe as common—of an entirely opposite description, permit me to ask you what this sort of testimony amounts to. I allow you full credit for yours, allow me full credit for mine, and the result is very simply a nullification of the one by the other statement, and a proof that there is as much good as evil in the details of slavery; but now, be pleased to throw into the scale this consideration, that the principle of the whole is unmitigated abominable evil, as by your own acknowledgment you hold it to be, and add, moreover, that the principle being invariably bad beyond the power of the best man acting under it to alter its execrable injustice, the goodness of the detail is a matter absolutely dependent upon the will of each individual slaveholder, so that though the best can not make the system in the smallest particular better, the bad can make every practical detail of it as atrocious as the principle itself; and then tell me upon what ground you palliate a monstrous iniquity, which is the rule, because of the accidental exceptions which go to prove it. Moreover, if, as you have asserted, good preponderates over evil in the practice though not in the theory of slavery, or it would not maintain its existence, why do you uphold to us, with so much complacency, the hope that it is surely, if not rapidly, approaching its abolishment? Why is the preponderating good, which has, as you say, proved sufficient to uphold the institution hitherto, to become (in spite of the spread of civilization and national progress, and the gradual improvement of the slaves themselves) inadequate to its perpetuation henceforward? Or why, if good really has prevailed in it, do you rejoice that it is speedily to pass away? You say the emancipation of the slaves is inevitable, and that through progressive culture the Negro of the Southern states daily approaches more nearly to the recovery of the rights of which he has been robbed. But whence do you draw this happy augury, except from the hope, which all Christian souls must cherish, that God will not permit much longer so great a wickedness to darken the face of the earth? Surely the increased stringency of the Southern slave laws, the more than ever vigilant precautions against all attempts to enlighten or educate the Negroes, the severer restrictions on manumission, the thrusting forth out of certain states of all free persons of color, the atrocious Fugitive Slave Bill, one of the latest achievements of Congress, and the piratical attempt upon Cuba, avowedly, on the part of all Southerners, abetting or justifying it because it will add slave territory and 600,000 slaves to their possessions—surely these do not seem indications of the better state of things you anticipate, except, indeed, as the straining of the chain beyond all endurable tightness significantly suggests the probability of its giving way.

I do not believe the planters have any disposition to put an end to slavery, nor is it perhaps much to be wondered at that they have not. To do so is, in the opinion of the majority of them, to run the risk of losing their property, perhaps their lives, for a benefit which they profess to think doubtful to the slaves themselves. How far they are right in anticipating ruin from the manumission of their slaves I think questionable, but that they do so is certain, and self-impoverishment for the sake of abstract principle is not a thing to be reasonably expected from any large class of men. But, besides the natural fact that the slaveholders wish to retain their property, emancipation is, in their view of it, not only a risk of enormous pecuniary loss, and of their entire social status, but involves elements of personal danger, and, above all, disgust to inveterate prejudices, which they will assuredly never encounter. The question is not alone one of foregoing great wealth or the mere means of subsistence (in either case almost equally hard); it is not alone the unbinding the hands of those who have many a bloody debt of hatred and revenge to settle; it is not alone the consenting suddenly to see by their side, upon a footing of free social equality, creatures toward whom their predominant feeling is one of mingled terror and abhorrence, and who, during the whole of their national existence, have been, as the earth, trampled beneath their feet, yet ever threatening to gape and swallow them alive. It is not all this alone which makes it unlikely that the Southern planter should desire to free his slaves: freedom in America is not merely a personal right; it involves a political privilege. Freemen there are legislators. The rulers of the land are the majority of the people, and in many parts of the Southern states the black free citizens would become, if not at once, yet in process of time, inevitably voters, landholders, delegates to state legislatures, members of Assembly—who knows?—senators, judges, aspirants to the presidency of the United States. You must be an American, or have lived long among them, to conceive the shout of derisive execration with which such an idea would be hailed from one end of the land to the other.

That the emancipation of the Negroes need not necessarily put them in possession of the franchise is of course obvious; but, as a general consequence, the one would follow from the other; and at present certainly the slaveholders are no more ready to grant the political privilege than the natural right of freedom. Under these circumstances, though the utmost commiseration is naturally excited by the slaves, I agree with you that some forbearance is due to the masters. It is difficult to conceive a more awful position than theirs: fettered by laws which impede every movement toward right and justice, and utterly without the desire to repeal them—dogged by the apprehension of nameless retributions—bound beneath a burden of responsibility for which, whether they acknowledge it or not, they are held accountable by God and men—goaded by the keen consciousness of the growing reprobation of all civilized Christian communities, their existence presents the miserable moral counterpart of the physical condition of their slaves; and it is one compared with which that of the wretchedest slave is, in my judgment, worthy of envy.

SLAVE NO MORE

"Slave No More" is a chapter from The Negro in Virginia, *compiled by the Writer's Project of the Works Progress Administration for the state of Virginia.*

THE FIRST RECORDED REVOLT against white rule in Virginia was led by Sam, a black man of Northern Neck, who in 1687 organized slaves to overthrow their masters. When one of the members revealed the plans, Sam was found guilty and sentenced, according to the official court record, to be

> whipt att a cart tayle from the prison round about the town (Jamestown) and then to the Gallows, and from thence to the prison againe and . . . that hee have a halter about his necke during that time, & afterwoard that hee have a strong Iron collar affixed about his necke with four spriggs wch collar he is never to take or gett off nor to go off his master or masters plantation during all the time that he shall live, and if he shall goe off his said master or masters plantation or gett off his collar then to be hanged.

Revolts did not cease when slavery had been established by law. In 1710 slaves of James City and Surry counties set Easter Sunday as the day to rebel. When Will, one of the conspirators, turned traitor, he was promptly set free by his owner because of his "loyalty," while three of his former companions were hanged.

The example was not entirely effective. In 1722 a group of Rappahannock slaves decided to strike for freedom by slaying their masters during public worship. As usual, news of the plot leaked out. When the Negroes approached the church, the worshipers confronted them with leveled muskets.

To the Colonial fathers, running away was the same as rebellion; after 1691 death was the penalty. In 1729 fifteen Tidewater slaves quietly departed from their plantation on the James, taking along "arms and ammunition . . . some provisions, their clothes, bedding, and working tools." They settled in the mountains near Lynchburg, where they built themselves houses. Their master found them, however, and "obliged them, after exchanging a shot or two by which one of the slaves was wounded, to surrender and return back, and so prevented for this time a design which might have been proved . . . dangerous."

In 1730 the coming of Colonel Spotswood precipitated a rumor among Negroes in Williamsburg that the new Colonial governor brought orders from the King to free all baptized slaves. While many slaves sought an early baptism, others "improved this to a great height" and started to enjoy liberty immediately. Stung to desperation when the rumor proved false, a number of slaves determined to be free anyway. But the odds were against them. "Five counties were in arms," with orders to kill all who would not submit.

The American Revolution, during which the "spirit of freedom" was in the air, rekindled in Negroes the hope of liberty. Of the seventy-two revolts or threatened insurrections of slaves in Virginia, sixty-three occurred in the post-Revolutionary years.

The Gabriel Prosser conspiracy at the turn of the century was certainly the most carefully planned slave insurrection. On the morning of August 30, 1800, two Richmond slaves, Tom and Pharoah, told their master a "fantastic" story. That very night eleven hundred Negroes were to assemble at the head of Old Brook Swamp and march the six miles into Richmond, where they would seize the penitentiary and the arms recently stacked there, capture the powder house, kill all who resisted "except the French inhabitants," and then crown one Gabriel, slave of Thomas Prosser, "King of Virginia, with Richmond as the capital." The conspirators expected that thirty thousand Negroes would join them in a week, a force that would enable them to hold Richmond and Petersburg against any number of whites. Out of Virginia would be carved a separate Negro state. If they were repulsed, they planned to withdraw to the mountains, where they could "defend themselves indefinitely." "They could scarcely have failed of success," wrote a Richmond correspondent of the day, "for, after all, we could only muster four or five hundred men of whom not more than thirty had muskets."

Whether the Negroes actually started the march on Richmond will perhaps never be known. Richmond citizens believed that the hand of God alone saved them from destruction. For, instead of an uprising, "the most furious tempest known in Virginia burst upon the land that day." Roads and plantations were submerged; bridges were carried away; and, according to Thomas W. Higginson, "the country Negroes could not get in, nor those from the city get out. The thousand men dwindled to a few hundred. . . . There was nothing to do but to dismiss them, and before they could reassemble they were betrayed."

Still, fear of what might have happened threw Richmond into a turmoil, especially when Ben Woolfolk, another slave, admitted that Gabriel Prosser had given him three shillings to be used for recruiting. Another slave, John Scott, "astonished his master by accidentally pulling ten dollars from a ragged pocket which seemed inadequate to the custody of ten cents." "Where there's coin there must be conspiracy" became the motto of Richmond's vigilantes. Woolfolk, Tom, and Pharoah were granted freedom for their loyalty. Martial law was proclaimed, and all "suspicious-looking" Negroes were arrested. Higginson reports that "men were convicted in one day, and hanged on the next—five, six, ten, fifteen, at a time, almost without evidence."

A three-hundred-dollar reward was offered for Gabriel Prosser, described as "a fellow of courage and intellect above his rank in life, who was about twenty-five years old, but looked to be thirty, he had lost two front teeth and had several scars on his head." The same amount was offered for Gabriel's supposed chief lieutenant, Jack Bowler, alias "Ditcher," who was "a black man about twenty-eight years of age, six feet and four inches high, stout, and perhaps as strong as any man in the state. . . ." Bowler was persuaded to surrender by Peter Smith, who, because he was a Negro, was granted only fifty dollars of the three-hundred-dollar reward. Bowler protested his innocence, but was executed. On September 24 Prosser was discovered in the hold of a schooner which had just sailed from Richmond to Norfolk. A week later crowds mobbed the Richmond courthouse during Prosser's trial. He is said to have "maintained the utmost composure, and with the true spirit of heroism seemed ready to resign his high office and even his life, rather than gratify the officious inquiries of the governor."

On October 7 he was hanged, without having confessed or implicated a single confederate. Further execution of suspected Negroes was halted, a necessary measure, noted a contemporary writer, "owing to the immense number who are interested in the plot, whose death . . . will nearly produce the annihilation of the blacks in this part of the country."

Slaveowners could not understand what motives had prompted so mad a scheme. One rumor spread that the state seal—Virtus standing all-conquering over Tyrannus—had been responsible for the uprising. Deluded by the impression the seal gave on dark wax, Negroes were supposed to have thought it symbolic of the freed slave standing triumphant over his master. Sentiment spread to change the seal. At the state capitol an armed sentinel was stationed for more than a dozen years

—symbol of the fear that another deliverer might arise to carry on where Gabriel left off.

And other "deliverers" were to come. Two slaves of Norfolk, Jeremiah and Ned, planned to burn the town on Easter morning of 1802, according to an accomplice who betrayed them to the authorities. Sentenced to death and driven atop their coffins to the place of execution, the two ringleaders found a tremendous crowd awaiting them. Jeremiah was "turned off" with the cheers of the crowd ringing in his ears; but Ned, "trembling under the gallows," was granted a reprieve, with the hope probably that he would reveal the names of other conspirators.

In 1810 Richard Byrd wrote the governor that an insurrection in Smithfield "is contemplated beyond all doubts." He alleged that a Negro boy, watching a white man blunder through the manual of arms, had observed, "You will all have to use your muskets before long, and if you knew what I know it would be well for you." After twenty lashes the boy admitted that the Negroes he heard talking were from North Carolina. Hearing that he had been named, another slave boy ran away. And, according to Richard Byrd, "Preacher Peter" of Smithfield had told his congregation to come early to meetinghouse on Sunday, since there "was to be an Earthquake, and he wished to explain it to them all." A fourth Negro was heard to declare that "he was entitled to his freedom, and he would be damn if he would not have it in a fortnight." "I am convinced," wrote Byrd, "that the Negro preachers are more dangerous than any other description of blacks."

In January 1811 a mysterious letter came to light in Richmond, addressed to General T. R. and signed with the initials J. B.:

> . . . keep everything silent till that fatal night which will show to the world that slavery will no longer exist in Virginia.
>
> The plans you laid down was good; you say you have 60 under you armed with guns, scythe blades, &c., I have 20 armed with muskets, the rest with old swords and clubs. I think you say we can set fire to Todd's lane, and while the people are there we can set fire up the town. Very good. I will divide my men into 4 divisions. I will command 25. Peter the Bearer, the second; Bob the third, and Henry the 4th. I will be stationed by or near the capitol. Peter near the Eagle tavern, behind the houses. Bob near the Market bridge on the right, and Henry on the left when the houses burn or the alarm is given. We shall set fire to the alley opposite the Bell Tavern. You lay off your men—conduct everything with secrecy and we trust in God. If we succeed we will be very rich. We are moulding balls every night. N. B.—I have a keg of Powder.

If Peter, Bob, Henry, or the ambitious J. B. were located, their fates were never divulged. Relations with England were already strained. Recalling Lord Dunmore's use of Negroes at the outbreak of the Revolution, Virginians were not advertising unrest among their slaves. When the war came in 1812, there arose in many slaves the same hope that had been aroused by the Revolution. One Negro is said to have killed his master, after having heard "that these British people was out to rise against this country." When the American forces planned an attack on Canada at the beginning of the war, John Randolph declared, "We have too much reason to shudder for our safety at home. . . . From the spreading of the infernal doctrine [of French fraternity] . . . the whole South has been thrown into a state of insecurity."

With British soldiers once more on Virginia soil, numerous Negroes in the vicinity of Norfolk went over to the enemy, to be converted, according to one American military officer, into "troops vindictive and rapacious . . . with most minute knowledge of every bypath, they return upon us as guides and incendiaries." Several hundred slaves were landed at Trinidad and emancipated by the British after the war. Just as in post-Revolutionary years, the period following the War of 1812 brought numerous slave uprisings. When George Boxley, a white storekeeper and mystic, let it be known that "a little bird had brought him a holy message, which was that he was to deliver his fellow men from bondage," numerous Negroes of Louisa and Spotsylvania counties conspired with him to carry out the heaven-sent command. Again someone talked—this time a slave woman. Boxley and about two dozen Negroes were arrested, six of whom were hanged and six transported from the state. Boxley mysteriously escaped jail and disappeared.

While his fellow slaves danced, young Nat Turner brooded in silence on July 4, 1826, the fiftieth anniversary of American independence. His mother, transported to Virginia from native Africa in early childhood, had tried to kill the newborn babe rather than have it grow up a slave, and his father, also African-born, finally escaped to Liberia after countless attempts. Nat was superior in intelligence and appearance. He often amused himself by casting different things in molds made of earth; he is said also to have experimented in making paper and gunpowder.

After running away and staying for thirty days in the swamps, Nat astonished other slaves by reporting that "he had lived without food, and that he had seen white spirits and black spirits engaged in battle, and blood flowing in the streams." Turning to his Bible, Nat read about the great man Jesus, to whom also visions had appeared and spirits had talked. He brooded for ten years, during which period he married, led an industrious life, preached, and neither swore nor drank intoxicants. Finally, on May 12, 1828, according to Nat's confession, the Holy Spirit appeared before him and proclaimed that "the yoke of Jesus must fall on him, and he must fight against the serpent when the time appeared."

One August morning in 1831, "the sun's disk seemed, on rising, to have changed from its usual brilliant golden color to a pale, greenish tinge . . . and in the afternoon the naked eye could see on its surface a 'black spot.' "

The time had come. Nat turned to his well-worn Bible, perhaps to the passage that read

From that time began Jesus to show unto his disciples, that he must go unto Jerusalem, and suffer many things of the elders and chief priests and scribes, and be killed.

There was a Jerusalem in Virginia, the county seat of Southampton County, fifteen miles from Cross Keys. Henry Porter, Mark Travis, Nelson Williams, and Samuel Francis were his disciples, to whom were added two new conspirators, Jack Reese and Will Francis. Nat fixed the night of Sunday, August 21, 1831, as the date, and—in order not to arouse suspicion—planned a barbecue feast after church services. While the Negroes feasted, Nat outlined his plan. The sign had come; they must march on Jerusalem that very night. His six disciples grasped their crude weapons and followed Nat.

The first stop was the home of Nat's master, Joseph Travis. Nat ascended a ladder to the upper story of the house, crept down, and admitted his followers. His men insisted that he strike the first blow; he stole to his master's bedside and struck the aroused man with his hatchet. Travis jumped from bed and called his wife. These were his last words. Mark split his skull with an ax, and another slave dispatched the man's wife. In his confession Nat said that, seeing the little baby "sweetly smile as he reached down to take it in his arms," he put it back in the cradle. As he left the house, however, he reflected that "nits make lice." He sent two men back to "take it by its heels and dash its brains out against the bricks of the fireplace."

While the others drank their fill at the cider press, Nat gathered up the muskets and shot and issued them to his band. Then he lined the men up in ranks and paraded them up and down the barnyard, making them rehearse over and over in the few military maneuvers that he knew. From the Travis place they cut a swath of quick death through the countryside, gathering recruits at each house. With practice came efficiency—grab the guns and powder, kill the whites, take the horses, and on to the next house. Now they divided; those on foot proceeded to the nearest house, while the mounted force galloped to places farther off, to unite again at some prearranged station—always a mile or two nearer Jerusalem.

With daylight the news spread, and panic-stricken whites fled their homes. Hysterical crowds gathered in Jerusalem, many to pause there only for a moment's breath. The more intrepid barricaded the old Rochelle homestead and sent couriers posthaste to beg the governor to send troops.

The disciples grew to sixty men, armed with every conceivable weapon. Two miles from Jerusalem a group entered the Parker estate to enlist the slaves, while Nat remained at the gate with seven men. The reconnoitering party, finding that the owners had fled and that the slaves were afraid to join them, loitered to sample the Parker brandy. Nat finally had to go for them. The delay was disastrous. On the county road they met their first resistance—a band of eighteen whites. The whites retreated, and Nat's men pursued them for two hundred yards but halted when they saw white reinforcements approaching. Instead of pressing his advantage, Nat turned back, although it was afterwards said by members of this white troop that Nat could easily have routed their small force and marched straight into Jerusalem. It was now late afternoon, and not another white could be found. Though his men returned to their owners, prepared to swear that they had not participated in the uprising, his six disciples stood guard while he lay in the swamp to rest for the night. The next day was no better; gunfire met them whenever they approached a dwelling. One shot hit Mark, Nat's trusted lieutenant—their first casualty. At daybreak the depleted band swooped down on Dr. Simon Blunt's house, where watchers had waited during the night. The loyal slaves had been armed and drilled, and now Nat was met by gunfire from those he sought to free.

Nat called his remaining followers together and bade them shift for themselves. He went into hiding beneath a pile of fence rails near the Travis house, venturing out only at night for fresh water. Within a week three thousand persons were searching for him.

For six weeks he eluded capture. In the meantime there were many rumors: Nat had been drowned; abolitionists had helped him to escape to Norfolk; he was concealed on a boat bound for Norfolk. Crowds rode to Southampton for the "Negro-hunting." One group of horsemen asked directions of a Negro who was hoeing his garden.

"This is Southampton County," the Negro, a free man, is said to have replied. "My property is right on the county line."

"So you live in Southampton County, do you?" Before an answer could come, the spokesman shot the Negro dead.

According to the editor of the Richmond *Whig,* who was on duty with militia, "Men were tortured to death, burned, maimed, and subjected to nameless atrocities. The overseers were called upon to point out any slaves whom they distrusted, and if any tried to escape they were shot down." A committee of Southampton citizens in a letter to President Jackson declared that "so inhuman had been the carnage . . . that were the Justices to declare a slave innocent, we fear a mob would be the consequence." The heads of some Negroes were impaled on fences to give "warning to all who should undertake a similar plot." At Cross Keys, among a group of prisoners, Mr. Francis discovered Easter, one of his slaves. She had saved his wife's life, and in gratitude he embraced her and ordered that she be freed. But on seeing there Charlotte, who was supposed to have tried to hold his wife for the riders, he "dragged her out, tied her to an oak tree, and fired the first bullet into her." The tree, it is said, "died from the number of shots which pierced it."

For Nat there was no escape. One morning, just after a patrol group had passed without discovering him, he charged from a fodder stack full in the face of one Benjamin Phipps. Exhausted, emaciated, with only a rusty sword for protection, Nat suffered himself to be tied and led at gun's point to the nearest house. When horsemen rode into Jerusalem shouting, "Nat is caught," many rushed for the swamps, thinking the cry to be "Nat is coming."

On Monday, October 31, nine weeks to a day after "bloody Monday," Nat arrived at Jerusalem, not in triumph, but still not in despair. And at what a price! Thirteen men, eighteen women, and twenty-four children—fifty-five whites in all, though estimates vary, and blacks unnumbered—the innocent with the guilty, had met violent death. Estimates of Negroes killed in reprisal ran as high as two hundred. One man boasted that he alone had accounted for fifteen.

Nat was saved for two weeks, with the hope that he would expose other associates. Composed and speaking "intelligently, clearly, and without the least confusion," he answered all questions but declared that he alone had planned the insurrection. With head erect and level gaze, Nat heard Judge Jeremiah Cobb pronounce the sentence of death. And on November 11, Armistice Day now—commemorative of a million others who died for freedom—Nat swung from an old tree in Jerusalem.

Nat Turner's spirit remained to haunt Virginia slaveowners. Houses were locked, and groups of blacks seen talking together were promptly thrown in jail and, in many cases, banished to the cotton country—the worst fate, other than death, that could befall a Virginia slave. Within the year numerous uprisings, or suspected uprisings, were reported throughout Virginia and the Carolinas, while more Negroes were legally executed than in any previous period.

At the next meeting of the General Assembly, Governor Floyd urged the revision of all laws intended to "preserve in due subordination the slave population of our State." The legislature of 1832 enacted Virginia's "black laws," restrictions that were enforced until the end of the Civil War.

For three decades, despite many alarms, there were no serious outbreaks. But the spirits of Prosser and Turner were still slumbering in the hearts of Virginia slaves, if the judgment of John Brown can be relied on. That is what brought old Ossawatomie to the state in 1859.

Late in the summer of 1859, John B. Floyd, Secretary of War, received an anonymous letter, sent from Cincinnati, which read:

> Sir, I have discovered the existence of a secret association, having for its object the liberation of the slaves at the South by a general insurrection. The leader of the movement is "old John Brown," late of Kansas. They will pass down through Pennsylvania and Maryland, and enter Virginia at Harper's Ferry. They have a large quantity of arms at their rendezvous, and are probably distributing them already. As I am not fully in their confidence, this is all the information I can give you. I dare not sign my name to this, but I trust that you will not disregard the warning on that account.

On August 20, the very day the letter was postmarked, Frederick Douglass, runaway slave, abolitionist editor and orator, met John Brown in a rendezvous at a stone quarry near Chambersburg, Pennsylvania. Douglass was accompanied by Shields Green, better known as the Emperor, a South Carolina fugitive, anxious to rescue his wife and children from slavery. A more famous fugitive, Harriet Tubman, who had guided more passengers along the Underground Railroad than any other conductor, was unable to come.

Brown revealed to Douglass that his plan was to capture the government arsenal at Harper's Ferry. For two days Douglass violently opposed the old man, arguing "that such a measure would be fatal to running off slaves [the original plan] and fatal to all engaged." To the old man's eloquence Douglass was deaf, even when Brown begged, "Come with me, Douglass, I will defend you with my life. I want you for a special purpose. When I strike, the bees will begin to swarm, and I shall want you to help hive them." Refusing for the last time, Douglass turned to Green and asked if he was ready to go. But Green, who had taken no part in the long discussion, had made up his mind. "I b'lieve I go wid de old man," he said.

Shields Green became the sixth Negro in John Brown's small force of twenty-two fighters. The others were two Virginians—Lewis Leary and Dangerfield Newby—and John A. Copeland, Osborn Anderson, and John Anderson. Lewis Leary, a 25-year-old mulatto, whose white ancestor of the same name had won glory in the Revolution, had left his young wife and baby in Oberlin, Ohio, to join Brown's forces. A respectable saddle and harness maker, Leary had fallen under John Brown's sway at a meeting in Cleveland. At Brown's summons he had hastened to Harper's Ferry, bringing with him his young nephew, John Copeland. Better educated than the other Negroes, Copeland seems to have appreciated the hopelessness of Brown's plans but to have sensed the psychological effect of the venture.

Osborn Perry Anderson, born in 1830, having escaped from slavery while a young boy, had met John Brown in Canada. When the call came, friends advised against his return to slave soil, but he had no intention of failing his leader. Newby, six feet two inches tall, was described by John Brown's daughter as "quiet, sensitive, and very unobtrusive." Of Scotch and Negro ancestry, he had escaped from Fauquier County, leaving a wife and seven children. That very August Newby's wife had written begging that he buy her and the baby. "Oh, Dear Dangerfield," she wrote, "come this fall without fail, money or no money, I want to see you so much; that is one bright hope I have before me."

Brown's orders were that the whites must be seen only singly, and the Negroes not at all. There was an inquisitive neighbor, a "worse plague than flese." When she was seen approaching, the men would gather the dinner things, tablecloth and all, and climb the ladder into the loft. The furtive waiting was nerve-racking, but the "cause" and the fierce spirit of the "old man" held them together. Watson Brown, the youngest son, wrote his wife during the summer:

> I do want to see you and the little fellow very much but must wait. There was a slave near where we live whose wife was sold South the other day and he was found hanging in Thomas Kennedy's orchard, dead, the next morning. I cannot come home as long as things are done here. I sometimes think perhaps we shall not meet again.

At last the time arrived. At sundown on Sunday, October 16, John Brown quietly told his men, "Get your arms; we will proceed to the Ferry." They loaded into a wagon the pikes, fagots, a sledge hammer, and a crowbar; buckled on arms; drew over their shoulders the long gray shawls, which were to become their winding sheets; and marched two by two down the gloomy road to the Harper's Ferry bridge, defying all military principles by separating themselves from their supply base. Crossing the bridge to Virginia soil at half-past ten in the evening, they made a prisoner of the watchman, William Williams, who "thought it a good joke," then proceeded to take the United States Armory and the rifle works without a shot having been fired.

A raiding party was dispatched to the plantation of Colonel Lewis W. Washington, great-grandnephew of George Washington, with orders to capture the slaveowner, free his slaves, and secure the pistol and sword presented to George Washington by Lafayette and Frederick the Great, respectively. And, to make the act more symbolic, Brown ordered that the tokens be delivered into the Negro Anderson's hands by Colonel Washington himself. The orders were carried out, and in Harper's Ferry the prisoners and their slaves were lodged inside the armory.

When the eastbound train was halted at the bridge, Sheppard Hayward, a free Negro who served as baggagemaster, started toward it to see what the commotion was about. When he did not halt upon command, he was dropped in his tracks, to die twelve hours later on the floor of the railroad station. Thus a free Negro was the first casualty in John Brown's attempt to free Virginia slaves.

When Brown permitted the train to proceed, the tidings were telegraphed ahead. By noon volunteer troops from Charles Town arrived, who forced the guard at the bridge to retreat to the armory. Dangerfield Newby was the first of the invaders to die; a spike bullet slit the Negro's throat from ear to ear.

At the rifle works a quarter of a mile away, Kagi, with the Negroes Leary and Copeland, was less protected than the force in the armory. They tried to ford the Shenandoah River but were forced back to the top of a rock in the middle of the stream, where they presented an easy target. Kagi and Leary were shot down; and Copeland, his powder soaked and useless, surrendered to the citizens. The town physician lodged him in a safe place, though his captors had improvised a rope with their handkerchiefs.

Soon after sundown on Monday night, soldiers of the regular United States Marine arrived with Colonel Robert E. Lee in charge and Lieutenant J. E. B. Stuart as aid. In answer to a demand for his surrender, Brown insisted that his men and their hostages should be allowed to cross the bridge to the outskirts of town, where they would "take their chances." When Stuart reported that no surrender could be arranged, Colonel Lee, as a gesture of state pride, "tendered the assault" to the Virginia volunteers. They "declined the honor," for fear of endangering Brown's hostages. Lieutenant Israel Green of the marines, detailed for the task, ordered eighteen men to ram the enginehouse door with a heavy ladder. Three assaults split the door open, and the marines rushed in "like tigers." Lieutenant Green showered Brown's head with blows that "laid him flat, brought the blood, and seemed to the onlookers as if they must reach his skull."

Of the original force only five of the eleven men captured (Brown, Stevens, Coppoc, Copeland, and Green) were sufficiently alive to be considered prisoners. Watson Brown was past all medical aid. Stretched out in the paymaster's office on a cot, John Brown was surrounded by a crowd of Virginia notables. In spite of his great pain, Brown answered all questions directly and firmly, but refused to name any Northern backers. "Mr. Brown, the silver of your hair is reddened by the blood of crime," remarked Governor Henry A. Wise of Virginia. Brown replied:

> Governor, the difference between your tenure and mine is trifling, and I want to therefore tell you to be prepared; I am prepared. You all [referring to slaveholders] have a heavy responsibility, and it behooves you to prepare more than it does me.

One week after the capture, John Brown, Coppoc, Stevens, Copeland, and Green were brought into Charles Town Courthouse. "I do not know which most to admire," wrote young George H. Hoyt of Brown's legal staff, "the thorough honor and admirable qualities of the brave old border soldier, or the uncontaminated simplicity of the man. . . . The people here, determined to have him die for his alleged offenses, generally concede and applaud the conscientiousness, the honor, and the supreme bravery of the man." When the foreman of the jury pronounced Brown guilty on three counts—murder, treason, and inciting slaves to rebel—the old man "readjusted the covers of his pallet and stretched himself upon it as if he had no interest in the proceedings."

When asked whether he had anything to say before sentence was pronounced, the old man pulled up from his pallet and spoke in clear and confident tone:

In the first place, I deny everything but what I have all along admitted: of a design on my part to free slaves . . . I never did intend murder, or treason, or the destruction of property, or to excite or incite slaves to rebellion, or to make insurrection.

. . . Had I interfered in the matter, which I admit, and which I admit has been proved—for I admire the truthfulness and candor of the greater portion of the witnesses who have testified in this case—had I so interfered in behalf of the rich, the powerful, the intelligent, the so-called great, or in behalf of any of their friends, either father, mother, brother, sister, wife, or children, or any of that class, and suffered and sacrificed what I have in this interference, it would have been all right. Every man in this Court would have deemed it an act worthy of reward rather than punishment.

This Court acknowledges, too, as I suppose, the validity of the law of God. I see a book kissed which I suppose to be the Bible, or at least the New Testament, which teaches me that all things whatsoever I would that man should do to me, I should do even so to them. It teaches me, further, to remember them that are in bonds as bound with them. I endeavored to act up to that instruction. I say I am yet too young to understand that God is any respecter of persons. I believe that to have interfered as I have done, as I have always freely admitted I have done, in behalf of His despised poor, I did no wrong, but right. Now, if it is deemed necessary that I should forfeit my life for the furtherance of the ends of justice, and mingle my blood with the blood of my children and with the blood of millions in this slave country whose rights are disregarded by wicked, cruel, and unjust enactments, I say, let it be done.

No one spoke. Judge Richard Parker pronounced the death sentence. A single spectator clapped his hands and was instantly suppressed. The execution date was set for December 2.

Immediately after Brown's conviction, the trial of the other men—Coppoc, and Cook and the two Negroes, Green and Copeland—proceeded. "Copeland was the prisoner who impressed me best," wrote Judge Parker fifty years later. "He had been educated, and there was a dignity about him that I could not help liking. He was always manly." Andrew Hunter, the prosecutor, is quoted as having said, "Copeland was the cleverest of all the prisoners . . . and behaved better than any of them. If I had the power and could have concluded to pardon any man among them, he was the man I would have picked out." For the Negroes, the unique plea was made that a Negro, having no right of citizenship in Virginia, could not be convicted of treason. When the plea was acceptable to the court, the prosecution obtained quick convictions on two other charges—murder and insurrection.

Talking with his wife for the last time, John Brown declared that he wanted no religious ceremonies, "from ministers who consent or approve of the enslavement of their fellow creatures." Instead he would prefer to accompany him to the scaffold

a dozen slave children and a good old slave mother, with all their appeal to God for blessings on his soul, than all the eloquence of the whole clergy of the commonwealth combined.

But the next morning, when John Brown was brought from the jail wearing the same clothes he had worn to Harper's Ferry, six companies of infantry and one troop of cavalry escorted him to the place of execution. He greeted several persons in the crowd, stepped into the wagon, and took his seat on the white pine coffin. Several thousand witnesses were hemmed into the space between two circles of soldiers—among whom was a man soon to be known as Stonewall Jackson. Brown shook hands with his jailors, thanked them for their kindness, then stood calmly surveying the crowd until a cap was drawn across his head. At eleven o'clock the trap was sprung, and for thirty-five minutes John Brown hung between heaven and earth.

Execution day for the two Negroes, Green and Copeland, was two weeks later. Copeland wrote farewell to his parents in Oberlin:

my fate as far as man can seal it is sealed, but let this not occasion you any misery for remember the cause in which I was engaged, remember that it was a Holy Cause . . . remember that if I must die I die in trying to liberate a few of my poor and oppressed people from my condition of serveatud. . . .

To one newspaper correspondent the Negroes "seemed downcast and wore none of that calm and cheerful spirit evinced by Brown"; while another wrote that "they mounted the scaffold with a firm step," determined to show that "Brown's men could die like himself." After a brief prayer by the clergy, the ropes were drawn tight around their necks. Copeland waited calmly, but Green continued in earnest prayer up to the time the trap was drawn. A moralizing newspaper correspondent is authority for the statement that Green, who had prayed, had his neck broken immediately, while Copeland "writhed in violent contortion for several minutes." The bodies were buried beneath the gallows.

With John Brown and his comrades "moldering in their graves," many Northerners were agreed that the "rope had two ends—one around the neck of a man, the other around the system." At the burial in North Elba, New York, Wendell Phillips declared that "John Brown has loosened the roots of the slave system; it only breathes, it does not live, hereafter." But John Brown himself had been more prophetic. On leaving his cell for the last time, he handed an attendant his final message to the world:

> I, John Brown, am now quite certain that the crimes of this guilty land will never be purged away, but with Blood.

LET MY PEOPLE GO

Henrietta Buckmaster

Henrietta Buckmaster has long been a student of the background history of the Negro during the slavery period. Her latest book is Dark River, *a novel built around the white antislavery sentiment in the hill country of north Georgia.*

TORTURED TO DEATH! We shall torture it "even unto DEATH!" A cold shiver ran down the spines of those who heard. Then this was a war between men of the same race—a civil war? The Underground Railroad men, the abolitionists, saw it as civil war when they mentioned the name of Texas.

Texas had been fitfully in and out of the national consciousness ever since that day in 1836 when Mexico had recognized her independence and Sam Houston had become first president of the new republic. The slavocracy had never forgotten her. Slaveowners regarded her as part of themselves, for were not her blood ties and her slave ties as close as two fingers on a hand? And if Texas looked on Mexico, lying below the Rio Grande, as her enemy, neither did the South equivocate, for in Mexico slaves were free. And if Texas were slow to see the sinister designs of a slaveless England, offering her trade and treaties, the South was quick to show her the dangers that lay with such abolitionists. Clearly these two parts of one whole must melt their destinies into each other!

Annexation—annexation. And on the wings of "annexation" came the spades that would prepare the ground. All the darkest machinations of the British Foreign Office were laid before the startled eyes of Americans. The terrible web she was spinning from Canada down through Oregon on one side, and the West Indies on the other, would knot itself in Texas, and the United States would be trapped, for with England, the small man was told, came freed slaves, Negro insurrections, and cotton competition. Mexicans, moreover, were planning war. Border raids were magnified to such an extent that Texas women were set to molding bullets and making cartridges. Northerners were whipped into concern over vast undeveloped markets which would be lost to them if England were allowed to have her way.

These intrigues dazzled the Texans. They were swift to see the advantages of statehood in the Union. When Mexico threatened that annexation "would be equivalent to a declaration of war," they merely said that Mexico had threatened war before.

But the question was buzzing through the North. Was the United States willing to fight the war that would follow an annexation treaty? The offer of an annexation treaty was the answer. War was a small price to pay to keep the British threat of abolition out of the Southwest and to open up those great plains for slavery.

President Tyler drew up the treaty, signed it, and in April 1844 submitted it to the Senate. The Senate would have nothing to do with it. The Constitution forbade the acquisition of land by treaty. Well, said Tyler, this is not my only plan. The people will decide.

The future of Texas obscured all other issues that election year. Abolitionists, unexcelled now in agitation, stirred many hearts with their warnings against the slavocracy, warnings that sprang from a deeper moral basis than all the justifications of imperialism, of westward destiny, of American investments in Texas. The South, wildly apprehensive, shouted itself hoarse at disunion meetings from Virginia to Louisiana. "The possession of Texas is infinitely more important to us than a longer connection with the Northern States, and if we have to yield either it cannot and shall not be Texas!" a manifesto read. The Democrats declared for annexation, the Whigs equivocated. That the Democrats won the election was all the answer needed by annexationists. "The will of the people had prevailed." This time Congress would obey.

Many people claimed that the Whig votes and the Liberty party votes, counted together, gave a majority against annexation. But the machine could not be stopped. Texas belonged to the slave power. Texas would be cut into four states, and these multiplied representatives would be sent to speak for slavery in Congress.

This, said William Channing in a letter to Clay, "is but the first step of aggression." In the House, John Quincy Adams led the anti-Texans. In Detroit petitions were circulated demanding the annexation of Canada and a return of the balance of power. In Boston a large number of Whigs and a few Democrats called a meeting the first of the new year, 1845—an Anti-Texas Convention—to meet in Faneuil Hall. "The antislavery spirit of the convention was surprising," said Edmund Quincy. "The Address and the speeches of the gentlemen, not abolitionists, were such as caused Garrison to be mobbed ten years ago."

How quickly ten years had passed! To some who had seen a broadcloth mob lead Garrison bound through these very streets it seemed only yesterday. And yet here was a broadcloth convention cheering to the rafters that same Garrison and his words which fell like "fiery rain." He was elected a delegate from his ward, and there was but one thing they failed to do for him that day. They would not act on a certain proposal. But that proposal called for the dissolution of the Union.

It is probable that when Garrison sat down, his thin hawk face imperturbable, his eyes piercing through his spectacles, he was content for the time—*for the time*—to be the only revolutionist. But things would move fast now. Sixteen years would go past more quickly than one could believe.

NO UNION WITH SLAVEHOLDERS had lain across the masthead of the *Liberator* for a year or more. Garrison had made quite clear what he thought of the democratic paraphernalia which cradled slavery so comfortably. "The ballot box is not an antislavery but a proslavery argument, so long as it is surrounded by the U. S. Constitution, which forbids all approach to it except on condition that the voter shall surrender fugitive slaves—suppress Negro insurrections—sustain a piratical representation in Congress, and regard man-stealers as equally eligible with the truest friends of human freedom and equality."

Some of his coadjutors might disagree with him on this point—Ellis Gray Loring, Edmund Quincy—or some of those who accused him of leaving the Negroes in outer darkness while the slaveless North withdrew within its own borders. For them he had the words of John Quincy Adams, "If slavery be the destined sword in the hands of the destroying angel which is to sever the ties of the Union, the same sword will cut asunder the bonds of slavery itself." But to others his dogma of revolution did not need to be explained—to men with minds as hard and smashing as his own, men like Phillips who dazzled and pummeled with his brilliant invectives against the Union, "that unholy alliance of slavery and freedom"; men like Stephen Foster, the theological student, who invaded churches whose members would not come to antislavery lectures and interrupted the services with denunciations of their intrenched conservatism, their tacit consent to slavery, their "Brotherhood of Thieves" ("This hat was crushed for me," he would shout to an antislavery gathering, "in *a church in Portland!*" and his battered topper became the very symbol of the oppressed, the very fount of horror); men like Parker Pillsbury, great, black-bearded Pillsbury, "tearing up words like trees by the roots," as Lowell said, who would turn slowly about on the abolition platform and show his coat, ripped from hem to collar by a pious mob.

The deadly apprehension, the sense almost of doom that harried antislavery men was not out of proportion to the facts. If the Missouri Compromise had troubled men's consciences, the treaty of annexation stirred them deeply, for the intervening years had laid a heavy hand upon the future. When, in March 1845, the outgoing Tyler, with "indecent haste," signed a Senate resolution annexing Texas and left to his successor, the Tennessean, Polk, the disposition of military and naval forces to hold the prize, and when Polk coolly informed his Cabinet that California would soon cease to be a Mexican possession, all the doubts and wonderings were over. The slavocracy had won. The abolitionists acknowledged it with their customary realism. But did it mean that antislavery men would let the challenge pass? No indeed. It meant merely that they would make their cause clang like a fire bell in the North.

They were prepared for a challenge on any front. The diminishing membership of the antislavery societies showed that the fight was broadening its front, was assuming political action. All during the summer of 1845 they held meetings, agitated, kept the question alive, waiting, always, for that Mexican declaration of war. Their power to act was limited, but they could sting the conscience, they could make slavery the most hated thing in the country. On the Fourth of July and on August first, the anniversary of West Indian emancipation, they held great rallies. Eloquence was a golden torrent, intended to tear to pieces the pretensions of the slave power. Jonathan Walker was there, shocking, fit to be gazed at with round eyes, confirming in his own person all that they had said.

Jonathan Walker's story had sizzled through the North like the branding iron on his skin. Anyone there could have told you about him. How he, a New Englander, went to Florida to assist in the building of a railroad. How he treated his black workers in the manner of a Christian, allowing them to eat with him and pray with him, and how he won their friendship. Wasn't it natural—the story passing from ear to ear—for those black men to come to him when they wanted to leave the prison house of Florida? And wasn't it natural that such a man as Captain Walker would agree to help them? In 1844 seven of them, with the captain, pushed off in an open boat from Pensacola for a Bahaman island. They rounded the capes of Florida. But the beating sun prostrated the captain, and the slaves knew nothing of navigation. A shipwrecking sloop found them, drifting and desperate, and seven black men and one white were hauled aboard. Walker was sent to Pensacola in chains, where he lay in a jail, fastened to a ringbolt for fifteen days without bed or chair. After two trials he was stood in a pillory for an hour while a "renegade Northerner" threw rotten eggs at him, and then he was taken out and a branding iron heated. By order of the Federal court the letters SS were burned upon his hand, slave stealer, to bring him glory among the friends of the fugitive. Returned to prison, he was chained until the seven fines for the seven slaves and the costs of his trial were paid, and the seven terms of imprisonment for the seven slaves were served.

Within the year the fines were paid by the abolitionists of the North and the imprisonments were waived. And Jonathan Walker was able to stand at an abolition meeting in Massachusetts and raise his branded hand against the slavocracy. What if the meeting were emotional? Captain Walker, solid, blue-eyed, a son of their own, was asking them to give a hundred times less than he had.

In September they went to another convention—not of the abolitionists but of the still uncertain Whigs. Yet the abolitionists were the ones who saw the issue squarely and made the best speeches. Everywhere anti-Texas men were hastily preparing a unified front against the awful juggernaut of the slavocracy. In Massachusetts, public meetings were held all over the state, and some of her most distinguished men let their oratory mount to stirring heights. Petitions, signed by tens of thousands, were gathered and borne off to Washington by Henry Wilson and John Whittier.

It was a fine effort, but too many of the antislavery politicians had already admitted defeat. Seward wrote a public letter to Chase, submitting to the annexation, deploring the talk of disunion, and urging that the abolition work be concentrated, not on whipping a dead horse, but on electing an "independent Congress" which would stem the slave trade. One by one they submitted, and by their submission sapped the courage of many brothers.

Yet New Englanders were aroused. Pride in their revolutionary antecedents had been stirred. Faneuil Hall was jammed in November; Palfrey, the secretary of state, was chairman of the meeting. On that day Charles Sumner rose in his seat and took his first public part in the fight that would carry him to the Senate, to the cause of "Bleeding Kansas," to the pummeling stick of Preston Brooks, to emancipation. He fought valiantly on that occasion against the defeatism of those who professed antislavery principles and yet accepted the Texas annexation with a bowing of the head. The meeting was fervent. Committees were organized in the best New England fashion. There was something deeply stirring in their freshness, vitality, and inexhaustible faith in good. Had abolitionists ever accepted defeat before? Never! And they let the cry ring around Faneuil Hall, whip at lagging spirits, and sweep Garrison, the saturnine, onto the committee that was authorized to rouse the state into action. How true to himself Garrison always was. The misfit, the radical, with the faint smile that rounded his lips, consented to the post as "an experiment to demonstrate the futility of any and every attempt to assail slavery in its incidents and details." Texas was a detail. He had larger game to catch. He had the whole slave power to fasten on the end of his hook.

When the emotions had subsided, when the cold days of winter arrived and Texas became a state, they saw that he was right. They saw that with the division among themselves—Whigs, Liberty men—the slave power could always seep in through the cracks.

When Congress convened, they waited to hear what John Quincy Adams, aged, the fire in him subsiding, had to say. There was not very much to say. He laid the petitions they had gathered, thousands of signatures, before the House, and the House tabled them. Stephen Douglas, the cherubic little man from the West with the sly eyes and the barroom manners, presented a resolution to admit Texas to statehood. A majority of five to two agreed with him. Daniel Webster, with the ravages of ambition catching at his beetling brows, darkening his deep-sunk eyes, protested in the name of Massachusetts. Others stood up, men dedicated to an expanding North, and solemnly voiced their condemnation, their words echoing with a hollow solemnity in the restive chamber, a consciousness possessing them that the day would come when their fine expanding North would outgrow scenes like this, would be strong enough to sit elbow to elbow with the slavocracy and speak with a lusty voice.

Antislavery men in the North might admit discouragement, but the abolitionists laughed. Garrison wrote jovially to a friend, "Apparently the slaveholding power has never been so strong—has never held such complete mastery over the whole country—as at the present time; and yet never has it in reality been so weak, never has it had so many uncompromising assailants, never has it been so filled with doubt and consternation, never has it been so near the downfall as at this moment." And Edmund Quincy, writing to the same friend, took up the note: "Garrison is in good spirits as he always is, and as we all have a trick of being. Mrs. Follen says that when she wants to be put in spirits, she goes among the abolitionists, and there she is sure to find cheerfulness, wit, humor, and fun. And who should be cheerful and merry in this country but the abolitionists?"

They knew why they were merry. Civic consciousness was roused. Agitation like this would make men realize that occasional voting was not the sum of their duty, that all the wide promises of freedom must be kept for others if they were to be kept for themselves. Garrison was not the only man to say that the slavocracy had overreached itself, that Texas, with its million acres, slave-hungry, was the swan song of a swollen oligarchy.

Boston was deeply alive those days in the searching of its spirit. Men still made money on State Street, workers still sat fifteen and twenty hours a day at spinning looms, but New England was flowering in the deep places of the heart and mind, and her great men were bringing her the exquisite immortality that was to lie like a balm on the brutality of a new industrial age. The Boston of the 1830s and '40s was a world of new ideas. German idealism, French enlightenment, Swedenborgian mysticism, spiritualism, possessed the underlying channels of thought and mingled with the doctrines of revolution—Communism, women's rights, temperance, protection for the insane, rehabilitation of prisoners—all social panaceas for a new age. Emerson, who had cut away from his church, searching for truth, had propounded his intellectual Declaration of Independence seven years before and pulled at the roots of orthodoxy with his challenges. Young Theodore Parker, with the round, formidable skull and the vigilant eyes, had found his "soul so aroused" by this "declaration . . . so beautiful, so terribly sublime," that within three years he had proclaimed his own iconoclasm and left his church—at its request. By 1845 he was preaching not to the handful who had filled his regularly appointed church but to the thousands who filled Melodeon Hall to enjoy the fine clear blast of his championship of freedom, of the soul, the mind, and the body. That year he joined the antislavery society and began fourteen years of agitation that was paralleled only by Garrison and Phillips. He made the North his parish and became a self-appointed conscience, his name and his fame spreading from Maine to Mississippi. Over the principle of abolition he threw the fabric of transcendentalism, so that it became not merely a material agitation but a profound intuition of the spirit; into its mouth he put his own inexhaustible erudition; finally to the cause itself he gave his vivacity, his humor, and his love of action.

In Cambridge, Longfellow, the most popular author of his America, was writing thunderously on slavery, and what he said stood for a while, although by 1848, when he refused to allow his abolition poems to be included in his collected works, his thunder had muttered away and left him face to face with the indignant abolitionists. James Russell Lowell, ecstatically a bridegroom, was a perfect zealot of a reformer, writing for a pittance a stream of antislavery articles and shouting gloriously while his fervor was still fresh. Alcott, happy, ardent, dreaming, could not keep himself from something that so closely touched on life, and lent his sweet unworldliness to a cause that seemed a whole soul removed from him, yet was in reality a deep spirituality translated into action. Thoreau, dwelling in a world where there was no slavery of black or white, quite naturally, with no struggling of the intellect or the conscience, reached out a hand to the fugitive.

In the antislavery world away from Boston, politics were more powerful than cultural philosophy.

In Congress, Giddings and Adams were no longer fighting a solitary battle. Owen Lovejoy was there, the brother of the martyr. And Gates and Tilden from New York, Mixson from Ohio, Slade from Vermont, as well as former Governor Crafts, who was vice-president of the Vermont Antislavery Society, Clarke of western New York, a section now becoming a roadbed for the "railroad." Ohio also sent a Tappan to the Senate, a brother of the redoubtable pair in New York City. They were all products of a rising political thought, yet all outcasts, all hated and abused.

What peculiar leaven, then, was knitting the small men of the North loosely—very loosely—into a new way of thinking? Had the slavocracy indeed overreached itself? Were industrial ambitions perhaps stronger than devotion to Southern interests? Yet the farmer of Ohio, where politics flourished in such congenial soil, had very little concern with the manufacturers of the East.

He must have sensed something that was blowing fresh across the Eastern hills and the Western prairie land—a new world that ran on iron rails and that gave to life a curious exhilaration. A generation ago someone's father had been the first man to nail two boards together and begin a house and a town out this way. That town had grown, whether it was called Springfield, Illinois, or Akron, Ohio, and people had grown with it. They weren't sophisticated people; when an Abe Lincoln started off for the Illinois legislature and a Ben Wade started off for the Ohio legislature, and put on their shiny stovepipe hats, this did not mean that the world was coming in; it merely meant that two men were going to another town of mud streets where rooting pigs and cows contested the way with them. But there they learned something—learned maybe that a railroad had been built in Russia, that in England people were sending ships across the Atlantic to buy their corn and wheat. Russia and England weren't much farther off than the Alleghenies, then? Just beyond those mountains, down those long iron rails, were people who needed the men of Ohio, of Indiana, of Illinois, even the men of that terribly faraway Pacific coast. The world was drawing very close. Railroads were beginning to shape the thoughts of men. They brought new things for the women, sewing machines and other curiously natural devices that the new power-driven factories of the East were producing; they brought tools to men—quick and cheaply—so that men no longer had to cut and shape their own implements. From Chicago they brought a new harvesting machine which a man named McCormick promised would mean riches for the farmers. Railroads were the explanation of a new life, a panacea for old ills.

All that railroads signified gave men a new attitude toward that huge commanding land below the Ohio River which had no railroads to speak of, which talked instead of its power in cotton, which made fractional representation out of their slaves in order to keep Congress jumping according to their plan. (They knew about it in Ohio and especially in Illinois because of the men who crossed over to make their homes among them.) Maybe those men in the South had a right to their slaves; they weren't going into that; but they were beginning not to like the airs they gave themselves. When a runaway came along, white-eyed with nerves, it was a slap at the high-and-mightiness of his master if space were made in the corncrib. After all, men of the North didn't need black boys to work for them. They weren't ashamed of their own two hands!

Into all this, Garrisonism was growing, in Ohio and Michigan where the Liberty party was strong, growing enough to make a pipeful of talk, perched on the rail of the crossroads store, for Garrison and none-resistance, Garrison and non-voting had never found such root before in the Western temperament. Maybe it was the people who came preaching Garrisonism—Abby Kelly and Stephen Foster and Parker Pillsbury—nobody's fools, with voices as loud as any hecklers', plain people. Abby Kelly looked like one of their women, no furbelows, no foolishness, arms primly crossed above her stomach, a nice hot temper. And Pillsbury and Foster made dandy stump speeches and didn't mind the words they used, or those their audience used. You could laugh them down, but they just roared a little louder and threw in a story for good measure. Maybe most people went away laughing, but some did not. Some stayed to talk a little longer. In Salem, Ohio, where the Quakers were strong, they even founded a paper and called it the *Anti-Slavery Bugle*. It blew its little tune for twenty years, while other antislavery papers rose and fell, and its little tune never varied—"No Union with Slaveholders!"

Probably some of these things were unimportant—small people using small means to create a revolution—but they fell into the pattern of those years, and their small design added to a larger scroll, a big scroll that was just beginning to unwind itself in the Texas annexation.

The excitement had grown with the summer. Florida had come in as a slave state with a constitution that attempted to prohibit, *forever,* the possibility of freedom. Northern men hurriedly presented Iowa, and the balance was restored, precarious, artificial. The country was subtly, within its own heart and mind, preparing for war. The farmer in Ohio, the artisan in Pennsylvania, the schoolteacher in New England, might not have recognized war in the food they ate, the newspapers they read, the spinning looms they manipulated, the plow they guided; and the shopkeeper in Louisiana, the small planter in Georgia, might not have seen war in the cotton, going up the slow rivers and disappearing into the hungry doors of Northern factories, or in the rising price of slaves or the rising value of manufactured goods, but certainly they must all have known that the new quickening of the eyes, the pregnant silences and exchange of glances when free land was spoken of carried a threat as far as the Pacific, as far as the Rio Grande. Free Land! It brought a swifter response than Free Man had ever done. Whig turned against Whig, Democrat against Democrat.

The German immigrants, flying to America from political oppression, took up the cry with a contagious zeal. The young and gangling trade-unions recognized in it the very shape and color of the proletariat. The abolitionists saw in it the deathblow to the slavocracy.

But the slavocracy had seen it too. Without slavery extension, the industrial North would outstrip it; the balance of power would be lost; the domination of the Supreme Court, the foreign service, the army, the navy, and the administrative branches would be gone. Hysteria was strengthened by atrocity stories. When Mexico moved she must face a United States bound together by a common hatred of the dark men below the border. As the summer went on, many of the real issues were lost in the stimulated hatred.

But Mexico moved too slowly. When a "border incident" was invoked early in 1846, when Polk ordered General Zachary Taylor to advance into Mexican territory, the slavocracy, much as it might deplore the effect of war, drew a deep breath. The West would now be made safe for slavery.

The excitement was electric. Polk had moved adroitly and inconspicuously. Protests and acclamations were both anticlimaxes. He calmly declared that a state of war existed, and Congress without delay voted men and money. A year before, orders had gone to the commander of the Pacific fleet to seize California when the word was given, and the word was now given. More than half of Mexico was demanded by the United States.

Voices in Congress were a cheap commodity. Yet Giddings' roar filled the chamber, as he stalked, rough-haired, bushy-browed, up and down the aisles, shaking his fury under the nose of Southern Democrats. And Corwin of Ohio wrote his epitaph when he flung out his arms and shouted to a turbulent House, "If I were a Mexican, I would greet you with bloody hands and welcome you to hospitable graves!" But from their long, thin friend Lincoln, from Illinois, fell the counsel of the future, the "sacred right of the people . . . to rise up and shake off the existing government, and form a new one that suits them better [since] it is the quality of revolutions not to go by old lines or old laws, but to break up both and make new ones."

The abolitionists—well, they were not surprised. Perhaps even, in the secret of their beds at night, they were a little glad that the hand of slavery had shown itself so clearly. Garrison merely reiterated, with his inspired monotony, "What the people need is a new government—a free government—NO UNION WITH SLAVEHOLDERS!"

Garrison had had an invitation to go to an antislavery convention in London. He hesitated for a little while, for this was no time for leaders to be away from home, and Elizur Wright and Arnold Buffum were both absent, and Frederick Douglass was already triumphantly in England. But, after all, there was nothing new here. A crisis would not arise from the Mexican War, although the Mexican War would lay the groundwork for a crisis. And he was needed in England. His friend George Thompson was making it evident that reactionary forces were slowly gaining control of abolition sympathy in England, and English support was invaluable to the American abolitionists. Someday there would be a showdown, and England must be on the side of freedom.

In the South the recognition of war rose here and there among the slaves. In Pensacola, "as soon as a sufficient number of white men went off to war" they intended to rise, and martial law was declared in the navy yard, and patrols filled the city. In Louisiana, Solomon Northup, free colored man of New York, who had been kidnaped and lived for twelve years in slavery, found that "the news of victory filled the great house with rejoicing, but produced only sorrow and disappointment in the cabins."

All the while in Washington, that dusty, dirty city where soldiers on parade at the last inauguration had sprawled in the slippery mud, where pickpockets worked their trade at the best receptions, where every dialect could be heard, but mostly the soft or nasal tones of the South, where pigs rooted in the streets and slave coffles shuffled past the Capitol, here in this fierce town the forensics rose and fell with the course of the war, and Lincoln, who hated the war, became an intimate of Alex Stephens, that "little pale star from Georgia," who saw, bound into the war, all that he believed. Here Andrew Johnson, come from Tennessee with the rooted bitterness which made one know him for a "poor white," sneered at that other poor man from Ohio, Josh Giddings, and the exquisites from Massachusetts listened with startled good manners to Steve Douglas, who, by the testimony of Adams, "in the midst of his roaring stripped off and cast away his cravat, to save himself from choking, unbuttoned his waistcoat, and had the air and aspect of a half-naked pugilist." Here men hated at the tops of their voices and drew a fierce line, more visible than Mason and Dixon's, between their individual interests and concerns. Even the Southern Whigs, who were theoretically against annexation, saw the wisdom of adding their voices to the Democrats, for the only alternative was a denunciation of slavery expansion, and slavery politics were more important to them than a plank in a badly nailed platform. Only Calhoun, gaunt and burned out but mighty, was filled with dismay at the thing that he had done. This was the Texas he had maneuvered, as Secretary of State for Tyler, out of the hands of the British and therefore out of the hands of emancipationists. But he had not intended this; he had not meant to drown it in blood or bring slavery with the sword to a free half-breed population. Some of his Southern Whig disciples attempted to find a compromise, perhaps even a solution. "They were for their country right or wrong, but Congress had the right to declare War, and it was the President who had done it." But a new kind of politician, full of hot chauvinism, arrogant with thousands of miles of cotton furrows, was putting aside such men as Calhoun. At their hands the war was legalized.

By August 1846, Polk was asking for more money "for the purpose of settling our difference with Mexico." He suggested that two million dollars would be an adequate sum. The dissident Whigs and those few Democrats who could not go with the war party were not prepared to let such an opportunity pass. Voices were raised sharply. Party lines were broken. This congressman would not vote for the appropriation unless he were assured that slavery would be limited. Another seconded him. Another rose to repeat the same thing in different words. Finally David Wilmot of Pennsylvania stood up with a carefully drafted amendment.

He moved that slavery should be forever barred from any territory taken in this war. The champions of slavery rose with a roar, yet the proviso burned through all the questions of the war that session and the next. It lay on the lips of men and women everywhere, for it had become a greater issue than the war itself. Sectional lines were broken through again and again. And meanwhile the war went on without the two-million-dollar appropriation.

Had the Northern forces been united, had the proviso been acted upon quickly, some comfort might have been taken from the months of debate. But by January 1847 it was evident that the slavocracy had recovered whatever ground was lost and set its machinery to work. Whatever fight was left was merely a matter of principle. On the last day of the session Wilmot again offered his amendment as the appropriations bill came up, and 102 voted against it, 97 in its favor. The President now had two million dollars with which to negotiate a peace. And slavery was unrestricted.

For antislavery men who were not abolitionists it was a dark and disturbing moment. To the Garrisonians it was merely further proof that political action was futile. To other abolitionists it was a clear call for a new political party. Soon—very soon—America must know its own mind.

That summer Garrison went on his first Western tour. It was not a pure triumph, for his reputation met him everywhere, and sometimes he was not able to contend with it, but it was on the whole a remarkable success for Garrisonism, that strange flower in the Middle West. Edmund Quincy edited the *Liberator* while he was gone, and Frederick Douglass accompanied him. A Frederick Douglass now sure of himself, beginning to show his superb talents, infusing the facts in which he dealt with the warm splendor of a magnificent voice. England had done a great deal for him. He had traveled there alone, lecturing and being received without a trace of prejudice. To England he was a man of talent and virtue, and Englishmen did not seem in the least concerned by the color of his skin. It had been hard to come back to America, where, on one occasion, he had been forced to tear up the plush seats of the general passengers' coach on his way to forceful exile in the Jim Crow car. Yet now he was a celebrity, and other celebrated men in the North were pleased to meet him, although lesser men still greeted him and other colored abolitionists with stones.

The tour of Garrison coincided with the fall of Mexico City and the virtual end of the war. Garrison, who missed nothing, who explained everything according to the undeviating pattern of his principles, carried the battle of disunion as far as Ohio, where crowds pressed eagerly to hear him debate the question with Giddings, his outspoken admirer. Middle Westerners were not afraid of the rough-and-tumble; they were more realistic, more willing to admit that the possibility of a political upheaval might be closer upon them than they suspected. Farther West, in Indiana, the ground had been well covered by antislavery lecturers, telling their stories at meetings in log cabins, in schoolhouses, in places where ox teams were the only means of locomotion, where they had to carry their own supply of candles to light the poor back-country meeting-houses, where tracks of split logs, unsoftened by earth, jogged their wagons to pieces as they looked for a night's hospitality.

The Mexican War had aided them. It had taken more time, cost more money, and given people more opportunity to study the purpose and mentality of the slavocracy than the war enthusiasts had anticipated. And the wind that was blowing carried the questions and the doubts not only to those Middle Western men who were making their own futures and knew well their own pasts, but to the settlers of the West, where modern industrialism was a farfetched phenomenon, and to the God-hungry, trade-hungry men of New England and the Atlantic States. For they remembered things that the slave power had forgotten, remembered a country which had produced men like Jefferson, the revolutionist, and Franklin, the philosopher of freedom. The overflow meetings, come to hear the Fosters, Stephen and Abby Kelly, Burleigh with the head of a fierce and uncouth Jesus, Pillsbury, and now Garrison and Douglass, made these remembrances increasingly evident. "I have seen nothing like it," Garrison wrote his wife. "Yesterday we held three large meetings, two of them in the open air, and concluded last night with the greatest enthusiasm. The place seems to be electrified, and the hearts of many are leaping with joy."

Abolition was not the only topic which drew the crowds, for Garrison was ready to expose the Church and the State, to preach the doctrine of disunion and combat the budding dogma that the Constitution was an antislavery document—an attitude of mind which he regarded as flagrant wishful thinking. A reshapen public opinion on all these matters would, he was convinced, break the mesmerism that made blind devotion to inflexible values seem the very form of integrity, the exact sum of patriotism. Garrison was not a man to see the minutiae of the future; he had no political training or social philosophy to allow him to prognosticate: he saw only an evil and its destruction. The vibrations in the air could not be identified by him. It is questionable if any man had the vision to see what lay so soon in the future.

By the summer of 1847 several inescapable facts had been established. Stung by the Mexican War, by the impact of fugitives on the emotions, and by the dynamics of abolitionists which brought forth friends and enemies, fully grown, it was evident that antislavery sentiment had grown with startling impressiveness within the rigid limits of the Whigs and Democrats and would play a large part in the forthcoming presidential campaign and provide a challenge that was bigger than the Liberty party had met in 1844. Yet the party itself was at a standstill. From Maine came word that it was merely holding its own and anticipating "certain death" if something were not done to relieve its static condition. Gerrit Smith spoke frankly of a falling away on all sides, and proved this statement by carrying off the most influential of the Negro supporters, Henry Highland Garnet and Frederick Douglass (who had by now split irremediably with Garrison on the question of politics), into the new Liberty League.

In a Massachusetts by-election the original Liberty party polled only ten thousand votes, and in a similar New York election it fell from sixteen to twelve thousand. The strong political abolitionists were still among the Whigs.

It was evident that political abolition must find a new policy, adopt some method that would compete successfully with that political dreadnaught, the Democratic party, and with the ailing but still sprightly Whig. Garrison, pleased by the small flowering buds of his Western trip, stopped over in Buffalo long enough to heap scorn on the Liberty party convention which was attempting to find a solution for this restive problem. To him the dilemma had been easily anticipated and was now justifying the jeremiads of himself and Phillips. They had predicted that antislavery alone would prove insufficient for a political group, and this fact was now being discovered by the very men who had found Garrison's reform movements too scattered for concentrated loyalty. Birney, Smith, Goodell, Beriah Green were urging free trade, direct taxation, government monopoly of mails, disbandment of the army and navy, distribution of public lands, as necessary concomitants of a sound reformation party. (Women's suffrage was still too much for them. That must be left to the women themselves, meeting at Seneca Falls the next year, and to the colored conventions meeting a few weeks after that at Cleveland and Philadelphia. At Seneca Falls the women recognized their common interests with the slaves by nearly electing Frederick Douglass chairman; at Cleveland and Philadelphia resolutions of feminine equality were among the first to be passed.) Discontented Whigs and Democrats would thus be disarmed and absorbed and would find themselves imbibing antislavery with other advanced ideas. This was still heresy to the original framers of the party, yet the two factions came together at Worcester, Massachusetts, in September, and mended their breaches for a few months until bigger things and larger issues wiped out the Liberty party forever.

Seen with even a limited vision, these events were all of a single design: they all made antislavery a fitfully sleeping giant in the land. To some observers the antislavery forces might appear disturbed and breaking; to others they might appear to be losing their pure absorption in the liberation of the black man and his unequivocal right to citizenship. From an absolute point of view both were perhaps right. That which came from political and economic necessities could not have the same pure altruism, the same infinite compassion as that which had come with the early zealots. Expediency might bring the end of slavery, but would expediency build a strong world for the Negro? Yet antislavery, a bare ten years after the gag rule, was in the consciousness of all Americans.

Even some of the border states were roused over the further extension of slavery. Delaware came so close to legislation providing for gradual emancipation that Calhoun, prophesying a new balancing of power, cast Delaware on the side of the free states. Western Virginia, where slaves were proving a bad economic investment, allowed the antislavery forces a power that threatened for the time to draw it from the orbit of the slavocracy. While in Kentucky, Cassius Clay, the scion who had heard Garrison speak in New Haven, was agitating with all the powers of his impeccable Southern name and his unassailable social position for the abolition of slavery, although his life was scarcely worth a farthing, his vicissitudes being taken from the same book as those of Birney, or of Daniel Goodloe, who was waging the fight in North Carolina.

In every case the oligarchic machine worked fast and ruthlessly, but there was a not unnatural perturbation in the very swiftness forced upon it. Many straws were in this now new and unpredictable wind. Passage or attempted passage of laws protecting the Negro from slave hunters were rousing the legislatures of all states which did not have personal liberty laws. The boycott of slave produce was growing with small but impressive strides. Levi Coffin had been forced to leave his Indiana home and move to the larger city of Cincinnati in order to act upon the money subscriptions and resolutions passed by free-labor conventions which authorized immediate organization of free-labor associations in the West.

For some time Westerners had been faithful supporters of free-labor products, but their demand for sheeting, yarn, muslin, exceeded the cotton supply of free-labor planters. As a Southerner, Coffin knew that the South was filled with small farmers, non-slaveholders, whose small patches of cotton were in hopeless competition with the great plantations. By correspondence he now learned that contacts might be made with some of these small farmers for free-grown cotton. But that was not enough, since slave labor ginned and baled it. At last, with the cooperation of the Philadelphia Free Labor Association, a gin was bought and shipped to a Quaker farmer in Mississippi who agreed that the entire process should be done by himself and his hired labor. The associations agreed to buy all the cotton in reach of that "Abolition gin" provided it were shipped to Memphis, the nearest shipping point that used free labor. In Memphis it was to be handled by a well-recommended commission merchant who used no slave labor, and shipped up the river on boats, manned by free men. Large quantities of cotton were thus made available, and the Philadelphia Association was able not only to keep Levi Coffin supplied, and through him the mills and the free-labor consumers of the West, but to ship good quantities to the Manchester mills of England in exchange for a finer grade of goods than they were then producing. A Quaker agent was hired to keep a continuous check on the producers and middlemen in the South, and local agents were employed to pay for the cotton on the spot and arrange for its shipping to Memphis.

Coffin himself went as far south as Mississippi, carrying with him his staunch abolition views, his fearlessness, and his humor. His Quaker dress set him apart. Men accepted the fact that he probably did not believe in slavery, and many times a stranger fastened himself to Coffin with an eager volubility, curious to hear the statements of an abolitionist, eager to argue against them, or, as Coffin had occasion to discover a number of times, eager to agree that slavery was the greatest curse of the South.

He was thankful, he said to his abolition friends later, that he had found such an open field for spreading antislavery principles. Every journey through the South to buy free-labor cotton, every encouragement to paid labor, was in reality a plea for the cause of the slave.

His free-labor business grew so rapidly that difficulties were soon upon him. The demand for free-labor goods had spread so far that he was receiving orders from all the free states west of the Alleghenies, from Canada, and from Kentucky and western Virginia. His supply was not equal to the demand, and neither he nor the Philadelphia Association had the equipment to fill orders. He needed a larger capital investment, and men with money were not interested in free-labor products. The Free Labor Association in Indiana attempted to organize a stock company, but antislavery men were not the ones with money to invest. It was a tantalizing uphill struggle, but he was able to fight for his growing business for ten years, while the market for free-labor goods developed all over the free states and in England.

When he left Indiana for Cincinnati he had fondly believed that his Underground Railroad work was over. He had been a conductor for twenty years, and other aspects of the cause seemed now to demand his time and energies. Familiar with the abolitionists of Cincinnati, he had believed that the work was in good hands. It took him only a short time to discover that the fugitives were mainly dependent on their own endangered and exposed people, and that the "railroad" was in much the same condition here as it had once been in Newport, Indiana. Cincinnati, that half-Southern city, was consistently hostile to abolitionists; they were ostracized in religious and political associations, and it took courage to assume the work of underground activities. It was a foregone conclusion that Coffin would not be able to leave the situation as he found it. He resumed his acquaintanceship with the abolition workers of Cincinnati and organized a more successful resistance to the slave catcher as well as a lively and active station for the Underground Railroad. The word spread rapidly, in that inexplicable manner which characterizes all underground activity, and it was only a matter of days before the fugitives were finding their way once more to a Coffin house.

They came from directly across the river and from Ohio River boats. They also came, now and then, from Rankin's famous "Abolition college" at Ripley, where that indefatigable little man, with his spotless white stock, unending geniality, and nine sons, was doing a thriving and dangerous business.

What effect the Mexican War had on the underground work is undetermined. When he moved to Cincinnati, Coffin was struck by the increase of runaways. How much of this was due to the position of the city itself on the banks of the river, and how much to the underswell of restlessness in the South, cannot be said. In any case, the work intensified to such an extent that the need for vigilance deepened in proportion, and Coffin was obliged to nip off more and more time from his business in order to supervise the concealment and safe conveyance of the runaways.

With runaways multiplying, the cost of the work increased. More material must be supplied to the antislavery sewing circles, more wagons and teams hired to make the journey to the next station, twenty or thirty miles away. A two-horse team cost ten dollars, and often two or three teams were required at one time. Coffin dealt with a German livery stable, sending an innocent colored man to transact the business and pay in advance for the wagons. The German seemed to understand that no questions were expected, and Coffin counted on this discretion. It was necessary to take every precaution in order to keep clear of the law. He himself seldom saw the colored man who hired the wagons, but gave the money and instructions to an intermediary. The drivers of the wagons were generally chosen in the same way, from colored men who owned no property and therefore would lose nothing if they became entangled with the law. These drivers must, first of all, have courage and resourcefulness, for although they always left at night, their drive might not be completed until the early hours of the daylight, and with daylight came all the dangers of discovery and arrest.

But the danger of the underground work did not, apparently, put any limits on the sex or previous condition of the workers. No man could have shown more courage and enterprise than Laura Haviland. She was a plain, prim-mouthed little Quakeress who lived in northern Michigan and brought up her children with a brisk concern for the details of integrity and self-reliance. But domesticity was not enough for her. Her energy needed wider scope. In 1837 she had started Raisen Institute because she believed in mixed education, both as to sex and color. For some time she had followed the example of other energetic abolition women by running an Underground Railroad station. Not entirely satisfied with the limitations of her plot of earth, she made several trips with fugitives into Canada to see them safely out of the eagle's claw, and braved slave catchers' pistols on more than one occasion. To her Levi Coffin was the leader and the guiding mind of these enterprises, and she thought nothing of packing her small reticule and going to Ohio to consult with him.

She went to see him promptly when, in 1847, a fugitive named John White, who worked on a farm near Raisen Institute, begged her to do something to rescue his wife from slavery. The Vigilance Committee of Cincinnati seemed the natural consultants, and Coffin, never surprised by any exploit, suggested that she go to Rising Sun, Indiana, and consult several colored friends of John White who had escaped from the neighborhood of his plantation and settled in that neighborhood.

They conferred for several days. Mrs. Haviland, in her prim, sober Quaker dress, her prim little lips folded meditatively, her prim little finger following the black figures, young and old, that traced a path for her, her bright eyes looking into black ones and disposing of the dangers beforehand, finally nodded her head, snapped shut her reticule, shook hands all around, and returned to Cincinnati. Coffin heard her plans, offered only tentative advice, and saw her onto the ferry that carried her to the Kentucky shore.

In Kentucky she made her way, in as conventional a manner as possible, to the neighborhood of the Stevens plantation, where Jane White was a slave. A free mulatto woman named Rachel, who showed no trace of her colored blood, agreed to pass her off as the aunt whom she was expecting from Georgia. Dressed in shabby clothes, with berry pails over their arms, "Aunt Smith" and Rachel walked up boldly to the Stevens plantation and joined the slaves at their noonday meal. "Aunt Smith" did not have much to say, as her Yankee twang would have turned her into a doubtful Georgian, but Rachel asked permission of Mrs. Stevens to take Jane with them berrypicking. Bending over the bushes, heads close together, voices low, Mrs. Haviland gave Jane her husband's message and attempted to cover up the wild storm of weeping that seized the girl. When she had been calmed, Mrs. Haviland told her to be ready when plans for escape had ripened. Berry pail filled, she slipped away and, before the day was over, had resumed her Quaker clothes and was on her way back to Michigan.

Within a few weeks there she was in Kentucky again, as ladylike as you please, busy establishing a contact with a slave friend of John White whom John had selected as the pilot of the enterprise. But she found the countryside in an unexpected ferment. In every stranger a counterfeiter was seen, for the countryside had taken upon itself the task of uncovering a predatory ring. Even the self-possessed little woman in the Quaker dress was regarded with deep suspicion. Because of this enforced conspicuousness, she could not speak for more than a moment with John's friend. But he said that when the excitement had died down he thought the escape could be made. She did not leave Kentucky emptyhanded, though, for she arranged for the immediate escape of a slave woman and her children, an exploit that was a blessing to everyone but the Indiana station keeper into whose hands she gave the family. The law closed down upon him, and he lost his farm and lands.

The weeks went by, and still Jane did not come. Impatient, apprehensive, John started alone for Kentucky and, weathering the unabated excitement of the neighborhood, smuggled Jane and a friend to the Indiana shore. This was almost freedom—almost. By nightfall they would reach a depot. But between noon and nightfall the slave catcher fell upon them, and three fine prizes were returned to Kentucky.

Jane and John were separated. Through an intermediary he managed to send word to his Michigan friends. A price of four hundred dollars had been set on him; his wife's fate he did not know. Soon he learned that she was dead.

In Levi Coffin's "council room" the Vigilance Committee of Cincinnati discussed the situation. Three hundred and fifty dollars was raised before the next day, and within three weeks Mrs. Haviland was returning to Raisen Institute under the escort of John White.

This war within a war showed how illusory were any lasting triumphs of arms for the slavocracy. With Levi Coffins, and, to a lesser extent, Laura Havilands, duplicated in action over and over in the North, and with small or mighty Garrisons to echo the words of their prototype in Boston, "If you come to us and are hungry, we will feed you; if thirsty, we will give you drink; if naked, we will clothe you; if you need a hiding place from the face of the pursuer, we will provide one that even bloodhounds will not scent out," there was little to calm and reassure the more coolheaded of the slavery champions. They tried again in Congress, as they had tried at frequent intervals for fifty years, to procure a law that would protect their absconding property. Now, in 1847, Kentucky again asked Congress to frame new laws that would allow her citizens to reclaim their slaves after they had reached the relative security of the North. The Senate bill never got beyond its second reading. Something bigger was in store—something much bigger.

By the close of 1847 the end of the Mexican War was in sight, with hundreds of miles of new territory with the look and spirit of cotton upon it. Upper California, New Mexico, Arizona, parts of Nevada and Colorado—territory almost as large as the original thirteen colonies—was to be given to the United States; fifteen million dollars was to be paid to Mexico. Mexico tried vainly to include in the treaty she was about to sign an agreement to keep this vast land free of slavery, but Nicholas Trist, the agent of President Polk, told the Mexican commissioners "that if it were in their power to offer the whole territory, increased tenfold in value, and in addition to that covered a foot thick with pure gold, upon the single condition that slavery be excluded, he could not entertain the offer for a moment, nor even think of communicating it to Washington."

In February 1848 a formal treaty was signed, and over one half of what had been the Mexican Empire came under the moral suasion of slavery. Moral suasion it remained for a suitable time, as even the politicians in Washington could not arrive at a compromise that would not be a complete submission to the demands of the slavocracy. The Southern politicians fought stubbornly. Jefferson Davis, a tall, handsome war hero, was sent from Mississippi as senator to persuade, exhort, but there were antislavery representatives now to keep the issue ablaze, to keep alive in the minds of Northern voters the arguments against the extension of slavery. Compromises were offered—specious compromises, such as the proposal to admit New Mexico, California, and the new acquisition, British-dominated Oregon, in one measure, leaving the Supreme Court—five slaveholders to four non-slaveholders—to decide whether slavery should be admitted as well.

The politicians of slavery were a-dream with arrogance. All the country would be theirs. Adams spoke darkly of secession; Northern members looked from under their brows and wondered whether peace was not more desirable than union. To placate the South meant not compromises but complete capitulation. There was California, for example. While Trist was still wrangling with the Mexican commissioners, gold had been discovered in California. A wilderness of Mexican villages turned suddenly into a settlement of a hundred thousand lovers of free labor. Could anything persuade them to give California to the slave power? The slave power said, "Yes."

But while the masters fought up and down the halls of Congress to make their "Yes" a valid fact, the California legislature, emboldened by the streams of fortune seekers from the North, from Europe, where competition with slave labor was an economic horror, ratified a constitution which forbade slavery or involuntary servitude forever from the territory. Constitution in hand, they asked admission as a state.

They came at a singularly inopportune moment. The glamor and the chivalry of the Mexican War, the troops and the bands and the tearful pride of the Southern women—for the Northern women saw it in a different light—had been transformed into a chimera. The Wilmot Proviso had not been laid to rest. It hung like a sword over the seats of Southern congressmen. They had never lost a fight before—were they prepared to lose one now? No, they cried almost as one man, and prepared to use the time-honored weapons that had always insured their victory.

Victory was more sweet and necessary than ever. Had not the South fought and paid for the gold fields of California; had not the price of slaves risen as a result of the war and the prospects of new territory? Fine things had been gained by the slavocracy; the brightest days of its civilization lay ahead . . . then let us say so in words and prove it in deeds, and the violence of the deeds will not matter so long as the proof is clear.

The slavocracy was hypersensitive these days. Its power had not been questioned in this manner before. Antislavery men, however prudent or moderate, felt the full weight of its displeasure. Mobs, violence, and suppression had supplemented this displeasure before. They were called upon again.

Yet they faced a subtle difference now, a difference which the slave power had not anticipated and which it was unable to subdue. When its wrath fell on Gameliel Bailey, who had founded a Liberty party paper, the *National Era,* in Washington, it discovered that Mr. Bailey was using a new kind of worldliness—a worldliness that bore little relation to the heroic martyrdom of Lovejoy—and that his political astuteness baffled all the efforts to suppress his journal. Within sight of the Capitol building it was inadvisable to call out a mob.

In Baltimore an antislavery newspaper, the *Saturday Visitor,* had been established, and citizens set out to suppress it. They called on its editor, Dr. Snodgrass, and presented their demands. Then and there one saw what the 1830s had done for the abolition cause. The battle for a free press had been fought, and Dr. Snodgrass could enjoy the fruits. He defied the citizens' delegation, proclaimed his right to publish, and, probably to his own surprise, lived to see the day of emancipation.

Yet John H. Pleasants—the editor of the *Richmond Whig,* a partisan paper as its name will indicate—was not so fortunate. He had inserted a few articles on the economic aspects of slavery. The machinery of opposition moved with precision, and Mr. Pleasants found himself in a cold world, outside the editorial offices. He was challenged to a duel by the son of a proslavery editor, and fell in the futile exchange that followed.

In Wilmington they caught up at last with that doughty miracle worker, Thomas Garrett. Thomas Garrett is a story and a song and a legend, and he should share no page with any other. But he was always one to find great enjoyment on the fringes of lesser people's mighty trivialities.

Born a Pennsylvania Quaker, hatred of slavery was in his blood. When he was twenty-four he had followed the kidnapers of a colored woman employed by his family halfway across the state and rescued her without ado. During that ride, he later said, the horror of slavery had so beat upon his brain that he seemed to hear a voice, telling him that his life's work must be devoted to the persecuted and enslaved. Through the heart of a slave state he accordingly passed over twenty-seven hundred fugitives.

He had come to Wilmington, Delaware, in 1822. His work had begun immediately. It took only a short time for slave and master to know that Thomas Garrett's house was a station of the Underground Railroad. And yet the consummate skill of the man was such that for over twenty years he was able to carry on his avocation just outside the reaches of the law. No evidence could be obtained against him. His business reputation was so impeccable that he made friends against their will. His house was continuously under the surveillance of the police and the slaveowners. His calmness and his physical impressiveness added weight to his refusal to be intimidated. He never denied that he aided fugitives, but he usually received only those fugitives of whom he had been notified by a conductor farther South, forestalling, by the advance precautions he was able to take, any damaging proofs against himself.

He had, at the start, assumed a share of the dangerous burden borne by certain free colored people, and as the work increased, white friends were drawn in to lend a hand when they least expected it. "Even numbering," as one of his biographers put it, "singular as it may seem, some ardent Democrats." When he heard that Maryland had offered ten thousand dollars for his capture, he wrote an open letter saying that he was worth at least twenty thousand, and if that sum were forthcoming he would collect in person. Threats of murder were so frequent that many of his colored friends established a watch in his front yard and took turns guarding him at night, although his expostulations could be heard clearly through the window.

The success of his work depended—as truly it did with every conductor—on the fertility of his imagination. He prescribed like a doctor, according to an individual's need. Often he would give a fugitive man a scythe, a hoe, a rake, and send him onto the street with instructions to walk calmly, as though he were going to work, to a certain bridge near the outskirts of the town. There he was to conceal his implement and from that point follow implicit directions to the next station, the implement being recovered by one of Garrett's friends and used again. Several times he dressed a woman fugitive in his wife's clothes, leading her to their carriage and driving off, smiling comfortably at the stragglers who were invariably about his door.

Sometimes he would direct fugitives to the home of Isaac and Dinah Mendenhall, ten miles from Wilmington. His directions were brief. "Go on and on until you come to a stone gatepost and then turn in." Frequently (as times grew more dangerous and spies lurked along the underground line) he gave them a note for the next station keeper, saying sometimes, "I send thee two [or four or six, as the case might be] bales of black wool," and at other times openly, "This man needs help." Now and then he sent fugitives to Chandler and Hannah Darlington, over the line in Pennsylvania. Their house was too exposed for frequent use and too generally filled with boarders of undetermined sympathies to be more than a switch house on the line, but the Darlingtons recognized an emergency when a tap, generally around eleven at night, came at their window and the voice of a conductor called softly, "Can you care for these people?" They seldom saw the conductor, transacting their business in the dark, in order to claim truly, if the need arose, that they did not know the personnel of the line.

Garrett knew that these friends and others, whom he had tested, could be trusted to outmaneuver the law as well as any. Better than he, he might have thought with a wry smile when in 1848, at a moment of extreme caution on his part, the law descended upon him in all its majesty. Why it came then and not sooner no one was prepared to say. But it is not unlikely that it sought him out at a time when the crisis in the South was reaching a climax, when for the first time the slavocracy doubted the invincibility of its power and determined to make an example, through a Federal law, of a man who had flouted it for twenty years.

His trial, for aiding two slave children, was called in the spring of 1848 in Newcastle, Delaware, with Garrett and a fellow conductor, John Hunn, in the defendant's box. When the verdict was returned, every cent of his property had been swept away. Every cent of John Hunn's property had been swept away, but John Hunn was a younger man. Thomas Garrett was sixty years old.

When his sentence had been pronounced, he rose in the courtroom, a tall, rather stooping old figure with white hair, soft as a baby's, and drooping lids that did not conceal the fire that suddenly blazed in his eyes. "Judge," he said, "now that thee hast relieved me of what little I possessed, I will go home and put another story on my house. I want room to accommodate more of God's poor." After a bare glance at him Garrett turned to the courtroom and for an hour expounded on the evils of slavery. He spared no one. He spoke in this room, dominated by slave laws, as men seldom had the courage to speak. Mostly he was listened to in silence; occasionally someone applauded; now and then a hiss cut across his words. When at length he sat down, breathing only a little more deeply than when he had begun, one of the jurors who had convicted him ran across the courtroom and seized his hand. "Give me your forgiveness," he said, "and let me be your friend." "Freely given," said Garrett, his stiff little smile breaking across his lips, "if thee cease to be an advocate of the iniquitous system of slavery."

Everything was sold. He watched his household goods and his merchandise carried out to the auctioneer. When the sale was over the auctioneer turned to him and said with a glint of righteousness, "Thomas, I hope you'll never be caught as this again." Only as quickly as it took him to put the words together, Garrett answered, "Friend, I haven't a dollar in the world, but if thee knows a fugitive who needs a breakfast, send him to me."

Thus at sixty he was forced to remake a life not only for himself but for "God's poor." In the twenty-one years that were left him he found a greater success in business than in the forty-odd years of adulthood behind him. His friends bought his possessions and returned them to him. With great pride he told Wendell Phillips that, proslavery as Wilmington was, his credit was so good that he got an immediate loan at the bank. He built the extra story to his house, true to his promise, and his name penetrated more deeply into the South. Persecution was excellent publicity for the underground road. Fugitives came in greater numbers. Friends in England sent him money, and every penny he paid back. Life seemed to increase for him rather than diminish, for with his public championship of the slave, he became an abolitionist in the fullest sense: a champion of women's rights, an advocate of temperance, a defender of the Indians, and an agitator in behalf of white working men and women. He even performed the miracle of turning Negro-hating Irishmen into conductors, for the poor Irish of Wilmington knew that he was their friend, and if "Father Garrett" wanted them to help a fugitive, they asked no questions.

Thus Garrett became an abolition hero, and in a few months Daniel Drayton was catapulted after him. Daniel Drayton represented that hardy specimen, a seafaring hater of slavery. It was a wonder that all seamen who carried the dull and torpid slaves in their bottoms were not antislavery men, but most of the sea captains were tough men who cared more for the prize in their holds than for the pros and cons of humanity. Daniel Drayton admitted that once he thought Negroes were fit only for slavery, that he had often turned away from thinly veiled pleas for assistance. Methodist meetings were the only gatherings he frequented, and, as he said, "Nothing was heard there about slavery." But one night, when his ship lay tied to a Washington wharf, a strange thing happened to him. A colored man came on board as Drayton was idly smoking his pipe and began to talk to him. The Negro was a man with easy manners, and his white teeth shone in his dark face as he talked with apparently aimless garrulity. Presently he slipped in, "Cap'n seemed to be from the No't'. I s'pose they is all pretty much ab'litionists up th-yah?" Drayton looked at him a moment and turned over in his mind how such information could have come to so poorly appearing a slave. He put his pipe back into his mouth and nodded. The black man hesitated, then, stumbling a little, he came to the point. A woman and her five children wanted to escape to her husband, a free colored man. The woman had been working under an agreement with her master for her freedom, but when she asked for a settlement the master threatened to sell her. "Cap'n"—the black face bent close—"will yah talk t'her? Kin Ah bring her on the bo't?" Drayton took one puff and then nodded abruptly.

He did not know what had moved him, and he did not understand why he agreed to the woman's importunities. Later, when he saw the woman caught in the arms of her husband, he admitted that something got into his blood. He went back to his home in Philadelphia to muse about it for several months. He mused about it until he received a letter from a person whose name he did not know but who asked him to come to a certain place at such and such a time. He did so, a weathered eye, no doubt, looking behind and before him. He learned, at the meeting, that word of his exploit had filtered through Washington, and here was a messenger from that city, asking if he could be persuaded to help two other families who expected hourly to be sold. The letter that he brought was touching, and Drayton pulled on his pipe while the intermediary anxiously folded up the sheet of paper. Finally Drayton shook his head. It can't be done, he said; he had no vessel and he could not take another man's through the dangers of the stormy season.

He must have left the matter open, though, for he saw the intermediary again a fortnight later and agreed to go to Washington to see what arrangements could be made. In the secretive channels of underground work in Washington—for Washington was an increasingly important junction of the Underground Railroad—he met the colored friends who were attempting to negotiate the escape of the slaves and promised that he would find a vessel and see what he could do.

Washington, one evening in April, was aflame with torchlight. The White House and the homes of secretaries and prominent politicians were illuminated inside and out as for a fete. Crowds swarmed through the streets, splashing through the spring mud. Bands played all the fine marching tunes they had ever learned, and the torchlight procession, impatiently gathering, stamped off at length to the stir and rattle of the drums and the whistles and huzzas of transported watchers. Dignitaries as well as common people dirtied their trouser hems as they wheeled down Pennsylvania Avenue, past the government buildings where people waved flags and shouted lustily, past the militia drawn up impressively, to a speaker's stand where more notables were setting aside their silk hats and fumbling with the speeches which were to make this occasion ring in the annals of republican history.

For—glory of glories—that nurse of revolution, that sister across the sea, had sent her king into exile. Revolution had triumphed. France had now taken her place among the democracies of the world.

As dusk came the excitement mounted with the rising torchlight and the crescendo of eloquence. Senator Foote of Mississippi was stirred to strange words: "The age of tyrants and slavery is rapidly drawing to a close. The happy period, to be signalized by the universal emancipation of man from the fetters of civil oppression and the recognition in all countries of the great principles of popular sovereignty, equality, and brotherhood, is visibly commencing."

"Visibly commencing . . ." Drayton had stayed on board his ship that night, and to all those with a dark skin who came up the ship's plank he promised this fulsomely praised liberty if they were aboard by eleven o'clock, three nights hence.

Three nights hence Drayton's eyes swept over the low fields that ran down to the river. Darkness had barely set in when he saw the first figure coming across the field, stooping low, running fast, darting swiftly up the plank that stretched to the vessel, and disappearing without a word into the shadows of the ship.

Several times he went aboard the vessel and learned from his mate that the hold was filling rapidly as several additional slaves had taken literally the enthusiasm for liberty that was filling Washington. Sometime past ten o'clock seventy-eight had run swiftly up the plank onto the vessel, and Drayton now went aboard. Around eleven, Sayres, who was to pilot his own ship, came aboard, and it was evident that they must start immediately as a dead calm had settled and it was necessary to maneuver the vessel into the river in order to pick up whatever wind sprang up. Toward midnight a wind began to stir, setting the halyards to creaking faintly, and Drayton and those on deck watched the low shores going slowly past. So far—*fine*.

All the next day they moved under a restless, sporadic wind; the next night Drayton went to his bunk and fell asleep to the slow roll of the ship, and he did not waken until the cries of a boarding crew rang in his ears.

They were taken back in triumph to a Washington still intoxicated by French liberty. The fugitive men had begged to be allowed to fight the boarding party, but Drayton had refused, knowing that no firearms were aboard. They came back to a crowd of several thousand spread out along the road that led to the jail, for the city of Washington was wildly concerned to see the $100,000 worth of property which had slid down the river in the night and only been recovered through the betrayal of a hackman who had carried a fugitive to the wharf. The fugitive men were driven by whips through the city, tied together two by two, the women following. The crowd shouted itself hoarse in taunts and jeers, although here and there a long wail rose above the noise, and once a relative fell insensible.

Congress was immediately reassembled, and Giddings, who had been warned to keep out of sight, swung hurriedly into action, drawing his antislavery colleagues with him as fast as they would go. He went first, with Hamlin of Ohio, to offer his services to Drayton and Sayres. Then he demanded a congressional investigation to determine why the jail was being used to house eighty individuals who had as yet been convicted of no crime.

But neither Congress nor Washington was prepared to take a judicious view of the affair. Within two days mobs had taken possession of the city, attacked the office of the *National Era,* where the press and the papers were saved only by the gifted tongue of its editor, Gameliel Bailey, and the stubbornness of the captain of police, and were threatening members of Congress. While in Congress for three days the uproar drowned out everything but the personal vilifications and the shouted challenges to bloody combat that made a journey down the aisles an unpredictable adventure.

By the second day fifty of the runaways had been sold to Hope Slatter, the principal slave dealer of the neighborhood, and silent congressmen, watching from the windows, saw the coffle marching by the Capitol.

The Southern members realized that the tide was running in the wrong direction—the antislavery members were using this occasion to introduce a resolution against the rule of mobs. In such a resolution the slaveowners saw only a threat to the reclamation of fugitives, and Calhoun, more superbly the politician as age dug great rivers in his face, rose like Jeremiah to foretell the end of things. Slavery was the only question—he repeated himself deliberately, *the only question*—that could divide the Union, and a crisis was not far away. If at one grasp seventy-eight of their slaves could be carried off, the apathy of the public must be roused. He promised insurrections as terrible as San Domingo if the fanaticism of certain antislavery congressmen was not rebuked. But he offered no remedy for the rift that was separating the minority of antislavery men from the great body of their opponents, a rift that was deeper than politics . . . as deep as the past and the future.

Forty-one indictments were drawn against Drayton. Bail for him, Sayres, and the mate of the *Pearl* was set at $228,000, and seventy-five additional indictments hung perilously above his head. Horace Mann, the successor of Adams in the House, Seward, and Chase had offered themselves as counsel and fought stubbornly, although the verdict was evident from the start. Some of the indictments were dismissed, but when sentence was pronounced, the hungry-faced and taciturn Daniel Drayton had accumulated a lifetime in jail, for his fines amounted to over ten thousand dollars.

Perhaps the slavocracy gained from all of this. It renewed its demand for a competent Fugitive Slave Law; it raised again the threat of disunion in

Congress; it threw the weak-spirited into a frenzy of conciliation. But certain things had been observed that neither time nor words could alter. The *Pearl* had tried to escape when liberty-loving speeches filled the air. The effect of this was not lost. Eighteen forty-eight was "the year of revolutions." Kings had been overthrown; Garibaldi, Mazzini, Kossuth were heroes on every tongue; freedom had become a taut word not to be used idly.

From the pulpit of Plymouth Church, Brooklyn, young Henry Ward Beecher, newly come out of the West, was selling slaves into freedom. To denounce slavery in this open manner was to make him as popular as is one who denounces private property today, and his more conventional parishioners urged him for his own success to leave such dangerous topics alone. "I don't know what it is," he replied, "but the moment you tell me that a thing is unpopular I am right there every time." And they had to bear the sight of a small black girl being auctioned off on a Sunday morning. It was shocking, true. Sobbing was heard all over the church, but her freedom was guaranteed when the collection plates were quickly passed.

Of course it was sensational, but no one can rightly speak against the dramatizing of the dramatic. As Beecher himself observed, "He is the best fisherman who catches the most fish whatever epithet may be flung at him about the kind of bait he uses."

Abolitionists were only too glad to cry out the drama of freedom if in this way the imagination could be stirred. When the Crafts escaped, a thrill went through the cohorts of Boston such as Greece must have felt when Phidippides ran from Marathon to Athens.

William and Ellen Craft were Georgia slaves who had determined that, no matter what the hazards, they would make the dash from the Deep South to freedom. They considered and rejected ways of escape, until they finally decided on a daring disguise that might succeed because of its boldness. Ellen's skin was white; William's was dark. Ellen would, therefore, become a young planter, and William would become the gentleman's servant. The plan seemed foolproof until Ellen's womanliness promised to betray them. But perhaps the young planter had a toothache and could muffle half his beardless face in linen! Perhaps he had weak eyes and needed the protection of green glasses! Their plan, predicated on boldness, necessitated stopping openly at the best hotels on the way North and registering their names, yet neither of them could write. Neuritis—or a sprain—would dispose of the young gentleman's right hand. William was ideally suited to act the part of the alert, devoted servant whose sole desire was to be the eyes, ears, hands, and feet of his debilitated young master, a devotion which would encourage only the kindliest co-operation from all whom they encountered.

The strain of the trip was immense, but William was always at hand to explain the unsociability of his young master when a stranger attempted to make his acquaintance. Perhaps, as slaves, they had been allowed to hire their time; perhaps they had made a little money by vegetable or cotton raising after dark—in any case they had sufficient funds to allow them to stop at the best hotel in Charleston, while they waited for their train, and at a first-class hotel in Richmond. Toward nightfall they arrived in Baltimore and went immediately to the station to buy tickets for Philadelphia and the end of the journey.

William handled the matter of tickets, and apparently he gave away none of his dismay when told by the ticket man that his master might have a ticket but that a bond must be posted for him as required for all Negroes journeying north through Baltimore. William had to reverse this decision then and there, with other ticket buyers pressing with impatience behind him. "My master is in a very delicate state of health. We are afraid he may not be able to hold out until he reaches Philadelphia, where he is going for medical treatment. It's out of the question to post a bond, and he cannot be detained." He waved toward his young master, sitting ill and drooping close at hand, and the ticket seller took a brief look and pushed two tickets toward him.

How feebly that poor young master got into the train, how tenderly his servant supported him, brought him water, arranged his blankets. Only a few more hours . . .

The Vigilance Committee in Philadelphia never forgot the first few moments of their arrival—the pale young man and his solicitous servant. First the tall hat was removed, then the green glasses and linen muffler. Finally the arm was freed from the sling and a few experimental dancing steps were attempted. When the final metamorphoses had taken place in an adjoining room, they were able to appreciate the full effect of ingenuity and courage.

They wished to send them on immediately, as such fine specimens would bring a swarm of interested slave catchers, but Ellen's nerves had gone to pieces. For several days she was prostrate. Yet the word of their exploit went ahead to Boston, and when she was well enough to travel, the Boston abolitionists greeted them as heroes and took care to spread their story North and South, as well as to England and to Europe. Antislavery workers, men and women, came to shake their hands.

These were the kind of people we have been fighting for, they said. Isn't the battle worth the powder?

That William and Ellen Craft provided so spontaneous a reunion of dissident abolitionists showed that differences of opinion did not penetrate to the heart of the cause. Beyond that, it indicated how things should be, and wakened grief in many hearts that by their discords an excuse was given men who held aloof from the antislavery fight. Yet, if one took the trouble to examine the reasons for these factions, they would have been found, not caprices, not the result of some leader's inflated ego, but rather an expression of deep perplexity, a perplexity that wondered a thousand times how a handful of men and women could render powerless a power that had laid its mark on the compromises of the Founding Fathers and then had bound itself inextricably to the governing function of the country, interweaving itself with every aspect of society—political, commercial, social, and religious. To agree how to disentangle such a monster from the mazes of the national house without bringing down the entire structure must have seemed impossible. And yet they did agree, fundamentally, on the means of accomplishment. "The formation of a new republic, that shall be such not in name only, but in full living reality and truth," was what the Garrisonians envisioned, and the political abolitionists found their hopes embodied in the same dream. They differed only on the interpretation of the Constitution. If it was a "Covenant with Death and an Agreement with Hell," as the Garrisonians maintained, then it must be utterly repudiated, and to accustom minds to such iconoclasm all the pernicious growths which hampered freedom and kept the mind in a mold of antiquated forms must be uprooted. Everything that perpetuated slavery—the degradation of women, the rigidity of the churches, the poor-spirited social reforms, the economic, intellectual, and social orthodoxies, the devotion to the ballot and to political and religious organizations—must be condemned.

If, on the other hand, the Constitution was read as an antislavery document, polluted by the proslavery forces which had gained control of national policies, then action on a political front, the unremitting use of the ballot, the tireless support of antislavery men in Congress, were all that could wipe out such a national disgrace. Perhaps only a national calamity would show which one was right.

The recriminations which passed between the antislavery camps made unhappy dissonances in friendly ears. Men from the old political parties, watching with experienced and worldly eyes, saw that in spite of the golden eloquence of the Garrisonians and the inspired writings of their faithful, in spite of the belief that "Duty is ours, results are God's" of the new Liberty League, in spite of the bold words of the emaciated Liberty party, the slave power was going on from victory to victory. Nothing had stopped it yet; appeals to reason were useless, consciences had been invoked in vain. Impassioned and brilliant as the Garrisonians might be, it was unlikely that the country would ever be brought to an espousal of disunion; the political abolitionists therefore held the stronger position, for ballots could be made to carry an unequivocal message. Even though the Liberty party had sickened because its platform was too narrow for men of different minds to stand upon, and even though orthodox politicians were still evading *the* issue and pouring out a stream of demagoguery to cover their omission, there were still abundant signs to show that the balances were settling in favor of a new political party. "Conscience" Whigs were in revolt against the "Cotton" Whigs, who by adroit maneuvering had hung upon them, as presidential nominee, a Mexican War hero, a Louisiana slaveholder, General Zachary Taylor, and had not even given the "Conscience" Whigs assurance that he would support the Wilmot Proviso or oppose the extension of slavery. The Democratic Convention had been forced to trample swiftly on its own rebels, the "Barnburners," who disclaimed being abolitionists but claimed a right to protest against corruption and patronage and urge the proviso. How furiously the revolt was flaming was proved when the "Barnburners" called their own convention, offered their own candidate, Martin Van Buren, in opposition to Lewis Cass of Michigan, the choice of the Southern Democrats, and made their platform one of undeviating hostility to the extension of slavery. The "Conscience" Whigs, fanning the flames, saw what they believed was a more practical solution. If a new party was formed, it could absorb the dissidents of the old parties and be in a position to take an uncompromising stand for freedom. For seven years they had worked for this moment, when the powerful Democrats and Whigs, fed by the same blood stream, could be cut in two. Nothing must now be left to chance or faulty leadership. They looked among the "Barnburners" and the "Conscience" Whigs for their leaders; that is to say, to men like Hale, King, and Wilmot among the Democrats, Giddings, Palfrey, Seward, and Mann among the Whigs. Free soil, the defeat of Taylor and Cass, the non-extension of slavery were to be the cries calculated to draw delegates to the convention set for Buffalo.

In August the delegates assembled, divided with representative equality between the Whigs, Democrats, and Liberty party men. Many famous names were there—Dana, Giddings, Lovejoy, Adams, Sumner, Fletcher, Webster, as well as Samuel Ringgold Ward and certain eminent "station keepers." Salmon Chase was chairman, and the keynote of the convention was quickly struck. Unity—unity!

Their purposes were set forth quickly: the Constitution was an antislavery document, promulgated in the spirit of Thomas Jefferson and the Northwest Ordinance, which forbade the spread of slavery; states' rights, which prevented the abolition of slavery, must be circumvented by the admission of free states only.

They added other things as well to make their platform roomy: cheap postage, government economy, land grants to settlers, a settlement of the national debt, an adequate but not proscriptive tariff. "On our banners we inscribe, 'Free Soil, Free Speech, Free Labor, and Free Men,' and under it we will fight on and fight ever, until triumphant victory shall reward our exertions."

Of course the matter of candidates tickled the sensibilities. And, in the matter of candidates, this political party showed the fundamental weakness it shared with all its kind. The Massachusetts "Conscience" Whigs had determined that they would accept only the ballot which swung in the "Barnburners" and forced them to share the burden of election. When candidates had been proposed and the rolls were called, the Democrats voted for Van Buren, and the Whigs took the hint. The men of the Liberty party with few exceptions stood by John Hale. When the delegates had responded, Van Buren had a clear majority.

This ironic choice must have made the terrible days of the 1830s seem like hazy figments. Was no abolitionist prepared to remind the convention that Van Buren, as President, had been such a faithful servant of the slave power that he had been known as "a Northern man with Southern principles," that his sudden devotion to antislavery was due to his dereliction over the matter of Texas annexation which had lost him the Democratic nomination?

But enthusiasm and satisfaction were all that the delegates displayed. They went home to call for state conventions and the whirlwind campaigning that characterized such an election year. The state conventions even reached within the bulwarks of the enemy, for local conventions and small meetings took place in Delaware, Virginia, North Carolina, Kentucky, and Missouri, and antislavery men in the border states wrote fervently and daringly of the paralyzing effect of slavery on industry, of the degradation of labor, of the stifling of education.

The Free-Soil party entered the fight, unencumbered by any "Southern wing." They could say what they chose, in conformity with their platform, and potential voters knew that it held no hidden meanings, unless Van Buren could be construed as a hidden meaning. The center plank had now been laid which was to lead the voters to that significant day, a few years hence, when the Free-Soil party would consign its spirit and its purposes to the larger scope of the Republican party, and when the slavocracy would, with negligible prompting, foretell its own end.

There was little doubt that the Free-Soil party was a child of the abolitionists. And yet could Garrison bring himself to believe that any abolition promise lay in that direction? He wrote to Edmund Quincy directly after the convention, and his argument had the sting of truth behind it.

> As for the Free Soil movement, I feel that great care is demanded of us Disunionists in giving credit to whom credit is due, and yet in no case even seeming to be satisfied with it. It is only placing the country in precisely the same condition, on the subject of slavery, that it occupied a quarter of a century since—to wit, that slavery ought not to be extended to new territories; that it ought to be abolished (when or how is not stated in the new creed) in all our territorial possession—(nothing, I believe, is said about its abolition in the District of Columbia): and that Congress has no Constitutional power to meddle with it in the several states.
>
> Our Disunion ground is invulnerable, and to it all parties at the North must come e'er long. The temptation to vote, however, at the coming election, will be so great that I fear a considerable number of Disunionists, and even of professed non-resistants, will fall into the snare, and try to persuade themselves that, for this once, they may innocently, and even laudably, "bow down to the house of Rimmon." Calm yet earnest appeals must be made to our friends to preserve their integrity, and not to lose sight of the true issue. Already, in this region, I hear it said that a number of those who have hitherto acted with us think they can now vote, even for Martin Van Buren. What infatuation!

The infatuation swept through the ranks like a wind. In Ohio, Chase, with all his impressive skill, organized mass meetings, drafted resolutions, delivered his slow methodical speeches, wrote stirring addresses for others. The importance of this Free-Soil campaigning could not be exaggerated. In Ohio, where men drew in politics with their breath, the Free-Soil doctrines found a surprisingly rich reward. Young Whigs went over to their camp by the hundreds; non-voting antislavery men were caught in the fervent belief that this was indeed their party. As the day of election drew closer, Edmund Quincy wrote to his friend Webb in Ireland that Free-Soilism "has carried off multitudes of our abolitionists, and it is to be feared that many of them will never recover themselves."

They came to the polls that November two hundred and ninety thousand strong; prognosticators of the future, whether they knew it or not, untutored prophets of a new economic order. Even Garrison was moved by this drama of political revolt. "I am for hailing it as a cheering sign of the times, and an unmistakable proof of the progress we have made, under God, in changing public sentiment. Those who have left the Whig and the Democratic parties, for conscience sake, and joined that movement, deserve our commendation and sympathy." Yet, spectacular as this rebellion was—"unprecedented" was Quincy's word, "taking into consideration its brief existence and formidable foes"—it had not delivered the anticipated blow. Van Buren carried no state in the Union, and only in New York, Vermont, and Massachusetts did the Free-Soil ticket climb beyond third place. They gained no electoral votes and sent only five members to Congress. But the election of Taylor—an enigma with no political views which could be ascertained—and the consequent defeat of the powerful Democratic machine were unmistakable attacks on the slavocracy.

In Ohio, Free Soil accomplished its greatest moral triumph in the repeal of the "Black Laws" which had lain like a canker on the statute books. Now the Negroes of Ohio needed no longer to give bonds before making their homes in the state; their children were no longer excluded from the schools; they might testify in court against a white man. And from Ohio, "the attorney-general for the fugitives," Salmon Chase, took the long and dusty journey to the Senate, where he met William Seward, elected on a freedom platform from New York. Although politicians first of all—rivals between whom no love was lost—their devotion to individual fugitives had been proven on numerous occasions.

The slavocracy which was seldom guilty of self-deception was beginning to realize that its gains had been ephemeral. Within the Southern States a renewed oppression struck at the free colored people. Old laws which had become inoperative were revived again, new laws were framed. The Border States attempted to quell their white dissenters and bolt their doors. But their arguments were less persuasive than usual. Although their dogma remained the same, counterbalancing forces were disturbing the minds of many Southern men, who questioned: Once you said that slavery was an entailed evil, something acquired by an earlier generation, something sectional, yet now you say that slavery is a positive good, that it is permanent, that it is national. What is true?

The men who questioned were mostly small clergy, living in the western parts of Virginia and North Carolina, the eastern parts of Tennessee and Kentucky—in the mountains—where slavery had never gained a hold. This subdued struggle, born to defeat, rubbed the raw wounds of those Southerners who wondered and could not understand what had happened to the fine imperial sway of the slavocracy. General Taylor—what had they acquired with General Taylor? One might have justifiably expected a slaveowner with a son-in-law like Jefferson Davis to be the very thing they needed. Yet they were discovering that he did not intend to be unduly swayed by his Southern attachments or his natural concerns with slavery. The tumult in the South was deeply seated. It raged like a furnace now that the Whigs were in power. The Wilmot Proviso, the Missouri Compromise, were living monsters bent on destroying the slaveowner's concept of freedom: the right to take his property and settle in any district which he chose. He was fit to stifle in the South with all the vast broad plains of the West closed, by moral suasion, to him. The governor of Georgia, in a burst of sectional devotion, proposed that his people should embark on a holy march to Washington and dissolve the government. Southern legislatures and newspapers were sending up a single chorus—disunion—disunion—if the tide did not soon turn in their direction.

Disunion came onto the floors of the Senate through the voice of Calhoun. The whip, which had always kept the ranks in good order, now seemed to have lost some of its immediate potency. Calhoun's usual adroit and brilliant persuasion offered no remedy for the threat of secession; he contented himself mostly with an attack on emancipation, picturing the horrors of racial equality in the South. When Congress adjourned, nothing had been decided. California was still waiting on the doorstep. Although no action had been taken to admit her with her free constitution, no effort had been made to bar her demands. Armed settlers started out from the South for the disputed territories, carrying their slaves with them, willy-nilly. Disunion conventions intensified the heat of the Southern summer, and just before the reassembling of Congress, committees of the Georgia and South Carolina legislatures made quite sure that certain Northern "doughfaces" understood the position of the slavocracy on the question of secession if, by an unforeseen chance, the new Congress should prove as unpredictable as the last.

Many people, in 1849, looked for war before the year was out.

Although, in terms of all who were enslaved, the number of successful fugitives might be slight, its proportion nevertheless reached figures that were alarming to the master. And at all the doors in the North their recovery was blocked by personal liberty laws. Masters of Maryland, Virginia, and the Ohio Valley were turned back time and time again. The Virginia legislature wildly denounced Pennsylvania when she withdrew state aid to kidnapers, and cried that such actions might "lead to war between independent nations." From Virginia and from Missouri went insistent pleas to other states to lend all their pressure to a new Fugitive Slave Law which would give to Federal postmasters or Federal collectors of custom the same authority to arrest, hold, convict, and return fugitives as was possessed by the courts, and the governor of Virginia added a further plea for a system of taxation by license "so arranged as to transfer entirely the trade from those states which have trampled under the foot the Constitution of the United States [in the matter of fugitive slaves] to those which are still willing to abide by its compromises and recognize our rights under it." At the same time Kentucky shifted her desperate, continuous complaints against Ohio to Michigan, which, she claimed, was blocking every effort to recover fugitives.

All this made Garrison proud and perhaps a little overconfident. "The times have indeed changed, and a radical alteration has taken place in public opinion on this subject," he exclaimed. "Probably not another slave will be allowed to be seized on the soil of New England, to say nothing of the other free states." At the Antislavery Convention in May, Edmund Quincy supplemented this by maintaining that the duty of the abolitionists was to keep the subject of slavery agitated in New England, to fight with all their power against any law which prevented New England from giving asylum to any fugitive from oppression. A few days later, at the same convention, Wendell Phillips pointed to the fruits of their earlier proclamation in the presence on the platform of William and Ellen Craft and the amazing Henry Box Brown, whose exploit was a nine-day wonder.

Probably five people out of six at that convention would have pinned you firmly against a wall while these stories were told again, and you would not have been able to choose which was the more remarkable—the stark bravery of the Crafts or the utter recklessness of Henry Box Brown, whose middle name told in one word his story. A Virginia slave of no little inventive ability, as his master had discovered to his advantage, he had found none of the usual avenues of freedom open.

He therefore hit upon a plan that would mean either death or liberty. He would have himself nailed in a box and shipped as freight to Philadelphia! He made the box according to specifications that would allow him a modicum of comfort. In it he carried a bladder of water and a few small biscuits. The friend who nailed him in the box and took charge of this peculiar freight was a shoe dealer by the name of Smith, a white man who for many years had been helping fugitive slaves to the North. The box was addressed to a member of the Philadelphia Vigilance Committee, William H. Johnson, and sent to Adams Express Office in a dray.

Word came cryptically to the Philadelphia committee, hinting that a box might be expected on the three o'clock morning train from the South and in the box would be—could it be a *man?* The members of the committee looked at each other.

They were quite willing to agree later that the strain of the next few hours was more than they enjoyed. When the box was carried in by a drayman they looked at this uncanny object with an apprehensive silence. What would be inside? Would it be alive or dead? Several friends had gathered to witness the "resurrection," and when the door had been locked James McKim rapped quickly on the lid of the box and called out, "All right?" "All right, sir," came the muffled answer.

The witnesses never forgot that moment. With saw and hatchet they cut the hickory loops that bound the box and pried out the nails. Brown sat up quickly but shakily, and no one said a word. Then, with all the aplomb of a Stanley meeting a Livingstone, he reached out his hand. "How do you do, gentlemen."

The effect of Brown's escape spread North and South. In Boston, where he was promptly sent, he was greeted as the Crafts had been—a hero. In Richmond, where his friend Smith plied his inconspicuous shoe trade, the news was received with such incredulity as to allow Smith to repeat the exploit with two other slaves. But this repetition had unfortunate results, for the fugitives and Smith were betrayed, the fugitives recaptured, and Smith sent to eight years' confinement in the state penitentiary.

When Congress came together again in December 1849, only the most dreamy believed that a clash could be avoided. A crisis hung over the Capitol, and no man going into the Houses could help but give a quick and harried look where trouble sat. Was this the end of the Union—a Union conceived in revolution and born in a fight for freedom? It took three weeks of violence that amounted sometimes to blows to elect a Speaker in the House. The balance of power hung like a thread. The South won.

The country was transfixed that winter; every ear from California to Maine strained to hear the forensics that swelled and battered against the walls of Congress. Was this a death struggle? How soon would the South or the North be brought to its knees? Words of the burning arguments that raged from day to day filtered through to the ears of the country. The Whigs were vacillating—could they be trusted? When the Wilmot Proviso was tabled—and thereby killed for the time at least—fourteen of the thirty-two Northern members who presided at the execution were Whigs. You see? . . . And what did Inge of Alabama say? He prophesied with infinite scorn that when the Democrats came to power they would hold the Mississippi River and demand tribute of all states, West and East, which sought to reach the oceans. Cuba, too, Congress was reminded, was ready for the Southern signal. With her in their embrace, and all the fields south and west of the Rio Grande, "with all these views of future wealth and grandeur lighting up the path of our destiny, can you feel that we fear to tread alone?" Robert Toombs of Georgia added the final curl of arrogance: "We have the right to call on you to give your blood to maintain the slaves of the South in bondage. Deceive not yourselves; you cannot deceive others. This is a proslavery government. Slavery is stamped on its heart!"

The small men of the North looked at each other, sitting in their shoe shops, leaning over their plows. The Whigs of the North looked at each other in their law offices and their dry-goods stores. The Democrats of the North looked at each other in their factories and their shipping offices.

Ears straining from the law offices and dry-goods stores heard Mr. Root of Ohio declare solemnly, "So help me God, I never will be a compromising man." God and the country must decide whether new territory was to be slave or free. Some, in the factories or shipping offices, held the corners of their ledgers and listened with a sick dropping of the heart to the attacks on Northern integrity. But there must be no recriminations, no stormy words to break the delicate cords that bound the factories and the cotton fields, the cotton fields and the shipping offices. Some, in the shoe shops and plowed fields, waited, waited, and heard Horace Mann speak up with a terrible directness of the horrors that the South would know if it persisted in disunion talk. "The South fosters in its home three millions of latent rebellions. Is there no Spartacus among them? Is the race of Nat Turner extinct?" And all of them, Whigs, Democrats, and Abolitionists, heard a fearful new voice raised for the first time in those halls.

A man's maiden speech should be decorous, tentative, but for Thaddeus Stevens it was merely an occasion for a blow as hard as his devastating wit and passion for equality could make it. "These Southern gentlemen," whose "well-defined object is partly to intimidate Congress and partly to occupy its time so that no legislation could be matured obnoxious to Southern gentlemen," found their most honorable pretensions exposed to the withering scorn of this dour-faced gentleman from Pennsylvania. "During the present session we have been told amid raving excitement that if we dared to legislate a certain way, the South would teach the North a lesson . . . Are the representatives of free men to be thus treated? You have too often intimidated Congress. You have more than once frightened the tame North from its propriety and found 'doughfaces' enough to be your tools. But I hope that the race of 'doughfaces' is extinct!" His voice was harsh and crisp. He refused to glance at the "Southern gentlemen" who had formed a ring about his desk, were putting their hands significantly into their pockets and interspersing his speech with such clearly articulated oaths that Stevens' friends heard little of his speech for watching over him.

The abolitionists greeted him with cries of joy. Northern papers were in an ecstasy of excitement. Here was a power which thev needed badly —if it had not come too late.

When Mr. Mason of Virginia rose one January afternoon in 1850, no very impressive representation was in the Senate to hear him offer an amendment to the Fugitive Slave Law of 1793. Antislavery men listened with a single ear, no more. His amendment sounded like a child of all those other efforts to bind slavery to the North, varying only slightly from the law of 1793. It merely reduced a man to bankruptcy for befriending a fugitive and left no possible loophole for a fugitive's escape if he were caught. But, as Mr. Mason pointed out, under the existing laws "you may as well go down into the sea and endeavor to recover from his native element a fish which had escaped from you as expect to recover a fugitive. Every difficulty is thrown in your way by the population." And Mr. Yulee of Alabama raised his hand insistently to tell about a convention, meeting *at that moment* in a church in Cazenovia, New York, called by the New York Vigilance Committee to consider ways of escape that could be passed on to restless slaves. One by one representatives stood up and told the number of the slaves in his state lost to the Underground Railroad: Kentucky, "hundreds of thousands of dollars'" worth each year; Maryland, $80,000 worth a year; Virginia, "losses too heavy to be endured . . . increasing year by year . . . already more than $100,000 a year." South Carolina and her neighbors, $200,000. From the District of Columbia, in ten years, the number of slaves had melted from 4,694 to 650 because of "Underground Railroads and felonious abductions." And Mr. Clingman of North Carolina summed it up angrily when he snapped that thirty thousand fugitives were living in the North; at current prices they were worth fifteen million dollars. What did the North propose to do about it? Thirty million dollars' indemnity was due for all that the underground lines had carried off in the last forty years.

Of course the figures were shocking. Antislavery congressmen wakened abruptly to the fact that if property losses were to be emphasized they must be on their guard. Northern men in Congress were taking occasion to shake hands sorrowfully with Southern colleagues and to insist, over a toddy, that as men of property themselves they would have to see that some protection was offered to their friends.

The ball was rolling fast. The South had presented a justifiable grievance. Around this grievance was built the session that followed, that dark turbulent period that was identified so disarmingly as a search for compromise. Before much time had passed compromise was a phrase found big enough to include every grievance that had festered North and South since the days of the Missouri Compromise. Perhaps the South did need protection for her slaves, but the North remembered that she needed protection for her free men. An empire of free men was waiting to stretch from the Atlantic to the Pacific. A slave empire was waiting to reach from one ocean to the other. What was to be given here to be gotten there?

The question was laid in the hands of three dying giants, bowed with age and honor and ambitions, whose search for an answer was to set fire to the fears and apprehensions of their countrymen.

Calhoun, from the Deep South, gaunt and spectral, Clay, from the Border States, surviving from the age of compromise to the age of violence, Webster, from the North, seeing still his dreams before his eyes, the presidency almost within his grasp, were giants all, who had held the destinies of the country in their hands before.

Clay spoke first, Clay the compromiser, Clay the union-lover, Clay who stood in the middle of the road, but with his eyes fixed on the fields of the South. Clay proposed his compromises to the moving refrain of patriotism, moderation, liberalism. Tears flowed freely.

How did this advocate of liberalism propose to heal the wounds of the country? He proposed it on the basis of the sacrifices that the North should be prepared to make. California should be admitted, and the question of slavery settled later; territorial governments should be without restriction or prejudice; the western boundary of Texas should be the Rio Grande; the abolition of slavery should be declared "inexpedient" in the District of Columbia, although the slave trader should be barred from the capital in order that he might not "establish his jails and put on his chains and sometimes mock the sensibilities of our natures by a long train of slaves passing through that avenue from the Capitol to the residence of the Chief Magistrate"; and finally, although the power to obstruct the slave trade between states should be unequivocally denied to Congress, the recapture of fugitive slaves should be made more effective, as Mr. Mason and other gentlemen had pointed out.

Yet some of his Southern colleagues objected. He did not go far enough. He did not say that slavery was a positive necessity. He compromised. Clay answered sharply, the equivocator baring himself with sudden cynicism: "Coming from a slave state, I owe it to myself, I owe it to truth, I owe it to the subject, to say that no earthly power could induce me to vote for a specific measure for the introduction of slavery where it had not before existed, either South or North of that line." He was visibly agitated. Perhaps for the first time he realized that a new South had risen which had no use for compromise.

Could anyone discuss these proposals calmly? Those who did not say so sensed that an ultimatum had been delivered. Would it be compromise again; would the North take what Clay had selected for her and allow the slavocracy to have the rest? Would the doughfaces, the Northern lovers of the slavocracy, bow—bow and vote as the South told them?

The debates raged in the newspapers, they spilled into the legislatures of the North, they whipped at the abolitionists, who knew that only a great miracle could snatch the power from the Southern masters of Congress and at the same time prevent disunion. Of twenty-seven standing committees in Congress, Southern chairmen presided over sixteen, while doughfaces chairmanned most of the others. From all important committees the irreconcilables, Hale, Seward, and Chase, had been excluded; Giddings, after nearly fifteen years, still had no committee of any kind. The House was theirs; the Senate would vote as they said. The Supreme Court would uphold any doubtful legislation; the foreign service would explain with urbanity any singular results.

And yet through those winter days the South rocked and tore at Clay's proposals. The South had been betrayed! California was to be given to the North—California which was larger than Georgia, the Carolinas, and Virginia—and what was the South to get? A Fugitive Slave Law that could not be enforced! A few hundred thousand dollars' worth of recaptured property, while free men staked out claims in gold fields and valleys rich in cotton-growing soil but richer still in representatives who would drag their greasy boots across the floor of Congress and vote for the North.

When word came that the giant of the South was to speak and that the third enigmatic giant was to answer for the North, the country held its breath. Calhoun and Webster, and the whole vast country between them!

Calhoun spoke first, and when he dragged himself into the Senate that day, wrapped in his long black cloak, one saw something of a dying age; one might have foretold that when his harsh, brilliant fire became extinguished the death of a civilization would have begun. He himself could not speak; Mason of Virginia read his speech for him, but the huddled, black-shrouded figure with the face of death and the burning eyes of life, opening now and then to sear the awe-struck chamber, arrested friend and enemy and bade all men be still.

The younger voice of Mason rang out the vindication of a system, the challenge to advancing times. Calhoun had forgotten nothing from a lifetime—the unchallenged power of the South, the sweep of a slave empire, the rise of a North which followed another way of life, a life that tore at the vitals of the slavocracy and showed its power like brazen youth. He remembered the Ordinance of 1787, the Missouri Compromise, the exclusion of slavery from Oregon, revenues and disbursements that did not coincide with slavery needs, a growing centralization of power that could only operate for the benefit of the North. And who was to blame for all this? From small beginnings "a fanatical party" had grown, now "become an object of courtship to both the great parties." (How his smoldering eyes must have opened and his black cloak stirred as he looked at the faces of the Free-Soil senators!) Mr. Clay's proposals he repudiated. They were no compromise. What was the answer? And his long withered fingers lay for a moment against his black shroud. Disunion—*disunion*—two presidents for two sections of the country—disunion in the manner of the churches, in the manner of the Methodists and the Presbyterians and the Baptists who had made their choice, and split peacefully North and South. (In the manner of the Quakers who were disciplining their radicals like Levi Coffin.) The North must decide, and Mason's voice took on fresh vigor. Either the North must give in, agree to an equal balance of power, admit California with no restrictions, cease her slavery agitations, and respect the law by returning fugitives, or the South would understand that the end of the United States had come.

There was no demonstration. That black figure had sat in his seat for thirty years, and in another month he would be dead. Perhaps he was the South. Perhaps it meant civil war. Many men's eyes passed that day to the other giant who had also sat in these halls for thirty years and seen his ambition pass him by as it had passed Calhoun. What would Webster answer? Would he speak for the North? There was uneasiness that night. What if Webster did not speak for the North? What if the South had won again?

His hour came on the seventh of March, and so momentous was that day that Webster's speech was ever after called by its name. When he rose, sunken-cheeked, black Daniel of the cavernous eyes, the Senate Chamber overflowed into all the halls about it, and an awful breathlessness hung in that moment of silence before he began to speak.

He spoke as a patriot—he chose his words with his customary test of their golden quality—"for the preservation of the Union. 'Hear me for my cause.'" Men remembered afterwards quite clearly what he said, but for the lovers of the antislavery cause it would have been a blessing to forget. For the slavocracy had won again.

If he had held something back, if he had conceded one thing for the antislavery cause, if he had agreed by a scintilla that the Southern demands were preposterous . . . but everything was given away. The hopes that had been laid in him went on a wind that bore two names—love of the Union and a last determined hand toward that presidential election which lay two brief years away. Ambition had consumed him since he was a young man: his reputation had been built on his devotion to the Union. Between those two his friends and his enemies might choose.

The slavocrats had listened to him with scorn, to his pleadings to the North that it had everything in any case, that slavery would never take root in California or the mountains of New Mexico. "He thinks to get the Southern delegates with a speech like *that,*" Toombs cried, "but, by God, how he'll find he's mistaken!" Yet they knew that they would not have won if Webster had not filled the breach for them.

Antislavery men could not find words for this perfidy. Emerson said for them sadly, "His finely developed understanding only works truly with all its force when it stands for animal good; that is, for property."

It was men of property who greeted him the day he returned to Boston. Nearly a thousand gentlemen signed their public thanks to a memorial, assuring him that "he had convinced the understanding and touched the conscience of the nation." Massachusetts divided very much as the country divided. The minority saw in him the betrayer of humanity and huzzaed when Faneuil Hall was denied his friends for a reception; the majority saw him in his well-worn role of defender of the Constitution.

As for Webster, his deep-seated conservatism, his distrust of all innovation and change, his well-known dedication to the interests of those friends whom he instinctively found among the bankers and the industrialists, led him to see only the hundreds of letters of congratulation from men of property, the letter from William Corcoran which spilled out canceled notes for six thousand dollars and an additional check for a thousand dollars. He had for the time forgotten the manner in which Calhoun had analyzed the political strength of the North.

> Abolitionists—about 5% of the voting population. Sober people, willing to see slavery abolished, but not by overthrowing the Constitution—70%. Highly respectable people who sympathize with the South—5%. The remainder—20%, who care less for principles than for spoils. Yet the abolitionists hold the balance of power from the nearly equal division of Democrats and Whigs. Hence the danger to the South should any party unite with the abolitionists.

He was not aware that those, East and West, who held the balance of power now despised the name of Daniel Webster. The Seventh of March had brought no peace to the Senate. Awful visions had been conjured up by extremists of both sides, of a country bleeding, paralyzed, and wantonly defaced. Public men were face to face with what had yesterday been mere political expediency but today was the very shape of terror. Could they reduce this terror to its former innocence or had a new day truly come? The fight that consumed another six months showed that they had found no answer.

Violence flared again and again. In the Senate, Foote, of Mississippi, his back against the President's desk, had flourished a pistol at Benton of Missouri, who had dramatically flung back his long coat and cried out to be assassinated. "Harry of the West," the great Clay, had cajoled, implored, argued, and maneuvered with a tirelessness that put to shame men less than his seventy years. Seward had sent shivers down the spines of Constitution deifiers when he shouted that "there is a higher law than the Constitution which regulates our authority!" In the House, antislavery was vociferous. Giddings was fighting as he had never fought before, casting aside party lines, leading the antislavery representatives, who were strengthened now by his son-in-law, George Julian of Indiana, and by Thad Stevens, whose remorseless wit and logic were more devastating than Giddings' bludgeons.

Blood had been rising all these months. The abolitionists had believed the days of mobs were over, but a nervous and apprehensive country turned upon them once again as natural scapegoats.

When, in May, Garrison went to New York for an antislavery convention, violence seemed to fill every corner of a violent city. The New York *Herald* had James Gordon Bennett for its publisher, and Bennett was freely presumed to have the devil in him.

He was busy now exhorting "the merchants, men of business, and men of property to frown down the meetings of these mad people, if they would save themselves." Each day his fine choice of words—"look at the black and white brethren and sisters, fraternizing, slobbering over each other, speaking, singing, praying, blaspheming and cursing the Constitution of our glorious Union"—grew more violent; each day they crept nearer to mob exhortation. The *Globe* was judicious rather than impulsive. It propounded one of demagoguery's favorite arguments: "The right to assemble peaceably for the overthrow of the Government is nowhere guaranteed by the Constitution."

A picked crew answered the exhortations and filtered into the hall of the antislavery convention to bring again the bloody days of the 1830s. Garrison knew they were there, above his head in the galleries, sitting in the backmost seats. But it was not in his nature to give them any dignity. He began without preamble. The proposed Fugitive Slave Bill was a monstrosity. Abolition was *the* Christian movement in the country, and he proved it, to his satisfaction, by a recital of the defections of organized sects. Dr. Furness felt a little rustling in the audience. "What does it mean?" he asked Wendell Phillips, who sat next to him. "It means there's going to be a row," that imperturbable gentleman answered, crossing one leg over the other and folding his arms.

Someone hissed from the gallery. Douglass and Phillips looked up, faint smiles ringing their mouths. Samuel Ringgold Ward sat, black as night, only the whites of his eyes showing. ". . . A belief in Jesus is no evidence of goodness," Garrison's voice was continuing. The hissing materialized when a man stood up in the gallery. Mr. Phillips may have given Dr. Furness a gentle nudge. It did not take farsighted eyes to recognize the bulk and shape of Isaiah Rynders, professional gambler, Tammany district leader, organizer of "roughs and desperadoes." "Are you aware," said Captain Rynders, letting his thunder bruise the head of Mr. Garrison, "that the slaves in the South have their prayer meetings in honor of Christ?"

Mr. Garrison, with his voice only slightly raised, sent a shock coursing down the spines of the respectable listeners who sat close to the platform. "Not a slaveholding or a slave-breeding Jesus. The slaves believe in a Jesus that strikes off chains. In this country Jesus has become obsolete. A profession in him is no longer a test. Jesus is the most respectable person in the United States."

The outcry was tremendous. Only the phalanx of abolitionists did not move an eye. Captain Rynders let out a roar and, forsaking his detached post in the gallery, pelted down the stairs, up the aisles, his pack at his heels. A visible agitation went over the audience as they heard the shouts, but no panic was evident. Mr. Garrison, with his tantalizing tranquillity, replied to the fist under his nose, "We go upon the principle of hearing everybody. If you wish to speak, I will keep order and you shall be heard." Francis Jackson, the impeccable gentleman who was presiding, coldly offered Rynders a seat on the platform and plenty of vocal opportunity as soon as Mr. Garrison had finished. The "roughs and desperadoes" hid their momentary failure by fulminating noisily and spitting on their hands. Garrison was very soon finished with one of his resolutions that was casually produced to bring down the house: ". . . indifference or hostility to this [abolition] movement indicates a state of mind more culpable than was manifested by the Jewish nation in rejecting Jesus as the Messiah, eighteen hundred years ago."

Captain Rynders, with his uncomfortable new piety, was thrown into a frenzy. "He vociferated and harangued," a witness said, "at one time on the platform, and then pushing down into the aisles, like a madman followed by his keepers." There was no stirring this gathering. Several hundred people sat quietly. Antislavery sentiment was not the despised, the outcast that it was when an earlier New York mob descended on a handful of men. Someone called out loudly for Douglass—Douglass of the lordly head. Rynders had the platform. He had taken it over without preamble and was prepared to administer business as he saw fit. "All right," he said to Douglass, "you can speak, but mind what I say, if you speak disrespectfully, I'll knock you off the stage."

Douglass only intended to use his logic. A few words would sum up what he had to say. "The gentleman who has spoken has undertaken to prove that blacks are not human beings. I offer myself for your examination. Am I a man?"

The affirmations rolled to him in a roar. Rynders tried to shout above them. *"You're* not a black man; you're only half a nigger!" Douglass turned with the blandest of smiles and a kind of half-affectionate bow. "Then I am a half brother to Captain Rynders." The place was beside itself with joy. Whatever Douglass chose to say after that was oracular. He spoke with passion of the unemployment and despair of his colored brothers; he tantalized Rynders with half asides; he finished his words with a gesture to call up Samuel Ringgold Ward, that inky black man who come up like a dark cloud from the rear of the stage and startled the audience by the very drama of his color.

His speech was the climax of the evening, for he put a period after every sentence of Douglass. "Never," said Dr. Furness later, "was there a grander triumph of intelligence over brute force. Two colored men whose claims to be considered human were denied had, by mere force of intellect, overwhelmed their maligners with confusion."

There were no more sessions in New York after that. The trustees of the Hall forbade it. "Thus closed," said the New York *Tribune,* "antislavery free discussion in New York for 1850." ". . .The great battle for free speech and free assembling," Whittier wrote Garrison a few days later, "is to be fought over. The signal has been given at Washington, and commercial cupidity at the North is once more marshaling its mobs against us." From Boston, Channing wrote to Theodore Parker that if they persisted in clinging to the old ways of giving help to the fugitives they would be crushed. An office must be rented, he urged, and kept open continually with a Negro with the intelligence of—say—William Nell, the historian, in charge. It would also be a wise move to print a small paper called the *Slave Catcher* to be issued when important fugitive cases were being discussed.

They were then not unprepared when the word finally came, one morning in September. Ominous political moves had been taking place, which had presaged some disturbing climax: the unending fight in Congress, the fear of the Northern politicians, even the death of Taylor, who as the crisis deepened had hinted that he would have nothing to do with compromises, especially if they emanated from Mr. Henry Clay.

Only a few weeks before, Fillmore had become President, and he was a man of small prejudices and determined conservatism, and conservatism in those days meant only one thing—proslavery bias. He had brought Webster with him into his Cabinet, and Webster had taken care to denounce the abolitionists in one of his last senatorial declamations.

What weapons did abolition possess with which to fight so powerful a government campaign, a campaign calculated for only one purpose: to drive through the program of compromise and appeasement? The program had become the frenzied concern of politicians who made it their business to see in the threats and the cries of the South a break in the Union, a disruption of trade, a financial debacle. The country had not been so prosperous within the memory of this generation. Fat years were blessing it, and the violence of a schism was unbearable. Businessmen had made no effort to conceal their share in organizing the procompromise meetings held in large cities of the North. Antislavery congressmen recognized the dimensions of the fight. They had seen government patronage violently utilized, the press whipped into line, and even the pulpits of the country invaded in such a manner that Simon Draper of New York observed caustically, "No Whig could have the confidence of the administration unless his heel was bathed in Negro blood." They had heard the endless forensics of the slavery champions, giving their fierce opinion that the adulterated and sickly dish of compromises would never nourish the extreme requirements of the South, and all the while secession became a darker and more bitter threat.

The fight had absorbed six months, and words that had, at the beginning, an honest meaning—"Union," "patriotism," "emancipation"—became fierce assaults on personal liberty and constitutional rights. The nemesis of all had been Henry Clay, cajoling the timid, persuading the stubborn, conceding here to gain there, altering his course until it became an inexplicable maze to some of his most devoted followers, all in an effort to marry the past and the future.

He had succeeded at last, however—he and Webster and the others who could not see the shape and the temper of the future. The climax had approached rapidly during the late summer of 1850, and all the compromise proposals had finally been shaped into an Omnibus Bill. The Texas bondholders were to realize on their securities by the adjustment of the Texas boundaries and by a large payment to be made by the government. The territories of Utah and New Mexico were to be organized on the basis of a rejection of the Wilmot Proviso, although without a guarantee of the extension of slavery, California was to be admitted with her free constitution, and the slave trade—not slavery—was to be banished from the District of Columbia. To be acted upon separately, and overshadowing all the rest in the popular mind because it came with such a ferocious impact, was the new Fugitive Slave Law.

The Omnibus Bill was passed, but the fight was carried up to the day the Fugitive Slave Law passed the Senate. It might even have failed in the House, for it had less than a two-thirds majority, had the opponents of both sides not been induced to see that a vote must be taken. Only three free-state senators voted for it. Restive, perplexed, uncertain, as the roll call droned on, the ominous implications of the law were heavy in the mind. Hale had pronounced a kind of doom over it for the anti-slavery senators, declaring that the influence of slavery had never been more powerfully exerted in a Congress before, while in the House George Julian pronounced the same obsequies. "The passage of the Fugitive Slave Act will open a fresh wound in the North, and it will continue to bleed as long as the law stands unrepealed."

From the twin days in September that the Senate passed the amendment and the President signed it, the consternation of the common people of the North grew as the words of the law expanded in meaning. The identification of a fugitive could be made on the affidavit of a slave catcher without effort to substantiate his word. The fugitive could offer no defense, could not testify for himself. He was not allowed a trial by jury. The fee of the commissioner who settled the case was to be ten dollars if he found for the master and only five dollars if he freed the fugitive. If a Federal agent hampered in any way the seizure of a fugitive, he was to be fined a thousand dollars, and if a fugitive escaped, with or without his help, he would be held responsible for the entire value of the slave. Bystanders could be forced to lend a hand if a fugitive tried to escape. And friends, in the underground work, or casual humanitarians, were liable to a fine of a thousand dollars or imprisonment for six months if they were convicted of passing him on.

It was said by some that the law was made deliberately barbaric so that Northerners of sensibility would be humiliated by its brutality and refuse to obey it, giving the slavocracy, thereby, sufficient grounds for secession. What truth there was in this could only be measured by the next ten violent years.

EMANCIPATION PROCLAMATION

January 1, 1863

BY THE PRESIDENT OF THE UNITED STATES OF AMERICA:

A Proclamation

The Emancipation Proclamation and the Thirteenth, Fourteenth, and Fifteenth amendments to the Constitution were meant to form a Negro Bill of Rights. Too often we overlook what they guarantee.

WHEREAS, on the twenty-second day of September, in the year of our Lord one thousand eight hundred and sixty-two, a proclamation was issued by the President of the United States, containing, among other things, the following, to wit:

"That on the first day of January, in the year of our Lord one thousand eight hundred and sixty-three, all persons held as slaves within any State, or designated part of a State, the people whereof shall then be in rebellion against the United States, shall be then, thenceforward, and forever free; and the Executive Government of the United States, including the military and naval authority thereof, will recognize and maintain the freedom of such persons, and will do no act or acts to repress such persons, or any of them, in any efforts they may make for their actual freedom.

"That the Executive will, on the first day of January aforesaid, by proclamation, designate the States and parts of States, if any, in which the people thereof respectively shall then be in rebellion against the United States; and the fact that any State, or the people thereof, shall on that day be in good faith represented in the Congress of the United States by members chosen thereto at elections wherein a majority of the qualified voters of such State shall have participated, shall in the absence of strong countervailing testimony be deemed conclusive evidence that such

State and the people thereof are not then in rebellion against the United States."

Now, therefore, I, Abraham Lincoln, President of the United States, by virtue of the power in me vested as commander-in-chief of the army and navy of the United States, in time of actual armed rebellion against the authority and government of the United States, and as a fit and necessary war measure for suppressing said rebellion, do, on this first day of January, in the year of our Lord one thousand eight hundred and sixty-three, and in accordance with my purpose so to do, publicly proclaimed for the full period of 100 days from the day first above mentioned, order and designate as the States and parts of States wherein the people thereof, respectively, are this day in rebellion against the United States, the following, to wit:

Arkansas, Texas, Louisiana (except the parishes of St. Bernard, Plaquemines, Jefferson, St. John, St. Charles, St. James, Ascension, Assumption, Terre Bonne, Lafourche, St. Mary, St. Martin, and Orleans, including the city of New Orleans), Mississippi, Alabama, Florida, Georgia, South Carolina, North Carolina, and Virginia (except the forty-eight counties designated as West Virginia, and also the counties of Berkeley, Accomac, Northampton, Elizabeth City, York, Princess Ann, and Norfolk, including the cities of Norfolk and Portsmouth), and which excepted parts are for the present left precisely as if this proclamation were not issued.

And by virtue of the power and for the purpose aforesaid, I do order and declare that all persons held as slaves within said designated States and parts of States are, and henceforward shall be, free; and that the Executive Government of the United States, including the military and naval authorities thereof, will recognize and maintain the freedom of said persons.

And I hereby enjoin upon the people so declared to be free to abstain from all violence, unless in necessary self-defence; and I recommend to them that, in all cases when allowed, they labor faithfully for reasonable wages.

And I further declare and make known that such persons of suitable condition will be received into the armed service of the United States to garrison forts, positions, stations, and other places, and to man vessels of all sorts in said service.

And upon this act, sincerely believed to be an act of justice, warranted by the Constitution upon military necessity, I invoke the considerate judgment of mankind and the gracious favor of Almighty God.

In witness whereof, I have hereunto set my hand, and caused the seal of the United States to be affixed.

Done at the city of Washington, this first day of January, in the [L. S.] year of our Lord one thousand eight hundred and sixty-three, and of the independence of the United States of America the eighty-seventh.

ABRAHAM LINCOLN

By the President: WILLIAM H. SEWARD, Secretary of State.

ARTICLE XIII

1. Neither slavery nor involuntary servitude, except as a punishment for crime whereof the party shall have been duly convicted, shall exist within the United States, or any place subject to their jurisdiction.

2. Congress shall have power to enforce this article by appropriate legislation.

ARTICLE XIV

1. All persons born or naturalized in the United States, and subject to the jurisdiction thereof, are citizens of the United States and of the State wherein they reside. No State shall make or enforce any law which shall abridge the privileges or immunities of citizens of the United States, nor shall any State deprive any person of life, liberty, or property without due process of law, nor deny to any person within its jurisdiction the equal protection of the laws.

Apportionment of Representatives in Congress.

2. Representatives shall be apportioned among the several States according to their respective numbers, counting the whole number of persons in each State excluding Indians not taxed. But when the right to Vote at any election for the choice of Electors for President and Vice-President of the United States, Representatives in Congress, the executive and judicial officers of a State, or the members of the Legislature thereof, is denied to any of the male inhabitants of such State, being twenty-one years of age, and citizens of the United States, or in any way abridged, except for participation in rebellion, or other crime, the basis of representation therein shall be reduced in the proportion which the number of such male citizens shall bear to the whole number of male citizens twenty-one years of age in such State.

Power of Congress to Remove Disabilities of United States Officials for Rebellion.

3. No person shall be a Senator or Representative in Congress, or Elector of President and Vice-President or hold any office, civil or military, under the United States, or under any State, who, having previously taken an oath, as a member of Congress, or as an officer of the United States, or as a member of any State Legislature or as an executive or judicial officer of any State, to support the Constitution of the United States, shall have engaged in insurrection or rebellion against the same, or given aid and comfort to the enemies thereof. But Congress may, by a vote of two-thirds of each House, remove such disability.

What Public Debts Are Valid

4. The validity of the public debt of the United States, authorized by law, including debts incurred for payment of pensions and bounties for services in suppressing insurrection and rebellion, shall not be questioned. But neither the United States nor any State shall assume or pay any debt or obligation incurred in aid of insurrection or rebellion against the United States, or any claim for the loss or emancipation of any slave; but all such debts, obligations, and claims shall be held illegal and void.

5. The Congress shall have power to enforce by appropriate legislation the provisions of this article.

ARTICLE XV

1. The right of the citizens of the United States to vote shall not be denied or abridged by the United States or by any State on account of race, color, or previous condition of servitude.

2. The Congress shall have power to enforce the provisions of this article by appropriate legislation.

THE NEGRO PROBLEM: A CASE HISTORY

Carey McWilliams

Although a lawyer by trade, Carey McWilliams is far better known for his writing. His deep interest in minority problems has resulted in such books as Prejudice: Japanese Americans *and* Brothers Under the Skin, *from which this excerpt was taken. He is also the author of* Factories in the Field.

1. A Forgotten Episode

PRIOR TO the Civil War, it was the institution of slavery, rather than the problem of the Negro, that engaged the attention of the nation. There was, in fact, no general recognition of the existence of *a* Negro problem. "Where distinctions based on class, caste, and race," writes Dr. Robert E. Park, "are part of the established social order, as they invariably are in a static society, each caste and class lives within the limitations of its own world and accepts the definition imposed upon it as if it were a part of the order of nature." Something like this state of affairs prevailed in the South prior to the Civil War. "A race problem developed for the first time," according to Charles S. Johnson, "when the fixed social position of the Negro slave was changed by his emancipation." An initial recognition of this fact is of extreme importance, since, if there is more racial conflict in America than in other democracies, it is in part owing to the fact, as pointed out by Dr. Park, that there is "more change, more progress. The Negro is rising in America and the measure of the antagonism he encounters is, in some very real sense, the measure of his progress."

As a matter of fact, "it was only with the advance of the invading armies farther and farther into Southern fields that the significance of the Negro as an element in the contest became more exactly defined and more generally apparent."[1] As the Union armies advanced, hundreds and later thousands of Negroes came to the Federal camps for support and protection. Here, for the first time, the North began to encounter the realities, and the true dimensions, of the Negro problem. At first the care of the Negroes who swarmed around the Federal camps was left to the judgment of the individual army commanders. Later various "freedmen's associations," made up of individuals who realized that the destruction of slavery as an institution did not imply that the Negro problem had been solved, were formed throughout the country. As a result of the acute problem faced by the military commanders and the agitation of the freedmen's associations, Congress was finally forced to take cognizance of the Negro.

Various ways and means of dealing with the problem were proposed in Congress during 1863 and 1864. It is interesting to note that one congressman thought that the care of the Negroes should be vested in the Department of Interior in "a bureau similar to the Bureau of Indian Affairs." To indicate the naïveté of the Northern leaders, suffice it to say that Lincoln himself was initially impressed with the desirability of colonization. Schemes for colonizing Negroes in Africa, South America, Central America, the West Indies, Mexico, and Texas were, in fact, seriously discussed, as witness an appropriation by Congress of $10,692.15 in 1864 to study such proposals. After the issuance of the Emancipation Proclamation, however, it became apparent that some affirmitive Federal program would have to be adopted in lieu of colonization proposals.

When a bill was finally drafted looking toward the establishment of a Freedmen's Bureau, it was opposed chiefly on the ground that it would "retard the development of independence and self-reliance in the freedmen"; and defended on the ground that it contemplated "not control, but aid and assistance." No one knew, in fact, just what should be done with the liberated Negroes since, previously, it had been slavery rather than the Negro which had concerned the nation. As one person observed: the Negro presented more than a task—he presented a problem. Hence it was only after *two years* of congressional debate that the bill creating the Freedmen's Bureau in the War Department was finally passed on March 3, 1865. One reason for congressional uncertainty was that the nation had assumed, without realizing it, an utterly unprecedented responsibility. No nation in the world had ever faced just such a problem; and surely there was little in our previous experience upon

[1]See *The Freedmen's Bureau,* by Dr. Paul Skeels Peirce, 1904, from which monograph much of the following information has been obtained.

which we could have drawn for guidance. There was, to be sure, our experience with the American Indian, but neither then nor later could anyone see a connection between the two problems.

Despite all the thunderous agitation over slavery, here was the nation suddenly and unexpectedly confronted with the problem of adjusting some 4,100,000 Negroes (92.2 per cent of all those in the United States) to a new way of life. Slavery had been abolished, but how were these uprooted, uneducated, and confused Negroes to be initiated into the essentially bewildering rites of freedom? Of these, nearly 1,700,000 were of school age. Not only were the adults largely illiterate, but the problem of providing schools for the children, in areas where no such schools had previously existed, presented an enormous task. It was not so much a matter of adapting existing institutions to new needs as of improvising an entirely new set of institutions, on the spur of the moment, to meet an unprecedented emergency. In creating the Freedmen's Bureau, Congress gave only vague and general directives and neglected to provide an initial appropriation. To head the new agency, President Johnson, following a suggestion by Lincoln, appointed General Oliver O. Howard. Without funds, without precedents, and with no clearly formulated policy, General Howard set about the task of dealing with the liberated Negroes. Systematically libeled in the works of reconstruction historians, the Freedmen's Bureau has been pointed to as the ultimate proof of the folly of governmental interference in race matters, as conclusively evidencing the corrupting propensities of all paternalism, and as a miserable failure. At the present time it is particularly important to revalue the work of the bureau, since it represents the *first,* and to date the *last,* attempt made by the national government to deal affirmatively and specifically with the Negro problem. In making such an appraisal, it is necessary to keep in mind that the bureau was only in existence from March 3, 1865, to June 30, 1872, that it was uniformly opposed in the South and only halfheartedly supported in the North, and that it became a central issue in reconstruction politics. When these factors are kept in mind, then, in retrospect, the work of the bureau is deeply impressive.

While it failed to meet the educational problem (some 500,000 children were not provided with the slightest schooling), nevertheless the bureau had under its supervision, when it was abolished, some 2,677 day and night schools, with 3,000 teachers and 149,581 pupils. In setting up secondary schools, it seems to have been rather impractical and to have emphasized Greek and Latin rather than vocational training; but in doing so it merely followed the educational bias of the times. Its schools, in any case, were extremely popular with the Negroes, who clamored for more and similar facilities. The bureau was also directly responsible for the establishment of Howard and Fisk universities—institutions which are, of course, still in existence. It also gave important and valuable aid to, and assisted in the establishment of, many other institutions of higher learning for Negroes.[2] It trained 1,871 teachers in 1869 alone, over half of whom were Negroes. And in many areas it laid the foundation for what later became a system of tax-supported public schools. These achievements were effected in the teeth of the most violent opposition. In many Southern communities mobs of irate Southerners dispossessed Negroes of their schools, teachers were not allowed to enter upon their duties, and churches and school buildings (built by the bureau) were burned to the ground. Nevertheless such bureau-sponsored institutions as Fisk, Hampton Institute, St. Augustine Normal School, and Howard University inaugurated, as Dr. Peirce states, "a system of professional, normal, and industrial training which is doing much to solve the Negro problem today."

The bureau also provided institutions for the care of the sick and the infirm, the insane and the crippled, the aged and the deaf-and-dumb. During its brief existence it established an excellent medical-aid program for Negroes, founded hospitals, provided direct medical treatment, and built asylums. Dr. Peirce estimates that at least one million Negroes received medical care from or through the bureau. It also aided in the care of orphans and provided for the destitute. Later an effort was made to induce some of the Southern states to take over the hospitals and other institutions established by the bureau, but in most cases the requests were refused and these sorely needed institutions simply passed out of existence.

In an effort to relocate Negroes who had drifted away from their homes, the bureau provided transportation for some thirty thousand freedmen. It arranged to have public lands in Mississippi, Missouri, Arkansas, and Florida thrown open for settlement and actually located some four thousand Negro families in these areas, and this despite the fact that it lacked funds to provide operating loans. It also sought, in an intelligent way, to adjust the Negro to a free-labor system. It intervened between the former slave and the plantation owner for the purpose of negotiating an equitable labor contract. Not less than fifty thousand such contracts were prepared under the supervision of the bureau—contracts that at least stipulated for food, fuel, shelter, and the payment of a stated

[2]See p. 78 of Dr. Peirce's monograph for a list of these colleges.

money wage. And, of still greater importance, the bureau served as a legal-aid clinic, advising the Negro in personal, property, and other legal matters. In many cases its agents appeared in court on behalf of Negro litigants. Moreover, it established its own courts to pass on certain types of disputes in which freedmen were involved. In Maryland and Virginia agents of the bureau forced the release of hundreds of Negro children who had been "farmed out" to employers under an outrageous apprentice system. Case after case may be noted in the bureau records where its agents successfully prosecuted those who had violated the civil rights of Negroes. To the Negro the agents "imparted a conception—inadequate and distorted though it may have been—of his civil rights as a freedman." The bureau was, as Dr. Peirce states, important as "a temporary adjustment, a plank in the *bridge* from slavery to freedom." It advised the Negro to vote, probably told him how to vote, and saw to it that he did vote. "In general," states Dr. Peirce, "it was to protect him [the Negro] against violence and outrage, to protect him from any permanent, temporary, or partial system of slavery, to defend his right to hold property, to secure the enforcement of his contracts, to see that he had a fair trial, that his testimony was received in court, and that his family relations were respected."

In response to the congressional mandate of providing every freedman with "forty acres and a mule," the bureau set about the task of distributing the abandoned and confiscated lands of which it had also been given jurisdiction. But by the time Congress had awarded the bureau jurisdiction over these lands it had begun to grant wholesale amnesties to former rebels and to reinvest them with title to confiscated properties. In all, the bureau had only 800,000 acres at its disposal, and the Treasury Department had already leased most of this acreage. Only two tenths of one per cent of the land in the insurrectionary states was ever held by the bureau; consequently it would have been impossible to have given one acre to every freedman. Such, in general, is the record of the bureau. Before it was abolished, however, it had become a football of reconstruction politics and, through the corruption of some (but only a few) of its agents, had become generally discredited. It was damned, however, not on its record—which was admirable—but as a matter of policy, as part of the reconciliation strategy.

It was not until years later, in fact, that belated justice was done the bureau in Dr. Peirce's important monograph of 1904. Even to this day few Americans have ever heard of the bureau or realize that, for a few brief years, the national government did take official cognizance of the

Negro problem with important, and beneficial, results. Involved in the discreditment of the bureau was the failure, in 1874, of the Freedmen's Savings and Trust Company, "morally and practically a part of the Freedmen's Bureau, although it had no legal connection." When the bank and trust company failed, as a consequence of the panic of 1873, Negroes lost three million dollars in savings, but the public forgot that the bureau had been responsible, in the main, for the fact that Negroes had accumulated any savings whatever.

"The accomplishments of the bureau," write Messrs. Abram Harris and Sterling Spero, "were undeniable. It set going a system of free labor and small holdings among the freedmen by aiding them in the purchase of public lands made available by the Act of Congress of June 1866; by supervising the terms under which Negroes were employed on land leased to former planters and northern whites; by allotting small parcels of land to Negroes and later by leasing lands for management and cultivation; and by organizing destitute and vagrant freedmen into self-supporting colonies, for which purpose lands ranging from one to ten thousand acres were used in each state. Moreover, it secured the recognition of the black man before courts of law and opened the free public schools to him and to the south generally." Referring to the opposition which the bureau faced, Dr. W. E. B. DuBois has written: "Even under such conditions, the Freedmen's Bureau in its short hectic life accomplished a great task. Carl Schurz, in 1865, felt warranted in saying that 'not half of the labor that has been done in the south this year, or will be done there next year, would have been or would be done but for the existence of the Freedmen's Bureau. . . . No other agency *except one placed there by the government could have wielded that moral power* whose interposition was so necessary to prevent southern society from falling at once into the chaos of a general collision between its different elements.'" (Italics mine.)

In retrospect, a striking fact about the bureau should be noted—namely, that the one time when the Federal government did attempt to deal, not negatively, but affirmatively, with the Negro problem, marked and permanent improvement resulted. During the time the bureau was in existence, General Howard on one occasion attempted to curtail some of its functions. His observations about what happened at the time foreshadow, clearly enough, precisely what happened on a larger scale when the bureau was abolished. "A reaction," he stated, "against the interests of the freedmen immediately followed. . . . The practical effect of discharging the officers and agents has been to close up the schools; to intimidate union men and colored people; and, in fact, to paralyze almost completely the work of education." Considering the status of the Negroes at the time, it is today perfectly apparent to any thinking person that some such agency was a vital necessity, in constituting *a bridge* across which Negroes might have passed rapidly from a feudal to a free-labor system, *had the bridge been permanent*. But to have expected that such a transition could be effected in *seven years* was incredibly naïve.

2. *A Deal Is Made*

If an exception be made of the Freedmen's Bureau, then it can be said that little progress was made during the reconstruction period to clarify the nature of "the Negro problem." What was called "the Negro problem" during these years was merely the political issue over the nature of reconstruction, which was fought on strictly sectional lines. The issue was finally decided in favor of the South in the great betrayal of 1876. It is impossible, here, to summarize the full sequence of events leading up to the so-called "compromise of 1876"; but the main facts are well known. Following the adoption of the Black Codes in the South, the Republicans enacted a radical reconstruction program in 1867. When confronted with this eminently realistic strategy, the South realized that, if the war were not to be resumed, a change in tactics was imperative. Thereafter, as Dr. Paul Buck has said, "'Reconciliation by acceptance' became the future basis of action. In the political parlance of the day this change of front was styled the 'New Departure' of the Democratic Party." Capitalizing upon the war-weariness of the nation, the campaign of reconciliation rapidly gained adherents in the North, as witness the defection of the liberal Republicans in 1872. The drive for reconciliation, moreover, was aided by the fact that Northern industrialists were eager to resume trade with the South and to exploit the Southern market. "Social peace was needed," writes Mr. James S. Allen, "to obtain the full benefits of the new plantation production and the tremendous internal market. . . . If peace could be obtained at the price of the hard-won rights of the Negroes, this was but a slight concession to ask of the bourgeoisie."

The signal of the new orientation in national affairs was the passage of the Amnesty Act of 1872, despite Sumner's warning that the nation should be just to the Negro before it became generous with the rebel. Taking advantage of the split in the Northern alignment, the South pressed hard for the restoration of white supremacy. The bargain of reconciliation was actually sealed in 1876 when the deadlock between Hayes and Tilden was finally broken. There can be but slight doubt today that the basis of the deal whereby Hayes was elected was the surrender of the Negro to the South. "The bargain consisted," writes Dr. DuBois, "in allowing the southern whites to disenfranchise the Negroes by any means which they wished to employ, including force and fraud, but which somehow was to be reduced to a semblance of legality in time. And then that the south hereafter would stand with the north in its main industrial policies and all the more certainly so, because northern capital would develop an industrial oligarchy in the south." It is not necessary to imply such an intention in the bargain of 1876, for the chief actors have themselves left records clearly indicating that such was the understanding.[3] "Hayes was tacitly committed," writes Dr. Buck, "to the restoration of white rule in the south, and southerners seemed perfectly satisfied with their share of the spoils." Henceforth, as the *Nation* observed in its issue of April 5, 1877, "the nation as a nation will have nothing more to do with the Negro."

The complete story of how this reconciliation was achieved is admirably told in Dr. Buck's volume, *The Road to Reunion* (1937). So thoroughly was the propaganda of reconciliation disseminated that, thirty years after the war, Thomas Wentworth Higginson—ardent abolitionist, commander of a Negro regiment in the war—is pictured by Dr. Buck with a copy of *Marse Chan* on his lap, actually shedding tears over the death of a slaveowner. Even the most progressive elements in the North came to accept, at face value, the South's theory of what was called "the Negro problem." For decades subsequent to 1876, as Dr. Charles A. Beard has written, "agitation of the Negro question became bad form in the north." How great was the South's ideological triumph is indicated by the almost universal acceptance in the North of the dogma that "the South will solve its own problem." To indicate how thoroughly this dogma came to be accepted in the North, Dr. Buck has prepared an interesting summation of contemporary views:

1. The mass of Negroes are unfit for suffrage.—R. W. Gilder, A. D. Mayo, and James Bryce.
2. The only hope for good government in the South rests upon the assured political supremacy of the white race.—Edward Atkinson, E. L. Godkin, Carl Schurz, Charles Eliot Norton, C. D. Warner.
3. The Negroes are the American peasantry.—N. S. Shaler, J. B. Harrison, H. M. Field.

[3]See *Reconstruction: The Battle for Democracy,* by James S. Allen, p. 205.

4. One race or the other must rule; the true interests of both races require that control should be in the hands of the whites.—Hugh McCulloch, A. K. McClure, G. F. Hoar.
5. If there is a race problem, time and education can alone supply its solution.—R. C. Winthrop, A. W. Tourgee, C. F. Adams.
6. The Negro is better off in Southern hands.—A. D. Mayo, T. W. Higginson, R. W. Gilder.
7. The history of the Negro in Africa and America leads to the belief that he will remain inferior in race stamina and race achievement.—A. B. Hart.

So far as official attitudes were concerned, there was no Negro problem after 1876. The problem had been "solved" by surrendering the Negro to the tender mercies of his former master. This change in Northern sentiment and thinking is the real explanation of much that subsequently happened.

In order to safeguard the rights established by the Civil War, the radical Republicans had forced the adoption of the Thirteenth, Fourteenth, and Fifteenth amendments to the Constitution. "The fourteenth amendment was not intended to confer new rights," points out Mr. Louis B. Boudin, "but to furnish a means of protecting old ones."[4] The amendment was adopted for the express purpose of making it abundantly clear that Congress had power to legislate for the protection and the enforcement of civil liberties—the civil liberties defined in the Bill of Rights to the Constitution. The Thirteenth, Fourteenth, and Fifteenth amendments provide that Congress has power to enforce the amendment by appropriate legislation. That Congress intended to enforce the amendments is indicated by its adoption of the so-called Enforcement Acts and the Civil Rights Act. What happened to this legislation? But, first, what happened to the Fourteenth Amendment?

In the famous Slaughterhouse Case in 1872, the Supreme Court, with an eye on the new strategy of reconciliation, held that the Fourteenth Amendment, despite its clear wording, despite the unmistakable contemporary evidence of congressional intention, did *not* accomplish the purpose for which it was adopted. Essentially such was the holding, for the court said that the "privileges and immunities" referred to in the amendment only had reference to those rights which existed solely by reason of national sovereignty, such as the right to travel from state to state. Later, in its celebrated decision in the Civil Rights Cases (1883), the court went further and struck down as unconstitutional the very

[4]"Truth and Fiction About the Fourteenth Amendment," *New York University Law Review*, November 1938.

measures which had been enacted pursuant to the clear authorization of the Fourteenth Amendment. And this was done despite the fact that Mr. Justice Miller, speaking for the majority in the Slaughterhouse Case, had stated that the Fourteenth Amendment was enacted specifically, if not solely, for the benefit of the Negro race, as to which there could not, in fact, be much doubt. In the Civil Rights Cases, Mr. Justice Harlan, in a famous dissent, asked the question: "Were the states against whose protest the institution [of slavery] was destroyed, to be left free, so far as national interference was concerned, to make or allow discriminations against that race, as such, in the enjoyment of those fundamental rights which by universal concession, inhere in a state of freedom?" The answer, of course, was that the decision *to do just that* had already been made; it had been made in 1876.[5]

In the Cruikshank Case (1876), in the Harris Case (1889), and in the Civil Rights Cases (1883), the Supreme Court had, in effect, put the Federal Bill of Rights outside the protection of the Fourteenth Amendment. Presumably these rights were to be vindicated, if at all, by "resort to the laws of the state." This outrageous amputation of the Fourteenth Amendment was not effected by any inherently plausible or inescapably sound legal reasoning. On the contrary, the decisions by which the amendment was robbed of its original intent were actually "bad law," a perversion of legal reasoning. These decisions, in fact, can only be explained, as Mr. Boudin has stated, "as part of that general movement which a recent writer has called 'The Road to Reunion.' The south and the Democratic Party had fought bitterly the war amendments and particularly the Fourteenth Amendment; and they never really became reconciled to them. The 'road to reunion' had to be paved with the sacrifice of the rights granted by these amendments and every device had to be resorted to to destroy or at least minimize the protection offered by these amendments to the Negro race, and incidentally to other individuals and minorities. The Supreme Court decided that the sacrifice should be made, and it acted on that decision in interpreting these amendments." The real decision was, therefore, based upon purely political, not legal, considerations.

The importance of the highly artificial and strained construction which the court placed on the Fourteenth Amendment can scarcely be overemphasized. The decision in the Civil Rights Cases, for example, was a "green light" to the South. It resulted in the passage by practically every

[5]See also "The Supreme Court and Civil Rights," by Louis B. Boudin, *Science and Society,* Vol. I, No. 3.

Southern state of Jim Crow laws enforcing the segregation which the Civil Rights statute had prohibited. Henceforth, as Messrs. Harris and Spero have said, the South "was free to handle Negro political aspirations according to its own standards." At first through terror, and later by a pretense of legality, the South proceeded to rob the Negro of his constitutional rights in a systematic and thoroughgoing fashion. Discrimination was not limited to the right of suffrage; but, quickly and efficiently, other types of discrimination were devised: residential segregation; discrimination in public conveyances, in public institutions, in schools, in employment, in places of amusement. So much, of course, is generally known. But the holding of the Supreme Court had other and even graver consequences, for it effectively denationalized the sphere of civil-liberties legislation. It not only opened the door to the South to establish a system of white supremacy, but it effectively tied the hands of Congress. And, lastly, it made for the existence of a mood of futility in so far as the Negro problem was concerned. If the *nation* could not act, if it was powerless to protect the Negro, just what in fact could be done, except to pray with the Southerner? (Which is about all that the nation has done in relation to the Negro problem since 1876.)

Had there been no supreme Court decisions, however, it is doubtful if Congress would have acted; in fact, Congress itself would probably have repealed the Civil Rights statute. For the decision to get rid of it was, as I have said, essentially based upon political considerations. The consequences, however, have been continuing in character. "Congress," writes Mr. Charles S. Mangum, Jr., "has remained discreetly silent since the days of the Civil Rights Act, and hence the problem and its control have been left in the hands of the individual carriers (referring to public conveyances). The railways in various sections of the country have therefore been permitted to handle the problem in any way they saw fit. Southern carriers have thereupon adopted a Jim Crow policy. It has been said that *congressional inaction* is equivalent to a declaration that railways and other interstate carriers may make such regulations."[6] Thus even with respect to one phase of the problem concerning which Congress could still have acted despite the Civil Rights Cases (the regulation of interstate commerce), it has not acted. Congress, therefore, as well as the Supreme Court, adhered to the bargain of 1876.

As a consequence of the national decision to vest control of the Negro problem in the South, a fixed dogma developed in this country—namely, that the Negro problem was essentially insoluble. "The race question,"

[6]*The Legal Status of the Negro,* 1940.

wrote Mr. John Moffatt Mecklin in 1914, "belongs to this class of essentially insoluble problems." "Relations between American Negroes and American whites," wrote Mr. Scott Nearing in 1929, "occupy a frontier of conflict which is beyond the pale of organized society." "I have been forcibly impressed," wrote Mr. William P. Pickett in 1909, "by the constant repetition of the thought that the problem is in its essential character insoluble." "No matter which way we turn in the north or the south," wrote Mr. André Siegfried in 1927, "there seems to be no solution. The color problem is an abyss into which we can look only with terror." "In spite of growing race consciousness and the development of a 'New Negro,'" wrote Dr. Everett V. Stonequist in 1929, "the problem of creating a race-wide program of action remains unsolved." Similar quotations, covering the period from 1876 to date, might be endlessly multiplied.

How could anyone propose a program of remedial legislation under the circumstances? Congress had been stripped of authority to legislate for the protection of civil rights by the Supreme Court; and the South was firmly in the grip of the whites. Only by recognizing this impasse is it possible to account for the sense of political frustration, reflected in the myth of the insolubility of the Negro problem, which prevailed after 1876. This sense of political frustration has had important psychological implications. It has made for uneasiness, unrest, bad consciences, a studied attempt to shy away from the Negro problem, an overemphasis upon education as a solution, and the propagation of numerous crackpot theories. The frustration of the political will of the nation only increased when, at a later date, the Supreme Court proceeded to place its stamp of approval upon the Jim Crow legislation which sprang into existence after it had nullified the Civil Rights statute. Just ponder this hypocritical statement by Mr. Justice Brown in Plessy vs. Ferguson (1890): "The object of the fourteenth amendment was undoubtedly to enforce the absolute equality of the races before the law, but in the nature of things it could not have intended to abolish distinctions based upon color, or to enforce social, as distinguished from political, equality, or the commingling of the two races upon terms unsatisfactory to either." Or, again, "If one be inferior to the other socially, the constitution of the United States cannot put them upon the same plane."

Presidents of the United States have also acquiesced in the emasculation of the Fourteenth Amendment. The second section of the amendment (which it is hoped that the majority of Americans will get around to reading one of these days) provides for a reduction of the number of representatives in Congress where qualified voters have been prevented from participating in elections. I cannot find an instance where the President has called this provision to the attention of Congress. Harrison, Cleveland, McKinley, Roosevelt, Taft, and Wilson, points out Dr. Kelly Miller, all deplored lynchings, "but declared their impotence to deal with the evil." President Theodore Roosevelt, for all his expressions of sympathy for the Negro, "never made the slightest suggestion of an effective remedy through federal agency." It is this systematic perversion of a clearly expressed constitutional amendment, rather than any inherent obstacle, which is accountable for our national frustration over the Negro problem. "The evil," wrote Dr. Miller, "is indeed national. So must the remedy be. It is but hollow mockery of the Negro, when he is beaten and bruised and burned, in all parts of the nation, and flees to the national government for asylum, to be denied relief on the ground of doubtful jurisdiction. The black man asks for justice and is given a theory of government."

The year 1876, wrote Mr. George S. Merriam, "marked the disappearance of the Negro problem as the central feature of national politics."[7] For all practical purposes, it also marked the disappearance of the Negro in so far as congressional attention was concerned. Somewhat shocked by the violence with which the South suppressed the Negro after 1876, Senator Henry Cabot Lodge, in 1890, proposed a bill in the Senate which provided that Federal supervisors representing both parties should be appointed in any election district where five hundred voters petitioned the Federal authorities. These supervisors were to have power to pass on the qualifications of voters in Federal elections and to receive ballots. The bill was not pushed very energetically and was finally defeated in 1891. With the exception of this bill, and a measure proposed by Senator Blair of New Hampshire to grant Federal subsidies for educational purposes in the South, no "important federal legislation directed specially at the south," on the Negro problem, was proposed from 1876 to 1906.[8]

The absence of any type of social action, with respect to the Negro problem, from 1876 onward was, indeed, most striking. "Since the discontinuance of the Freedmen's Bureau," wrote Mr. Harry Earl Montgomery, "the United States has shirked its duty by ceasing to provide the means whereby the Negro might learn to properly exercise his privileges of suffrage."[9] In the absence of national assistance or effective state

[7]*The Negro and the Nation,* 1906.

[8]Ibid.

[9]*Vital American Problems,* 1908.

action, private individuals and organizations made a feeble attempt to meet the obvious educational needs. The Peabody Fund was established in 1867, the Slater Fund in 1882, the Hand Fund in 1888, the Jeanes Fund in 1907. While these and other foundations did do important demonstrational work, nevertheless Northern philanthropy quickly became, as Messrs. Harris and Spero have said, "a powerful instrument for fortifying white supremacy." By setting up separate Negro schools and churches, they laid the foundations for what later became the "dual educational and welfare systems characteristic of the southern states." This development was almost inescapable, in the absence of a national policy against discrimination, since the foundations had to conciliate the whites before they could even function in the South. After it became apparent that the foundations intended to respect the existing social structure, then "the new South," so called, welcomed their activities. The work of the foundations, however, clearly indicated the necessity for some type of action, and, in default of Federal or state action, at least a beginning was made. It was not, however, until the turn of the century that public opinion would permit a full development of even privately sponsored programs based upon a philosophy of improving race relations.[10] From 1870 to 1900 the outside assistance furnished by the Northern foundations and the Northern missionary societies, according to Mr. Johnson, constituted "the sole constructive influence from without a south that was itself poor, disorganized, and reactionary."

3. *The New Aggression*

Despite the earlier pretense that the Negro problem had been "solved," it began to be abundantly apparent after 1900 that such was not the case. To be sure Negroes, from 1865 to 1900, had made some important gains; they had been, as one of them stated, "inchin' along." The northward migration had commenced, but on a small scale, and might have developed rapidly had it not been for the reaction of Northern tradeunionists. Between 1880 and 1890 some fifty strikes were reported in the North against the employment of Negroes. The attitude of the tradeunion movement had, in fact, "increased the Negro's dependence upon agriculture and domestic service." Even later, in 1910, 2,881,454 Negroes were engaged in agriculture; and the number in branches of industry other than cotton production constituted less than 0.5 per cent. Under the leadership of Booker T. Washington, they had nevertheless made

[10]See *A Preface to Racial Understanding,* by Charles S. Johnson, 1936.

some important gains in the South. New industries were developing in the region, and by 1900 most of the losses of the war period had been regained. As the South began to be partially industrialized, the Negro assumed increasing importance. For since it had been largely unaffected by European immigration, the South remained dependent upon a Negro labor supply. Labor became scarce; wages tended to rise; and the Negroes began to leave the plantations. After the Civil War the South had restored its ancient edifice, but not completely or satisfactorily. "There *had* been a revolution," wrote Mr. Ray Stannard Baker; "society *had* been overturned." In the process unexpected opportunities had been created for the Negro, on a limited scale, and he had not hesitated to seize them. As Negroes began to accumulate property and to get a foothold in wage employment, they became less dependent and more self-assertive. Many observers, noticing these tendencies, concluded that a "new day" had dawned in "the new South" for the Negro.

But just to the degree that the Negro made progress, social tensions increased. "The more progressive and ambitious the Negro becomes," observed Dr. Kelly Miller, "the less tolerable he seems to be to his white lord and master." For as the feudal structure of Southern society began to disintegrate, the poor whites (of whom there were 5,250,000 in 1860) began to be affected by the same social forces that had resulted in a measure of improvement for the Negro. As class antagonisms developed within the white group, both "poor white" and "Southern aristocrat" began to manipulate the Negro question to political advantage. While he had ceased to be a national political issue, the Negro had become an issue in intra-Southern politics. Beginning about 1890, the "poor whites" began to revolt against the dominance of Southern politics by the post-bellum aristocracy. Under the leadership of such men as Tillman, Jeff Davis, Hoke Smith, Vardaman, and Tom Watson, the poor whites commenced to assert themselves. "Wherever the whites divided as Democrats and Populists," writes Dr. Buck, "the rival factions courted the colored vote and some of the turbulence of Reconstruction came back again." Tillman discovered, for example, that the old-line Bourbon Democrats were voting the Negroes of the Black Belt against him. "In 1895," said Senator Tillman, "we changed our constitution and disenfranchised every Negro we could." This development, and fear of the passage of Senator Lodge's so-called Force Bill, compelled the South to place the disenfranchisement of the Negro upon a pseudo-constitutional basis, rather than to rely upon the extralegal and illegal methods employed during the reconstruction period. Also by 1895 most of the remaining enforcement legislation had been repealed by Congress. Commencing therefore in Mississippi, in 1890, the South began systematically to disenfranchise the Negro by "constitutional enactment": through grandfather clauses, literacy tests, poll taxes, and other devices. Similarly Jim Crowism was placed upon an official basis, as every Southern state (with the exception of Missouri) enacted, between 1881 and 1907, statutes requiring that white and colored persons be furnished separate accommodations in public conveyances, in schools, and in almost every phase of social life. As the poor whites came increasingly into competition with the Negroes, and as their demogogic leaders began to realize the vast possibilities of Negro baiting (which they seemed able to exploit more effectively than their opponents), the informal Jim Crowism of the post-war period crystallized into a rigid system of constitutional and legislative discrimination.

The new system was not merely a formal enactment of already existing discriminatory practices: it went much further and actually multiplied and expanded Jim Crowism in general. There developed, as Mr. George S. Merriam noted, "a new or a newly apparent aggression upon the weaker race." Official Jim Crowism has, in fact, assumed increasingly insane proportions since 1890, with new and stricter prohibitions being added almost every year right down to the present time. A new aggression was also apparent after 1890 in unofficial manifestations of Jim Crowism. Once it had been the proud boast of the South that, at least in that area, every Negro could work if he wanted to do so. But the poor whites, by so-called legal and extralegal means, have sharply curtailed the range of Negro employment opportunities. "Negroes," writes Mr. Edwin R. Embree, "have been losing ground steadily in many of their historic occupations in the south. Hotels are replacing Negroes by Europeans as waiters, cooks, bellboys, in all branches of service. Where Negroes formerly controlled teaming, trucking, and horse-drawn vehicles generally, they have not carried over in large numbers into taxi driving, garbage work, and other aspects of auto transport. As barbers and in other forms of personal service, and even in such menial and heavy tasks as street cleaning and road making, Negroes in the south are being shoved out by whites."[11] The new aggression, which began to be manifest in the South after 1890, soon challenged Mr. Booker T. Washington's famous theory that the Negro's best opportunity was in the South and that he could most readily utilize this opportunity by learning a trade.

Over a period of years the alienation of the races, which had begun

[11] *American Negroes,* 1942, p. 47.

during the years of reconstruction, gradually widened. The Jim Crow codes tended to deepen the breach and to extend the separation to all walks of life. "The tendency has been," wrote Mr. Merriam in 1906, "to a wider separation. Once the inmates of mansion and cabin knew each other's way. Now they are almost unacquainted." To keep the races separate and apart meant, in actual practice, to keep the Negro at a lower level. Not only is this the inevitable effect of separatism, but it also implies that the separate facilities provided for the Negro were, in each instance, inferior to those provided for whites. "A slow but widespread process of race separation in all parts of the country," wrote Mr. Mecklin in 1914, "is gradually divorcing the Negro from the white man's world. . . . The masses of the Negroes are today farther away from the white man's world than they were during slavery." This tendency was only evidenced by the increasing severity and complexity of the Jim Crow codes, which became constantly more rigorous. In the course of time the Negro came to have an almost distinct social and cultural heritage. "The Negro population," wrote Charles S. Johnson, "had its own social heritage which, in a relatively complete isolation, has had little chance for modification from within or without." Separatism or biracialism, far from minimizing, actually intensified race friction. Education for the Negro, within the framework of a biracial system, did not relieve these tensions; on the contrary, it probably increased them and created entirely new ones. The effect of the biracial system, noted Mr. Baker, was to make for "a silent, dogged, sanguinary struggle" in which the "combatants never rest upon their arms." In many areas educational facilities for the Negro, such as they were, were actually reduced. "Every man," said Tillman, "who can look before his nose can see that with Negroes constantly going to school, the increasing number of people who can read and write among the colored race . . . will in time encroach upon our white men." Increased work opportunities for the Negro, as a result of better training facilities, also tended to aggravate, not minimize, existing tensions.

The Negro was compelled, in effect, to go along with this new development. Once Northern support for his ambitions to rise in status had been removed, he was forced to seek some basis of accommodation or adjustment with his white neighbors. "One of the natural and inevitable results," wrote Mr. Baker, "of the effort of the white man to set the Negro off, as a race, by himself, is to awaken in him a new consciousness—a sort of racial consciousness. It drives the Negroes together for defense and offense." The essence of Mr. Washington's philosophy was to accept the principle of separatism and to seek to turn it to the Negro's advantage. Since Negroes were refused service in many businesses and could not obtain adequate professional attention from whites, they tended to create their own businesses and to patronize their own professional class. Every force, noted Mr. Baker, seemed to be working in the direction of building up a "more or less independent Negro community life within the greater white civilization." "Negro businesses," write Messrs. Harris and Spero, "are chiefly the product of segregation: they are defensive enterprises." Since the whites controlled the basic industries, the raw materials, and, above all, finance, it was impossible for the Negroes to develop a broad enough base to sustain a real middle class. Nevertheless, within a narrow range, Negro businesses rapidly developed, and, as they developed, Negroes became increasingly race-conscious.

Shortly after the turn of the century a number of events served to call the nation's attention to the fact that the South had not solved the Negro problem. For one thing, lynchings had increased. Between 1890 and 1900 there had been, on an average, 166 lynchings annually. The practice of lynching, as Mr. Johnson noted, took on a new impetus: it became "a hybrid of sport-vengeance." But no one event served so rudely to shatter the notion that the South had its own peculiar problem well in hand as did the savage race riots which took place in Atlanta in September 1906. After these riots, groups both North and South began to realize that it would no longer do to say that the Negro problem was insoluble and that some type of action was imperative.

A new attitude began to find expression in such books as Ray Stannard Baker's *Following the Color Line* (1908)—one of the most readable books ever written on the Negro problem—and in such rationalizations of biracialism as Edgar Gardiner Murphy's *The Present South* (1904) and *The Basis of Ascendancy* (1909). In these and other volumes the existence of a social problem, as distinguished from a political issue, was definitely recognized. It was generally indicated, however, that the approach to the problem was by way of prayer, interracial education, and the application of the golden rule (within the framework, of course, of a definitely biracial system). It is interesting to note that Mr. Baker, while clearly recognizing that the Negro had become a national problem,[12] never so much as hinted at Federal action. Later, in 1913, he wrote that "there is now no disposition anywhere in the north to interfere in the internal affairs of the south—not even with the force of public opinion."

[12]See p. 233 of *Following the Color Line.*

Many intelligent Southerners, after the turn of the century, also began to have a change of heart. They came to recognize the essential inconsistency of their position: by increasing the severity of Jim Crow regulations, they were driving the Negro from the South. This, assuredly, would never do. The creation of the Commission on Southern Race Questions, in May 1912, indicated a growing awareness that "something had to be done." The commission agreed, at one of its early meetings, that there was in the South "a realization of the pervasiveness of the problem; that in reality it is not an isolated situation out of touch with the affairs of the south at large, but an intimate, ever-present problem touching the life of the south at every turn, and involving the hygienic, economic, and moral well-being of every citizen of the south." At various religious meetings and conferences Southerners, with a feeling of almost unspeakable self-righteousness, began to forgather with Negroes and to "discuss the problem." The dogma became pretty thoroughly established, judging by practice, that the Negro problem might be solved by "discussion" and the "spread of enlightenment." This development was, in turn, paralleled by the formation of race-conscious Negro organizations in the North: the National Association for the Advancement of Colored People (1909) and the Urban League (1910). "We refuse to allow the impression to remain," said Dr. DuBois at the Niagara conference, "that the Negro-American assents to inferiority, is submissive under oppression and apologetic before insults." The Negro problem had thus been recognized by two widely divergent groups: a small minority of enlightened Southerners and a fairly large group of militant Negroes.

A number of Northern whites also began to realize that, with the passing of the old order in the South, the Negro problem had increased in magnitude and importance. "With the passing of the generation of whose life it [slavery] was an accepted fact, both black and white, the relations which it slowly evolved," wrote Dr. A. H. Stone in 1907, "are passing also. A new basis of contact is presented—that of unconditional equality." The existence of this changed situation did not imply more peaceful relations; on the contrary, it clearly indicated that there would be more, not less, friction. "Not only will there be race friction," wrote Dr. Stone, "but it will increase as the weaker race increases its demands for the equality which it is denied." About this time a Captain H. A. Wilson of the English Army, traveling in Africa, noted that the natives, even in the most remote areas, had heard some vague report that somewhere, in the unknown outside world, a yellow nation had defeated a white nation in war. "There can be no doubt," wrote Dr. Stone, "in the mind of any man who carefully reads American Negro journals that their rejoicing over the Japanese victory sounded a very different note from that of White America. . . . It was a clear cry of exultation over the defeat of a white race by a dark one."

4. *The First World War*

The First World War measurably changed the proportions of the Negro problem in the public mind. To fight a war a democracy must have a measure of internal unity; war naturally serves, therefore, to emphasize basic faults in the social structure. Aroused by the stirring slogans of 1918, Negroes were soon made to realize that they were second-class citizens. Appealed to in the name of democracy, they were constantly discriminated against in the armed forces. While their enemies in the South cast aspersions on their fighting ability, they seemed quite willing to let the Negro be drafted. From Mississippi, 24,066 colored men, by comparison with 21,182 white men, joined the colors; in South Carolina the figures were 25,789 colored, 19,909 white; in Florida, 12,904 colored, 12,769 white. According to a former special assistant to the Secretary of War, the Negroes contributed many more to the armed forces than their quota. Draft boards in numerous localities conscripted Negro married men "in defiance of both the spirit and the letter of the draft law." The first report of the provost marshal general indicated that of every hundred colored citizens called, thirty-six were certified; but of every hundred white men called, only twenty-five were certified. Negroes had "practically no representation upon the draft boards which passed upon their appeals."[13] Once in the service, Negroes were segregated, assigned to disagreeable and degrading tasks, and socially discriminated against. The South was horrified at the friendly attitude shown by the French people to the Negro troops. Major J. E. Spingarn of the American Expeditionary Forces publicly accused Southern officers of treason, "in that they preferred white ascendancy in the army to the measures necessary for efficiency and for victory."[14] This friction in the armed services naturally had its echoes in civilian life.

During the years 1917, 1918, and 1919 an estimated 500,000 Negroes moved from Southern rural areas to Northern industrial centers. In large measure this migration was stimulated by the fact that, with the

[13] *The American Negro in the World War,* by Emmett J. Scott.

[14] *The Negro Faces America,* by Herbert J. Seligmann, 1920, p. 136.

outbreak of war in Europe in 1914, immigration had sharply decreased. At a later date, between 1921 and 1924 (when the exclusionary Immigration Act was passed), an additional 500,000 migrated North to seek employment in the booming industrial areas. This movement made for increased tension North and South. "Whole sections of the south," writes Mr. Embree, "were depleted of labor. Southern planters who for decades had railed against the Negro masses suddenly were in panic at the threat of losing them. By edicts, by offers of better conditions, by force and threat, southerners tried to stem the flood." In the North the use of Negro labor, particularly as strikebreakers, made for sharp conflicts, as witness the frightful riots in East St. Louis in 1917, when six thousand Negroes were driven from their homes and thirty-nine were killed. "Both in the north and in the south," wrote Mr. Seligmann, "each increase in prosperity for the Negro made feeling about race relations correspondingly tense." Noting this tendency, many people began to wonder whether the emphasis placed upon finding industrial opportunities for the Negro was, after all, likely to make for improved social relations. "A disenfranchised working class in modern industrial civilization," said Dr. DuBois, "is worse than helpless. It is a menace not simply to itself but to every other group in the community. It will be diseased; it will be criminal; it will be ignorant; it will be the plaything of mobs, and it will be insulted by caste restrictions." Even many Negroes began to wonder, in the postwar years, if their position was not worse than it had been before the war. It should be noted, however, that few of them showed any tendency to return to the South. For in moving North they had at least been subjected to what Mr. Johnson calls "the galvanizing shocks of change."

The real crisis developed, however, not with our entrance into the war, but immediately afterwards. This fact should be of particular significance to Americans at the present time. "A week before the Armistice, November 11, 1918," to quote from a publication of the Interracial Commission, "a traveler in the south would have been struck by the apparent solidarity of the population, white and Negro. In support of the war they were united as never before. Two hundred thousand Negro men were fighting in France and many more were preparing to go over. The millions of Negroes at home were responding heartily to every wartime appeal and, in proportion to their means, quite as generously as any other groups. A week after the Armistice one might have observed a subtle but ominous change. Distrust was awakening. What would be the attitude of the Negro troops when they returned from

France? Rumors filled the air and . . . fear had taken a deep hold upon both races."

The public did not have long to wait in order to discover what would happen. In June 1919 bloody riots occurred at Longview, Texas; in July 1919 the disastrous riots occurred in Chicago; in Omaha a Negro was lynched, the courthouse was burned, and riots swept the city as Major General Leonard Wood, in charge of a detachment of Federal troops, was sent in to restore order; riots occurred in Knoxville, in Charleston, in Elaine, Arkansas, in Washington. In all, some twenty-six riots were reported in 1919. In 1920 riots were reported in Duluth, in Independence, Kansas, and in Ocoee, Florida. In 1921 riots were reported in Springfield, Ohio, in Rosewood, Florida, in Chester, Coatesville (where a Negro had been burned alive a few years previously[15]), and Johnstown, Pennsylvania. In Phillips County, Arkansas, riots had occurred in 1919 in which five white men and an estimated twenty-five Negroes were killed. It is worth noting that in several cases order was only restored when Federal troops were sent into the areas of unrest.

Mr. Seligmann, who has graphically described these riots, notes that the war had not so much improved the position of the Negro as it had increased his strategic importance; and as his strategic position improved, tension gradually mounted. Far from tending to harmonize the two races, the war created a situation where the problem of the two living together in the same society "was made immensely more urgent *and more menacing*" (italics mine). The accuracy of the observation is established, not merely by the postwar race riots, but by the subsequent rise of the Ku Klux Klan. The rise of the Klan was, in turn, stimulated by highly provocative stories in the press, throughout 1919 and 1920, about the alleged susceptibility of the Negro to radical propaganda. For a time the Negro became associated with the Bolsheviks—in the public mind—and this despite the fact that not a single Negro was arrested for subversive activities.

The postwar riots merely indicated, as Mr. Seligmann has observed, that the "south's color psychosis became extended, during the war, throughout the nation." Migration of the Negro merely spread the pattern of segregation to other areas, and segregation in the North tended to retard advancement as much as outright disenfranchisement. For segregation means unequal facilities, conditions, and opportunities. Lynchings in Delaware, Pennsylvania, Ohio, Indiana, Illinois, Colorado, and Kansas certainly indicated that the South did not have a monopoly

[15]See John Jay Chapman's famous Coatesville address, *Memories and Milestones,* 1915.

on race prejudice. Even Jim Crow legislation began to appear in the North, particularly in the form, after 1910, of devices aimed at residential segregation. The most urgent issue faced by the NAACP, after 1915, was that of residential segregation, mostly in Northern areas.

As a matter of fact, no better or more convincing demonstration of the *national* character of the Negro problem could have been imagined than the race riots themselves. Faced with these riots, many people were forced to a realization of the fact that some type of affirmative program was essential. If the states refused to act, if the Federal government was powerless to act, then private individuals would act. The creation of the Commission on Interracial Co-operation, in 1919, definitely indicated the existence of such a realization. Even with the stimulation of such organizations, however, the growth of local co-operation remained extremely slow. And toward the end of the decade 1920–30, when, to quote from one of its reports, "the doves of peace and tranquillity seemed to have settled over the south," the interracial commission began to shift its emphasis from field work to that of "research and study of college curricula."

Fortunately the significance of the 1919 riots was not altogether missed. In 1919 and 1920 two resolutions were introduced in Congress calling for an investigation of the shockingly high number of lynchings. The mere fact that such resolutions were introduced indicated that Congress had been forced to take cognizance of the problem. Even one or two states were moved to create commissions of inquiry. It is significant that, in reviewing the situation in 1920, Mr. Seligmann should have observed that he was tempted "to urge as an immediate step the creation of a federal department of race relations, with a cabinet officer responsible not only for investigating maladjustments where they show themselves, but of initiating campaigns of information and education of which the body of United States citizens are sorely in need." He pointed out that, given the state of the press in the United States, it was necessary that the government assume the responsibility of impartial investigation and an honest reporting of the facts. "The first step in an approach to the problems of race relations," he wrote, "will be a demand upon the part of United States citizens for information, exact information not only of the anthropologist, but with regard to the treatment of colored men and women by white men and women in the United States."

Once the necessity for such information was recognized, others were quick to observe that the Federal government was the only agency which could undertake such a task. "The Negro problem," wrote Herman Feldman in 1931, "is much too wide in scope and national in character for research of a merely local or unco-ordinated kind. The United States government itself, through one or more of its agencies, should study the problem for the benefit of the country at large. The same recommendation could, of course, be made concerning other races and groups. Thus, while the U. S. Census supplies information about Negro population, the bare fact of residence does not give sufficient data on which to base conclusions as to the nature of migration, its volume from year to year in relation to industrial demand, the adjustments between migrating types, and the specific labor needs of different regions."[16]

It is interesting to note that, recognizing just such a need, the government had established in 1918 a Division of Negro Economics in the Federal Department of Labor. This division was of great service during and immediately after the war, not only in disseminating information but in securing co-operation between white and colored citizens and in the placement and adjustment of Negro workers. "Opposition," states Mr. Feldman, "to the maintenance of the Division soon arose on the part of certain congressmen from the south, and the life of the Division was short. On April 26, 1921, the Secretary of Labor issued a statement which was supposed to be an explanation of the reason for doing away with this agency. It is shallow and obvious word-shuffling." Certain attitudes which may be read between the lines of this announcement are illustrated by the first two paragraphs:

> The so-called Division of Negro Economics has been abolished by the Secretary of Labor largely because there is no such thing as segregating the "economics" of Negro wage earners from those of any other race. It is fundamentally un-American to create classes or to recognize classes. Our laws do not distinguish between white men and Negroes or any other class or classes.
>
> It is recognized that there is a race distinction and sometimes it is very convenient to have the assistance of a representative of a race in dealing with the members of that race. So far as labor matters are concerned the race distinction becomes more pronounced in the field of collective bargaining when troubles between employers and employees threaten. For that reason a member of the Negro race has been appointed a commissioner of conciliation, who has been detailed to service wherever the Secretary may feel the need of race representation and to advise the secretary.

[16]*Racial Factors in American Industry.*

It will be noted: first, that Mr. Feldman does not accept the explanation offered; and, second, that the explanation does not square with the fact that objection to the division stemmed initially from Southern congressmen. The division was only in existence from May 1918 to April 26, 1921. Under the direction of Dr. George E. Haynes, the division had a staff of about forty members, thirty of whom were distributed in the eleven states where the division had a paid personnel operating. Representatives of the division in turn organized voluntary state and county committees, on which, at one time, some thousand citizens were serving.

Being somewhat curious concerning the work of this division, I wrote to Dr. George E. Haynes, its first and only director. In a letter to me under date of October 9, 1942, Dr. Haynes makes the following observations:

> At the close of the war and the reconstruction period we made an effort to get through congress an amendment to the Organic Act under which the Department of Labor operates to make the work permanent. Politics defeated the effort. The experiment, however, along with that of a similar advisory to the Secretary of War, set a pattern that has been continued and expanded in the Federal government service since that time. This has been greatly expanded during the present administration so that practically all of the principal departments and commissions of the national government have some outstanding race relations advisor or aide. The step, however, of having Negroes as administrative officers with administrative authority, which would have been the case if the special service in the Department of Labor had been made a permanent bureau as was the Women's Division, has not to date been made.
>
> Three other things have happened as a sequel to that war experience: in Ohio, Michigan, and Pennsylvania, special services to Negro populations or services to deal with the problems of Negro labor and their relations to white employers and fellow employees have continued and some form of service started in several other states, notably: Missouri, New Jersey, New York, and Illinois. Most, if not all of these can be traced directly to the relationships the United States Department of Labor established with the states through our field representatives in those states during the first world war.
>
> The effort to gather and make available special studies of experience with Negroes in industry was pioneered by the Department of Labor.
>
> Finally, in the development of the United States Employment Service, special personnel or policies to deal with race relations in the industrial field have been included. The present setup to deal with Negro workers

under the Manpower Commission has utilized the experience in handling Negro labor during the period 1918–21, and some of the present policies stem from that experience.[17]

In a somewhat similar way, the establishment in 1922 of a Department of Race Relations, by the Federal Council of Churches of Christ in America, was an indication of a growing recognition of the necessity for affirmative action. The basis of such a recognition was clearly indicated by Dr. Kelly Miller in 1913 when he said that "broadly speaking, the Negro is hardly governed at all by the state, but merely coerced and beaten into obedience. He is not encouraged to have any comprehensive understanding of or participating hand in the beneficent aims and objects of government."

5. Postwar Period

Down the years from 1900 one can detect a growing recognition of the national character of the Negro problem. For one thing, the expanding scope of governmental activity in the war and postwar years necessarily brought the government into closer contact with the Negro. "Race relations," writes Mr. T. J. Woofter, Jr., "have become more national and less sectional because, in its expansion, the federal government has come into contact with the Negro in new ways. The use of Negro troops, aid to the Negro farmer, application of the various funds appropriated for education and public health, the relation of the Negro to the labor problems of the nation, and the influence of the presence of large numbers of Negroes on the immigration policy are all concrete instances of the growth, altogether apart from party politics, of a national attitude to replace the old sectional view of race contacts."[18]

Even in the field of national party politics, however, it came to be recognized that the Negro was, in many ways, an enormously influential factor. With the Republican party in the South becoming as "lily white" as the Democratic, the two-party system ceased to function. "Politics in the south," writes Dr. Buck, "became a game for professionals, and in every state where constitutional disenfranchisement occurred the number of white voters diminished in alarming proportions." Thus in South Carolina in 1902 an average of about forty-six hundred voters cast their ballots in the election of each congressman, while in

[17]See, in addition, *The Negro at Work During the World War and During Reconstruction*, 1921, Department of Labor.

[18]*The Basis of Racial Adjustment*, 1925.

New York over forty thousand votes were cast in congressional elections. The South began to have a wholly lopsided representation in Congress, which, in turn, was reflected in the whole course of national legislation and national policy. "This rejected black man," wrote Mr. Baker, "whom the south has attempted to eliminate utterly from politics, has been for years changing and warping the entire government of this nation in the most fundamental ways." Southern race attitudes fusing with Northern industrial ambitions served to delay the granting of autonomy to the Philippines, and also embarrassed the nation in other ways. For example, in the early years of the century the Turkish Ambassador became *persona non grata* when, in replying to a sharp note from this country to Turkey on the mistreatment of Armenians, he pointedly called attention to our treatment of the Negro. Obsessed with the Negro problem, the South could not give expression to new and vital issues in American democracy. It could ill afford to espouse measures for progressive change, notes Dr. Buck, until those measures had been conservatively adjusted to the biracial nature of its population. Thus a vicious circle existed: the South contended that the Negro should not vote because he was illiterate; and at the same time Dr. DuBois contended, very plausibly, that the Negro's schools were bad because he could not vote. The strain of attempting to support two sets of institutions—schools, colleges, hospitals, reformatories, insane asylums, jails and prisons, and so on—imposed an insupportable burden on the South. Services for the Negroes were bad; but the services for whites were not good either. As a consequence many people came to see that some outside intervention was necessary in order to break the deadlock.

Also, with the passage of time, the Jim Crow system became increasingly unworkable. A glance at Mr. Gilbert Stephenson's *Race Distinctions in American Law* (1910) is sufficient to demonstrate the point. Litigation over Jim Crow regulations became, as it still is, one of the main props to any Southern law practice. Legal distinctions multiplied as life became more complex. Enough litigation developed over common carriers alone to fill a dozen volumes. To what extent are Southern Jim Crow regulations applicable to interstate carriers? What are equal accommodations? How should separate waiting rooms be designated? Should Jim Crow regulations be applied to Negro nurses attending white passengers? Who is a Negro, anyway? Do these regulations apply to steamboats, and, if so, to what extent? Do Jim Crow regulations apply to colored postal employees working on Southern trains? These and other equally horrendous issues have been engaging the attention of Southern appellate courts for the last fifty years and in an ever-increasing volume. In general these cases constitute the richest field of unmined Americana in our entire national life. The average American would not believe that educated adult persons could subject their minds to the ignominious task of spinning out, endlessly and minutely, these crazy distinctions.

"While prior to the World War," write Messrs. Harris and Spero, "Negroes constituted an industrial reserve upon which employers could draw in times of labor shortage, or strikes, they had become by 1929 an integral part of the labor force in practically every important industry." In 1930 they constituted 22.7 per cent of the building laborers, 16.2 per cent of the unskilled workers in steel, and 25 per cent of the unskilled workers in the meat-packing industry. The growth of Negro settlements in urban areas was accompanied by the establishment of more Negro newspapers, the development of more Negro businesses, and the expansion of Negroes in the professions. The appearance of Mr. Alain Locke's anthology of Negro writing, *The New Negro,* in 1925, called the attention of the nation to the outstanding achievements of a small but growing group of Negro intellectuals. The rising tide of race consciousness among Negroes was indicated by the spectacular career of Marcus Garvey in the early twenties. With every insistence by the white world upon race separatism as the instrument for maintaining white supremacy, the Negro group became increasingly unified and more militantly race-conscious. After 1917 Negroes appeared in the legislatures of such states as Michigan, Illinois, Missouri, New Jersey, California, New York, Pennsylvania, Kansas, Ohio, and West Virginia; they also appeared as city councilmen, as public officials, and as judges. The Negro vote began to be of increasing significance in many states, and in one or two it became of crucial importance.

Two events in the early thirties served to dramatize the growing strength of the Negro minority: first, the fight which the Negro organizations effectively waged against the confirmation of Judge Parker as a Supreme Court justice in 1930; and, second, the militant manner in which Negroes rallied to the defense of the Scottsboro boys. The Supreme Court, always preoccupied with political currents, was quick to note this change. Over a long period of years the court began to reconsider its interpretation of the Fourteenth Amendment. By a strained and historically inaccurate construction of the "due process clause" of that amendment, it began, slowly and cautiously, to reinvest the amendment with the meaning which its sponsors had intended it should have in 1868. In Moore vs. Dempsey (1923) the court suddenly discovered that it could, if it desired, guarantee a Negro a fair trial. Mr. Mangum, commenting upon the decision, suggests that perhaps it was due to "the shifting of the social outlook of some of the justices." In 1936, in Brown vs. Mississippi, the court said that Southern courts might regulate their own procedure, but not in a manner to offend "some principle of justice so rooted in the traditions and conscience of our people as to be ranked as fundamental."

In the last decade Negroes have won increasingly important victories in the Supreme Court. They have established, for example, the rights of Negroes in states having separate schools to every type of training available to any other citizen; they have established the right of Negro teachers in segregated schools to equal pay for equal training and work; and they have established, in the Mitchell case, the right to equal accommodations on common carriers. Two important observations should be noted about these and the other victories which Negroes have won in the Supreme Court: first, the victories have been important primarily in establishing *rights,* not in implementing rights; and, second, most of these decisions have failed to arouse sharp antagonism in the South.[19] What needs to be done at the present time, therefore, is to implement by Federal action rights firmly secured in theory for Negroes by the Supreme Court. For the court no longer believes—any more than the nation believes—that the South should be allowed to deal with Negroes as it wishes.

As the Negro became increasingly enmeshed in the processes of national life, important changes occurred in the concept of the Negro problem. For some years after 1900 a number of strange theories about the Negro continued to receive serious public attention. Some of the stock "solutions" of the problem that kept recurring were: biological extinction, colonization (or deportation), segregation (or biracialism), and autonomy. In retrospect, the crudity of some of these proposals is most striking; but it can be demonstrated that their sponsors were driven to the adoption of an extreme point of view by the assumed impossibility of Federal action. The extinction theory, advanced by Dr. Willcox in 1900, was, of course, quickly proved to be fallacious: Negroes, as Negroes, will be with us for a long time to come, despite racial mixture. Colonization, strongly urged by Mr. Pickett in 1909, became

[19]See "The Color Line Cracks a Little," by Dr. Will Alexander, *New Republic,* September 22, 1941.

increasingly unfeasible and, for all practical purposes, collapsed with the Garvey movement. The idea that a separate economy could ever be established for Negroes is, today, no longer credible. In 1936 Mr. James S. Allen suggested that a separate Negro republic be formed of the counties in the Black Belt having a Negro majority. "Only by the complete realization of the right of self-determination," he wrote, "is it possible to overcome the age-old national enmities and prejudices." Quite apart from the obvious impracticality of such a proposal (given the present dispersal of Negroes all over the United States), is it not apparent that it does have a measure of validity *if* it be assumed that the national government, as such, is powerless to protect the Negro? (A similar proposal was advanced by John Temple Graves in 1900, and by Professor J. W. Gregory in 1924.) Even complete racial separatism has a measure of validity, if the same assumption is made. For if the government cannot protect Negroes, then they should seek, as a matter of self-protection, to minimize all contacts with the white world. Even colonization proposals have some validity, assuming that the national government cannot even assure the Negro free access to public institutions.

American thinking on the Negro problem was also strongly influenced, until recently, by the widespread acceptance of such pronouncements as W. G. Sumner's that, in so far as folkways are concerned, "it is not possible to change them by any artifice or device, to a great extent, or suddenly, or in any essential element. It is possible to modify them by slow and long-continued effort, if the ritual is changed by minute variation." While no one would quarrel with this statement as a general proposition, nevertheless the prevalence of such thinking in the social sciences tended to support a counsel of despair. With people intellectually reconciled to the fact that only over centuries could any change be effected in race attitudes and that nothing could be done to accelerate the process, then the doctrine of the insolubility of the Negro problem found new adherents. Other doctrines having much the same effect were also widely accepted: the Negro problem, for example, was a "race" problem; "race" was essentially a biological fact; "race antipathy" was an instinct; the interbreeding of widely different types was generally believed to result in "weak, inferior offspring." Thousands of intelligent and well-disposed Americans were actually intimidated, in their thinking, by these pseudoscientific pronouncements. Volumes were devoted to stupid "cranial measurements," alleged intelligence tests, and supposedly scientific verdicts on inborn racial traits and tendencies.

Above all, people inclined to the belief that racial prejudice was a "natural antipathy," and therefore that it was not subject to any type of regulation or control. An uncritical reliance upon, and possibly a misinterpretation of, these and other doctrines led to the rash of "race doctrine" books after 1914, in particular those of Madison Grant, Lothrop Stoddard, Henry Fairfield Osborn, and Dr. C. C. Josey. Later it was interesting to note, as Dr. Kelly Miller has said, "how these philosophers of Negro subordination have been compelled to shift from one discredited theory to another, like a frightened bird that flutters and flits from twig to twig, as they bend and break beneath its tremulous weight."

With the general improvement of techniques and methods in the social sciences, many of these limiting assumptions came to be rapidly discarded. This development is most strikingly illustrated by a comparison of the volume devoted to the Negro problem by the American Academy of Political and Social Science in 1913 with a later volume on the subject in 1928. "Much has happened since 1913," stated the editor of the 1928 volume, "to make it desirable that another volume be devoted to the relations between the colored and white races in the United States. In fact, since that time students of race as well as laymen have had to discard or even reverse many of their theories concerning 'trends' and 'solutions' of Negro development and 'problems.'" It is interesting to compare, for example, the meager report on Negro criminality in the 1913 volume with the searching report on the same subject in 1928. The author of the 1928 report on criminality clearly recognized that the race question went to the very heart of our institutions and that Negro criminality could not be studied except in relation to the functioning of these same institutions. He was quick to note, for example, that Negroes were more commonly arrested than white persons, that they were more frequently convicted, that they received proportionately heavier sentences and fewer pardons and commutations. All along the line Negro studies became increasingly more penetrating: they developed, so to speak, in scope and in depth. An author in the earlier volume had noted that the Negro problem, so-called, was "human and economic. . . . Insufficient food, housing conditions incompatible with health or decency, a childhood spent unprotected in the streets—these things produce, not in this race or that, but in humanity, certain definite results: ill-nourished bodies, vacant and vicious minds, a craving for stimulants, lack of energy, weak wills, unreliability in every relation of life."

Noting the prevalence of crime, poverty, ill-health, and delinquency among immigrants, many Americans had jumped to the conclusion that these groups were somehow racially inferior. But careful studies (for the most part after 1920) quickly refuted the assumption. Much this same sort of demonstration had to be made with reference to the Negro before the public could see the possibility of some workable solution to the problem. As more emphasis was placed upon specific problems of Negro health, housing, and education, the purely "racial" aspect of the question began to assume less importance. "Social science," wrote Mr. Woofter, "has made its contribution to the lessening of prejudice by greatly increased research in Negro problems. Prejudice in the past has rested on popular misconceptions as to the health, morality, and mentality of the Negro, and the discovery and dissemination of the truth has ameliorated prejudice among well-read people."[20] *Among well-read people,* but whose task was it to see that these newer findings, this latter-day research, actually got to the masses of the people?

As these recent studies became more widely known, many people realized that there were Negroes and Negroes in the United States and that it was stupid to think of them as though they constituted a single homogeneous group of twelve million people. Scientific research was necessary, however, before the "problem" could be removed from the domain of opinion and fixed in the realm of fact. As Mr. Robert L. Sutherland has pointed out in his report to the American Youth Commission: "For years the Negro has been a problem in Sunday-school quarterlies, textbooks, and public addresses, but an understanding of the full and exact nature of the problem has seldom been attempted. Typically, these approaches have lumped all twelve million Negroes—black, brown, and light yellow, rich and poor, good and bad—together as a homogeneous group deserving the white man's sympathy, contempt, or assistance." Even the research specialist, obsessed with statistics on health, employment, and dependency, frequently failed to see the problem in its over-all proportions and failed conspicuously to relate it to the problems of other colored minorities in the United States.

Further progress in the direction of a realistic grasp of the problem developed during the depression. The notion of a self-sufficient Negro economy received its deathblow in 1929. "Last hired, first fired," became the order of the day, as Negro dependency mounted in all areas of the nation. It became quite obvious that Negroes were suffering proportionately greater hardships than whites. With the advent of the

[20] *Recent Social Trends,* 1933, p. 592.

New Deal, people began to regain some degree of political confidence and to use the powers of government for many novel purposes. While Negroes were discriminated against in relief and work projects, the mere fact that the government had acted to relieve distress helped to improve their position. Symptoms of marked unrest, however, were not lacking. On March 19, 1935, the Harlem riot occurred, during which Negroes invaded the business sections of Harlem by the thousand and destroyed upwards of two million dollars' worth of property—a riot which was later characterized by an official investigation as a "spontaneous and an incoherent protest."

As research into the Negro problem improved, the pertinence of this research to larger questions became apparent. The Negro, said Dr. Edward Reuter, offers one of the best and one of the most neglected opportunities for scientific study of any group in the modern world. In the Negro group the various stages of cultural development and adjustment can be traced; the development of personality can be studied from many new points of view; and the functioning of social institutions can be newly evaluated by studying their relation to Negroes. "The United States thus becomes," said Dr. Miller, "the world's most interesting laboratory for working out the intricate issues of race adjustment." As the Negro began to be studied from the point of view of cultural adjustment, the scope of the problem rapidly assumed, not merely national, but world-wide, implications. With the appearance of such volumes as *The Negro Around the World,* by Willard Price (1925), and *The Negro in the Americas,* edited by Charles H. Wesley (1940), an entirely new perspective was injected into considerations of our favorite "social problems." "In a world composed for the most part of colored races," wrote Mr. Seligmann, "fully embarked on new adventures toward autonomy, Americans had to be reminded, not only by a great northward migration of colored people during the war, but by race riots, that new movements and aspirations were stirring on their own continent." The mere fact that the Negro problem can today be seen as part of a larger —a world—issue has already shifted the basis of our thinking on the subject. At the same time it has made imperative the formulation of an affirmative national policy.

PART II

Black and White Mores

THE FLYING AFRICANS

Kenneth Porter

Kenneth Porter is a member of the history department at Vassar College. He has written widely on protest manifestations among oppressed minority groups in America.

THE PLANTATION BARGE had not reached the wharf—it was not indeed long from the slave ship moored in a secret harbor to avoid patrol vessels—when it was known in the quarters that there were Ibos on board.

Perhaps the boat, rowing upriver, had at points hugged the shore so closely that plantation hands could discern the Ibo tribal scars, or at least so near that a shout could carry. Perhaps there were drums hidden in the swamps. There was curiosity among the tribesmen, sitting at their doorsteps over the evening meal—some themselves only a few years from the Coast—as to what acquaintances or friends, what relatives even, what enemies perhaps, might be among the newcomers.

But none was prepared for the tall, powerful figure with the set face and blazing eyes whom the overseer herded, first of three, into the compound.

Quaco, a man without reverence, was first to recover. "Oho! Are sorcerers' eyes then so dull they cannot discern the snare in the trail?"

"The old lion leaped into the pit to find the way his cubs went," the other returned calmly.

"When the ship anchored and put out a red flag," one of the newcomers explained later, "we went out in canoes to trade. They took us into the cabin and gave us tafia, and when we awoke we were at sea.

Certain of us leaped overboard to return to our homes, so they chained the rest in the hold and allowed us on deck only in fetters. It was the half-caste linkster, it seems, who proposed that the white men thus complete their cargo, but he himself profited little, for in mid-passage, it is said, he endeavored to walk upon the sea after the manner of their prophet, and sank."

Narrator and listeners glanced involuntarily, and almost simultaneously, to where the witch man sat impassively on a log, staring into the cooking fire, the light shining on his muscled shoulders and scarred chest.

As on all well-conducted plantations, the new arrivals were given a week or so of "seasoning" to accustom themselves to their surroundings before being put to work. But at last the day came when the overseer led them into the field, handed them hoes, and gave them their orders, in the few words of "Congo"—the West Coast pidgin—that were necessary. The older in slavery looked furtively at the witch man as he stood hoe in hand, but after a moment he began to wield it with contemptuously accurate strokes.

"It has been said," remarked Quaco in a loud voice as they crossed one another, "that Certain Persons have the power to cause their tools to work by themselves."

"The hoe must be taught its way in new soil before it can walk alone," replied the other, maintaining the rhythm of his strokes.

So the days passed. None knew how his mind, which, ever since he woke in the ship's hold, he had striven to keep tight against the old life, was giving way—memories pouring in as water into a leaky canoe. At night in his cabin the impassive countenance, which in the presence of men he wore as a wooden ceremonial mask, slipped, crumbled, and he lay awake for hours, straining his ears for the chattering of monkeys, the screeching of parakeets, the throbbing of the forbidden drums. The swine flesh, the maize gruel, began to writhe and leap in his belly.

There came a day when in midafternoon, in mid-row, he dashed his hoe to the ground and stood staring desperately eastward as if his eyes might grapple the horizon and draw to him what was beyond. The overseer strode toward him, rasping curses, whip raised; but the sorcerer turned, and what was in his face caused the arm of the white man, despite the pistol in his belt, to swerve, so that the lash cut the air instead of falling on flesh, and the man slouched swaggeringly on, his curses falling to a grumble. For the rest of the day the witch man sat under a tree, alternately gazing into the sky and making marks on the palm-smoothed earth. By next morning a plantation on either side knew that the Ibo witch man had with a look made powerless the arm of the overseer, and that his hoe had worked all the afternoon alone.

That night, after the evening meal, the sorcerer suddenly arose among his fellow tribesmen. "Ibos!" he announced. "I grow weary of this place. I am returning to Africa. Those who desire may go with me."

There was a period of stunned silence.

"How shall this be done, oh, Great One?" cautiously inquired at last the elder.

"Have ye not heard that Certain People can go from place to place through the air, as the flamingos? I shall fly, certainly—and ye with me! Do ye doubt?"

There was an excited babble of denial. "No, no, it is true. . . . It is well known. . . . My mother has said . . . My father told me . . . My grandmother saw . . . It was said of my grandfather's brother . . ."

"Very well. No one doubts. It is decided."

"There are certain preparations to be made?"

"Yes. Provide the black chickens. Drums also."

"Drums are forbidden," the elder replied thoughtfully.

"And the cattle pen to the lion. Drums are necessary."

"I know of a fallen bee gum," ventured one.

"Skins will be provided," was the brief word of a long-limbed fellow, suspected of having a bow in a hollow tree.

"Good. Let that which is necessary be prepared."

"And the day?"

"The morning of the day sacred to their god, when we are not in the fields, and at sunrise, that we may have light for the journey. Let the word go to the Ibos on other plantations."

He turned on his heel and entered his cabin.

On the nights which followed he withdrew from the circle immediately after the evening meal and spent the hours until the driver made his rounds casting the bones again and again on the packed earth of the floor, examining them carefully after each throw by the light of a fat pine splinter stuck between the logs. They gave no clear answer. They were saying something, it was sure, and something not altogether unfavorable; the road was shadowy—shadowy rather than dark—but the moonlight did not stream down it, and leopards might lurk in the bushes, serpents hang from the limbs.

After the driver had passed and the light was extinguished, he lay upon the straw and stared unseeingly at the rafters. To fly! He had never doubted before. He was a wizard, and it was well known that wizards could fly, even as they could cast a spell for good or evil. Only, to fly had never before seemed to him necessary or advisable—even desirable. He remembered that sometimes, at a dance, among the leaping flames, the throbbing drums, the chanting, it had seemed that his feet were not moving on the packed dance ground but in air, and he had thought at the time, incuriously, unexcitedly, "Yes, this is how one feels just before rising into the sky," but he had never actually attempted it. And with a stab of fearful uncertainty he recalled that even flying wizards did not share their power with others—though he did recall a story of their flying with one person under each arm. But when he had spoken to the Ibos in the compound, the words had been put into his mouth.

He sat upright on his pallet. A figure was blocking out the moonlight. "Oh, Great One!" came a husky young whisper.

"Enter and sit," he replied ritualistically. Then, after a sufficient pause, "Speak, young one." The moonlight fell on the face of a boy of about fourteen.

"Oh, Mighty One, it is whispered that thou and the Ibos are to return, flying, to their own country. Now, I am Ibo by blood, but born in this land, of parents born in the Ibo country. Is this word for me also?"

"Thy parents—where are they?"

"Dead. Dead. My mother—the overseer sent her into the field too soon after she bore me. The master was angry with the overseer, for he said my mother was worth a great sum, even eight hundred dollars. My father was angry also, so that presently the overseer lay in a furrow with his skull halved and my father was in the swamps. But there came a season when the whites hunted the swamps with dogs and many men, and they brought him in across a horse, the bones of his legs broken by lead. They were minded to keep him until the bones were mended and he could walk, that they might choke him with a rope, publicly; but he, not caring to be a spectacle for the white men, resolved to die otherwise, and did so, though his hands were tied . . ." He paused, choking; then, after a little, continued. "He swallowed his tongue."

The sorcerer half put out his hand, then withdrew it, unseen. "Verily, thy father was an Ibo! And thou, too, art an Ibo!"

"Then, I may . . . ?"

"Yea, boy. What knowest thou of Africa?"

"Only what my foster parents, now dead—Ibos also—have told me."

"Think of it, then. See in thy mind the palmetto huts and the fields springing green seven years without planting. Hear the sound of the jungle, the monkeys chattering, the screaming of parakeets. Listen to the throbbing of the drums, the feet of the dancers. Smell the cooking fires. Hear the adze and the hammer as they shape wood and metal to the will of the workers. Think of the Ibo people. Think most of all of thy mother in labor, thy father in the swamps. Remember them both at the hour of their deaths. Thou too art an Ibo. Thou shalt see Africa!"

When the boy had gone, the witch man lay again on his back, eyes wide and unseeing. "We shall fly! Yea, we shall fly!" he whispered. He turned on his side and slept.

In the old field above the river that Sunday morning, just before dawn, the witch man numbered his followers: his own two companions of the voyage, the four earlier at the plantation—including even Quaco—two from the upper plantation, three from the lower, the boy from across the river. All were ceremonially painted, amulets at throat, rattles at wrist.

He raised his hand, and the drums began to pound like a distant cataract beating on the rocks, the rattles pouring through it the sound of a rushing torrent. They began to circle, at first slowly, then faster and wilder and faster. The drums picked them up and carried them along; the rattles sustained them. He felt the Power coming upon him. His head grew lighter and lighter—was one in substance with the air; his chest and belly followed, his loins, his thighs and legs, his ankles. The faces of his companions showed they were caught up with him.

"Forward! Run forward!" he cried. "We shall mount up like the buzzards!"

He ran, scarcely feeling his feet upon the ground. Then he felt them no more at all. They had left the earth and the air was bearing them up!

And then his feet were pounding, stumbling, on hard-baked earth and dried clods. . . .

He came to a stop, his chest heaving. His eyes moved around the crestfallen circle. "This air, it seems, is too thin for flying," he commented with wry casualness.

Then he straightened, chest expanding, eyes blazing. "Only one trail is open." He gestured toward the river pouring its flood toward the sea, the sea which lapped the shore of the Ibo country.

Quaco managed a sickly smile. "It is too far," he muttered. "We will get footsore!"

"Return, then." The witch man jerked his chin toward the quarters. "Thy mother was a Mandingo!"

He turned to the others, then swept the landscape with his gaze. They looked with him, and after that brief glance at their own, the Ibo, country this land was of a sudden unspeakably drab and evil. The drums began to throb, softly, insistently. Stiffly, stepping high and jerkily, as men sleepwalking, the line moved down the slope. An Ibo song began and passed from one to the other until all were singing.

The witch man extended a hand and took the boy's in his. A smile molded his face into new, unfamiliar lines. "Come, lion's cub!" he said gently.

The other slaves, watching from a distance in fascination and horror, agreed that the drumming and the Ibo singing never faltered and were clearly heard as long as the line of heads could be seen above the water—some said until long after. A few were able to see, far out in midstream, a flock of great water birds take flight and wing their way into the rising sun, with exultant cries.

MISTER McGREGOR

Andrew Nelson Lytle

Andrew Nelson Lytle is the author of a novel called The Long Night *and numerous short stories. A Southerner, he has written objectively about the region in which he lives.*

"I WANT to speak to Mister McGregor."

Yes sir, that's what he said. Not marster, but MISTER McGREGOR. If I live to be a hundred, and I don't think I will, account of my kidneys, I'll never forget the feelen that come over the room when he said them two words: Mister McGregor. The air shivered into a cold jelly; and all of us, me, Ma, and Pa, sort of froze in it. I remember thinken how much we favored one of them waxwork figures Sis Lou had learnt to make at Dr. Price's Female Academy. There I was, a little shaver of eight, standen by the window a-blowen my breath on it so's I could draw my name, like chillun'll do when they're kept to the house with a cold. The knock come sudden and sharp, I remember, as I was crossen a T. My heart flopped down in my belly and commenced to flutter around in my breakfast, then popped up to my ears and drawed all the blood out'n my nose except a little sack that got left in the point to swell and tingle. It's a singular thing, but the first time that nigger's fist hit the door I knowed it was the knock of death. I can smell death. It's a gift, I reckon, one of them no-count gifts like good conversation that don't do you no good no more. Once Cousin John Mebane come to see us, and as he leaned over to pat me on the head—he was polite and hog-friendly to everybody, chillun and poverty-wropped kin especial—I said, "Cousin John, what makes you smell so funny?" Ma all but took the hide off'n me; but four days later they was dressen him in his shroud. Then I didn't know what it was I'd smelled, but by this time I'd got better acquainted with the meanen.

Ma was rollen tapers for the mantel. She stiffened a spell like she was listenen for the north wind to rise; rolled out a taper and laid it down. She went to the door and put her hand square on the knob, hesitated like she knew what was comen, then opened it. There stood Rhears. He was the coachman. Him and his wife Della was Ma's pets. The both of'm was give to Ma by her pa at the marryen; and in a way that folks don't understand no more, they somehow become a part of her. Ma liked horses that wanted to run away all the time, and Rhears was the only nigger on the place that could manage'm. He was a powerful, dangerous feller. He'd killed the blacksmith and two free niggers in the other county before Ma brought him to Long Gourd. His shoulders jest but stretched across the opening, as he stood there in a respectful-arrogant sort of way with a basket knife in his hand.

"What do you want, Rhears?" his mistress asked.

"I want to speak to Mister McGregor," he said.

Pa had been scratchen away at his secretary. At "Mister" the scratchen stopped. That last scratch made more noise in my ears than the guns at Shiloh. Without a word, without even looken behind him, Pa stood up and reached for his gun. The secretary was close to the fireplace and had a mirror over it. He didn't waste no time, but he didn't hurry none either. He just got up, took off his specs, and laid them as careful on the secretary, just like he meant to set'm in one special place and no other place would do. He reached for the gun and turned.

Rhears warn't no common field hand. He was proud, black like the satin in widow women's shirtwaists, and spoiled. And his feelens was bad hurt. The day before, Pa had whupped Della, and Rhears had had all night to fret and sull over it and think about what was be-en said in the quarters and how glad the field hands was she'd been whupped. He didn't mean to run away from his home like any blue-gum nigger. He ject come a-marchen straight to the house to settle with Pa before them hot night thoughts had had time to git cooled down by the frost.

Pa turned and walked towards him. He still moved as steady and solemn. I watched the even distance each boot heel made and calculated that two more steps would put him up to the threshold. Just to look at him you might have thought he was a-goen towards the courthouse to pay his taxes or walken down the aisle to his pew. All of a sudden he come to a stop. Ma's brown silk skirt had spread out before him. I looked up. There she was, one hand tight around the gun stock, the othern around the barrel. Her left little finger, plunged like a hornet's needle where the skin drew tight over Pa's knuckles, made the blood drop on the bristly hairs along his hand, hang there, then spring to the floor. She held there the time it took three drops to bounce down and splatter. That blood put a spell on me.

A gold shiver along Ma's dress made me look quick at their faces. Her hair was a shade darker than the dress she was wearen and slicked down around her ears. There wasn't no direct sun on it, but a light sorghum color slipped up and down as if it was playen on grease. The light might have come from her eyes, for they was afire. She was always fine to look at, although her face wasn't soft enough to rightly claim her beautiful. But she would have taken the breeches away from any ordinary man, I tell you. She'd rather manage folks than eat. Pa ought to have let her do a sight more of it than he did. She was happier than I ever seen her the time he went to the legislature. But he didn't take to politics somehow. He said the government rooms smelled too strong of tobacco and stale sweat. He couldn't abide the smell of tobacco. He was a mighty clean man, the cleanest I ever come across. Took a washen once a day reg'lar. When I come to think about Ma, I see her a-studyen about somethen, with a wrinkle in her eyes. She didn't have to tell the servants not to bother her then. They stayed out of her way or went tippen around if their work took'm near her.

Well, Pa saw he couldn't get his gun out of her grip without acting ungentlemanly. He gave her a curious look and a low bow, then turned it loose. Taken off his coat and folden it, he laid it across a chair. Ma was marbly-pale when she stepped out of the way, but she moved easy and steady.

For a long time I never could make out the meanen of them looks, nor why Ma done what she done. And she never set us right about it. She wasn't the explainen kind, and you can bet nobody never asked. I'd just as soon've asked the devil to pop his tail. It's bothered me a heap in my time, more'n it's had any right to. I reckon it's because I always think about it when I'm taperen off. That's a time when a man gits melancholy and thinks about how he come not to be president and sichlike concerns. Well, sir, when I'd run through all my mistakes and seen where if I'd-a done this instead of that how much better off I'd be today, and cuss myself for drinken up my kidneys, I'd always end up by asken myself why that woman acted like that. I've knowed a sight of women in my day, knowed'm as the Bible saints knowed'm, as well as in a social and business way; and I'm here to say, sir, they are stuffed with dynamite, the puniest of'm.

It was a question of authority, and a time when whuppen was out of the argyment. All you had to do was look at Rhears and that basket knife sharpened thin like a dagger, a-hangen as innocent agen his pant leg, to see he didn't mean to take no whuppen. He must have felt in his Afrykin way that Pa had betrayed him. Folks jest didn't whup their house servants, and Rhears was a-meanen to teach Pa his manners. Niggers can think straight up to a certain point, and beyond that the steadiest of'm let their senses fly like buckshot, high to scatter. It never struck him that Della needed her whuppen. No sir, he was jest a-standen in the door tellen Pa he warn't his marster.

Now Ma might have thought that Pa ought, with his proper strength, to show him who his marster was. There ain't no doubt but what he had to show it in some way, or he might as well have sold all his niggers for any work he could-a got out'n them. Still it was a powerful big risk to run. And it was plain she was a-meanen for him to run it.

Anyway, that was the construction the kin put on it, and it was natural they would. But it never satisfied me. I got it in my head that Rhears warn't the only person on Long Gourd who didn't claim Pa his marster. Before I tell you what I mean, give me a little taste of that shuck juice—half a glass'll do, jest enough to settle the dust in my belly. I'm about to choke to death with the drought.

Aah . . . that's sweet to the taste. Now, sir. You'll excuse me if I lean over and whisper this. *That other body was Ma.* I know it ain't a-goen to sound right, for she and Pa had the name of be-en a mighty loven couple. But a man and woman can fight and still love. Most of'm enjoy fighten. I ain't never seen one get wore out with it. They can go on with a fight for years. Can git fat on it. When they win out, they put the man down amongst the chillun and give him a whuppen when he forgits his manners or sasses back. But if he's stout enough to put her and keep her in her place, she don't hold it agin him. She's proud to think she picked such a game one. That's how come I never married. I'm peaceful by nature. Ain't but one thing ever gits me fighten mad: that's putten salt in my whisky. That riles me. I'll fight a elyphant then.

Well, sir, that morning Della was late. Ma had had to send for her twice, and she come in looken like the hornets stung her. She fluffed down to her sewen and went to work in a sullen way, her lip stuck out so far it looked swole. And they ain't nothen meaner-looken than a blue-black, shiny lip of a sullen nigger woman. It looks like a devil's pillow.

Directly Ma said, "Della, take out that seam and do it over again."

"Take it out yourself, if it don't suit," she flounced back.

In a second Pa was on his feet: "Woman, lay down that sewen and come with me."

Them was his words; and if a nigger can git pale, Della done it. She seen right away what a mistake she'd made. She fell on the floor and commenced to grab at Ma's skirts. "Don't let him whup me, mistiss. Don't let him." For a while Ma didn't say a word.

"Get up off that floor and come with me," said Pa again.

"Mister McGregor, what are you going to do with this girl?"

Pa never made her no answer. He walked over and lifted Della up by the arm.

"Don't you tech me; you don't dare tech me. I belongs to mistiss."

Pa shuck her till her teeth rattled; then she stopped her jumpen and goen on and stood there a-tremblen like a scared horse.

"Mister McGregor," come Ma's even tones, "you're not going to punish that girl. She's mine."

And with that Pa turned and said in a hard, polite way he never used before to Ma: "And so are you mine, my dear." Then he nodded to Della to go before him, and she went.

When he came back Ma was standen in the middle of the floor just where he had left her. She hadn't moved a peg. She just stood there, stiff as a poker, her head thrown up and her eyes as wide as a hawk's.

"I have whipped Della and sent her to the field for six months. If at the end of that time she has learned not to forget her manners, she may take up again her duties here. In the meantime, so you will not want, I've sent for P'niny. If you find her too old or in any way unsuitable, you may take your choice of the young girls."

He waited a breath for her answer and, when it didn't come, got on his horse and went runnen over the back road down to the fields. No other words passed between them that day. At supper the meal went off in quick order. There wasn't no good old-fashioned table talk. Everybody was as polite to one another as if they was visiten. Ma sat at the foot, froze to her chair. Pa at the head like a judge expecten shooten in the court. We knew somethen was bound to blow up and bust; and I do believe if somebody had tromped on a hog bladder, we chillun'd-a jumped under the table.

Next mornen it come. That bow of Pa's, as he let go of the gun, was his answer to the challenge. For you might almost say Pa had whupped Ma by proxy. And here was Rhears, agen by proxy, to make him answer for it . . . a nigger and a slave, his mistress's gallant, a-callen her husband and his marster to account for her. I don't reckon they'd been any such mixed-up arrangement as that before that time, and I know they ain't since.

I scrouched back in the corner and watched, so scared my eyes turned loose in their sockets. If Jesus Christ had-a touched me on the shoulder and said, "Come on, little boy, and git your harp," I'd-a no more looked at him than if he'd-a been my dog come to lick me. For Pa and Rhears was a-eyen one another. This fight was to be accorden to no rules. I saw straight off it would start fist and skull and work into stomp and gouge. If Pa didn't manage to git that knife away from the nigger, it would be cut and grunt as well.

Pa was the slimberer of the two, but he wouldn't-a looked it away from Rhears. From neckèd heel up he was six feet—no, six feet four—and his boots raised him an ench higher. Right away he took a quick easy step forward, and both of'm tied their muscles together. Rhears tightened his fingers around the knife. I looked at Pa's breeches. They fit him tight; and the meat rolled up, snapped, then quivered under the cloth. His butt give in at the sides and squeezed away its sitten-down softness. His waist drawed in and pumped the wind into his chest, a-pushen out his shoulders just as easy and slow. I don't believe you could have found a man in the whole cotton country hung together any purtier.

Pa, quick-like, sunk his hand in and around the black flesh of Rhears's neck. The knife swung backwards, but Pa grabbed it with his left hand before it could do its damage. A breath, and Rhears was a-spinnen round the room. The basket knife lay in the door as still as any of the pine floor boards. This rattled the nigger some. He had figured on gitten Mister McGregor in the door, where he could-a used the knife to advantage. Fighten in his mistress's room, a place he didn't feel at home in, rattled him some more. So before he could come to himself good, Pa lambed a blow into his black jaw. It was a blow fit to down a mule, but Rhears shook his head and run in to close, changed quick, dropped low and butted. Four quick butts jambed Pa agen the wall, where he saved his guts by grabben Rhears's shoulders—to hold. That kinky hunk of iron slowed down. Both men shook under the strain. The noise of destruction held up. All you could hear was a heavy, pumpen blowen, like two wind-broke horses drawen a killen load . . . then a rippen cry from Rhears's coat—and it was good broadcloth—as it split both ways from the small of his back. Both men drawed in their breaths for a long second.

Sudden-like Pa's head and chest went down and forward. His feet pressed agen the wall. Slow as candy pullen he broke the nigger's holt on the front muscles of his thighs. But that nigger's grip never give. No sir. What give was two drippen hunks of leg meat. Just the second that holt was broke Pa shifted neat and shoved hard. Rhears smashed a sewen table top into kindlen wood before he hit the wall. That table saved his neck, or I'm as good a man as I used to be. Before he could get his bearens, Pa was a-pounden his head into the hard pine floor. I looked for the brains to go a-splatteren any time, and I begun to wonder how far they would slide on the floor's smooth polish. But God never made but one thing tougher'n a nigger's head—and that's ironwood. Slowly Rhears raised up and, with a beautiful strain of muscles, got to his feet. Then him and Pa went round the room. It looked like that bangen had set the nigger crazy. A stranger comen into the room would-a thought he was set on breaken up ever stick of furniture, a-usen Pa for his mallet. Once the two of'm come close to Ma, so close the wind they made blowed her skirts, but never a peg did she move. She held as rigid as a conjure woman.

Directly the nigger begun to wear some. All that crazy spurt of energy hadn't done him no good. Gradually Pa's feet touched the floor more and more; then they didn't leave it. The panten got heavier, more like bellows. A chair got in their way. They went over it. They did a sight of rollen—up to the door crowded with house servants, all a-looken like they had fell in the ash hopper. You could follow how far they'd rolled by the sweat on the floor. It looked like a wet mop had been run by a triflen hand. Then, sir, my hairs straightened up and drawed in to hide under the scalp. Rhears had ended up on top and was a-shiften to gouge. Pa looked all wore down. I tried to holler to Ma to shoot, but my throat was as parched as it is right this minute. . . . Thank you, sir. You are very generous.

Have you ever seen a long dead limb stretched between sky and droppen sun? Well, that's how still Ma held on to that gun of Pa's. I couldn't stand to see them black thumbs go down. As I turned my head I heard the nigger holler. Pa had jerked up his knee and hit him in a tender spot. He fell back and grabbed himself. It must have been an accident, for Pa made no move to take advantage of the break. He just lay there and let Rhears take hold of himself and git at Pa's throat. I never seen such guts in nobody, nigger or white man. Bump went Pa's head on the floor. Bump and agen. Ever time he lifted Pa, he squeezed tighter. Ever time he come down, he pushed him forward.

It had been one of them frosty December mornens, and a fire had been burnen in the chimney since first light. The front stick had been burned in two and left between it and the back stick a heap of red and blue hickory coals. They don't make no hotter fire than that. I saw right away what Rhears had in mind. Every time he bumped my father's head against the floor, he was that much nearer the hearth. Pa wriggled and jerked, but his wind was cut and the black blood ran into his eyes. Those heavy black hands growed deep in the red, greasy flesh of Pa's neck.

They moved slower towards the fire, for Pa had at last clamped his legs in a way to slow'm down. Then I saw him reach for his pocket. Rhears didn't see this move. His eyes was bucked on what they had in mind to do, and the heat from the hickory logs made'm swell with a dark, dry look of battle luck. After some fumblen Pa finally brought out his knife. He opened it in a feeble way over the nigger's back, and let it rip and tear through his ribs. The blood first oozed, then spouted. It fell back from the knife like dirt from a turnen plow. Then Pa made a jab back of the kidneys. That done for him. He grunted, turned loose, and rolled over like a hunk of meat.

Staggering to his feet, Pa went over and leaned agen the mantel. Directly Rhears spoke up, so low you could hardly hear him:

"Marster, if you hadn't got me, I'd-a got you."

Then he shook with a chill, straightened out, and rolled back his eyes. Mister McGregor looked at him a minute before he turned to his wife. And then no words passed his mouth. He reached out his hand, and she walked over and handed him the gun. He reached over the mantel and, his arms a-tremblen, set the gun back in its rack.

"Bring me a pan of warm water, the turpentine, and the things out of my medicine chest." That was Ma speaken, sharp and peremptory, to the servants in the doorway. "And take this body out of here," she added in a tone she used when the girl Sally failed to dust behind the furniture.

"Sit down in that chair, Mister McGregor, so I can dress your wounds."

Pa done what she told him. She worked away at him with deft, quick fingers. Directly I heard her in a offhand way, her head benden over and her hands busy wrappen:

"Colonel Winston will be through here on his way South. I think it would be best to sell him Della."

"I think that, my dear," said Pa, "would be the most sensible thing to do."

LITTLE WHITE GIRL

Sara Haardt

The late Sara Haardt passed away at a time when her deep insight into her native South was just beginning to take shape. The wife of H. L. Mencken, she was the author of numerous short stories and one novel.

Susie Tarleton spread out her skirts and sat down on the patch of Bermuda grass under the big oak tree. When she had scooped out a triangular hole in the ground approximately the size of the piece of broken window glass she was using as a trowel, she laid the glass down and rested her chin on her knees. For a moment it came to her, with a twinge of guilt, that she shouldn't be here digging in the dirt in her fresh afternoon clothes—she should be out on the front veranda or stringing four-o'clocks in the garden like a good little white girl. But she hated playing by herself when there was Pinky to play with.

Pinky was Aunt Hester's little girl, born the month before Susie, and they played on the same pallet spread under the big oak tree when they were babies, for Aunt Hester was Susie's mammy as well. Now that she was eight years old Susie didn't need a mammy any more, except to help her dress in the afternoons, but she hadn't missed a day playing with Pinky—and she never would!

"Pinky, Pinky," she called in high treble, "here I am under the big oak tree!"

There was a scurrying, as of a frantic little animal, along the path from Aunt Hester's cabin, and Pinky dropped down on the ground beside her. She wasn't very black—her satiny yellow skin merely looked as if she had a good tan—and Aunt Hester had trained her stiff black hair to lay flat to her head. Susie loved the feel of Pinky's skin, and the smell of the magnolia balm Aunt Hester greased her hair with, and the fresh starchy smell of Pinky's calico dresses. She loved everything about Pinky with all her heart.

"You can pick the flower bouquet of roses while I'm finishing the nest for them," Susie told Pinky now, and Pinky ran as fast as her skinny legs could carry her to the flower garden.

Susie continued digging in the damp ground with the triangular piece of glass, and when she had finished she leaned her head against the trunk of the big oak tree. She closed her eyes and sniffed in the sweetly saturated afternoon air. It was nice, she told herself, to play with Pinky.

Even on the hottest day the big oak tree with its mauve cool shade was a wonderful playhouse. It was very quiet here, so quiet and faraway no grown-up person could intrude upon it without a warning rustle of leaves and boughs. Susie was sure the little white girl who was moving on the next plantation and who was coming to spend the day with her tomorrow would think it was wonderful too. It was strange to think of a little girl living near her—a little white girl named Alice Louise Pratt.

She stood up quickly and curtsied, as she would do tomorrow when Alice Louise came to see her. "I am Susie Tarleton," she rehearsed in a small voice. "Who are you?"

"I's hurryin'," Pinky answered her from the flower garden, "I's comin' fas' as I kin."

Susie dropped her skirts and stiffened. She hadn't told Pinky about Alice Louise, and for some reason unknown to her she didn't want to tell Pinky.

She stood there motionless with her hands clasped tightly behind her while Pinky fluttered along the garden path like a gay butterfly with the flower bouquet held high for her to see.

"Here I is!" Pinky called joyously.

Susie parted her lips to answer, but her throat was dry and no sound came. She looked at Pinky's shining face and reached out her hands for the bouquet.

The next instant both of them dropped on the ground beneath the big oak tree, and Susie forgot all about Alice Louise. Nobody could play Penny-Poppy Show like Pinky! Susie held the bouquet while Pinky patted the sides of the hole in the ground she had made with the piece of glass, leaving a few clods of earth loose to stick the flower stems in. Swiftly yet carefully Pinky lined the hole with camphor leaves; then she selected first one rose and then another.

When she was through she paused and drew a bunch of lavender from the bosom of her calico dress. "I dunno why I picked this, when you said the show was to be onliest of roses, but seem like I couldn't pass it by."

"Oh, it looks sweet, Pinky!" Susie cried. The pungent smell of the lavender thrilled her nostrils more than the fragrance of the roses. She flashed a warm smile across the gathering dusk: Pinky's taste was perfect; the lavender and the roses looked far lovelier together than the roses ever could have looked by themselves.

Pinky tucked in the last plume of lavender and started to polish the piece of window glass on her plain little ticking underskirt. Then she held up the glass expertly by the very edge so she would not leave any fingerprints on it, and Susie smiled because Pinky's gesture reminded her of all the times she had polished her mood and then held it carefully, tenderly, for fear of spoiling it. The secret of Penny-Poppy Show was to cover the flowers in the ground with the shining glass, then to cover the glass with dirt scraped out of the hole, and to scrape a peephole in the dirt to look through; but somehow, this afternoon, she couldn't bear to see the flowers covered up.

"Wait just a minute!" she cried, and, stooping swiftly, buried her nose in the flowers as if this were the last time she would ever fill her nostrils with their fragrance.

Pinky waited silently until she sat up; Susie helped her to put the glass over the flowers and, finally, to pat the earth over the glass until the ground was as smooth as it had been before. Pinky gathered up the fallen petals and looked inquiringly at Susie.

According to rule, Susie should scrape back the earth now so they could see the flowers, framed in their nest like a picture, but she sat still, her eyes staring fast at the ground.

"Dey'll be jes' as fresh tomorrow," Pinky said very softly. "I wuz careful to stick their stems clean th'ugh the wet dirt."

"Let's wait until tomorrow to look at it," Susie answered quickly, before Pinky had got the words out of her mouth.

"Dey'll be jes' as pretty," Pinky promised in her soft musical voice.

"Tomorrow, then." Susie got up and walked with Pinky to the far edge of the shadow cast by the big oak tree in the deepening twilight. It was Pinky's suppertime, and she waved a hand to Susie as she disappeared down the path to Aunt Hester's cabin.

Susie stood watching the tall grass on the sides of the path that Pinky's flight had set in motion, then she turned and walked back to the big oak tree. It was quite dark underneath the sheltering branches, and invisible insects flew with a humming sound past her ears. A light bloomed in the kitchen of the house. It would soon be her suppertime, time for her to go up the trim paths of the garden to the house, yet she lingered in the spooky shadow of the big oak tree.

When, at last, she did go, she ran with all her might and main, staring hard at the bright light in the kitchen and passing unheeded the white evening flowers that bloomed newly at her feet.

II

In the morning Susie waited on the front veranda behind the Madeira vines for the shiny black automobile that would bring Alice Louise. She wore a fresh afternoon dress and her black patent-leather Mary Jane slippers, and her eyes blazed with excitement until they blotted out the rest of her round white little face. Impatiently she rehearsed her meeting with Alice Louise.

She stood up and curtsied. "I am Susie Tarleton. Who are you?"

Before Alice Louise had time to reply, "I am Alice Louise Pratt, your new playmate, who has come to see you," a shiny black car turned off the road on to the drive and stopped at the side of the house.

Susie felt like skipping down the steps to meet Alice Louise, as she skipped down the kitchen steps every morning to meet Pinky, but she stood motionless in a breathless hush. Through a hole in the Madeira vine she saw a white man in a uniform climb out of the driver's seat and open the back door of the car. After an incredibly long moment a little girl stepped out sedately; she walked past the man without a word, and the man followed her, carrying a small tan bag with gold letters on it.

They had only a few steps to walk from the car to the veranda steps, yet every detail of the little girl's perfection was imprinted upon Susie's mind. She saw the expensive plainness of the little girl's white dress, the pin tucks and carefully fitted sleeves and rich creamy material. She saw the little girl's slippers, so finely made of dull leather with the tiniest shaped heels. She saw the little girl's finely woven straw hat with a blue velvet ribbon—velvet in summer!—round the crown.

Susie thought of her old sun hat made of plaited grasses, forgotten until now on the landing upstairs, that she wore when she wore any hat at all, and blushed. She was blushing furiously when she faced the little girl at last, and instead of curtsying, as she had practiced, she backed shyly a few steps.

The little girl bowed to her and said, "I am Alicia Pratt. Are you Susie Tarleton?"

Susie bowed then and answered her, "Yes, I am Susie Tarleton. I am so glad you have come. But my mother said your name was Alice Louise."

"I changed my name," Alicia announced in a clear precise voice. "I was named for my Grandmother Pratt, but she's dead, and I won't be named such a funny name any more."

"Won't you—won't you take off your hat?" gulped Susie. She had never, even in storybooks, seen anybody as pretty as Alicia. Her skin was really-truly as pale as the petals of a white japonica; her hair, now that her hat was off, was as fine as silk and a beautiful golden color all the way through, not just streaked with golden lights like her own brown mop. And she had what Aunt Hester called "airs and graces."

"You can leave my bag, George," she told the man carelessly. "I'll expect you at five."

Susie was aghast. Perhaps she had better invite Alicia into her mother's drawing room until Alicia decided what she wanted to play. "Did you want to change your dress first—or anything?" she asked shyly.

"Oh no," Alicia assured her. "I don't suppose we'll hurt anything. I hate rough games."

"Do you know any games?" Susie inquired eagerly.

"I knew about twenty games before I got tired of them," Alicia answered with royal detachment. "I had a playroom all to myself in our house in town where I used to play bagatelle with my governess."

"Bagatelle?" Susie marveled. She held back the curtains of the drawing room and waited for Alicia's next move.

Alicia smiled. "Tell me about your games," she commanded.

For a moment Susie was so rattled that she could not speak. She couldn't, she decided swiftly, tell Alicia about the Penny-Poppy Show, or about the corn-silk dolls that she and Pinky played with, or about catching doodles with a broomstraw dabbled in spit. "Well"—she hesitated—"I know a few games, but I'm afraid you'll hurt your dress, and your dress is beautiful."

"Name one," persisted Alicia, the light in her gray eyes changing into a smile.

Susie wet her dry lips. "I like to catch doodles," she ventured. "I know a song to sing to them that charms them right out of their holes."

"Ugh!" shivered Alicia. "I wouldn't touch one of the nasty things for a fortune."

"We might play Greenie," Susie ventured.

"How very silly." Alicia's soft syllables took away their sting. "It's only a baby game."

"I tell you what," Susie warmly promised, "let's go out under the big oak tree and call Pinky. I'll take a pillow so you won't hurt your dress. Pinky's a million times better at games than I am!"

There fell a strangely chilling silence, broken by Alicia's polite question, "And who—who could be Pinky?"

Susie blushed. "Why, Pinky's my—my playmate," she answered simply, and though she knew Alicia herself had never had such a wonderful playmate, she felt vaguely apologetic and unhappy.

III

The sun was shining brightly, but it was cool under the big oak tree. Susie laid the pillow on the ground close to the trunk, and Alicia sat upon it daintily, her delicate little hands in her lap, like a princess upon a throne.

"Pinky, Pinky," called Susie happily, reassured by her familiar outdoors.

Pinky came running along the path from Aunt Hester's cabin like a streak of flame, for she was wearing one of her red calico dresses. She stopped short and bobbed her head with the friendliest of smiles when she reached the shade of the big oak tree.

"Hurry up, Pinky," Susie called. "We're waiting for you to play games." Then, with naïve pleasure, she turned to Alicia. "This is my playmate Pinky, Alicia. She's the one I told you about."

Alicia stared and stared at Pinky with her cool gray eyes until Pinky picked at the hem of her dress nervously. "How do you do?" Alicia said at last, icily. "Miss Susie said you could play games, but I think I'd rather look over her mother's fashion books. I'd like a glass of water, too, if you please."

Pinky's mouth opened distressedly and closed. She looked at Susie for help, and Susie gulped at last, "Please bring us a pitcher of water, Pinky. And all Mother's fashion books on her sewing table."

Pinky flashed her a strange drowning look and began walking slowly to the house. All the life was gone from her steps. Susie felt the blood boiling in her veins as she watched her out of sight; she could have turned upon Alicia and clawed her to pieces. Yet she didn't. She didn't lift her hand or say a word.

Alicia stirred on her cushion, and her finely starched dress rustled like tissue paper. "She's a nigger," she declared in her sharp little voice. "The very idea of your playing with a nigger!"

"I like her," Susie said stubbornly, the red burning in her cheeks. "I've always played with her."

"Maybe you did when you were a baby"—Alicia's syllables fell silvery cool—"but you're entirely too big to play with her now. Why, you're as grown as I am, and I haven't played with a nigger in ages!"

Susie moved into the darkest part of the shade and sat down. She felt, literally, sick inside, as if her stomach were twisting in agony and her heart were too hurt to beat any more. The worst of it was she could not answer Alicia easily; Alicia's manner had made her feel differently about Pinky—as though she were siding with Alicia against Pinky—whether she wanted to or no.

"Pinky is my mammy's little girl, and we grew up together," she explained again, carefully, despising herself the while.

"Well, you don't have to play with her any more—now," Alicia said.

Susie nodded and looked up with a half-smile, but her pleasure in Alicia, in the clear golden morning, was gone. She started digging in the earth with a broken twig, to keep from thinking of what she would say to Pinky when she came back. I'll say I'd rather play with her any day in the week, that's what I'll say, she told herself. I'll say, Alicia or no little white girl will ever make me stop playing with her, that's what I'll say!

Presently Pinky came out of the kitchen door and walked slowly toward them with a pitcher of water and some glasses on a tray. The twig dropped from Susie's hand; she made a quick motion to Pinky to set the tray beside Alicia.

"Miss Alicia would like some water," she said in a flat voice, faintly imitative of Alicia's.

Pinky nodded. Her little yellow face with her sparkling chinquapin eyes had hardened into a mask of sober deference. She set the tray down and carefully poured a glass of water, without looking either at Susie or at Alicia. Susie was amazed. Pinky's manner was as remote, as impersonal, as if they had never met before. In the short space it had taken her to walk into the house and back, she had become a little colored girl who knew her place. Not even when Susie caught her eye at last and smiled warmly did she blink an eyelid.

"Here are the fashion books," she said in a flat tone, and put them beside Alicia. Then she did something that caught at Susie's heart like a spasm of pain—she backed away a few steps and curtsied, as the older servants habitually did to her mother, their mistress. The gesture was so admirable that Alicia bowed in acknowledgment.

Susie closed her eyes to hide the tears swimming in them, and when she looked up again Pinky was gone. In the deepening shade of the big oak tree Alicia seemed paler, more precious, than ever. Like a white japonica, Susie thought with a sharp twinge of jealousy.

Yet she moved over to her obediently a moment later, when Alicia called to her to come choose paper dolls.

IV

All during the time she was choosing paper dolls with Alicia, and even while she was accepting Alicia's invitation to spend the day with her tomorrow, Susie was looking forward to the time when Alicia would be gone and she could call to Pinky to come look at their Penny-Poppy Show under the big oak tree. At last Alicia went home in the shiny black car, and she was alone. It was getting dark, but no darker than yesterday, when they had made the Penny-Poppy Show. And Pinky had said the flowers would be as fresh as the day they were picked.

Susie ran to the big oak tree, calling, "Pinky, Pinky!" at the top of her lungs. How free she felt as she ran along the path without Alicia tagging her! It was darker under the tree than she had thought, but if Pinky would hurry they would still be able to see the Penny-Poppy Show. "Pinky, Pinky!" she called softly, urgently, and tilted her head sideways so she could hear Pinky's first running steps.

At first she heard only the hum of invisible insects, flying past her ears, and then the humming deepened to the sound of human voices.

She recognized Aunt Hester scolding Pinky; her words came clear and hard, like the sound of hickory nuts falling onto the frozen ground.

"You kin go an' speak to her if it'll ease yo' pain, but you tell her you know the diff'ence between a white chile and a black chile, and y'all caint play together no more. Hit was boun' to come. Quit that sniffin' and go yonder an' tell her lak I tole you."

After a while Pinky came up the path from the cabin. She did not run like a streak of light this time, but came slowly, and wiped her eyes on the hem of her calico dress.

Susie waited for her under the big oak tree near the Penny-Poppy Show, but she knew only too well that they would not look at the Penny-Poppy Show or ever make another together.

"I heard Aunt Hester," she told Pinky. "I heard what Aunt Hester said." Although her voice sounded calm and grown-up like Alicia's, her heart felt as if it would break.

Pinky stood before her in the dim light, rubbing one lovely yellow hand over the other, and it came to Susie that it was really Aunt Hester who had stopped Pinky from playing with her—not Alicia or herself. Susie had given in to Alicia while Alicia was guest, as was proper, but Pinky knew she would come back, Pinky knew Susie loved her better than all the little white girls in the world.

"I can't play with you no more." Pinky said at last. "Mammy says I can't play with you no more."

"I heard her," Susie answered, and in the dim light her face looked as white as Alicia's. In the strangest way her whole body stiffened with pride; she not only acted like a little white girl, without meaning to, but she looked like a white japonica, delicate and remote and cool.

"I have to go back," Pinky whispered, and curtsied as she had before Alicia, "unless—unless you want anything."

Susie nodded imperiously, as Alicia had nodded before her, as all the little white girls for generations had nodded to their little black playmates. Only, Susie felt the tears in her throat, and so bitter were they that they tasted like brine in her mouth. "No"—she mimicked Alicia completely—"I don't care for anything."

For the briefest moment Pinky hesitated, then she turned and walked slowly down the path the way she had come.

Susie watched her go, and such a loneliness swept over her as she had never imagined except in the breasts of old people who had lost all their kin and were left without a soul to love them. She went over to the Penny-Poppy Show and stretched out her hands as if she would scrape the dirt away from over the glass that covered the flowers, but her hands dropped like wilted petals, and she stood there, stiffly, helplessly, listening to the terrible beating of her heart.

THE REVOLT OF THE EVIL FAIRIES

Ted Poston

Ted Poston is a newspaperman of long standing, now serving with the Office of War Information in Washington.

THE grand dramatic offering of the Booker T. Washington Colored Grammar School was the biggest event of the year in our social life in Hopkinsville, Kentucky. It was the one occasion on which they let us use the old Cooper Opera House, and even some of the white folks came out yearly to applaud our presentation. The first two rows of the orchestra were always reserved for our white friends, and our leading colored citizens sat right behind them—with an empty row intervening, of course.

Mr. Ed Smith, our local undertaker, invariably occupied a box to the left of the house and wore his cutaway coat and striped breeches. This distinctive garb was usually reserved for those rare occasions when he officiated at the funerals of our most prominent colored citizens. Mr. Thaddeus Long, our colored mailman, once rented a tuxedo and bought a box too. But nobody paid him much mind. We knew he was just showing off.

The title of our play never varied. It was always *Prince Charming and the Sleeping Beauty,* but no two presentations were ever the same. Miss H. Belle LaPrade, our sixth-grade teacher, rewrote the script every season, and it was never like anything you read in the storybooks.

Miss LaPrade called it "a modern morality play of conflict between the forces of good and evil." And the forces of evil, of course, always came off second best.

The Booker T. Washington Colored Grammar School was in a state of ferment from Christmas until February, for this was the period when parts were assigned. First there was the selection of the Good Fairies and the Evil Fairies. This was very important, because the Good Fairies wore white costumes and the Evil Fairies black. And strangely enough most of the Good Fairies usually turned out to be extremely light in complexion, with straight hair and white folks' features. On rare occasions a dark-skinned girl might be lucky enough to be a Good Fairy, but not one with a speaking part.

There never was any doubt about Prince Charming and the Sleeping Beauty. They were *always* light-skinned. And though nobody ever discussed those things openly, it was an accepted fact that a lack of pigmentation was a decided advantage in the Prince Charming and Sleeping Beauty sweepstakes.

And therein lay my personal tragedy. I made the best grades in my class, I was the leading debater, and the scion of a respected family in the community. But I could never be Prince Charming, because I was black.

In fact, every year when they started casting our grand dramatic offering my family started pricing black cheesecloth at Franklin's Department Store. For they knew that I would be leading the forces of darkness and skulking back in the shadows—waiting to be vanquished in the third act. Mamma had experience with this sort of thing. All my brothers had finished Booker T. before me.

Not that I was alone in my disappointment. Many of my classmates felt it too. I probably just took it more to heart. Rat Joiner, for instance, could rationalize the situation. Rat was not only black; he lived on Billy Goat Hill. But Rat summed it up like this:

"If you black, you black."

I should have been able to regard the matter calmly too. For our grand dramatic offering was only a reflection of our daily community life in Hopkinsville. The yallers had the best of everything. They held most of the teaching jobs in Booker T. Washington Colored Grammar School. They were the Negro doctors, the lawyers, the insurance men. They even had a "Blue Vein Society," and if your dark skin obscured your throbbing pulse you were hardly a member of the elite.

Yet I was inconsolable the first time they turned me down for Prince Charming. That was the year they picked Roger Jackson. Roger was not only dumb; he stuttered. But he was light enough to pass for white, and that was apparently sufficient.

In all fairness, however, it must be admitted that Roger had other qualifications. His father owned the only colored saloon in town and was quite a power in local politics. In fact, Mr. Clinton Jackson had a lot to say about just who taught in the Booker T. Washington Colored Grammar School. So it was understandable that Roger should have been picked for Prince Charming.

My real heartbreak, however, came the year they picked Sarah Williams for Sleeping Beauty. I had been in love with Sarah since kindergarten. She had soft light hair, bluish-gray eyes, and a dimple which stayed in her left cheek whether she was smiling or not.

Of course Sarah never encouraged me much. She never answered any of my fervent love letters, and Rat was very scornful of my one-sided love affair. "As long as she don't call you a black baboon," he sneered, "you'll keep on hanging around."

After Sarah was chosen for Sleeping Beauty, I went out for the Prince Charming role with all my heart. If I had declaimed boldly in previous contests, I was matchless now. If I had bothered Mamma with rehearsals at home before, I pestered her to death this time. Yes, and I purloined my sister's can of Palmer's Skin Success.

I knew the Prince's role from start to finish, having played the Head Evil Fairy opposite it for two seasons. And Prince Charming was one character whose lines Miss LaPrade never varied much in her many versions. But although I never admitted it, even to myself, I knew I was doomed from the start. They gave the part to Leonardius Wright. Leonardius, of course, was yaller.

The teachers sensed my resentment. They were almost apologetic. They pointed out that I had been such a splendid Head Evil Fairy for two seasons that it would be a crime to let anybody else try the role. They reminded me that Mamma wouldn't have to buy any more cheesecloth because I could use my same old costume. They insisted that the Head Evil Fairy was even more important than Prince Charming because he was the one who cast the spell on Sleeping Beauty. So what could I do but accept?

I had never liked Leonardius Wright. He was a goody-goody, and even Mamma was always throwing him up to me. But, above all, he too was in love with Sarah Williams. And now he got a chance to kiss Sarah every day in rehearsing the awakening scene.

Well, the show must go on, even for little black boys. So I threw my soul into my part and made the Head Evil Fairy a character to be remembered. When I drew back from the couch of Sleeping Beauty and slunk away into the shadows at the approach of Prince Charming, my facial expression was indeed something to behold. When I was vanquished by the shining sword of Prince Charming in the last act, I was a little hammy perhaps—but terrific!

The attendance at our grand dramatic offering that year was the best in its history. Even the white folks overflowed the two rows reserved for them, and a few were forced to sit in the intervening one. This created a delicate situation, but everybody tactfully ignored it.

When the curtain went up on the last act, the audience was in fine fettle. Everything had gone well for me too—except for one spot in the second act. That was where Leonardius unexpectedly rapped me over the head with his sword as I slunk off into the shadows. That was not in the script, but Miss LaPrade quieted me down by saying it made a nice touch anyway. Rat said Leonardius did it on purpose.

The third act went on smoothly, though, until we came to the vanquishing scene. That was where I slunk from the shadows for the last time and challenged Prince Charming to mortal combat. The hero reached for his shining sword—a bit unsportsmanlike, I always thought, since Miss LaPrade consistently left the Head Evil Fairy unarmed—and then it happened!

Later I protested loudly—but in vain—that it was a case of self-defense. I pointed out that Leonardius had a mean look in his eye. I cited the impromptu rapping he had given my head in the second act. But nobody would listen. They just wouldn't believe that Leonardius really intended to brain me when he reached for his sword.

Anyway, he didn't succeed. For the minute I saw that evil gleam in his eye—or was it my own?—I cut loose with a right to the chin, and Prince Charming dropped his shining sword and staggered back. His astonishment lasted only a minute, though, for he lowered his head and came charging in, fists flailing. There was nothing yellow about Leonardius but his skin.

The audience thought the scrap was something new Miss LaPrade had written in. They might have kept on thinking so if Miss LaPrade hadn't been screaming so hysterically from the side lines. And if Rat Joiner hadn't decided that this was as good a time as any to settle old scores. So he turned around and took a sock at the male Good Fairy nearest him.

When the curtain rang down, the forces of Good and Evil were locked in combat. And Sleeping Beauty was wide awake and streaking for the wings.

They rang the curtain back up fifteen minutes later, and we finished the play. I lay down and expired according to specifications, but Prince Charming will probably remember my sneering corpse to his dying day. They wouldn't let me appear in the grand dramatic offering at all the next year. But I didn't care. I couldn't have been Prince Charming anyway.

WHITE ON BLACK

Tess Slesinger

The late Tess Slesinger is best remembered by her novel The Unpossessed *and her brittle short stories, gathered into a volume called* Time: The Present.

ONE OF THE PRIVATE SCHOOLS attended by the "nice" children of the West Side some twenty years ago followed not only the liberal practice of mixing rich and poor, Gentile and Jew, but made a point also of including Negroes. Not many, of course—just enough so that when the eye of a visiting parent roved down the rows of pink and white faces collected for the Harvest Festival or the Easter Play, it stumbled complacently here and there—perhaps three or four times in all the auditorium—on an equally scrubbed black one sticking out like a solitary violet in a bed of primroses. For, except in the case of two sisters, or of a brother and sister, these black children never made friends among themselves, seldom even to the extent of choosing seats side by side in assemblies.

I suppose that the effect upon the rest of us was, as it was intended to be, on the whole good. It must have taught us well-bred little boys and girls at the least the untruth of the common slander that Negroes have an unpleasant odor; for certainly none of the Wilsons and Whites and Washingtons in our school ever smelt of anything but soap. And we were brought up, through weekly ethics lessons and the influence of the inevitable elderly lady teacher who had never got Harriet Beecher Stowe out of her mind, to the axiom that all men were created equal.

The few scattered colored children in clean clothes, then, contributed practically to our liberal education. But what effect we, in our more than clean, our often luxurious clothes and with our pink and white faces, had in turn upon them, it is impossible for one of us to judge. Although I can tell you today what has happened since to a number of my old schoolmates, even to those in whom I have long ceased to be interested, and although I run every year across gossip concerning still others, none of us has any idea what happened to our colored classmates. Some of them left school before the high-school years were over; some of them were graduated and stood at our elbows with their rolled-up diplomas; but all of them have equally dropped out of our common knowledge since. Where are they now? Did they drift back to Harlem, those Wilsons and Washingtons and Whites? How do they look back upon their ten years' interlude with white children? I cannot imagine. But I remember vividly the school careers of the two who were in my class.

The Wilsons, brother and sister, joined us in the sixth grade. Paul was exquisitely made, his face chiseled and without fault; a pair of delicately dilated nostrils at the end of a short fine nose, and an aureole of dim black curls. Elizabeth was bigger, coarser, more negroid; darker, her lips were thick, her nose less perfect; but still she was a beautiful child, luxuriously made, and promising to develop into a type of the voluptuous Negro woman at her best. Elizabeth was older than Paul; but her brain, like her nose, was less sharp, and both were put into the same class.

For the first week or two our kind teachers paid them the surplus attention which was always extended to Negro or crippled or poverty-stricken children. They suggested that Paul be chosen when the boys were choosing up sides; they asked the girls to take Elizabeth as partner. The children stood off from them no more than they stood off from any newcomers. We were not adultly snobbish; we merely glared at all newcomers in our world until they should prove themselves worthy. But by the end of the month there was no longer any question of choosing Paul: Paul himself was the chooser and the permanently chosen; likewise Elizabeth was besieged with requests for the seats on either side of her in assembly, and it became an honor to have a seat in the same row; and the teachers turned round and were given rather to suppressing the colored Wilsons than to bringing them out.

For after a certain natural humility had worn off, Paul and Elizabeth were not merely taken into the group; they took over the group. Including the faculty. They were a smashing success. For one thing, they feared nothing; furthermore, they proved marvelous athletes, and they were born leaders. Electing Paul to the captaincy of the basketball team was a mere formality; even if he hadn't richly deserved it, he would have permitted no one else to hold it. Elizabeth was as strong as a horse, less skillful, less graceful than he, but easily outshining, by her animal strength and fearlessness, all the white girls in the class. Beside their athletic prowess, which alone would have won them popularity in a class of eleven-year-olds, both of them were gifted with an overpowering jubilancy and a triumphant bullying wit, which inevitably made them czars.

They ruled the class with a rod of iron, chose their intimates, played with them, dropped them, and patronized the teachers. Their power spread to politics: by the end of the first year Paul was president of the class, and Elizabeth, who could not spell, secretary. Their class meetings were masterpieces of irreverent wit and bedlam, subtly dominated by the tacitly authoritative Paul. The teachers turned over to them the difficult business of controlling the class after recess, and Paul, in his double capacity of legal president and illegal czar, easily succeeded where they had long failed. Even his sister, who was no small power among the girls, feared and adored him. If her authority was for one moment questioned, she had only to say, "I'll call Paul. . . ."

I remember myself—and probably not a few others of the dazzled little white girls did the same in secret—going home to dream about marrying Paul and taking Elizabeth to live with us. I remember a moment of certainly unprecedented and of almost unsurpassed voluptuous pleasure on an occasion when Paul, twisting his wiry body into one of those marvelous knots from which he unrolled himself to shoot a basket, stretched so far that his shirt left his trousers and revealed a few inches of coffee-colored skin glistening with sweat, which caused me to gasp with delight. We girls chose to play against the boys of the class rather than among ourselves, and I was surely not the only girl who had voted favorably for the pure delight of being tossed on the ground and swung round the hips by the jubilant Paul, who had, beside his lovely body and fierce little nostrils, not the slightest inhibition.

For two years the noisy Wilsons demoralized the entire class into a raucous group that was never tired of wrestling, playing basketball, shouting jokes, and merrily defying the teachers. Not even the famous Seventh Grade Trouble, which involved the Wilsons as central figures, subdued them. Not even the visit, upon that terrifying occasion, of their mother. All of us made a point of walking past the principal's office to view Mrs. Wilson, who sat there, dressed in black and with her face held low and ashamed as though she were the culprit herself. We whispered afterward, among ourselves, of what a lady Mrs. Wilson was; we had never before seen a colored lady.

The high-school years loomed ahead. We were to be joined by another section of the same grade, and we were determined to maintain our solidarity with Paul at our head. Our reputation as a champion class had preceded us; but with it, we soon noticed, a reputation for rowdiness. Paul was instantly elected captain of the basketball team. But he was just nosed out of the presidency by a white boy belonging to the other section, who must have gained some treacherous votes from among our own. Although the other boy occupied the chair, Paul managed, for half a year, to bully even the new section into slowly waning submission to the last echoes of his power.

Elizabeth's popularity remained limited to the girls in our own old section. The others adopted her at first as a novelty, but they had not been trained to her loud hearty jokes and her powerful wrestling, and soon tired of her and left her to her old companions. These dwindled slowly, as we girls gained consciousness of our status as girls and wished to dissociate ourselves from anything rowdy. Of course it was our fault—we could have pushed Elizabeth forward and remained loyal to her—but we had so many things to think of in those days. And I think something of the sort was bound to happen to Elizabeth anyway; she did not have the native personality to warrant and sustain the unlimited popularity which had fallen on her partly because of her strength and partly because she was her brother's sister. There was a quiet girl in our class, less mature than the rest of us—who were, in that first year of high school, more fiercely mature than some of us are today, which is ten years later. This girl, Diana, fastened upon Elizabeth as a chum, and from now on the curious pair were inseparable.

I remember the early days when it became the thing for the boys to take the girls to the corner soda store after basketball games and for each boy to treat one girl to a fudge sundae. We couldn't help noticing that the boys, so eager to roughhouse with Elizabeth in the classroom, hesitated among themselves as to which should treat her and that the same one never treated her twice. We noticed, too, that the soda clerk stared at the dark blemish in our small white group. Elizabeth never seemed to notice anything; she developed a habit of kidding the soda clerk in a loud professional voice, and soon our indignation was shifted to her, and we told her to lower her voice and not fool around with soda clerks. Toward the end of the year Diana and Elizabeth dissociated themselves from our group and began to occupy a little table by themselves in a corner. Here they would sit and pretend to be alone, and we could hear them giggling and whispering happily. Paul, of course, was still too young and too "manly" ever to join these parties.

In the course of that first year in high school many things beside the soda parties happened to us. Wrestling between boys and girls was outlawed, the girls began to loop their hair in buns over the ears, and the boys began to appear in navy-blue long trousers.

I remember Paul in his first longies. Instead of navy blue, he appeared in a sleek suit of light Broadway tan, nicely nipped in at the waist, which harmonized with his clear mocha skin and showed off his dapper little figure to perfection. But it didn't quite fit in our school. I noticed that day, standing in line behind him to buy lunch tickets, that he wore brand-new shoes: they were long and very pointed and polished a brilliant ocher; they were button shoes, with cloth tops; they squeaked like nothing else in the world. I remember staring at them and wondering where I had seen shoes like those before: was it in the elevator at home?

We were so grown-up that year that instead of shooting baskets in the twenty-minute recess that followed lunch we got one girl to play the piano and the rest of us danced. Only about half of the boys were bold enough to dance; Paul still belonged to the group which stood in a corner and laughed and imitated their bolder friends, waiting for younger girls to be imported into the high-school department next year. With one boy to every pair of girls, it was not surprising that Elizabeth danced more than half of her dances with her friend Diana. The rest of us paired off with our girl friends equally often.

But for no reason that anyone could see, Elizabeth's friends still diminished week by week. She had occasional spurts of her old popularity, but these were chiefly occasioned by reaction against some more stable idol, who would soon be restored to her post. Elizabeth's one permanent friend was Diana, the quiet little blonde girl who had no other friends. As far as I know, Diana was the only girl who ever invited Elizabeth to her house, and it was rumored that Diana was the only one who had seen the inside of the Wilson house, but Diana could be made neither to say whether it was true nor what it was like if she had seen it. As for the rest of us, we were a little uncomfortable about omitting Elizabeth at afternoon parties at our homes; but somebody's mother settled it for us by saying that she thought it would be an unkindness to the little colored girl to invite her to a home where there would be none of her own people.

This conflicted, of course, with the lesson of our ethics classes, but we were thirteen-going-on-fourteen, and we had too much to think about, so we let it go at that.

Meanwhile Paul, who had remained captain all the first year, failed to be elected for the second. Some of his classmates started propaganda to the effect that, while still their best player, he was no good as a captain, and they self-righteously elected the second-best player in his stead. Paul took out his anger in refusing to co-operate with the team, and developed into a poor sport, that worst of anathemas in school, successfully hogging the ball so that no one else had a chance. The epithet poor sport began to be whispered about the classroom, and when class elections for the second year were held, Paul was not even nominated for an office. Our section had sworn to stand by him when we had suffered defeat at the beginning of the year, but when the time came we simply sat and held our tongues and elected another boy from the hostile section.

When the Wilsons returned for the second year after vacation, they looked a little different to us. Paul had turned into something resembling an uptown beau, and Elizabeth's face had grown coarser. Elizabeth joined her friend Diana at once, and their companionship remained unbroken. Paul, however, held in considerably less esteem, remained aloof, making no effort to regain his lost popularity, and pursued his way sullenly and almost defiantly among us. He met our reproaches with indifference.

That year evening dances broke out among us. For the sake of girls who might never be asked, there was a rule that everyone must come unescorted and unescorting. It was easy enough, of course, to break the rule. Most of the girls came regularly attended by boys from the upper classes. Elizabeth came the first few times with her brother, which was as good as coming unattended. Paul stood in a corner with the stags; Elizabeth sat with the other girls who had come unattended or attended by brothers, looking very dark and strange in her short-sleeved light dresses, and accepted gratefully her few opportunities to dance.

There began to be whispers among us of what we would do if Paul asked one of us to come to a dance with him or offered a treat to a soda. We admitted to feeling uncomfortable at the thought of being seen on the street with him. At the same time we realized that what we were contemplating was horribly unfair. But Evelyn—Evelyn, who led our class in social matters because at fourteen she wore rouge and baby French heels—said, "School is school; it's not the World; it's not our Real Lives," and we let it go at that. As we had tacitly adopted policies toward Elizabeth, we now officially adopted one toward Paul: we were to be extra nice to him, but not in the way that one treats a boy, and we were to dance with him when he asked us but very kindly refuse his invitations to escort us anywhere outside the school walls. Fortunately for our peace of mind, ethics lessons were that year changed to weekly lessons in elocution for the girls and public speaking for the boys.

But none of us was given the chance to refuse him. So far as I know, he never asked a girl to go anywhere with him, never left the stag line at our Friday-night dances, and after the first half dozen he never even came with Elizabeth. He scrupulously avoided even the careless physical contacts in the elevator, of which the other boys took modest advantage. Also, when we followed our policy of being nice to him in school, we found ourselves politely ignored. Paul grew increasingly sullen, even occasionally rude, and one girl reported that he had passed her on the street and pretended not to see her, neglecting to lift his elegant tan felt hat.

In the middle of that year Elizabeth's friend Diana was withdrawn from the school by her parents and sent to a boarding school in the South, rumor said to get her away from the black girl and teach her a proper sense of color.

With her friend gone, Elizabeth picked up smaller fry and dazzled them, because, unlike Paul, she seemed to want never tc be alone. But even with these she learned to disappear at the school door, or at most to walk no farther with a white classmate than the end of the school block. There, making some excuse about having to hurry, or going in another direction, she would dash away with a good-humored smile. I remember watching her running away from us once and wondering to what strange world she disappeared every day after school.

Of course not one of the nice girls in our school would have dreamed of hurting Elizabeth's feelings by suggesting that she leave us on the street, but there must have been some hesitating on the corner before Elizabeth so effectively learned that her position with her white schoolmates ended with the school door. Or could it have been that dark lady, who had sat in the principal's office with her head lowered as though she were the culprit, that time of the Seventh Grade Trouble? But no matter, we were in our third year of high school now, and had forgotten the seventh grade as we had forgotten the famous trouble, and were used now to seeing our dark classmate hurry off after school and run down the long block, leaving us standing on the corner, discussing our this and that, which was so awfully important to us. . . .

In the third year of high school, Paul simply did not appear. We were,

I suppose, faintly relieved, in so far as we thought about him at all. He removed, after all, such uncomfortable questions as playing other schools with a Negro on our first team. And our own old section, our merry, rowdy section, of which Paul had once been undisputed king, had imperceptibly melted away; the boundary line was wavery, our old loyalty vague, a thing of the past; Paul, so far as he was anything in our minds, was a memory belonging to our lost section. When we asked Elizabeth what had happened to him, she told us he was going to another school because he didn't like girls and considered our private school sissy. She carried it off rather well, I think. One or two of us suggested that he might have been fired, because we all knew that his work had gone off badly in that last year.

Elizabeth herself, in those last two years, toned down considerably. Her prowess in studies had never been great, and she seemed now to be devoting more time to them. Her athletic ability had not lived up to its promise, because she had been after all primarily interested in roughneck play and seemed unable or unwilling to tame her strength and spirits into rules and skill. She abandoned the bright colors she had worn as a child and came to school in neat and modest dresses. She dropped without reluctance into the common order of students, learned to toady as she had once been toadied to, and managed to keep up a decent sober reputation which ensured her a mild amount of companionship, restricted, of course, to within the school walls. On committees Elizabeth volunteered for unpleasant jobs and carried them out cheerfully and efficiently. She grew generous and sweet-tempered and a little like a servant; and, like a servant, she was thanked for her services and forgotten.

Paul had dropped out of our existence.

The last time I saw either of them was at our graduation dance. Elizabeth had long ago given up coming alone to our dances, but she came, of course, to this one, looking rather too burly and black in the prescribed white dress, with bare arms which hung like bones from her ungainly shoulders. She was the whole of the committee on refreshments, and all during the first part of the evening she stood behind a table with her diploma tucked on a rack over her head—nobody from her family had come to see her be graduated—and cheerfully dispensed sandwiches and ice cream.

Everybody was mingling proudly in the big assembly room, waiting for the chairs to be removed for dancing; everybody was very nice to Elizabeth and even took down her address as a matter of form, but in the rush of taking addresses that really meant something and comparing notes about future colleges she was forgotten, and if it hadn't been for a teacher who came to her rescue, she might have been completely alone. When the dancing began the teacher led her away from the buffet table with her arm around her, to bring her to the row of chairs where girls sat waiting for partners.

Some of us must have had compunctions—I know I did—floating by her in our partners' arms, for on that night the least popular girl had achieved a faithful escort, if only by importing boys from classes below who felt it an honor to be there at all. But none of us felt badly enough to urge our partners to leave us and dance with Elizabeth. Later one or two boys danced a waltz with her, because a waltz was the least difficult thing to sacrifice. She sat all evening and talked cheerfully to the teacher. She looked uncomplaining, as though she had quietly learned her place. She even seemed to enjoy watching the rest of us dance.

The evening broke up on a high note of "See you again," "Don't forget," and "Oh, the most marvelous time!" and I remember emerging from the dance room in a fever of happiness, walking on winged feet. I pushed my way through the gay crowd outside the door. Somebody tapped me on the arm: "Miss!" I turned and saw, for the first time in three years, Paul Wilson, the king of our old section! I smiled eagerly, delighted to see him again. "Why, Paul!" I exclaimed, holding out my hand.

He was as beautiful as he had been three years before, but his face was different, hardened perhaps, so that the dapper tan clothes he wore made him cheap and flashy. He still wore pointed button shoes with cloth tops. He was standing by the wall with his hat pulled down over his eyes. "Why, Paul!" I said.

He looked up, caught my eye, and shifted his away as though he had failed to recognize me. He looked down at the floor and spoke in a low voice. "Miss, would you mind finding my sister, Elizabeth Wilson, inside and say her brother is waiting for her?" He stuck his hands suddenly into his pockets with something of his old sullen gesture.

I remember turning from him with an overpowering sense of guilt to spare him embarrassment, and going back with tears burning my eyes to find Elizabeth. I left him standing there against the wall, with his hat over his eyes, snubbing his former classmates, while they passed their former god and leader, some of them too happy to distinguish his features under that hat, others no doubt turning from him to prevent his embarrassment, and even, on that happy night, to spare themselves. . . . This should have been his graduation.

AFTER YOU, MY DEAR ALPHONSE

Shirley Jackson

Shirley Jackson, a frequent contributor to the New Yorker, *is well known for her short stories.*

MRS. WILSON was just taking the gingerbread out of the oven when she heard Johnny outside talking to someone.

"Johnny," she called, "you're late. Come in and get your lunch."

"Just a minute, Mother," Johnny said. "After you, my dear Alphonse."

"After *you,* my dear Alphonse," another voice said.

"No, after *you,* my dear Alphonse," Johnny said.

Mrs. Wilson opened the door. "Johnny," she said, "you come in this minute and get your lunch. You can play after you've eaten."

Johnny came in after her, slowly. "Mother," he said, "I brought Boyd home for lunch with me."

"Boyd?" Mrs. Wilson thought for a moment. "I don't believe I've met Boyd. Bring him in, dear, since you've invited him. Lunch is ready."

"Boyd!" Johnny yelled. "Hey, Boyd, come on in!"

"I'm coming. Just got to unload this stuff."

"Well, hurry, or my mother'll be sore."

"Johnny, that's not very polite to either your friend or your mother," Mrs. Wilson said. "Come sit down, Boyd."

As she turned to show Boyd where to sit, she saw he was a Negro boy, smaller than Johnny but about the same age. His arms were loaded with split kindling wood. "Where'll I put this stuff, Johnny?" he asked.

Mrs. Wilson turned to Johnny. "Johnny," she said, "what did you make Boyd do? What is that wood?"

"Dead Japanese," Johnny said mildly. "We stand them in the ground and run over them with tanks."

"How do you do, Mrs. Wilson?" Boyd said.

"How do you do, Boyd? You shouldn't let Johnny make you carry all that wood. Sit down now and eat lunch, both of you."

"Why shouldn't he carry the wood, Mother? It's his wood. We got it at his place."

"Johnny," Mrs. Wilson said, "go on and eat your lunch."

"Sure," Johnny said. He held out the dish of scrambled eggs to Boyd. "After you, my dear Alphonse."

"After *you,* my dear Alphonse," Boyd said.

"After *you,* my dear Alphonse," Johnny said. They began to giggle.

"Are you hungry, Boyd?" Mrs. Wilson asked.

"Yes, Mrs. Wilson."

"Well, don't you let Johnny stop you. He always fusses about eating, so you just see that you get a good lunch. There's plenty of food here for you to have all you want."

"Thank you, Mrs. Wilson."

"Come on, Alphonse," Johnny said. He pushed half the scrambled eggs onto Boyd's plate. Boyd watched while Mrs. Wilson put a dish of stewed tomatoes beside his plate.

"Boyd don't eat tomatoes, do you, Boyd?" Johnny said.

*"Does*n't eat tomatoes, Johnny. And just because you don't like them, don't say that about Boyd. Boyd will eat *any*thing."

"Bet he won't," Johnny said, attacking his scrambled eggs.

"Boyd wants to grow up and be a big strong man so he can work hard," Mrs. Wilson said. "I'll bet Boyd's father eats stewed tomatoes."

"My father eats anything he wants to," Boyd said.

"So does mine," Johnny said. "Sometimes he doesn't eat hardly anything. He's a little guy, though. Wouldn't hurt a flea."

"Mine's a little guy too," Boyd said.

"I'll bet he's strong, though," Mrs. Wilson said. She hesitated. "Does he . . . work?"

"Sure," Johnny said. "Boyd's father works in a factory."

"There, you see?" Mrs. Wilson said. "And he certainly has to be strong to do that—all that lifting and carrying at a factory."

"Boyd's father doesn't have to," Johnny said. "He's a foreman."

Mrs. Wilson felt defeated. "What does your mother do, Boyd?"

"My mother?" Boyd was surprised. "She takes care of us kids."

"Oh. She doesn't work, then?"

"Why should she?" Johnny said through a mouthful of eggs. "You don't work."

"You really don't want any stewed tomatoes, Boyd?"

"No, thank you, Mrs. Wilson," Boyd said.

"No, thank you, Mrs. Wilson, no, thank you, Mrs. Wilson, no, thank you, Mrs. Wilson," Johnny said. "Boyd's sister's going to work, though. She's going to be a teacher."

"That's a very fine attitude for her to have, Boyd." Mrs. Wilson restrained an impulse to pat Boyd on the head. "I imagine you're all very proud of her?"

"I guess so," Boyd said.

"What about all your other brothers and sisters? I guess all of you want to make just as much of yourselves as you can."

"There's only me and Jean," Boyd said. "I don't know yet what I want to be when I grow up."

"We're going to be tank drivers, Boyd and me," Johnny said. "Zoom." Mrs. Wilson caught Boyd's glass of milk as Johnny's napkin ring, suddenly transformed into a tank, plowed heavily across the table.

"Look, Johnny," Boyd said. "Here's a foxhole. I'm shooting at you."

Mrs. Wilson, with the speed born of long experience, took the gingerbread off the shelf and placed it carefully between the tank and the foxhole.

"Now eat as much as you want to, Boyd," she said. "I want to see you get filled up."

"Boyd eats a lot, but not as much as I do," Johnny said. "I'm bigger than he is."

"You're not much bigger," Boyd said. "I can beat you running."

Mrs. Wilson took a deep breath. "Boyd," she said. Both boys turned to her. "Boyd, Johnny has some suits that are a little too small for him, and a winter coat. It's not new, of course, but there's lots of wear in it still. And I have a few dresses that your mother or sister could probably use. Your mother can make them over into lots of things for all of you, and I'd be very happy to give them to you. Suppose before you leave I make up a big bundle and then you and Johnny can take it over to your mother right away . . ." Her voice trailed off as she saw Boyd's puzzled expression.

"But I have plenty of clothes, thank you," he said. "And I don't think my mother knows how to sew very well, and anyway I guess we buy about everything we need. Thank you very much, though."

"We don't have time to carry that old stuff around, Mother," Johnny said. "We got to play tanks with the kids today."

Mrs. Wilson lifted the plate of gingerbread off the table as Boyd was about to take another piece. "There are many little boys like you, Boyd, who would be very grateful for the clothes someone was kind enough to give them."

"Boyd will take them if you want him to, Mother," Johnny said.

"I didn't mean to make you mad, Mrs. Wilson," Boyd said.

"Don't think I'm angry, Boyd. I'm just disappointed in you, that's all. Now let's not say anything more about it."

She began clearing the plates off the table, and Johnny took Boyd's hand and pulled him to the door. " 'Bye, Mother," Johnny said. Boyd stood for a minute, staring at Mrs. Wilson's back.

"After you, my dear Alphonse," Johnny said, holding the door open.

"Is your mother still mad?" Mrs. Wilson heard Boyd ask in a low voice.

"I don't know," Johnny said. "She's screwy sometimes."

"So's mine," Boyd said. He hesitated. "After *you,* my dear Alphonse."

TROUBLE KEEPING QUIET

Leonard Wallace Robinson

Leonard Wallace Robinson has for some years been associated with various magazines in an editorial capacity. His short stories have appeared in the New Yorker *and* Harper's *magazine.*

It was after four o'clock in the morning, and the two colored men came along Twenty-third Street, stepping right out and talking with all their energy in spite of the heat which would not be cooled even by the heavy morning dew. They were both going home now, a little drunk, having, after finishing their work at the dock, gone into one of the river-front saloons and had several beers apiece. One was bareheaded, about fifty years old, and he wore a mustache and a pair of gold-rimmed glasses, and the other, much younger, had a cap on with a crown so high and wide that it covered the visor completely. They kept up their rapid pace along the street, crossing four avenues, and then, imperceptibly, they began to slow down, both in pace and in talk. Finally, after a brief silence, the man with the glasses fished through his overall pockets and tapped his blue shirt pocket.

"I'm outa smokes," he said. "You got a cigarette?"

"No," said the other man, "we been smokin' yours."

"That's what I thought," said the man with the glasses. "How about you loosen now and get us some cigarettes?" He pointed his finger at his friend and grinned. "*You* payin' for them this time."

"You know," said the other man, "you is a genius for good ideas, the only thing is being I ain't got one damned red cent only a nickel for the subway."

"Well, ain't that too bad for me," said the man with the glasses. "I guess that means I'm Mr. Pay again." He fished in his overall pockets and took out four dimes. "Only *where* in hell we get a cigarette down here unless we wait till we get up Harlem."

"I seen this one place open all night up here between Eighth and Seventh, and I guess they got a machine," said his friend.

"I like the way you know these places," the man with the glasses said, "so when we come up there you can go right in there and get them."

His friend looked at him for a moment out of the corner of his eyes, and he wasn't smiling now. "Like hell," he said emphatically. "You wanted that smoke, not me. I don't go in them places. It's too much trouble keepin' quiet when they treat you bad if there's a bad counterman. I just keep out."

"Okay, okay, don't get all steam," said the other. "I got no fears. I walk right in and ask for cigarettes, treat me bad, treat me good, treat me anyways."

"I wouldn't go in for nothin'," said his friend. "Charley Oakes went in one place like that on Forty-second Street last week and he said that counterman like to throwed that food at him. Charley says never again, it's too much trouble not sayin' anything."

"Okay," said the older man, "I go in, I got no fears." They walked on now in silence till they came to a white-fronted restaurant, the window of which had, written in English lettering across it, THE IDEAL. The two men paused outside for a moment, and then the man with the glasses opened the door and went inside. "I be right out," he said to his friend.

There were no people in the restaurant, and a lone counterman leaned on the long counter reading a copy of the *Mirror*. He did not look up as the Negro came in, and the colored man paused, then walked toward the back of the shop looking for a cigarette-vending machine. Halfway to the rear he encountered a rope stretched across the space between the counter and the wall, bearing the sign, "This Section Closed." The lights in the closed section were off and the back walls were almost in total darkness. He paused at the rope and the counterman looked up. He was very tough-looking, with a bald head and a hard, seamed face.

"Whadaya want?" he said to the colored man.

"I was just looking for a cigarette machine back here," said the colored man. "I want to get a package."

"Well, just duck under that rope," said the counterman, and he stood up straight, folding his paper. "It's way against that back wall."

"Okay," said the Negro. He went under the rope, getting down on his hands and knees to do so, and got up on the other side.

The counterman followed him down on his side of the counter, and when he came to the string from an overhanging light he snapped it on. "Now you can see," he said, his face expressionless.

The Negro glanced at him, then he smiled briefly. "Well," he said, "thank you, thank you."

"That's okay," said the counterman. "A guy comes down here in this dark and you could kill yourself falling down over something."

"That's right," said the Negro, "you could fall down over something without seeing it. Thanks."

"That's okay," said the counterman. The Negro felt in his pockets for the four dimes, then the counterman spoke again. "Those are all good except the slot for Pall Malls," he said. "That one's broken, so don't pull that one."

"Thanks," said the colored man. "I only wanted Chesterfields. I'll just pull that slot."

"Oh, that slot's all right," said the other, "only the Pall Mall one is broken."

The Negro put in two of the four dimes, pulled the lever, and got his cigarettes. He opened the package at once and tapped a cigarette up. "Have a cigarette?" he said to the counterman, and he extended the pack across the counter.

"Thanks," said the counterman, and his stolid face cracked slightly with a difficult smile. He reached under his apron into the pocket of his dirty white pants and took out some matches and lit one, and by that time the Negro had a cigarette in his mouth and the counterman extended the lit match. Then he lit his own cigarette and spoke again. "Ain't it hot out?" he said.

"Man, is it hot," said the Negro heartily. "I work over to them docks, and man, it's like hell it's so hot. Even at night."

"It's hot here," said the counterman. "That damned stove is hot with this weather."

"I bet it is," said the Negro.

They started to walk back toward the front of the store, and when he came to the electric-light cord the counterman snapped out the light and then the colored man ducked under the rope. He walked a few steps farther and then he turned to the counterman suddenly.

"Say," he said, "have you got a cup of tea here?"

"Sure we got tea," said the counterman. "You want a cup of tea?"

"Yes," said the Negro, "I think that would go good. A cup of tea is just what I need, I think."

The counterman poured some boiling water into a cup and put a tea ball into it and set it on the counter, and the Negro sat down. "What else?" said the counterman.

"I guess that's all," said the Negro, and he put a dime on the counter. "They say you take something hot and it cools you off."

"It does every time," said the counterman. "I drink two or three cups of that or coffee every night. If you're hot inside you get cool outside." He went to the cash register and rang up the dime. He stood now for a moment in front of the colored man puffing on his cigarette, then he went down the counter and picked up a large glass dish which bore on top of it a half loaf of crumb cake and he carried it back to the Negro. "You want something good, you take a piece of this," he said.

The Negro looked at the counterman smiling in a pleased manner, and he did not pause a second before he spoke. "You're the boss on things to eat," he said.

The counterman cut a piece of cake for the colored man and put it on a plate and gave it to him. The Negro fished into his pocket and took out his last dime. He looked at it, for the briefest moment hesitating, then he put it down and the counterman rang it up on the cash register. After the Negro had taken the first bite the counterman spoke again, and there was almost enthusiasm in his tone. "How's that?" he said. "That's pretty good, hey?"

"Man," said the colored man, "that sure is a good piece of cake." He ate it slowly, relishing it, sipping his tea between bites. The counterman returned to his paper, and neither spoke again until the Negro had finished and stood up. "Well," said the Negro, "the best of luck to you."

The counterman looked up. "I'll be seeing you," he said. The colored man walked to the door and waved his hand airily at the counterman. "Keep in the shade," said the counterman.

The Negro laughed out loud at this. "I sure will," he said, "I sure will, and you do too."

Outdoors his friend was leaning against the next building, and when he saw the older man come out he yelled at him. "Where in hell you been?" he said. "You been in there a hell of a time."

"Well," said the man with the spectacles, "I just got hot, so I took some tea."

"Come on," said his friend. "We won't be home by daylight like this." They covered the half block to the subway at a brisk pace, but when they came to the entrance uptown the man with the glasses stopped.

"I just been thinkin'," he said. "I ain't seen the sun come up for one hell of a time. I just think I'll walk uptown a ways. Maybe all the way home."

His friend stared at him incredulously for a long moment. "You're crazy," he said, "you're just plain crazy."

"Maybe I am," said the colored man with the glasses. He did not stop to argue further but walked off alone, rapidly, his hands thrust in his empty overall pockets, turning up Seventh Avenue in the direction of Harlem. For two blocks he walked up the deserted avenue, and then he said, half aloud, to the early-morning darkness, "Maybe I am. I guess maybe I am."

ARRANGEMENT IN BLACK AND WHITE

Dorothy Parker

For several decades Dorothy Parker maintained her reputation as America's keenest satirist. Her short stories and poetry have been collected into various editions.

THE WOMAN with the pink velvet poppies wreathed round the assisted gold of her hair traversed the crowded room at an interesting gait combining a skip with a sidle and clutched the lean arm of her host.

"Now I got you!" she said. "Now you can't get away!"

"Why, hello," said her host. "Well. How are you?"

"Oh, I'm finely," she said. "Just simply finely. Listen. I want you to do me the most terrible favor. Will you? Will you, please? Pretty please?"

"What is it?" said her host.

"Listen," she said. "I want to meet Walter Williams. Honestly, I'm just simply crazy about that man. Oh, when he sings! When he sings those spirituals! Well, I said to Burton, 'It's a good thing for you Walter Williams is colored,' I said, 'or you'd have lots of reason to be jealous.' I'd really love to meet him. I'd like to tell him I've heard him sing. Will you be an angel and introduce me to him?"

"Why, certainly," said her host. "I thought you'd met him. The party's for him. Where is he, anyway?"

"He's over there by the bookcase," she said. "Let's wait till those people get through talking to him. Well, I think you're simply marvelous, giving this perfectly marvelous party for him, and having him meet all these white people, and all. Isn't he terribly grateful?"

"I hope not," said her host.

"I think it's really terribly nice," she said. "I do. I don't see why on earth it isn't perfectly all right to meet colored people. I haven't any feeling at all about it—not one single bit. Burton—oh, he's just the other way. Well, you know, he comes from Virginia, and you know how they are."

"Did he come tonight?" said her host.

"No, he couldn't," she said. "I'm a regular grass widow tonight. I told him when I left, 'There's no telling what I'll do,' I said. He was just so tired out he couldn't move. Isn't it a shame?"

"Ah," said her host.

"Wait till I tell him I met Walter Williams!" she said. "He'll just about die. Oh, we have more arguments about colored people. I talk to him like I don't know what, I get so excited. 'Oh, don't be so silly,' I say. But I must say for Burton, he's heaps broader-minded than lots of these Southerners. He's really awfully fond of colored people. Well, he says himself he wouldn't have white servants. And you know, he had this old colored nurse, this regular old nigger mammy, and he just simply loves her. Why, every time he goes home, he goes out in the kitchen to see her. He does, really, to this day. All he says is, he says he hasn't got a word to say against colored people as long as they keep their place. He's always doing things for them—giving them clothes and I don't know what all. The only thing he says, he says he wouldn't sit down at the table with one for a million dollars. 'Oh,' I say to him, 'you make me sick, talking like that.' I'm just terrible to him. Aren't I terrible?"

"Oh no, no, no," said her host. "No, no."

"I am," she said. "I know I am. Poor Burton! Now, me, I don't feel that way at all. I haven't the slightest feeling about colored people. Why,

I'm just crazy about some of them. They're just like children—just as easygoing, and always singing and laughing and everything. Aren't they the happiest things you ever saw in your life? Honestly, it makes me laugh just to hear them. Oh, I like them. I really do. Well, now, listen, I have this colored laundress, I've had her for years, and I'm devoted to her. She's a real character. And I want to tell you, I think of her as my friend. That's the way I think of her. As I say to Burton, 'Well, for heaven's sakes, we're all human beings!' Aren't we?"

"Yes," said her host. "Yes indeed."

"Now this Walter Williams," she said. "I think a man like that's a real artist. I do. I think he deserves an awful lot of credit. Goodness, I'm so crazy about music or anything, I don't care what color he is. I honestly think if a person's an artist, nobody ought to have any feeling at all about meeting them. That's absolutely what I say to Burton. Don't you think I'm right?"

"Yes," said her host. "Oh yes."

"That's the way I feel," she said. "I just can't understand people being narrow-minded. Why, I absolutely think it's a privilege to meet a man like Walter Williams. Now, I do. I haven't any feeling at all. Well, my goodness, the good Lord made him, just the same as He did any of us. Didn't He?"

"Surely," said her host. "Yes indeed."

"That's what I say," she said. "Oh, I get so furious when people are narrow-minded about colored people. It's just all I can do not to say something. Of course I do admit when you get a bad colored man, they're simply terrible. But as I say to Burton, there are some bad white people, too, in this world. Aren't there?"

"I guess there are," said her host.

"Why, I'd really be glad to have a man like Walter Williams come to my house and sing for us sometime," she said. "Of course I couldn't ask him on account of Burton, but I wouldn't have any feeling about it at all. Oh, can't he sing! Isn't it marvelous the way they all have music in them? It just seems to be right *in* them? Come on, let's us go on over and talk to him. Listen, what shall I do when I'm introduced? Ought I to shake hands? Or what?"

"Why, do whatever you want," said her host.

"I guess maybe I'd better," she said. "I wouldn't for the world have him think I had any feeling. I think I'd better shake hands, just the way I would with anybody else. That's just exactly what I'll do."

They reached the tall young Negro standing by the bookcase. The host performed introductions; the Negro bowed.

"How do you do?" he said. "Isn't it a nice party?"

The woman with the pink velvet poppies extended her hand at the length of her arm and held it so, in fine determination, for all the world to see, until the Negro took it, shook it, and gave it back to her.

"Oh, how do you do, Mr. Williams," she said. "Well, how do you do. I've just been saying I've enjoyed your singing so awfully much. I've been to your concerts, and we have you on the phonograph and everything. Oh, I just enjoy it!"

She spoke with great distinctness, moving her lips meticulously, as if in parlance with the deaf.

"I'm so glad," he said.

"I'm just simply crazy about that 'Water Boy' thing you sing," she said. "Honestly, I can't get it out of my head. I have my husband nearly crazy, the way I go around humming it all the time. Oh, he looks just as black as the ace of—er. Well, tell me, where on earth do you ever get all those songs of yours? How do you ever get hold of them?"

"Why," he said, "there are so many different——"

"I should think you'd love singing them," she said. "It must be more fun. All those darling old spirituals—oh, I just love them! Well, what are you doing now? Are you still keeping up your singing? Why don't you have another concert sometime?"

"I'm having one the sixteenth of this month," he said.

"Well, I'll be there," she said. "I'll be there, if I possibly can. You can count on me. Goodness, here comes a whole raft of people to talk to you. You're just a regular guest of honor! Oh, who's that girl in white? I've seen her someplace."

"That's Katherine Burke," said her host.

"Good heavens," she said, "is that Katherine Burke? Why, she looks entirely different off the stage. I thought she was much better-looking. I had no idea she was so terribly dark. Why, she looks almost like—— Oh, I think she's a wonderful actress! Don't you think she's a wonderful actress, Mr. Williams? Oh, I think she's marvelous. Don't you?"

"Yes, I do," he said.

"Oh, I do too," she said. "Just wonderful. Well, goodness, we must give someone else a chance to talk to the guest of honor. Now, don't forget, Mr. Williams, I'm going to be at that concert if I possibly can. I'll be there applauding like everything. And if I can't come, I'm going to tell everybody I know to go, anyway. Don't you forget!"

"I won't," he said. "Thank you so much."

The host took her arm and piloted her firmly into the next room.

"Oh, my dear," she said, "I nearly died! Honestly, I give you my word, I nearly passed away. Did you hear that terrible break I made? I was just going to say Katherine Burke looked almost like a nigger. I just caught myself in time. Oh, do you think he noticed?"

"I don't believe so," said her host.

"Well, thank goodness," she said, "because I wouldn't have embarrassed him for anything. Why, he's awfully nice. Just as nice as he can be. Nice manners, and everything. You know, so many colored people, you give them an inch, and they walk all over you. But he doesn't try any of that. Well, he's got more sense, I suppose. He's really nice. Don't you think so?"

"Yes," said her host.

"I liked him," she said. "I haven't any feeling at all because he's a colored man. I felt just as natural as I would with anybody. Talked to him just as naturally, and everything. But honestly, I could hardly keep a straight face. I kept thinking of Burton. Oh, wait till I tell Burton I called him 'Mister'!"

SLAVE ON THE BLOCK

Langston Hughes

Langston Hughes is short-story writer, novelist, poet, and playwright. His best-known books are The Ways of White Folks, Without Laughter, *and several collections of poetry, the latest,* Shakespeare in Harlem.

They were people who went in for Negroes—Michael and Anne—the Carraways. But not in the social-service, philanthropic sort of way, no. They saw no use in helping a race that was already too charming and naïve and lovely for words. Leave them unspoiled and just enjoy them, Michael and Anne felt. So they went in for the Art of Negroes—the dancing that had such jungle life about it, the songs that were so simple and fervent, the poetry that was so direct, so real. They never tried to influence that art, they only bought it and raved over it, and copied it. For they were artists too.

In their collection they owned some Covarrubias originals. Of course Covarrubias wasn't a Negro, but how he caught the darky spirit! They owned all the Robeson records and all the Bessie Smith. And they had a manuscript of Countee Cullen's. They saw all the plays with or about Negroes, read all the books, and adored the Hall Johnson Singers. And they had met Dr. DuBois. Of course they knew Harlem like their own back yard, that is, all the speak-easies and night clubs and dance halls, from the Cotton Club and the ritzy joints where Negroes couldn't go themselves down to places like the Hot Dime, where white folks couldn't get in—unless they knew the man. (And tipped heavily.)

They were acquainted with lots of Negroes, too—but somehow the Negroes didn't seem to like them very much. Maybe the Carraways gushed over them too soon. Or maybe they looked a little like poor white folks, although they were really quite well off. Or maybe they tried too hard to make friends, dark friends, and the dark friends suspected something. Or perhaps their house in the Village was too far from Harlem, or too hard to find, being back in one of those queer and expensive little side streets that had once been alleys before the art invasion came. Anyway, occasionally a furtive Negro might accept their invitation for tea or cocktails, and sometimes a lesser Harlem celebrity or two would decorate their rather slow parties; but one seldom came back for more. As much as they loved Negroes, Negroes didn't seem to love Michael and Anne.

But they were blessed with a wonderful colored cook and maid—until she took sick and died in her room in their basement. And then the most marvelous ebony boy walked into their life, a boy as black as all the Negroes they'd ever known put together.

"He *is* the jungle," said Anne when she saw him.

"He's 'I Couldn't Hear Nobody Pray,' " said Michael.

For Anne thought in terms of pictures: she was a painter. And Michael thought in terms of music: he was a composer for the piano. And they had a most wonderful idea of painting pictures and composing music that went together and then having a joint "concert-exhibition," as they would call it. Her pictures and his music. The Carraways, a sonata and a picture, a fugue and a picture. It would be lovely, and such a novelty, people would have to like it. And many of their things would be Negro. Anne had painted their maid six times. And Michael had composed several themes based on the spirituals and on Louis Armstrong's jazz. Now here was this ebony boy. The essence in the flesh.

They had nearly missed the boy. He had come when they were out to gather up the things the cook had left and take them to her sister in Jersey. It seems that he was the late cook's nephew. The new colored maid had let him in and given him the two suitcases of poor dear Emma's belongings, and he was on his way to the subway. That is, he was in the hall, going out, just as the Carraways, Michael and Anne, stepped in. They could hardly see the boy, it being dark in the hall and he being dark too.

"Hello," they said. "Is this Emma's nephew?"

"Yes'm," said the maid. "Yes'm."

"Well, come in," said Anne, "and let us see you. We loved your aunt so much. She was the best cook we ever had."

"You don't know where *I* could get a job, do you?" said the boy. This took Michael and Anne back a bit, but they rallied at once. So charming and naïve to ask right away for what he wanted.

Anne burst out, "You know, I think I'd like to paint you."

Michael said, "Oh, I say now, that would be lovely! He's so utterly Negro."

The boy grinned.

Anne said, "Could you come back tomorrow?"

And the boy said, "Yes indeed. I sure could."

The upshot of it was that they hired him. They hired him to look after the garden, which was just about as big as Michael's grand piano—only a little square behind the house. You know those Village gardens. Anne sometimes painted in it. And occasionally they set the table there for four on a spring evening. Nothing grew in the garden really, practically nothing. But the boy said he could plant things. And they had to have some excuse to hire him.

The boy's name was Luther. He had come from the South to his relatives in Jersey and had had only one job since he got there, shining shoes for a Greek in Elizabeth. But the Greek fired him because the boy wouldn't give half his tips over to the proprietor.

"I never heard of a job where I had to pay the boss, instead of the boss paying me," said Luther. "Not till I got here."

"And then what did you do?" said Anne.

"Nothing. Been looking for a job for the last four months."

"Poor boy," said Michael, "poor, dear boy."

"Yes," said Anne. "You must be hungry." And they called the cook to give him something to eat.

Luther dug around in the garden a little bit that first day, went out and bought some seeds, came back and ate some more. They made a place for him to sleep in the basement by the furnace. And the next day Anne started to paint him, after she'd bought the right colors.

"He'll be good company for Mattie," they said. "She claims she's afraid to stay alone at night when we're out, so she leaves." They suspected, though, that Mattie just liked to get up to Harlem. And they thought right. Mattie was not as settled as she looked. Once out, with the Savoy open until three in the morning, why come home? That was the way Mattie felt.

In fact, what happened was that Mattie showed Luther where the best and cheapest hot spots in Harlem were located. Luther hadn't even set foot in Harlem before, living twenty-eight miles away, as he did, in Jersey, and being a kind of quiet boy. But the second night he was there Mattie said, "Come on, let's go. Working for white folks all day, I'm tired. They needn't think I was made to answer telephones all night." So out they went.

Anne noticed that most mornings Luther would doze almost as soon as she sat him down to pose, so she eventually decided to paint Luther asleep. The Sleeping Negro, she would call it. Dear, natural, childlike people, they would sleep anywhere they wanted to. Anyway, asleep, he kept still and held the pose.

And he *was* an adorable Negro. Not tall, but with a splendid body. And a slow and lively smile that lighted up his black, black face, for his teeth were very white and his eyes too. Most effective in oil and canvas. Better even than Emma had been. Anne could stare at him at leisure when he was asleep. One day she decided to paint him nude, or at least half nude. A slave picture, that's what she would do. The market at New Orleans for a background. And call it The Boy on the Block.

So one morning when Luther settled down in his sleeping pose, Anne said, "No," she had finished that picture. She wanted to paint him now representing to the full the soul and sorrow of his people. She wanted to paint him as a slave about to be sold. And since slaves in warm climates had no clothes, would he please take off his shirt.

Luther smiled a sort of embarrassed smile and took off his shirt.

"Your undershirt too," said Anne. But it turned out that he had on B.V.D.s, so he had to go out and change altogether. He came back and mounted the box that Anne said would serve just then for a slave block, and she began to sketch. Before luncheon Michael came in and went into rhapsodies over Luther on the box without a shirt, about to be sold into slavery. He said he must put him into music right now. And he went to the piano and began to play something that sounded like "Deep River" in the jaws of a dog, but Michael said it was a modern slave plaint, 1850 in terms of 1933. Vieux Carré remembered on 135th Street. Slavery in the Cotton Club.

Anne said, "It's too marvelous!" And they painted and played till dark, with rest periods in between for Luther. Then they all knocked off for dinner. Anne and Michael went out later to one of Lew Leslie's new shows. And Luther and Mattie said, "Thank God!" and got dressed up for Harlem.

Funny, they didn't like the Carraways. They treated them nice and paid them well. "But they're too strange," said Mattie. "They make me nervous."

"They is mighty funny," Luther agreed.

They didn't understand the vagaries of white folks, neither Luther nor Mattie, and they didn't want to be bothered trying.

"I does my work," said Mattie. "After that I don't want to be painted, or asked to sing songs, nor nothing like that."

The Carraways often asked Luther to sing, and he sang. He knew a lot of Southern work songs and reels and spirituals and ballads.

Dear Ma, I'm in hard luck:
Three days since I et,
And the stamp on this letter's
Gwine to put me in debt.

The Carraways allowed him to neglect the garden altogether. About all Luther did was pose and sing. And he got tired of that.

Indeed, both Luther and Mattie became a bit difficult to handle as time went on. The Carraways blamed it on Mattie. She had gotten hold of Luther. She was just simply spoiling a nice simple young boy. She was old enough to know better. Mattie was in love with Luther.

At least, he slept with her. The Carraways discovered this one night about one o'clock when they went to wake Luther up (the first time they'd ever done such a thing) and ask him if he wouldn't sing his own marvelous version of "John Henry" for a man who had just come from St. Louis and was sailing for Paris tomorrow. But Luther wasn't in his own bed by the furnace. There was a light in Mattie's room, so Michael knocked softly. Mattie said, "Who's that?" And Michael poked his head in, and here were Luther and Mattie in bed together!

Of course Anne condoned them. "It's so simple and natural for Negroes to make love." But Mattie, after all, was forty if she was a day.

And Luther was only a kid. Besides, Anne thought that Luther had been ever so much nicer when he first came than he was now. But from so many nights at the Savoy he had become a marvelous dancer, and he was teaching Anne the Lindy Hop to Cab Calloway's records. Besides, the picture of The Boy on the Block wasn't anywhere near done. And he did take pretty good care of the furnace. So they kept him. At least, Anne kept him, although Michael said he was getting a little bored with the same Negro always in the way.

For Luther had grown a bit familiar lately. He smoked up all their cigarettes, drank their wine, told jokes on them to their friends, and sometimes even came upstairs singing and walking about the house when the Carraways had guests in who didn't share their enthusiasm for Negroes, natural or otherwise.

Luther and Mattie together were a pair. They quite frankly lived with one another now. Well, let that go. Anne and Michael prided themselves on being different; artists, you know, and liberal-minded people—maybe a little scatterbrained, but then (secretly, they felt) that came from genius. They were not ordinary people, bothering about the liberties of others. Certainly the last thing they would do would be to interfere with the delightful simplicity of Negroes.

But Mattie must be giving Luther money and buying him clothes. He was really dressing awfully well. And on her Thursday afternoons off she would come back loaded down with packages. As far as the Carraways could tell, they were all for Luther.

And sometimes there were quarrels drifting up from the basement. And often, all too often, Mattie had moods. Then Luther would have moods. And it was pretty awful having two dark and glowering people around the house. Anne couldn't paint and Michael couldn't play.

One day, when she hadn't seen Luther for three days, Anne called downstairs and asked if he wouldn't please come up and take off his shirt and get on the box. The picture was almost done. Luther came dragging his feet upstairs and humming:

Before I'd be a slave
I'd be buried in ma grave
And go home to my Jesus
And be free.

And that afternoon he let the furnace go almost out.

That was the state of things when Michael's mother (whom Anne had never liked) arrived from Kansas City to pay them a visit. At once neither Mattie nor Luther liked her either. She was a mannish old lady, big and tall, and inclined to be bossy. Mattie, however, did spruce up her service, cooked delicious things, and treated Mrs. Carraway with a great deal more respect than she did Anne.

"I never play with servants," Mrs. Carraway had said to Michael, and Mattie must have heard her.

But Luther, he was worse than ever. Not that he did anything wrong, Anne thought, but the way he did things! For instance, he didn't need to sing now all the time, especially since Mrs. Carraway had said she didn't like singing. And certainly not songs like "You Rascal, You."

But all things end! With the Carraways and Luther it happened like this: One forenoon, quite without a shirt (for he expected to pose), Luther came sauntering through the library to change the flowers in the vase. He carried red roses. Mrs. Carraway was reading her morning scripture from the *Health and Life*.

"Oh, good morning," said Luther. "How long are you gonna stay in this house?"

"I never liked familiar Negroes," said Mrs. Carraway over her nose glasses.

"Huh!" said Luther. "That's too bad! I never liked poor white folks."

Mrs. Carraway screamed, a short, loud, dignified scream. Michael came running in bathrobe and pajamas. Mrs. Carraway grew tall. There was a scene. Luther talked. Michael talked. Anne appeared.

"Never, never, never," said Mrs. Carraway, "have I suffered such impudence from servants—and a nigger servant—in my own son's house."

"Mother, Mother, Mother," said Michael. "Be calm. I'll discharge him." He turned on the nonchalant Luther. "Go!" he said. "Go, go!"

"Michael," Anne cried, "I haven't finished The Slave on the Block." Her husband looked nonplused. For a moment he breathed deeply.

"Either he goes or I go," said Mrs. Carraway, firm as a rock.

"He goes," said Michael, with strength from his mother.

"Oh!" cried Anne. She looked at Luther. His black arms were full of roses he had brought to put in the vases. He had on no shirt. "Oh!" His body was ebony.

"Don't worry 'bout me!" said Luther. "I'll go."

"Yes, we'll go," boomed Mattie from the doorway, for she had come up from below, fat and belligerent. "We've stood enough foolery from you white folks! Yes, we'll go. Come on, Luther."

What could she mean, "stood enough"? What had they done to them? Anne and Michael wondered. They had tried to be kind. "Oh!"

"Sneaking around knocking on our door at night," Mattie went on. "Yes, we'll go. Pay us! Pay us! Pay us!" So she remembered that time they had come for Luther at night. That was it.

"I'll pay you," said Michael. He followed Mattie out.

Anne looked at her black boy.

"Good-by," Luther said. "You fix the vases."

He handed over his armful of roses, glanced impudently at old Mrs. Carraway, and grinned—grinned that wide, beautiful, white-toothed grin that made Anne say when she first saw him, "He looks like the jungle." Grinned, and disappeared in the dark hall, with no shirt on his back.

"Oh," Anne moaned distressfully, "my Boy on the Block!"

"Huh!" snorted Mrs. Carraway.

WHITE AS SNOW

Kay Boyle

Kay Boyle, one of our outstanding short-story stylists, has also written several novels.

THERE IS ONLY one history of any importance, and it is the history of what you once believed in, and the history of what you came to believe in, and what cities or country you saw, and what trees you remembered. The history of other things comes in one ear and goes out the other, and the history of places you have never been to is good as a picture, but with no taste or smell. Nor is it enough to speak the name of a city, for if the name of this one were said you might recall things no one else remembers. Easter gave that town a special glamour, not as Rome must have, but different, for it was not a religious place at all. It had no use for Christmas; winter was not its time of year.

Then it had long looped strings of lights hanging from pillar to post along the sea. It had gulls to it like a wilder place might, but that was not good enough for it; it had put theaters the length of the water front as well. It had a thing for every hour of the day and night: ponies to drive on the sand, and a merry-go-round as big as an island, and on days when the rain fell the rolling chairs made elegant as palaces with lights inside and glass panes set beside and out before. Riding at night in them, the rain could be heard at the wheels running swift but shallow, and the rain polished as wax would the splinters and the grain of the timber walk that stood the length of the sea.

That was the year Carrie came down as nurse with us instead of the other. She was colored sweet and even like sarsaparilla, and she had never before been near the sea. She was so thin that we took all the best things on the plates to give her, honey and corn and waffles in the morning, because when she was a little girl they had never heard of such things. The family ate in the hotel dining room, but Carrie sat in the ordinary between us with her hand on the edge of the table shaking in fear of what they might serve her next and whether a spoon or a fork should go beneath it. The first time the artichokes passed, she started laughing soft and high, as if she didn't care for them, but she remembered them forever. She always talked of them in the evening when she sat in the room waiting for the time to eat to come.

"If you children hadn't been talking so loudmouthed that time, I'd of seen better what they was," she said softly, holding her thin blue hands between her knees in mourning. Or just before lunch time she would remember. "I could of took hold of them leaves as neat as could be," she said to her own face in the glass, "if I'd had any idea what was passing."

Carrie would be twenty in a few years, but then she stood thin as a bone in the hall with her hair slicked back tight and shining. The porters were white men, but they had plenty of time to talk and linger, making little pieces of conversation with her whenever we went out or in. Here inside the house she had a strong sweet artificial odor on that took all other smells aside, but out on the beach there was nothing left of it. Everything in life there, the high or the low tide or good weather or bad, or whether or not we smiled, depended on one thing: it depended on Adamic and if he had come to the shore early that summer or if he wouldn't be coming until July. It was easy to know, for before you were out of the hotel bus you could see the marks of the tennis ball on the wall at the side, and if they were new he was there, and he was not there if they were fading away from the year before. Or maybe see Adamic standing, pulled out longer and longer every year, but with his face still like a child's face, the way a flower's head might be unchanged no matter how tall the stalk. This time when we came he had trousers that reached to his tennis shoes on, and he was standing knocking the ball back, standing still with his arm swinging to take the ball square on the racquet however it might come.

No word was ever said to him, but such things were thought in solitude of him that if the step of the tennis ball was not pacing the wall all summer, then the heart expired in the breast. Under the stone porches of the hotel there was never any word spoken. The chairs with the people sitting on them, one after another, were there, but children went speechless past them. For when people begin to speak their minds out, then something falters. It is easy to talk of one thing or another only when you do not believe any more in the purity and fervor of everyone else alive.

It was the time Carrie came with us; it was raining hard and she had cotton pansies on her hat, and she was afraid to get in the bus from the train and afraid to get out at the hotel for what the rain might do to the pansies' faces. When we stepped down, Carrie opened her handkerchief out and set it on top of her hat, and Adamic was standing under the shelter hitting the tennis ball back against the wall.

"It might just as well be Philadelphia," Carrie said to the man who took the bags in. "The rain's just as wet as."

We went up to the bedrooms, and in the elevator Carrie took out her powder and did her face light again, beating the flat puff hard in her thin hand. We did not speak about Adamic then, but when we were at the floor we went running away from our delight that he was there, leaping and skipping down the carpeted hall. Carrie came running on her sharp thin legs after, jumping from one design to the next and laughing.

"You look like Eliza on the ice!" I cried out, thinking with joy of Adamic maybe. And Carrie stopped dead in the hall, in the dark, thin and still and faceless against the light that was shining in the ceiling far in back.

"No, I don't," she said. "That's not true."

The white porter was coming with the bags, and we could not tell what her face was, for she was standing black as a paper doll against the little moon of light.

"I ain't anything like Eliza," she said. "I never'd of thought to hear you say it." She saw the porter coming down the hall behind her, and she said: "Why would you want to say a thing like that for, and before the gentleman that way?"

It did not come to an end when we were washed and dressed in white, but went on like a song all evening.

"If I wanted to tell you out, I could tell you out like some colored people as do," she said, and this was the first time she had been in a hotel anywhere, but her sorrow was so great that she could not keep it still. The other nurses were talking among themselves at the table, but whether they heard her or not she could not help it. "I've heard colored people all over the world treating people to names like 'white trash' and other things worse than. To some it comes easy," she said in grief, "and to others it comes hard."

Even when we gave her the three ears of corn it was no comfort to her. She ate them slowly, silently, one after the other, chewing the buttered grains and wiping the grease off her brownish lips. We sat one on each side of her watching her eat, each with a hand laid on her knees under the table. I said: "I'm sorry, Carrie, I'm sorry." But as soon as the corn was done with, her voice began again, mourning and sighing. "You got no reason to care," she said. "Anything gets harmed for you, folks get you a new one. Anything happens to me, it just stays that way. But I got a heart as red as yours, my blood runs the same color; if I was to cut my finger and you cut your finger, nobody'd be able to tell the two of us apart."

But even that was not the end, and she went on with it through the hotel parlors, speaking soft and low and blameful, as though she would never be the same. She put on our jackets and we went out on the stone piazza where the people were walking after dinner, and when she saw Adamic standing there in his white trousers hitting the tennis ball back again, over and over, she stopped at once as if a hand had been laid on her mouth. It may be only for the things not said that youth is remembered so sharply. We stood there a long time watching Adamic. Carrie did not speak any more and we had no thought of speaking; this is the special privilege given before the tongue turns womanly and bold with comment and intention.

The days were fair and long that year and the beach striped with thin blue lagoons. We had Mexican hats and each a tooth out in front, and the afternoons were so hot that the wax beads from Venice melted and changed color on our necks, and Carrie said: "My hair," and when she spoke she stopped digging in the damp sand and smiled, "it seems it might be getting straighter here. It seems the air on the beach, it's known it takes the curl out. I heard that," she said, "I heard it," but she wouldn't say where. "It seems colored people often found the seashore beneficial." Her thin hands turning gave the tunnels their long secret shape. "It seems colored fellows comes here in particular, and the sun does what it can to take their coloring away."

She was talking like this when Adamic came walking over the sand, with his head down to make himself a smaller man, and his feet bare, and letting his yellow bathrobe swing. He was not looking at us, nor looking either at the sea, nor watching, and he lay down as if unknowing near to us on the pure burning sand. Carrie was saying: "Maybe not as real white like a lily, but light enough so there was no telling," and then she saw Adamic and she stopped talking.

The waves came in and out for a little while, and Adamic was lying there on his face with his robe spread under him, lying in his black swimming suit, letting the sun shine on his back and legs.

"What was it I was telling you children?" said Carrie, moving her hands on the hard sand again, slapping and shaping it into stone.

"About the colored fellows," said my sister.

"Where ever did you hear that now?" said Carrie, laughing high and wild. "Can't you tell the truth once? Don't you recall? I was telling about the place my uncle had and all the servants waiting on him. That's where we was reared," she said, talking higher. "I was telling you. It was near to Boston, where the most of the good families inclines to be."

Resting on the damp sand, her hands seemed scarcely darker, and only under her chin on her throat when she turned her head towards Adamic did any shadow of color seem to be. Her bones were little and breakable under her skin, and her big lids in her sallow face swollen and smooth and blue. Her nose and her cheeks had freckles across them, colorless, like scattered drops of rain.

Adamic did not move, but suddenly his voice could be heard coming across the sand from under his folded arms where his face was hidden. "I come from Boston," he said slowly.

"Your father, he certainly looks like a real old Bostonian," said Carrie, arching and preening.

"I knew colored boys in high school there," said Adamic, looking straight over his arms to her.

"Oh, everywhere," said Carrie, and the sand ran through her fingers, "wherever you go the colored element's bound to be."

We all sat still on our knees, stricken with silence, waiting, with our ears gaping, for whatever next he might say.

For three days Carrie did not tell us, and then she told us that Adamic was going with us to the moving pictures. He would not walk out of the hotel with us, but when we got to the moving pictures Adamic would be waiting there. So Carrie stayed in from the beach that morning, doing over the blouse and the little hat, sewing the pansies up as tight as buds for a change, and passing to and fro before the glass, languid and slow. Because she did not go out, we must stay in the room with her, painting pictures until it was time for lunch.

"They should have been out in the sun all morning, Carrie," Mother said. And Carrie said:

"I couldn't make them move a step, ma'am, I couldn't do a thing."

"There are runs in their socks, Carrie," Mother said, and Carrie said:

"I know, ma'am, I know. But here I was cooped up with no needle or thread."

When we went out, Adamic was there, waiting with his back to the sea, leaning on the rail in the sunlight, tall as a grown man and smoking a cigarette hasty and short, as if the taste of it were bad. He was watching the crowds passing, his eyes moving hastily over everyone passing, but when we came along he made no sign at all. We could see his face very near as Carrie took us by him, and his eyes were fast on Carrie, on her hat and her smooth hair and the veil that went almost to her mouth. Her color was light with powder now, almost like chalk laid thick upon her skin, and she had put rouge on her cheekbones so that her sad sharp face seemed burning with delight.

"Afternoon, Mr. Adamic," said Carrie, and she went stepping by him on her high thin legs. But Adamic only threw his cigarette away over the rail and did not speak. We passed so close to him that we could see the invisible golden down that was coming on his chin. His head was everything it had ever been, but the long, lank, uneasy limbs were strangers to us; he might have been a carnival thing, the limber, grotesque members holding a small child's head on high.

He came following down the boardwalk behind us, as if he did not know us even, looking the other way. Only when Adamic was in the sea did his face seem natural and human to us, for the endless body was then lost swimming out of sight. But when he was out, dressed full length in his good clothes with his watch on his wrist, there was this difference: there was a stranger standing erect within, looking bitterly and selfishly out of Adamic's eyes.

"The weather is surely pretty," Carrie said. She kept her head turned a little, like a bird's head, on her shoulder, so that she could keep him in her eye.

"It's not so bad," said Adamic, walking with his head down, swinging uneasy, almost behind. From where he was we knew he could see the holes still running in our socks.

"It might just as well be Philadelphia," said Carrie. She was stepping in her elegant heels over the splintery walk. "The sun shining so strong, Mr. Adamic."

"It might be Boston," said Adamic, smiling with his lip turned up. But still he was laughing, with his head bent, the way he had laughed every other year. "If it wasn't for the sea out there, and the boardwalk, and if it wasn't for the sand——"

"Oh, I've found," said Carrie, speaking high on her shoulder, with her blue veil drawn tight across her eyes, "I've found no matter how wide you travel, things is everywhere mostly similar. Ain't that the way, Mr. Adamic?"

"Oh yes, that's true," said Adamic, talking slowly, as if he must shape the words stronger and braver in his mouth. "Sure," he said, and his head hung, swinging. "Girls, women——"

Carrie began laughing quick and soft, and she pulled her kid gloves up again over her bracelets to hide the pieces of her arms.

"What do you mean, Mr. Adamic? I'm sure I don't know what you mean," she said.

We were passing by a salt-water-taffy shop, and Adamic turned in the door and left us, and Carrie lingered at the window, seeming to look at all the fancy boxes, but staring straight into her own face reflected there within. She smiled her own small teeth at herself and moved the whites of her eyes in pleasure.

"Looks like I got a good sunburn," she said.

Adamic came out the door, carrying a box with a pink ribbon on it. He turned around quickly, as if he was not speaking to Carrie, and he put the box in her hands and said: "Here, that's for you."

"That surely is kind of your part, Mr. Adamic," said Carrie, and we started down the walk again, Carrie with one of us on each side, and Adamic following close but not quite behind.

"I used to know a gentleman in Pawtucket," said Carrie, speaking over her shoulder to him as she stepped. "He was always making gifts of some kind. It was like a habit with him."

"Sure, I know," said Adamic, talking low and hoarsely. "If you have a lot to do with women you get into that habit. I've been trying to break myself of it for some time now, but what's the use?"

We came to the moving-picture place and Henry Walthall was playing, and Adamic put his hand deep in his pocket and passed in before us. We stood before the posters in the entrance way looking at the posters of the Southern hats and the dust on the riding boots, holding Carrie's hands.

"It's what they call *The Birth of a Nation,*" Carrie said. "It has to do with what colored people there was they treated just like they was slaves."

When Adamic came back to us, a tide of shame had flowed across his face and was burning still and shifting there. He had no tickets in his hand, and he said:

"I waited to ask you. They haven't four seats left together. There's one left up in the balcony, if you'd like to take that one yourself," he said. He looked this way and that, but he could not look at Carrie.

"We can go to another moving picture," my sister said.

"I guess it's a crowded afternoon everywhere," said Adamic, looking from one thing to another. "I guess there isn't much use. They might all be that way."

The man in the ticket window was looking through the glass at us, looking down the length of carpet to where we stood. And when Adamic turned, uneasy on his heels, the man in the window shook his head slowly back and forth at him, smiling at him, but shaking in forbiddance his head. Carrie put her hands up to her cheeks, and suddenly she started laughing.

"The kind of sunburn I got," she said, "you couldn't tell one person from another." And she said: "It isn't as if I'd been fixed on seeing that picture. War and fighting all the time would of tired me out."

The man in the window was shaking his head still at Adamic, and Carrie took out her powder puff and beat it hard all over her face.

"We might walk as far as the shoot the chutes," said Carrie. "The weather looks so fine."

But Adamic said, looking at neither of us nor looking at Carrie: "I just remembered. I just remembered something I was supposed to do." He took his panama hat out folded from his pocket, and he set it on the front of his head. "I'd better get along," he said. "I promised." His hat cast a dark blind shadow over his eyes. He looked at the man selling tickets in the window, and the man looked out at him.

"Anyone makes a promise, he better keep it," said Carrie. "Or else it might turn out he wasn't a gentleman no more."

"Sure," said Adamic, and we watched him walking off, swinging his arms and his legs, off through the people, holding his child's face small and low.

That might have been the end of it, if Carrie hadn't laid down on the bed in the dark when we got to the hotel. She drew the curtains over the windows and lay there saying nothing at all. There was no reason to lighting the light, for no word or touch could move her. We sat still on the bed beside her, thinking of things to say.

"There'll be strawberry ice for supper tonight," I said to her. And my sister said: "There's going to be creamed chicken too." And after a while Carrie spoke and said to us: "I might just as well stay here in the dark for always, because there ain't going to be any more good things for me."

She lay silent, as if dead and shrouded in the strong artificial flowery scent she wore, cold and speechless with some knowledge we did not share. Her hands were crossed over her breasts, and her pointed feet stood upright at the end of the bed. After a little while she said: "You don't know, children. I'll never tell you what it was. You're too young to know."

But when it was time for dinner, she got up and put the light on, and she went and looked at her face close in the glass. She took the hairbrush off the table and sat there brushing her black hair back, brushing it tight and small.

"I knew all right," she said. "I wasn't fooled. It was the Jim Crow gallery. Colored people goes upstairs, other people goes down." And Mother came in and said:

"But, Carrie, you haven't changed the children's dresses for supper," and Carrie said:

"I know, ma'am, I know. They've been cutting up again. They're getting too much for me. Maybe I'm too young. They get out from under my control."

THE TEST

Angelica Gibbs

Angelica Gibbs is a short-story writer whose work has been featured in the volume Short Stories from the "New Yorker."

ON THE AFTERNOON Marian took her second driver's test, Mrs. Ericson went with her. "It's probably better to have someone a little older with you," Mrs. Ericson said as Marian slipped into the driver's seat beside her. "Perhaps last time your cousin Bill made you nervous, talking too much on the way."

"Yes ma'am," Marian said in her soft, unaccented voice. "They probably do like it better if a white person shows up with you."

"Oh, I don't think it's *that,*" Mrs. Ericson began, and subsided after a glance at the girl's set profile. Marian drove the car slowly through the shady suburban streets. It was one of the first hot days of June, and when they reached the boulevard they found it crowded with cars headed for the beaches.

"Do you want me to drive?" Mrs. Ericson asked. "I'll be glad to if you're feeling jumpy." Marian shook her head. Mrs. Ericson watched her dark, competent hands and wondered for the thousandth time how the house had ever managed to get along without her, or how she had lived through those earlier years when her household had been presided over by a series of slatternly white girls who had considered housework demeaning and the care of children an added insult. "You drive beautifully, Marian," she said. "Now, don't think of the last time. Anybody would slide on a steep hill on a wet day like that."

"It takes four mistakes to flunk you," Marian said. "I don't remember doing all the things the inspector marked down on my blank."

"People say that they only want you to slip them a little something," Mrs. Ericson said doubtfully.

"No," Marian said. "That would only make it worse, Mrs. Ericson. I know."

The car turned right, at a traffic signal, into a side road and slid up to the curb at the rear of a short line of parked cars. The inspectors had not arrived yet.

"You have the papers?" Mrs. Ericson asked. Marian took them out of her bag: her learner's permit, the car registration, and her birth certificate. They settled down to the dreary business of waiting.

"It will be marvelous to have someone dependable to drive the children to school every day," Mrs. Ericson said.

Marian looked up from the list of driving requirements she had been studying. "It'll make things simpler at the house, won't it?" she said.

"Oh, Marian," Mrs. Ericson exclaimed, "if I could only pay you half of what you're worth!"

"Now, Mrs. Ericson," Marian said firmly. They looked at each other and smiled with affection.

Two cars with official insignia on their doors stopped across the street. The inspectors leaped out, very brisk and military in their neat uniforms.

Marian's hands tightened on the wheel. "There's the one who flunked me last time," she whispered, pointing to a stocky, self-important man who had begun to shout directions at the driver at the head of the line. "Oh, Mrs. Ericson."

"Now, Marian," Mrs. Ericson said. They smiled at each other again, rather weakly.

The inspector who finally reached their car was not the stocky one but a genial, middle-aged man who grinned broadly as he thumbed over their papers. Mrs. Ericson started to get out of the car. "Don't you want to come along?" the inspector asked. "Mandy and I don't mind company."

Mrs. Ericson was bewildered for a moment. "No," she said, and stepped to the curb. "I might make Marian self-conscious. She's a fine driver, Inspector."

"Sure thing," the inspector said, winking at Mrs. Ericson. He slid into the seat beside Marian. "Turn right at the corner, Mandy-Lou."

From the curb Mrs. Ericson watched the car move smoothly up the street.

The inspector made notations in a small black book. "Age?" he inquired presently, as they drove along.

"Twenty-seven."

He looked at Marian out of the corner of his eye. "Old enough to have quite a flock of pickaninnies, eh?"

Marian did not answer.

"Left at this corner," the inspector said, "and park between that truck and the green Buick."

The two cars were very close together, but Marian squeezed in between them without too much maneuvering. "Driven before, Mandy-Lou?" the inspector asked.

"Yes sir. I had a license for three years in Pennsylvania."

"Why do you want to drive a car?"

"My employer needs me to take her children to and from school."

"Sure you don't really want to sneak out nights to meet some young blood?" the inspector asked. He laughed as Marian shook her head.

"Let's see you take a left at the corner and then turn around in the middle of the next block," the inspector said. He began to whistle "Swanee River." "Make you homesick?" he asked.

Marian put out her hand, swung around neatly in the street, and headed back in the direction from which they had come. "No," she said. "I was born in Scranton, Pennsylvania."

The inspector feigned astonishment. "You-all ain't Southern?" he said.

"Well, dog my cats if I didn't think you-all came from down yondah."

"No sir," Marian said.

"Turn onto Main Street here and let's see how you-all does in heavier traffic."

They followed a line of cars along Main Street for several blocks until they came in sight of a concrete bridge which arched high over the railroad tracks.

"Read that sign at the end of the bridge," the inspector said.

" 'Proceed with caution. Dangerous in slippery weather,' " Marian said.

"You-all sho can read fine," the inspector exclaimed. "Where d'you learn to do that, Mandy?"

"I got my college degree last year," Marian said. Her voice was not quite steady.

As the car crept up the slope of the bridge the inspector burst out laughing. He laughed so hard he could scarcely give his next direction. "Stop here," he said, wiping his eyes, "then start 'er up again. Mandy got her degree, did she? Dog my cats!"

Marian pulled up beside the curb. She put the car in neutral, pulled on the emergency, waited a moment, and then put the car into gear again. Her face was set. As she released the brake her foot slipped off the clutch pedal and the engine stalled.

"Now, Mistress Mandy," the inspector said, "remember your degree."

"Damn you!" Marian cried. She started the car with a jerk.

The inspector lost his joviality in an instant. "Return to the starting place, please," he said, and made four very black crosses at random in the squares on Marian's application blank.

Mrs. Ericson was waiting at the curb where they had left her. As Marian stopped the car the inspector jumped out and brushed past her, his face purple. "What happened?" Mrs. Ericson asked, looking after him with alarm.

Marian stared down at the wheel and her lip trembled.

"Oh, Marian, *again?"* Mrs. Ericson said.

Marian nodded. "In a sort of different way," she said, and slid over to the right-hand side of the car.

HE DON'T PLANT COTTON

J. F. Powers

J. F. Powers is a promising young short-story writer from the Middle West. His stories have appeared in the O. Henry Memorial Award Prize Stories.

Baby walked the block to the car line rapidly or slowly, depending on his hunch whether a car was coming. On some nights it was pleasant waiting, not cold, and he leaned against a store front and simply forgot about the car: it would be along. Other nights, the bitter nights, he fidgeted angrily, scraping his feet in the street, squinting down the lonesome tracks. The wind twisted snow into his eyes and he focused his eyes down the line again and again and blinked away the cold tears.

The seasons entered the Black Belt penitently, in ashes, dust, and drabness, without benefit of green. Time here wore itself away monotonously, with a slow drag: there was always time left over. The seasons were not rounded. You knew them only by the thermometer and the clothing of the people. Still there were nights when the air itself told you. On some spring nights, even here, the air seemed enchanted, the diminished echo of spring happening ardently in the distant prairies and the suburbs. When the street was a decaying hollow mouth hung open, breathing fetid breath, that was summer. And tonight, certainly, was winter.

The snow, just beginning, swirled down, fighting for the earth. Baby twisted his hands to make heat in his overcoat pockets. He saw a woman cross the street to catch the car, which was coming now, but the woman refused stiffly to run for it. The wind went hooting down the tracks. Baby got on.

A cold breeze swept the floor, rattling old transfers and gum wrappers. Baby placed his feet uneasily on the heater to make the meager warmth funnel up his pants legs. The dark flesh beneath the cloth was chilled to chalky gray at the joints. He listened to the wheels bump over segments in the track, and the warmth from the heater rose higher on his legs. Without knowing exactly when, he became warm and forgetful of the weather, except as scenery. The streets were paved evenly with snow twinkling soft and clean and white under the white street lights and velvet red or green from the neon signs. New York may be all right, he hummed to himself, but Beale Street's paved with gold. That's a lie, he thought. All my life playing jobs in Chicago and I still got to ride the Big Red. And that's no lie. Jobs for musicians were getting harder and harder to find. What they wanted was Mickey Mouse sound effects. Singing strings, electric guitars, neon violins. Hard to find a spot to play in, and when you did it was always a white place and drunken advertising men who wanted to hear A Old Song—"My Wild Irish Rose" or "That Old Gang of Mine." So you played it, of course, plenty of schmaltz. And the college kids who wanted swing—any slick popular song. So you played that too. And always you wanted to play the music you were born to, blue or fast, music that had no name. You managed somehow to play that too when there was a lull, or the place was empty and you had to stay until 4 A.M. anyway.

Baby got off the streetcar and walked two blocks over snow, comfortable to the feet, the same two blacks he saw every night except Tuesday. The wind had died down almost entirely and the snow whirled in big flakes end-over-end and coasting slow motion. The wind managed only to stir up little whirls here and there. Padding along, Baby told himself he liked winter better than summer. Then he came to the place, went down three steps, and forgot all about winter and summer. It was always the same here. It was not so much a place of temperatures as a place of lights and shades—dingy shades—and chromium, mirrors, the smell of beer, rum, whisky, smoke—a stale blend of odors and shadows, darkness and music. It was a place of only one climate and that was it.

Baby's overcoat, hat, and scarf went into a closet and settled familiarly on hooks. His old tuxedo walked over to the traps. Its black hands rubbed together briskly, driving out the chill. One hand fumbled in the dark at the base of the big drum, and a second later a watery blue light winked on dully and flooded the drumhead, staring like a blind blue eye. Immediately the tuxedo sat down and worked its feet, with a slight rasping noise, firmly on the floor. The fingers thumped testingly on the hide, tightened the snare. They knew, like the ears, when it was right. Gingerly, as always, the right foot sought the big drum's pedal. The tuxedo was not ready yet. It had to fidget and massage its buttocks around on the chair, stretch out its arms and hug the whole outfit a fraction of an inch this way and that. Then the eyes glanced at the piano player, signaling ready. The drumsticks paused a moment tensely, slid into the beat, barely heard, accenting perfectly the shower of piano notes. Everything worked together for two choruses. Then the piano player tapered his solo gently, so that at a certain point Baby knew it was his. He brought the number to a lifeless close. Too early in the evening.

"Dodo," Baby said to the piano player, "Libby come in yet?"

Dodo sent a black hand up, slow as smoke, toward the ceiling. "Upstairs," he said, letting it fall to the keyboard with a faint far-off chord. It stirred there, gently worming music from the battered upright. Notes drew nearer, riding on ships and camels through a world of sand and water, till they came forthright from the piano, taking on patterns, as the other black hand came to life on the bass keys, dear to Dodo. Baby picked up his sticks, recognizing the number. He called it Dodo's Blues, though he had never heard Dodo call it anything. Every night about this time, when there was no crowd and Dodo hadn't yet put on the white coat he wore servicing the bar, they would play it. Baby half closed his eyes. With pleasure he watched Dodo through the clouds of rhythm he felt shimmering up like heat from his drums. Baby's eyes were only open enough to frame Dodo like a picture; everything else was out. It was a picture of many uncommon dimensions; music, he could make out, was one of them. Here was a man, midgety, hunchbacked, black, and proud, mostly all back and music. A little man who, when he was fixing to play, had to look around for a couple of three-inch telephone directories. Piling them on top of the piano bench, he sat down, with all their names and streets and numbers and exchanges under him. He had very little of thighs or stomach; mostly just back, which threw a rotund shadow on the wall. When he leaned farther away from the piano, so the light slanted through his hands, his shadow revealed him walking on his hands down the keyboard, dancing on the tips of fingery toes. Sometimes it seemed to Baby through half-closed eyes, when Dodo's body was bobbing on the wall and his hands were feet dancing on the keyboard, the dim light shaped him into a gigantic happy spider. When he became a spider you could forget he was a man, hunchbacked, runtish, black, and he too could forget perhaps that he had to be careful and proud. Perhaps he could be happy always if his back and size and color and pride were not always standing in the way. The piano made him whole. The piano taught him to find himself and jump clean over the moon. When he played, his feet never touched the pedals.

People were beginning to fill the place. They finished off the number, Baby smiling his admiration, Dodo scrupulously expressionless.

"For a young man . . ." Baby said.

Dodo got down off the telephone directories and threw them under the piano at the bass end, beyond the blue glow of the big drum. He had seen Libby come down the steps from the dressing room, a red dress, a gardenia. Dodo went behind the bar and put on his white service coat. Libby sat down at the piano.

Helplessly attracted, several men came over from the bar and leaned on the piano. They stared, burdening Libby's body with calculations. Singly at first and then, gathering unity, together. Libby sang a popular song. The men went back to the bar to get their drinks, which they brought over and set on top of the upright. Libby sang the words about lost love, and the men licked their lips vacantly and grinned. At the end of the song they clapped fiercely. Libby ignored them with a smile.

"Say, that was just fine," one man said. "Where you from, anyhow?"

With a little grin Libby acknowledged Baby. Baby, beaming his veteran admiration of a fine young woman, nodded.

"Where you from?" the same man hammered away, sounding a note of embarrassment. "Huh?"

"New Orleans."

"Well, you don't say!" the man blurted out joyfully. "We're from down South too . . . Mississippi, matter of fact!"

Icily, Libby smiled her appreciation of this coincidence. She looked at Baby, who was also registering appropriately. Just think of that! Small world! And welcome to our city!

"Well, what do you know!" crowed the gentleman from Mississippi. "So you're from down South!" He was greatly impressed and already very drunk. He eyed his friends, four or five of them, distributing his discovery equally among them.

"You never know," he explained. The mantle of philosophy was draping over him when he appeared to suffer a pang of doubt. He turned quickly to Libby again, as though to make sure she was still there. His eyes jellied blearily and in them an idea was born.

"I know," he said. "Sing . . . sing——sing 'Ol' Man River' for the boys. They all'd sure like that."

Without responding, Libby looked down at her hands, smiling. She measured chords between her thumbs and little fingers, working her amusement into the keys. Baby stared at the mottled hide of his snare drum, at the big one's rim worn down from playing dixieland. The gentleman from Mississippi got worried.

"Aw, sing it," he pleaded. So Libby sang a chorus. The gentlemen from

Mississippi were overwhelmed. They loved the song, they loved the South, the dear old Southland. Cinnamon seed and sandy bottom. Look away! Look away! They loved themselves. Look away! Look away! There was the tiniest touch of satire in Libby's voice, a slightly overripe fervor. Baby caught it and behind the bar Dodo caught it, but the gentlemen did not. Dodo had put down the sherry glass he was polishing and look away! look away!—good.

At the bridge of the second chorus Libby nodded "Take it!" to Baby. He stood up, staggering from the heat of the fields, clenching his black toilworn fists. In profound anguish, he hollered, giving the white folks his all, really knocking himself out.

"Tote that bar!
Lift that bale!
Git a little drunk——"

Baby grimaced in torment and did his best to look like ole Uncle Tom out snatchin' cotton.

Behind the bar, unnoticed, Dodo's sad black face had turned beatific. *"And you land in jail!"* Dodo could not see the other faces, the big white ones, but he could imagine them, their heads fixed and tilted. It was too dark in the place, and he could only make out blurrily the outlines of craned necks. Always before, he was capable only of hating them. Now he had risen to great unfamiliar heights and was actually enjoying them. Surprised at this capacity in himself, yet proud he could feel this way, he was confused. He went further and started to pity them. But his memory stood up outraged at his forgetfulness and said kill that pity dead. Then he remembered he was really alone in the place. It was different with Libby and Baby, though they were black too. He did not understand why. Say their skin was thicker, only that was not why. Probably this was not the first time they had jived white folks to death and them none the wiser. Dodo was not like that; he had to wait a long time for kicks like these. From his heart no pity went out for the white men. He kept it all to himself, where it was needed. But he had to smile inside of him with Libby and Baby. Only more. Look at that fool Baby! Jam up!

"Bend your knees!
Bow your head!
And pick that cotton!
Tiiilllll you're dead!"

Baby sat down with a thud, exhausted. The gentlemen from Mississippi brayed their pleasure. My, it was good. It was good to see that black boy all sweatin' and perspirin' that way. They clapped furiously, called for drinks, gobbled . . .

"And bring some for the darkies!"

Baby swallowed some of his drink. He looked at the beaten rim of the big drum, then at the sticks. He took out his pocketknife and scraped the rough splintery places smooth. He glanced at Libby and ventured the kind of smile he felt and knew she did. He finished his drink. The gentlemen from Mississippi hung around the piano, getting drunker, shouting in each other's face. Nervously, Libby lighted a cigarette. A college boy tried to make conversation with her while his honey-haired girl assumed an attitude of genuine concern.

"Can you play 'Hot Lips'?" the college boy asked.

"Don't know it," Libby lied. If they did, she wished she didn't.

"Can you play 'Sugar Blues'?" Right back.

"Don't know it."

One of the gentlemen, heretofore backward, crowded up to the piano. He drained his drink. Then he moved closer to the piano, so as to brush Libby's left hand with the front of his trousers. Libby moved her hand. He followed it with his body, grinning lewdly

"That's all right," he snickered. "Play lots of bass, honey."

The first gentleman from Mississippi, with a drink in his hand, stumbled over from the bar. He told Libby to play that "Ol' Man River" song some more. Libby hesitated. Then she lit into it, improvising all around it and it was a pleasure for Baby, but the first gentleman from Mississippi was not pleased. He said if that was the best she could do she had better try singing. Libby sang only one chorus. The gentlemen from Mississippi, though they applauded in vigorous competition, were not gratified. There was an air of general petulance among them. They remembered another time they heard the song, but it was not clear now what had made it different and better. They saw Baby all right, but they did not remember that it was he who had sung before, the good one that toted their bars, lifted their bales and landed drunk in their jails. Something was wrong, but in their present condition they saw no remedy. Each gentleman suspected the fault was personal, what with him drinking so heavy and all. Dodo, behind the bar, had not enjoyed the song the last time, hating the coercion the white men practiced on Libby and Baby, and feared his advantage was slipping. Soon he would be down to earth again, or lower, and hate and fear them again. Yes, he could feel himself beginning to hate them to pieces.

"Can you play 'Tiger Rag'?"

Libbey made a face and then managed to turn it into a smile. "No."

The honey-colored girl wrenched her face into an attractive smile. Her lips puckered pregnantly.

"Can you play 'St. Louis Blues'?" she asked.

"How do you want it?" Libby said. She put out her cigarette. "Blues, rhumba . . . what kind a way?"

"Oh, play it low down. The way *you people* play it." So that Libby would understand perfectly, she executed a ponderous wink, narrowed her eyes and made them glitter wantonly behind the lashes.

"*You* know," she said.

Libby knew. She played "St. Louis," losing herself in it with Baby. She left the college boy and the honey-haired girl behind. Libby forgot she knew. She gazed at Baby with her eyes dreamy, unseeing, blind with the blue drum, her head nodding in that wonderful graceful way. Baby saw his old tuxedo in the mirror, its body shimmying on the chair, and he was pleased. The drums, beating figures, rocked with a steady roll. They were playing "Little Rock Getaway" now, fine young woman music, he thought.

And Libby was pleased, watching Baby. And then, somehow, he vanished for her into the blue drum. The sticks still danced at an oblique angle on the snare, but there were no hands to them and Libby could not see Baby on the chair. She could only feel him somewhere in the blue glow. Abandoning herself, she turned into the piano. Now, still without seeing him, she could feel him with a clarity and warmth beyond all vision. Miniature bell notes, mostly blue, blossomed ecstatically, perished *affecttuoso,* weaving themselves down into the dark beauty of the lower keys, because it was closer to the drum, and multiplied. They came back to "St. Louis" again.

"Stop." The first gentleman from Mississippi touched Libby on the arm. "When I do that to you, that means Stop," he said. Libby chorded easily. "Some of the boys like to hear that 'Ol' Man River' some more." He straightened up, turned to the other gentlemen, his smile assuring them it would not be long now.

"Kick off," Baby sighed.

But Libby broke into "St. Louis" again. Baby, with a little whoop, clambered after, slicing his sticks into the drum rim, a staccato dixieland.

The first gentleman frowned, touching Libby's arm meaningfully. "Remember what that means? Means 'Ol' Man River,'" he said calmly, as though correcting a slight error. "Toot sweet. Know what that means? That's French. Means right now." No harm done, however. Just that his friends here, a bunch of boys from down South, were dying to hear that song again, up to him to see that they got satisfaction, knew there would be no trouble about that.

"We'll play it for you later on," Libby said quickly. "We got some requests besides yours. How many you got now, Baby?"

Baby held up eight fingers, very prompt.

"Coming up," he said.

The first gentleman was undecided. "Well . . ." he drawled. Libby began a popular song. The first gentleman faced his friends. His eyes more or less met theirs and found no agreement. The boys looked kind of impatient, like a bunch of boys out for a good time and not doing so well. He turned to Libby again.

"We gotta have that 'Ol' Man River' some more. Boys got their hearts set on it," he said. "Right away! Toot sweet! Toot—away!" He'd gone and made a joke, and the boys all laughed and repeated it to each other. Libby played on, as though she had not heard. The first gentleman took hold of her arm. She gazed steadily up into his bleary eyes.

"Not now. Later."

"No you don't. You gotta play it right now. For a bunch of boys come up North from down South. They all got a hankerin' to hear that 'Ol' Man River' some more."

"So you best play it," another gentleman said, leaning down hard on the old upright piano. "On account of I'm gonna take and give ear. We kinda like how that old song sound up North. Whatcha all need. The drummer will sing," he said, and looked at Baby. Baby looked back, unsmiling.

Libby chorded lightly, waiting for the gentlemen from Mississippi to get tired. They could not see how it was with her and Baby.

"You ain't gonna play?"

Baby's eyes strained hard in their sockets.

"We ain't comin'," Libby said.

Baby's eyes relaxed and he knew the worst part was over. They had made up their minds. They felt the same way about it. The rest was easy. Baby was even a little glad it had happened. A feeling was growing within him, realization coming with the passing moments that he had wanted to do this for a long time, for years and years, in a hundred different places he had played.

Secretly majestic, Baby sat at his drums, the goal of countless uplifted eyes—beseeching him. For it seemed hordes of white people were far below him, making their little commotions and noises, asking favors of him, like Lord, please bring the rain, or Lord, please take it away. Lord Baby. Waves of warm exhilaration washed into him, endearing him to himself. No, he smiled, I am sorry, no favors today. Yes, Lord, they all said, if that's the way it is, so be it. O.K., Baby said indulgently, so be it.

But somebody objected. The manager's voice barked, far below. It was scarcely audible to Baby in his new eminence. ". . . honoring requests," he heard, and ". . . trouble with the local," and ". . . wanting to get 'a sweet-string trio' in this place a long time now." And the manager, strangely small, an excited pale pygmy, "That's all I can do in the circumstances," explaining to the gentlemen from Mississippi, also small, how it was, and them saying, "Well, I guess so, well, I guess so all right, don't pay to pamper 'em, to give 'em an inch."

Baby noticed Libby had got up from the piano and put on her coat, the long dress hanging out at the bottom, red.

"I won't change," she said, and handed Baby the canvas cover for the snare drum.

"Huh?" Baby said foggily. He set about taking his traps apart. Dodo came over, not wearing his white service coat, to help.

"You don't have to," Baby said.

They walked down the street towards the car line. Baby, going first, plowed a path for Libby and Dodo in the snow. Window sills, parked cars, and trees were ripe with it. The wind was dead and buried. Baby bore the big drum on his shoulder and felt the sticks pressing tight and upright in his vest pockets, two on each side. Libby had her purse and street clothes rolled up under her arm. Dodo carried the snare drum.

Softly as snow, Libby laughed. "That's all I can do in the circumstances," she said, laughing.

"I got your old circumstances," Baby said.

Then they were silent, tramping in the snow.

At the corner they waited in a store entrance for a southbound streetcar. Libby raised a foot now and then, shuddering with cold. Dead still, Dodo breathed covertly down inside the collar of his overcoat, retarding his breath, frowning at the little smoke trickling out as though it were the only thing left in the world to remind him he was alive. Baby talked of taking a cab and finally did go out into the street to hail one approaching. It slowed up, pulled over to the curb, hesitated . . . and lurched away, with Baby's hand reaching for the door. Baby watched the cab speed down the snowy street, following it for a few steps, speechless. There was nothing to do. Without looking, he saw Libby and Dodo shivering in the store entrance. They had seen the cab come and go. They had not moved an inch. They waited, as before and always, for the Big Red.

"What's wrong with you, Baby?" Libby called out. A tiny moment of silence, and then she was laughing, gradually louder, mellow octaves of melody, mounting, pluming . . .

Like her piano, it seemed to Baby, that fine young woman laughter.

"Why you laugh so much, woman?" he inquired plaintively from the street. Then he moved to join them, a few steps only, dallying at the curb to temper the abruptness of his retreat. Like her piano on "Little Rock," that fine young woman laughter.

FOR WHITE MEN ONLY

James T. Farrell

James T. Farrell is, of course, the creator of the Studs Lonigan novels. He has altogether six novels and three collections of short stories to his credit.

"Boy, I tell you, don' you go there," Booker Jones, a small and yellowish Negro, said.

"Booker, there is no white man alive who's gonna tell me where I is to go swimming, and where I isn't. If I wants to go swimming this lake here at Jackson Park, that's where I'm going swimming," Alfred, a tall and handsome broad-shouldered and coppery Negro, replied.

They were shirtless, wearing blue swimming suits and old trousers, and they walked eastward along Fifty-seventh Street.

"Oh, come on, Alfred, let's go to Thirty-ninth Street," Booker said with intended persuasiveness as they passed across Dorchester after they had ambled on for a block in silence.

"You go! Me, I'm going swimming over in Jackson Park, whether there's white men there or not," Alfred said, his face hardening, his voice determined.

"Alfred, you is always courtin' trouble, and just because you want to show off before that no-account mulatto gal . . ."

"What you say, nigger?"

"Well, no, I'm sorry, Alfred," Booker cringed. "But someday you'll go courtin' trouble, and trouble is just gonna catch right on up with you, and it's gonna say, 'Well, Alfred, you been courtin' me, so here I is with my mind made up to give you plenty of me.' "

"Shut up, black boy!" Alfred said curtly.

Booker shook his head with disconsolate wonder. As they passed under the Illinois Central viaduct, Booker again suggested that they go down to the Thirty-ninth Street beach, and Alfred testily told him that Thirty-ninth Street wasn't a beach at all, just a measly, overcrowded pile of stones. The black man had no beach. But he was aiming to go swimming where he had some space without so many people all around him. He added that if the Negro was to go on being afraid of the white man, he was never going to get anywhere, and if the Negro wanted more space to swim in, he just had to go and take it. And he had told that to Melinda, and she had laughed at him, but she was not going to laugh at him again. Booker just shook his head sadly from side to side.

They entered Jackson Park, where the grass and shrubbery and tree leaves shimmered and gleamed with sunlight. The walks were crowded with people, and along the drive a succession of automobiles hummed by. Alfred walked along with unconcerned and even challenging pride. Booker glanced nervously about him, feeling that the white men were thrusting contemptuous looks at him. He looked up at Alfred, admiring his friend's courage, and he wished that he were unafraid like Alfred.

Turning by the lake, they passed along the sidewalk which paralleled the waters. Sandy beach ran down from the sidewalk to the shore line, and many were scattered along it in bathing suits. Down several blocks from them they could see that the regular beach was crowded. More white people frowned at them, and both of them could sense hate and fear in these furtive, hasty glances. Alfred's lips curled into a surly expression.

Halfway along toward the regular beach Alfred jumped down into the sand, tagged by Booker. He gazed around him, nonchalant, and then removed his trousers. He stood in his bathing suit, tall and impressively strong, graceful. Booker jittered beside him, hesitating until Alfred, without turning his head, taunted him into haste. Booker removed his trousers and stood skinny beside Alfred, whose arms were folded and whose gaze was sphinx-like on the waters. They heard a gentle and steady rippling against the shore line.

Near by, white bathers stared with apprehension. A group of three fellows and two young girls who had been splashing and ducking close to the shore saw them and immediately left the water and walked down a hundred yards to re-enter it. Alfred seemed to wince, and then his face again became hard and intent. Booker saw various white bathers picking up their bundles and moving away from them, and, still afraid of these white men, he hated them.

Alfred trotted gracefully to the shore line, again plunged into the water, followed by Booker. They cut outward, and Alfred suddenly paddled around and playfully ducked Booker. They again hit outward. Catching his breath and plunging beside his companion, Booker told Alfred that they had made a mistake coming out here where they were two against a mob. Alfred retorted that he was not going to whine and beg the white man for anything. Some black men had to be the first to come, if they wanted to have the right of a place to swim. And he wasn't scared anyway. Booker shook a pained head, caught a mouthful of water, and splashed to keep himself up. Alfred dove under water and reappeared a number of yards away, laughing, snorting, glorying in the use of his body. After they had swum around, Booker again chattered that he was afraid.

"Here is one black boy that's not going to be mobbed," Alfred said.

II

Buddy Coen and his friends emerged from the water laughing, shaking their wet bodies and heads. They found a space of sand within the enclosure of the regular beach and dropped down, hunting for the cigarettes they had hidden.

"Well, boys, I was just going to say, if you lads want to provide the bottle, I'm all set for a bender tonight," Buddy said after lighting a cigarette.

"If you'd go back driving a hack, you'd have dough enough for your own liquor," fat Marty Mulligan said.

"What the hell have I got a wife working as a waitress for? So that I can drive a taxi all night. See any holes in my head, Irish?" Buddy said tauntingly.

"After the fight Buddy started last Saturday night with two dicks, I should think he'd stay sober once in a while and see how it feels," Morris said.

"Say, there's plenty of neat pickups around here, even if most of them are Polacks," the big Swede said.

"Boys, my girl is out of town tonight, and I'm dated up with a married woman I met out on my territory. Her husband works nights, and brother, she's the stuff," Marty bragged, following his statement with an anatomical description of her contours, charms, and sexual technique.

The big Swede began talking about the old days, and Marty told anecdotes of how he used to get drunk when he was going to St. Stanislaus high school. They talked on until suddenly from a group close to them they heard a lad say:

"There's niggers down a way on the beach."

They became tense, and Buddy asked was that straight stuff.

"Bad enough having Polacks dirtying up the lake without diseased shines," the big Swede said in hate.

"A few weeks ago a coal-black bastard tried to get into the lockers here, but he was told that there weren't any free. Then a couple of us boys just talked to him outside, you know, we talked, and used a little persuasion, and he's one black bastard that knows his place and knows that this is a white man's park and a white man's beach," Buddy said.

"Say, I just need to sock somebody to make the day exciting and put me in good spirits for my date tonight," Marty Mulligan said.

"Well, then, what the hell are you guys waiting for?" Buddy said, jumping to his feet.

They followed Buddy to the water, swam out around the fencing that extended along the formal beach limits, and walked along the shore line in search of the Negroes.

"I know I don't mind pounding a few black bastards full of lumps," Norton said.

"Me now, I ain't sloughed anybody since Christ knows when, and I need a little practice," Morris said.

III

"Alfred, I'm tired," Booker said.

"Nigger, shut up! Nobody's going to hurt you," Alfred said.

"Well, I is, just the same," Booker said, his voice breaking into a whine.

Ignoring Booker, Alfred turned over on his back and floated with the sun boiling down upon his coppery limbs. Booker paddled after him, afraid to go in alone. He turned and looked back along the avenue of sand, filled with so many white people. Blocks and blocks of sand, populated with all these whites. The fears of a mob assailed him. He wished that he had never come. He thought of Negroes lynched in the South, of many who had been beaten and mobbed in the Chicago race riots of 1919. He remembered as a boy in those times how he had seen one of his race, dead, hanging livid from a telephone post in an alley. He was afraid, and with his fear was hate, hatred of the white man, hatred because of the injustices to him, to his race, hatred because he was afraid of the white man. Again he glanced along the avenue of sand filled with white men, and each small figure along it was a potential member of a mob to beat him and Alfred. He turned and again looked at his friend who was floating, unconcerned. He wished that he had Alfred's courage. With chattering teeth, he shook his head slowly and sadly, feeling, sensing, knowing that they were going to pay dearly for this venture. He treaded water waiting for Alfred, wishing that he was out of it. He saw a group of white bathers stand at the shore and look out over the water. He had a premonition.

IV

"There they are," Buddy said, curtly nodding his head toward the water, and they saw two kinky heads and two Negro faces, diminished by distance.

"Let's drown the bastards!" Morris said.

Buddy said that they would walk off a little ways and wait until the two shines came in. They moved a few yards away and waited, keen and eager. Buddy lashed out contemptuous remarks, keeping them on edge, and Marty remarked that they had driven the white man out of Washington Park, and that if things went on, soon the whole South Side would be black.

"If they want Jackson Park, they got to fight for it!" Buddy sneered.

"Just think! Look at all these white girls bathing around here. With niggers on the beach, it ain't safe for them," Morris said.

"And do you fellows know, my sister nearly came out here swimming today?" Morris said.

They saw the two Negroes coming in and heard the smaller one trying to convince the big one about something, but they could not catch enough of what he said. The two Negroes walked slowly toward their small bundles of clothing, their wet bodies glistening in the sunlight. After they had sat down, Buddy arose and led the group toward them. Seeing the white fellows approaching, Booker grabbed his clothes and ran. Four of the white lads pursued him, yelling to stop that nigger.

With a sulky expression on his face, Alfred arose at the approach of Buddy and Morris.

"The water nice?" Buddy asked, his voice constrained and threatening.

"Passable," Alfred answered, his fists clenched.

"Been out here before?" Buddy continued.

"No. . . . Why?" Alfred said with unmistakable fearlessness.

A crowd gathered around, and excitement cut through the beach like an electric current because of the shouts and chase after Booker. A white bather tripped him as he ran and joined the four other pursuers in cursing and punching him, mercilessly disregarding his pleas to be let alone. They dragged him to his feet, knocked him down, kicked him, dragged him up, knocked him over again while he continued to emit shrill and helpless cries.

"Anybody ever tell you that this is a white man's beach?" Morris asked Alfred.

"You know we don't want niggers here!" Buddy said.

Buddy went down from a quick and surprising punch on the jaw, and Alfred countered Morris' left swing with a thudding right that snapped the white lad's head back. Buddy sat down, rubbed his jaw, shook his dazed head, leaped to his feet, and went into Alfred swinging both hands. While the Negro fought off the two of them, others dragged back the howling Booker to the fight scene. The big Swede broke through the crowd of spectators and clipped Alfred viciously on the side of the head. Two other white bathers smashed into the attack. Defending himself, Alfred crashed Morris to the sand and was then battered off his feet. A heel was brought against his jaw, and as he struggled to arise, five white bodies piled onto him, punching, scratching, kneeing him. Spectators shouted, females screamed and encouraged the white lads, and Alfred was quickly and severely punished. Booker opened his mouth to beg for mercy, and a smashing fist brought blood from his lips, and another wallop between the eyes toppled him over backward.

A bald-headed Jewish man with a paunchy stomach protested, and a small, pretty blonde girl screamed that he must be a nigger lover. A middle-aged woman with a reddish bovine face called in an Irish brogue for them to hit the black skunks, while a child strained at her waist and shouted.

A park policeman hurriedly shoved through the spectators, and the slugging ceased. The two Negroes sat in the sand, their faces cut and bleeding.

"You fellows better go home!" the policeman said roughly, sneering as he spoke.

They slowly got up, and Booker tried to explain that they had done nothing.

"Don't be giving me any lip," the policeman said. "I said you better go home or do your swimming down at Thirty-ninth if you don't want to be starting riots. Now move along!"

He shoved Booker.

"And you too," he said to Alfred, who had not moved.

Booker hurriedly put his trousers on and Alfred did likewise slowly, as if with endless patience. They wiped their bleeding faces with dirty handkerchiefs, and Booker sniffled.

"Go ahead now!" the policeman roughly repeated.

"We will, but we'll come back!" Alfred said challengingly.

The crowd slowly dispersed, and the six fellows stood there near the policeman.

"Shall we follow them?" asked Marty.

"They ain't worth hitting, the skunks, and the dirty fighting they do, kicking me that way," said Collins, limping.

They turned and walked heroically back toward the enclosed beach.

"That black bastard had the nerve to hit me," Buddy said, pointing to his puffed eye.

"Like all niggers, they were yellow," said Morris.

"Well, we did a neat job with them," Norton bragged.

"Boy, I caught that big one between his teeth. Look at my hand," Marty said, showing his swollen knuckles.

"Look at that, fellows! There's somethin'. I say there, sisters!" the Swede said to three girls who were coquetting on the sand.

Looking covertly at legs and breasts, they leered.

THE ETHICS OF LIVING JIM CROW

Richard Wright

With the publication of Native Son, *Richard Wright became one of the best-known writers in the United States. As a play starring Canada Lee,* Native Son *had a long run on Broadway. This piece, written and published some years ago, forms a chapter in his recent autobiography,* Black Boy.

MY FIRST LESSON in how to live as a Negro came when I was quite small. We were living in Arkansas. Our house stood behind the railroad tracks. Its skimpy yard was paved with black cinders. Nothing green ever grew in that yard. The only touch of green we could see was far away, beyond the tracks, over where the white folks lived. But cinders were good enough for me, and I never missed the green growing things. And, anyhow, cinders were fine weapons. You could always have a nice hot war with huge black cinders. All you had to do was crouch behind the brick pillars of a house with your hands full of gritty ammunition. And the first woolly black head you saw pop out from behind another row of pillars was your target. You tried your very best to knock it off. It was great fun.

I never fully realized the appalling disadvantages of a cinder environment till one day the gang to which I belonged found itself engaged in a war with the white boys who lived beyond the tracks. As usual, we laid down our cinder barrage, thinking that this would wipe the white boys out. But they replied with a steady bombardment of broken bottles. We doubled our cinder barrage, but they hid behind trees, hedges, and the sloping embankments of their lawns. Having no such fortifications, we retreated to the brick pillars of our homes. During the retreat a broken milk bottle caught me behind the ear, opening a deep gash which bled profusely. The sight of blood pouring over my face completely demoralized our ranks. My fellow combatants left me standing paralyzed in the center of the yard and scurried for their homes. A kind neighbor saw me and rushed me to a doctor, who took three stitches in my neck.

I sat brooding on my front steps, nursing my wound and waiting for my mother to come from work. I felt that a grave injustice had been done me. It was all right to throw cinders. The greatest harm a cinder could do was leave a bruise. But broken bottles were dangerous; they left you cut, bleeding, and helpless.

When night fell my mother came from the white folks' kitchen. I raced down the street to meet her. I could just feel in my bones that she would understand. I knew she would tell me exactly what to do next time. I grabbed her hand and babbled out the whole story. She examined my wound, then slapped me.

"How come yuh didn't hide?" she asked me. "How come yuh always fightin'?"

I was outraged, and bawled. Between sobs I told her that I didn't have any trees or hedges to hide behind. There wasn't a thing I could have used as a trench. And you couldn't throw very far when you were hiding behind the brick pillars of a house. She grabbed a barrel stave, dragged me home, stripped me naked, and beat me till I had a fever of one hundred and two. She would smack my rump with the stave and, while the skin was still smarting, impart to me gems of Jim Crow wisdom. I was never to throw cinders any more. I was never to fight any more wars. I was never, never, under any conditions, to fight white folks again. And they were absolutely right in clouting me with the broken milk bottle. Didn't I know she was working hard every day in the hot kitchens of the white folks to make money to take care of me? When was I ever going to learn to be a good boy? She couldn't be bothered with my fights. She finished by telling me that I ought to be thankful to God as long as I lived that they didn't kill me.

All that night I was delirious and could not sleep. Each time I closed my eyes I saw monstrous white faces suspended from the ceiling, leering at me.

From that time on the charm of my cinder yard was gone. The green trees, the trimmed hedges, the cropped lawns grew very meaningful, became a symbol. Even today, when I think of white folks, the hard, sharp outlines of white houses surrounded by trees, lawns, and hedges are present somewhere in the background of my mind. Through the years they grew into an overreaching symbol of fear.

It was a long time before I came in close contact with white folks again. We moved from Arkansas to Mississippi. Here we had the good fortune not to live behind the railroad tracks or close to white neighborhoods. We lived in the very heart of the local Black Belt. There were black churches and black preachers; there were black schools and black teachers, black groceries and black clerks. In fact, everything was so solidly black that for a long time I did not even think of white folks, save in remote and vague terms. But this could not last forever. As one grows older one eats more. One's clothing costs more. When I finished grammar school I had to go to work. My mother could no longer feed and clothe me on her cooking job.

There is but one place where a black boy who knows no trade can get a job. And that's where the houses and faces are white, where the trees, lawns, and hedges are green. My first job was with an optical company in Jackson, Mississippi. The morning I applied I stood straight and neat before the boss, answering all his question with sharp yessirs and nosirs. I was very careful to pronounce my sirs distinctly, in order that he might know that I was polite, that I knew where I was, and that I knew he was a white man. I wanted that job badly.

He looked me over as though he were examining a prize poodle. He questioned me closely about my schooling, being particularly insistent about how much mathematics I had had. He seemed very pleased when I told him I had had two years of algebra.

"Boy, how would you like to try to learn something around here?" he asked me.

"I'd like it fine, sir," I said, happy. I had visions of "working my way up." Even Negroes have those visions.

"All right," he said. "Come on."

I followed him to the small factory.

"Pease," he said to a white man of about thirty-five, "this is Richard. He's going to work for us."

Pease looked at me and nodded.

I was then taken to a white boy of about seventeen.

"Morrie, this is Richard, who's going to work for us."

"Whut yuh sayin' there, boy!" Morrie boomed at me.

"Fine!" I answered.

The boss instructed these two to help me, teach me, give me jobs to do, and let me learn what I could in my spare time.

My wages were five dollars a week.

I worked hard, trying to please. For the first month I got along O. K. Both Pease and Morrie seemed to like me. But one thing was missing. And I kept thinking about it. I was not learning anything, and nobody was volunteering to help me. Thinking they had forgotten that I was to learn something about the mechanics of grinding lenses, I asked Morrie one day to tell me about the work. He grew red.

"Whut yuh tryin' t' do, nigger, git smart?" he asked.

"Naw, I ain' tryin' t' git smart," I said.

"Well, don't, if yuh know whut's good for yuh!"

I was puzzled. Maybe he just doesn't want to help me, I thought. I went to Pease.

"Say, are you crazy, you black bastard?" Pease asked me, his gray eyes growing hard.

I spoke out, reminding him that the boss had said I was to be given a chance to learn something.

"Nigger, you think you're white, don't you?"

"Naw sir!"

"Well, you're acting mighty like it!"

"But, Mr. Pease, the boss said——"

Pease shook his fist in my face.

"This is a white man's work around here, and you better watch yourself!"

From then on they changed toward me. They said good morning no more. When I was just a bit slow in performing some duty, I was called a lazy black son-of-a-bitch.

Once I thought of reporting all this to the boss. But the mere idea of what would happen to me if Pease and Morrie should learn that I had "snitched" stopped me. And after all, the boss was a white man too. What was the use?

The climax came at noon one summer day. Pease called me to his workbench. To get to him I had to go between two narrow benches and stand with my back against a wall.

"Yes sir," I said.

"Richard, I want to ask you something," Pease began pleasantly, not looking up from his work.

"Yes sir," I said again.

Morrie came over, blocking the narrow passage between the benches. He folded his arms, staring at me solemnly.

I looked from one to the other, sensing that something was coming.

"Yes sir," I said for the third time.

Pease looked up and spoke very slowly.

"Richard, Mr. Morrie, here, tells me you called me Pease."

I stiffened. A void seemed to open up in me. I knew this was the showdown.

He meant that I had failed to call him Mr. Pease. I looked at Morrie. He was gripping a steel bar in his hands. I opened my mouth to speak, to protest, to assure Pease that I had never called him simply Pease and that I had never had any intentions of doing so, when Morrie grabbed me by the collar, ramming my head against the wall.

"Now, be careful, nigger!" snarled Morrie, baring his teeth. "I heard yuh call 'im Pease! 'N' if yuh say yuh didn't, yuh're callin' me a liar, see?" He waved the steel bar threateningly.

If I had said, "No sir, Mr. Pease, I never called you Pease," I would have been automatically calling Morrie a liar. And if I had said, "Yes sir, Mr. Pease, I called you Pease," I would have been pleading guilty to having uttered the worst insult that a Negro can utter to a Southern white man. I stood hesitating, trying to frame a neutral reply.

"Richard, I asked you a question!" said Pease. Anger was creeping into his voice.

"I don't remember calling you Pease, Mr. Pease," I said cautiously. "And if I did, I sure didn't mean——"

"You black son-of-a-bitch! You called me Pease, then!" he spat, slapping me till I bent sideways over a bench. Morrie was on top of me, demanding:

"Didn't yuh call 'im Pease? If yuh say yuh didn't, I'll rip yo' gut string loose with this bar, yuh black granny dodger! Yuh can't tell a white man a lie 'n' git erway with it, you black son-of-a-bitch!"

I wilted. I begged them not to bother me. I knew what they wanted. They wanted me to leave.

"I'll leave," I promised. "I'll leave right now."

They gave me a minute to get out of the factory. I was warned not to show up again or tell the boss.

I went.

When I told the folks at home what had happened, they called me a fool. They told me that I must never again attempt to exceed my boundaries. When you are working for white folks, they said, you got to "stay in your place" if you want to keep working.

II

My Jim Crow education continued on my next job, which was portering in a clothing store. One morning, while polishing brass out front, the boss and his twenty-year-old son got out of their car and half dragged and half kicked a Negro woman into the store. A policeman standing at the corner looked on, twirling his night stick. I watched out of the corner of my eye, never slackening the strokes of my chamois upon the brass. After a few minutes I heard shrill screams coming from the rear of the store. Later the woman stumbled out, bleeding, crying, and holding her stomach. When she reached the end of the block, the policeman grabbed her and accused her of being drunk. Silently I watched him throw her into a patrol wagon.

When I went to the rear of the store, the boss and his son were washing their hands at the sink. They were chuckling. The floor was bloody and strewn with wisps of hair and clothing. No doubt I must have appeared pretty shocked, for the boss slapped me reassuringly on the back.

"Boy, that's what we do to niggers when they don't want to pay their bills," he said, laughing.

His son looked at me and grinned.

"Here, have a cigarette," he said.

Not knowing what to do, I took it. He lit his and held the match for me. This was a gesture of kindness, indicating that even if they had beaten the poor old woman, they would not beat me if I knew enough to keep my mouth shut.

"Yes sir," I said, and asked no questions.

After they had gone, I sat on the edge of a packing box and stared at the bloody floor till the cigarette went out.

That day at noon, while eating in a hamburger joint, I told my fellow Negro porters what had happened. No one seemed surprised. One fellow, after swallowing a huge bite, turned to me and asked:

"Huh. Is tha' all they did t' her?"

"Yeah. Wasn't tha' enough?" I asked.

"Shucks! Man, she's a lucky bitch!" he said, burying his lips deep into a juicy hamburger. "Hell, it's a wonder they didn't lay her when they got through."

III

I was learning fast, but not quite fast enough. One day, while I was delivering packages in the suburbs, my bicycle tire was punctured. I walked along the hot, dusty road, sweating and leading my bicycle by the handle bars.

A car slowed at my side.

"What's the matter, boy?" a white man called.

I told him my bicycle was broken and I was walking back to town.

"That's too bad," he said. "Hop on the running board."

He stopped the car. I clutched hard at my bicycle with one hand and clung to the side of the car with the other.

"All set?"

"Yes sir," I answered. The car started.

It was full of young white men. They were drinking. I watched the flask pass from mouth to mouth.

"Wanna drink, boy?" one asked.

I laughed, the wind whipping my face. Instinctively obeying the freshly planted precepts of my mother, I said:

"Oh no!"

The words were hardly out of my mouth before I felt something hard and cold smash me between the eyes. It was an empty whisky bottle. I saw stars and fell backwards from the speeding car into the dust of the road, my feet becoming entangled in the steel spokes of my bicycle. The white men piled out and stood over me.

"Nigger, ain' yuh learned no better sense'n tha' yet?" asked the man who hit me. "Ain' yuh learned t' say *sir* t' a white man yet?"

Dazed, I pulled to my feet. My elbows and legs were bleeding. Fists doubled, the white man advanced, kicking my bicycle out of the way.

"Aw, leave the bastard alone. He's got enough," said one.

They stood looking at me. I rubbed my shins, trying to stop the flow of blood. No doubt they felt a sort of contemptuous pity, for one asked:

"Yuh wanna ride t' town now, nigger? Yuh reckon yuh know enough t' ride now?"

"I wanna walk," I said simply.

Maybe it sounded funny. They laughed.

"Well, walk, yuh black son-of-a-bitch!"

When they left they comforted me with:

"Nigger, yuh sho better be damn glad it wuz us yuh talked t' tha' way. Yuh're a lucky bastard, 'cause if yuh'd said tha' t' somebody else, yuh might've been a dead nigger now."

IV

Negroes who have lived South know the dread of being caught alone upon the streets in white neighborhoods after the sun has set. In such a simple situation as this the plight of the Negro in America is graphically symbolized. While white strangers may be in these neighborhoods trying to get home, they can pass unmolested. But the color of a Negro's skin makes him easily recognizable, makes him suspect, converts him into a defenseless target.

Late one Saturday night I made some deliveries in a white neighborhood. I was pedaling my bicycle back to the store as fast as I could, when a police car, swerving toward me, jammed me into the curbing.

"Get down and put up your hands!" the policemen ordered.

I did. They climbed out of the car, guns drawn, faces set, and advanced slowly.

"Keep still!" they ordered.

I reached my hands higher. They searched my pockets and packages. They seemed dissatisfied when they could find nothing incriminating. Finally one of them said:

"Boy, tell your boss not to send you out in white neighborhoods this time of night."

As usual, I said:

"Yes sir."

V

My next job was as hallboy in a hotel. Here my Jim Crow education broadened and deepened. When the bellboys were busy, I was often called to assist them. As many of the rooms in the hotel were occupied by prostitutes, I was constantly called to carry them liquor and cigarettes. These women were nude most of the time. They did not bother about clothing even for bellboys. When you went into their rooms, you were supposed to take their nakedness for granted, as though it startled you no more than a blue vase or a red rug. Your presence awoke in them no sense of shame, for you were not regarded as human. If they were alone, you could steal sidelong glimpses at them. But if they were receiving men, not a flicker of your eyelids must show. I remember one incident vividly. A new woman, a huge, snowy-skinned blonde, took a room on my floor. I was sent to wait upon her. She was in bed with a thickset man; both were nude and uncovered. She said she wanted some liquor and slid out of bed and waddled across the floor to get her money from a dresser drawer. I watched her.

"Nigger, what in hell you looking at?" the white man asked me, raising himself upon his elbows.

"Nothing," I answered, looking miles deep into the blank wall of the room.

"Keep your eyes where they belong, if you want to be healthy!"

"Yes sir," I said.

VI

One of the bellboys I knew in this hotel was keeping steady company with one of the Negro maids. Out of a clear sky the police descended upon his home and arrested him, accusing him of bastardy. The poor boy swore he had had no intimate relations with the girl. Nevertheless, they forced him to marry her. When the child arrived, it was found to be much lighter in complexion than either of the two supposedly legal parents. The white men around the hotel made a great joke of it. They spread the rumor that some white cow must have scared the poor girl while she was carrying the baby. If you were in their presence when this explanation was offered, you were supposed to laugh.

VII

One of the bellboys was caught in bed with a white prostitute. He was castrated and run out of town. Immediately after this all the bellboys and hallboys were called together and warned. We were given to understand that the boy who had been castrated was a "mighty, mighty lucky bastard." We were impressed with the fact that next time the management of the hotel would not be responsible for the lives of "trouble makin' niggers."

VIII

One night, just as I was about to go home, I met one of the Negro maids. She lived in my direction, and we fell in to walk part of the way home together. As we passed the white night watchman, he slapped the maid on her buttock. I turned around, amazed. The watchman looked at me with a long, hard, fixed-under stare. Suddenly he pulled his gun and asked:

"Nigger, don't yuh like it?"

I hesitated.

"I asked yuh don't yuh like it?" he said again, stepping forward.

"Yes sir," I mumbled.

"Talk like it, then!"

"Oh yes, sir!" I said with as much heartiness as I could muster.

Outside I walked ahead of the girl, ashamed to face her. She caught up with me and said:

"Don't be a fool; yuh couldn't help it!"

This watchman boasted of having killed two Negroes in self-defense.

Yet, in spite of all this, the life of the hotel ran with an amazing smoothness. It would have been impossible for a stranger to detect anything. The maids, the hallboys, and the bellboys were all smiles. They had to be.

IX

I had learned my Jim Crow lessons so thoroughly that I kept the hotel job till I left Jackson for Memphis. It so happened that while in Memphis I applied for a job at a branch of the optical company. I was hired. And for some reason, as long as I worked there, they never brought my past against me.

Here my Jim Crow education assumed quite a different form. It was no longer brutally cruel, but subtly cruel. Here I learned to lie, to steal, to dissemble. I learned to play that dual role which every Negro must play if he wants to eat and live.

For example, it was almost impossible to get a book to read. It was assumed that after a Negro had imbibed what scanty schooling the state furnished he had no further need for books. I was always borrowing books from men on the job. One day I mustered enough courage to ask one of the men to let me get books from the library in his name. Surprisingly, he consented. I cannot help but think that he consented because he was a Roman Catholic and felt a vague sympathy for Negroes, being himself an object of hatred. Armed with a library card, I obtained books in the following manner: I would write a note to the librarian, saying: "Please let this nigger boy have the following books." I would then sign it with the white man's name.

When I went to the library, I would stand at the desk, hat in hand, looking as unbookish as possible. When I received the books desired, I would take them home. If the books listed in the note happened to be out, I would sneak into the lobby and forge a new one. I never took any chances guessing with the white librarian about what the fictitious white man would want to read. No doubt if any of the white patrons had suspected that some of the volumes they enjoyed had been in the home of a Negro, they would not have tolerated it for an instant.

The factory force of the optical company in Memphis was much larger than that in Jackson, and more urbanized. At least they liked to talk and would engage the Negro help in conversation whenever possible. By this means I found that many subjects were taboo from the white man's point of view. Among the topics they did not like to discuss with Negroes were the following: American white women; the Ku Klux Klan; France, and how Negro soldiers fared while there; French women; Jack Johnson; the entire Northern part of the United States; the Civil War; Abraham Lincoln; U. S. Grant; General Sherman; Catholics; the Pope; Jews; the Republican party; slavery; social equality; Communism; Socialism; the Thirteenth and Fourteenth amendments to the Constitution; or any topic calling for positive knowledge or manly self-assertion on the part of the Negro. The most accepted topics were sex and religion.

There were many times when I had to exercise a great deal of ingenuity to keep out of trouble. It is a Southern custom that all men must take off their hats when they enter an elevator. And especially did this apply to us blacks with rigid force. One day I stepped into an elevator with my arms full of packages. I was forced to ride with my hat on. Two white men stared at me coldly. Then one of them very kindly lifted my hat and placed it upon my armful of packages. Now the most accepted response for a Negro to make under such circumstances is to look at the white man out of the corner of his eye and grin. To have said: "Thank you!" would have made the white man *think* that you *thought* you were receiving from him a personal service. For such an act I have seen Negroes take a blow in the mouth. Finding the first alternative distasteful and the second dangerous, I hit upon an acceptable course of action which fell safely between these two poles. I immediately—no sooner than my hat was lifted—pretended that my packages were about to spill and appeared deeply distressed with keeping them in my arms. In this fashion I evaded having to acknowledge his service and, in spite of adverse circumstances, salvaged a slender shred of personal pride.

How do Negroes feel about the way they have to live? How do they discuss it when alone among themselves? I think this question can be answered in a single sentence. A friend of mine who ran an elevator once told me:

"Lawd, man! Ef it wuzn't fer them polices 'n' them ol' lynch mobs, there wouldn't be nothin' but uproar down here!"

A SHORT WAIT BETWEEN TRAINS

Robert McLaughlin

Robert McLaughlin is a frequent contributor to the New Yorker *and other magazines. He is serving in the armed forces.*

THEY CAME into Forrest Junction at eleven-thirty in the morning. Seen from the window of their coach, it wasn't much of a town. First there were the long rows of freight cars on sidings with green-painted locomotives of the Southern Railway nosing strings of them back and forth. Then they went past the sheds of cotton ginners abutting on the tracks. There were small frame houses with weed-choked lawns enclosed by broken picket fences, a block of frame stores with dingy windows and dark interiors, a small brick-and-concrete bank, and beyond that the angled roof and thin smokestacks of a textile mill.

The station was bigger than you would expect; it was of dirty brick and had a rolling, bungalow-type roof adorned with cupolas and a sort of desperate scrollwork. The grime of thousands of trains and fifty years gave it a patina suggesting such great age that it seemed to antedate the town.

Corporal Randolph, a big, sad Negro, said, "Here we is."

Private Brown, his pink-palmed hand closed over a comic book, looked out the window. "How long we here?" he asked.

"Until one o'clock," said Randolph, getting up. "Our train west is at one o'clock."

The two other privates—Butterfield and Jerdon—were taking down their barracks bags from the rack. Other passengers bunched in the aisles —two young colored girls in slacks; a fat, bespectacled mother and her brood, with the big-eyed child in her arms staring fixedly at the soldiers; tall, spare, colored farmers in blue overalls.

As they waited for the line to move, Jerdon said, "Who dat?"

Grinning, Brown answered, "Who dat say 'Who dat?' "

Jerdon replied in a nervous quaver, "Who dat say 'Who dat?' when I say 'Who dat?' "

They both began to laugh, and some of the passengers looked at them with half-smiles and uncertain eyes.

Butterfield said, "Even the kid thinks you're nuts."

The child in the fat woman's arms looked at him sharply as he spoke, then her eyes went back to Jerdon and Brown.

"You think I'm nuts, baby?" asked Jerdon. "Is it like the man say?"

The line of passengers began to move.

"That baby don't think I'm nuts," said Jerdon. "That baby is sure a smart baby."

Their coach was up by the engine, and they descended to the platform into a cloud of released steam, with the sharp pant of the engine seemingly at their shoulders.

A motor-driven baggage truck, operated by a colored man wearing an engineer's cap, plowed through them. The three privates, with their bags slung over their shoulders, stood watching the corporal. He was checking through the papers in a large manila envelope marked "War Department, Official Business." It contained their railway tickets and their orders to report to a camp in Arizona.

"Man," said Brown, "you better not lose anything. We don't want to stay in this place."

"This don't look like any town to me, either," said Jerdon.

Butterfield, slim, somewhat lighter in complexion, and a year or two older than the others, looked around him. "Hey," he said, "look what's up there."

The others turned. Down the platform they could see two white soldiers armed with carbines and what appeared to be a group of other white soldiers in fatigues. A crowd was forming around them.

"They're prisoners of war," said Butterfield. "You want to see some Germans, Brown? You say you're going to kill a lot of them; you want to see what they look like?"

Brown said, "That what they are?"

"Sure," said Butterfield. "See what they've got on their backs? 'P.W.' That means 'prisoner of war.' "

The four soldiers moved forward. They stood on the fringe of the crowd, which was mostly white, looking at the Nazi prisoners with wide-eyed curiosity. There were twenty Germans standing in a compact group, acting rather exaggeratedly unconscious of the staring crowd. A small mound of barracks bags was in the center of the group, and the eyes of the prisoners looked above and through the crowd in quick glances at the station, the train, the seedy town beyond. They were very reserved, very quiet, and their silence put a silence on the crowd.

One of the guards spoke to a prisoner in German, and the prisoner gave an order to his fellows. They formed up in a rough double column and moved off.

Little boys in the crowd ran off after them and the knot of watchers broke up.

When the four soldiers were alone again, Brown said, "They don't look like much. They don't look no different."

"What did you think they'd look like?" Butterfield asked.

"I don't know," said Brown.

"Man, you just don't know nothing," said Jerdon. "You're just plain ignorant."

"Well, what did *you* think they'd look like?" Butterfield asked Jerdon.

Jerdon shifted his feet and didn't look at Butterfield or answer him directly. "That Brown, he just don't know nothing," he repeated. He and Brown began to laugh; they were always dissolving in laughter at obscure jokes of their own.

A trainman got up on the steps of one of the coaches, moved his arm in a wide arc; the pant of the locomotive changed to a short puffing, and the train jerked forward.

The colored baggageman came trundling back in his empty truck, and Corporal Randolph said to him, "They any place we can leave these bags?"

The baggageman halted. "You taking the one o'clock?"

"That's right."

"Dump them on the truck. I'll keep them for you."

Randolph said, "Any place we can eat around here?"

"No, they ain't."

"Where we have to go?"

"They ain't no place," the baggageman said, looking at them as though curious to see how they'd take it.

"Man," said Jerdon, "we're hungry. We got to eat."

"Maybe you get a handout someplace," said the baggageman, "but they sure no place for colored around here."

Butterfield said sourly, "We'll just go to the U.S.O."

"Oh, man, that's rich," Brown said, and he and Jerdon laughed.

"They got a U.S.O. in this here town?" Jerdon asked the baggageman.

"Not for you they ain't," said the baggageman.

"Man, ain't that the truth," replied Jerdon.

Randolph said stubbornly. "We got to get something to eat."

The baggageman said, "You want to walk to Rivertown you get something. That the only place, though."

"Where's Rivertown?" Butterfield asked.

"Take the main road down past the mill. It's about three, four miles."

"Hell, man," said Jerdon, "I'm hungry now. I don't have to walk no four miles to get hungry."

"You stay hungry, then," said the baggageman, and went off.

"Well, ain't this just dandy?" said Brown.

The men all looked at Corporal Randolph, who transferred the manila envelope from one hand to the other, his heavy face wearing an expression of indecision.

Butterfield said, "There's a lunchroom in the station. You go tell them they've got to feed us."

Randolph said angrily, "You heard the man. You heard him say there's no place to eat."

"You're in charge of us," Butterfield said. "You've got to find us a place to eat."

"I can't find nothing that ain't there."

"You're just afraid to go talk to them," said Butterfield. "That's all that's the matter with you."

Brown said, "Corporal, you just let Mr. Butterfield handle this. He'll make them give us something to eat." He and Jerdon began to laugh.

"O.K.," said Butterfield. "I'll do it."

Brown and Jerdon looked at Randolph.

"My God," said Butterfield, "you even afraid to come with me while I ask them?"

"You're awful loud-talking——" Randolph began, angrily but defensively.

"You coming with me or not?" Butterfield asked.

"We're coming with you," Randolph said.

The four soldiers went into the colored section of the station and walked through it and into the passage that led to the main entrance. The lunchroom was right next to the white waiting room. The four men moved up to the door, bunching a little as though they were soldiers under fire for the first time.

Butterfield opened the screen door of the lunchroom and they followed him in. There were five or six tables and a lunch counter and, although it was around twelve, only a few diners. A cashier's desk and cigarette counter was by the door, and seated behind it was a gray-haired woman, stout and firm-chinned and wearing glasses.

Butterfield went up to her, rested his hands on the edge of the counter, and then hastily removed them.

She looked up.

Butterfield said quickly, "Is there any place we could get something to eat, ma'am?"

She looked at him steadily, then her eyes shifted to the others, who were looking elaborately and with desperation at their shoes.

"This all of you?" asked the woman.

"Yes ma'am, there's just us four."

"All right," she said. "Go out to the kitchen. They'll feed you."

"Thank you, ma'am."

Butterfield, trailed by the others, started back toward the kitchen.

"Just a minute," said the woman. "Go out and around to the back."

They turned, bumping each other a little, and went back out the door.

Brown said, when they were outside, "Mr. Butterfield, he sure do it."

"That's right," said Jerdon. "You want to look out, Corporal. That Butterfield, he'll be getting your stripes."

Butterfield and Randolph didn't answer, didn't look at each other.

In the kitchen they found a thin, aged colored man in a white apron and a young, thick-bodied colored girl who was washing dishes.

"What you want?" asked the cook.

"Something to eat."

"Man, we're hungry," Jerdon told him. "We ain't put nothing inside us since before sunup. Ain't that right, Brown?"

"Since before sunup *yesterday*," said Brown.

"The lady say you come back here?" asked the cook.

"That right."

The cook took their orders and, as he worked, asked them what camp they were from, where they were going, how long they'd been in the Army. He told them about his two sons who were in the Engineers at Fort Belvoir.

"Labor troops," said Butterfield. "A bunch of ditchdiggers and road menders."

The cook stared at him. "What the matter with you, man?"

Butterfield didn't answer. He lit a cigarette and walked to the serving window, looking out at the woman at the cashier's desk.

Brown and Jerdon went over to the girl washing dishes, and Corporal

Randolph, his manila envelope under his arm, listened mournfully to the cook.

Suddenly Butterfield threw away his half-smoked cigarette and called to the others, "Come here and look at this."

"What?" said Randolph.

"You come here and see this."

They all came over, the cook, the girl, the three other soldiers.

Sitting down at the tables in the lunchroom were the twenty German prisoners. One of their guards was at the door with his carbine slung over his shoulder; the other was talking to the cashier. The other diners were staring at the Nazis in fascination. The prisoners sat relaxed and easy at the tables, lighting cigarettes, drinking water, taking rolls from the baskets on their tables, and munching them unbuttered, their eyes incurious, their attitudes casual.

"God damn! Look at that," said Butterfield. "We don't amount to as much here as the men we're supposed to fight. Look at them, sitting there like kings, and we can't get a scrap to eat in this place without bending our knee and sneaking out to the kitchen like dogs or something."

The cook said severely, "Where you from, boy?"

"He from Trenton, New Jersey," said Brown.

Butterfield stared around at them and saw that only Randolph and the cook even knew what he was talking about and that they were both looking at him with troubled disapproval. Brown and Jerdon and the girl just didn't care. He turned and crossed the kitchen and went out the back door.

The cook said to Randolph, "I'll wrap some sandwiches for him and you give them to him on the train." He shook his head. "All the white folks around here is talking about all the nigger killing they going to do after the war. That boy, he sure to be one of them."

Randolph cracked his big knuckles unhappily. "We all sure to be one of them," he said. "The Lord better have mercy on us all."

"COLOR TROUBLE"

Harold Garfinkel

Born in Newark, New Jersey, Harold Garfinkel attended the University of North Carolina and after graduating stayed on as a Fellow until he joined the Army.

According to the timetable, the bus traveling from Washington, D. C., to Durham, North Carolina, is scheduled to make the run in eight hours. "Lv. Wash. 2:30: Arr. Dur. 10:36," is the listing. An inconspicuous footnote, however, serves to make this pronouncement less categorical, for it points out, though in very fine print, that "the company will not be liable for unavoidable delays."

Now, it must be an undisputed point among bus company officials that the traffic manager in charge of routing buses between Washington and Durham is grossly underpaid when the difficulties with which he must deal are considered in comparison to those of the manager of the buses traveling, for instance, between New York City and Washington. The reason for this assumption is not hard to explain. Any delays occurring between New York and Washington are attributable to immediately discernible items, as, for instance, a flat tire. On the other route, however, the manager's job is infinitely more complex, for it is during this stretch that delays may occur which are attributable, according to one interpretation, to the denial of "the rights and privileges of a free citizenry," and, according to another, "color trouble." It is here that culture differences may be brought to keen consciousness, and clashes which are at once tragic and comical work themselves out upon an intricate background of prejudice and preconceptions.

In the clashing of perceptions are to be found all the elements of drama; and of peculiar interest value for purposes of this paper is the drama that was to be found on that bus that traveled from Washington to Durham on Saturday afternoon, March 23, 1940.

This particular bus rolled into the Petersburg bus depot on time, at a quarter to seven. Before it had stopped, a press of Negroes had formed at the door and stood there champing and grinning, waiting patiently for the door to be opened. Some of the darker faces were shining, and the laughter was spontaneous. The driver opened the door and slipped out sideways from behind the wheel in order to collect the tickets. The chatter outside increased, and the knot became tighter. The first two boarding the bus hardly hesitated long enough to hand him their tickets, but came on sticking out their passes in his general direction, their grinning faces searching the bus for seats. They came aboard in quick succession, the first, the second, the third—then two were jammed on the step.

"Now wait a second," the driver said. "Just hold it a minute. Get out there, go ahead, both of you. Wait till we get settled in here." Hands on hips, he waited for the doorway to be cleared and the group to come to order. Then he turned and rose on the balls of his feet to count the remaining seats.

A young colored girl and her youthful companion had slipped up behind the last white couple in the row, and now sat chatting and anticipating the crowd. She was perhaps twenty-four years old, high-spirited, loud and infectious in her laughter. Slender, light-colored, but not very good-looking, when she talked she enunciated her words clearly, almost self-consciously, and spoke without any trace of an accent. The young man with her was lighter than she, of slight build, thin shoulders, flat chest, sensitive, self-conscious in voice and manner. He carried with him a pile of books which were stacked laterally, in high-school fashion. The two had talked together for long, uninterrupted periods, now hushed, now loud, always eager, and always conscious of those around them.

By his glance the driver addressed himself to the couple. By nodding his head he indicated that he wanted them to move to the back of the bus. They did not respond. "Look," he called back, "you two will have to move to the back of the bus."

The girl paid no attention to him.

The driver looked at her sharply. After a pause he spoke to her in low, measured phrases.

"You heard me!" He pointed his finger at her. "Now go on, move back there like you're told."

"Say, who do you think you're talking to?" the girl flared. "Don't talk to *me* like that. What do you think I am?" She sounded angry, but by this time the situation had become clear to the driver, and after a hasty glance around the bus he turned and shut the door. Then he turned back to her.

"Well, I guess you're new down here. In case you don't know it, there's a law in this state which says that Nee-groes load a bus from the back forward. That's the law, and either you're gonna move back or we're not going to take on any more passengers until you do. Is that clear?"

"Certainly it's clear," the girl said. "It simply means that you won't take on any more passengers, because I have no intention of moving from this seat. I paid the bus company my good money for it and I'm staying right here. Besides, look here, there are enough people waiting outside to fill all the seats behind us, so I don't see any reason for our moving back."

"Now look, I'm not going to stand here wasting my breath arguing with you. I'm certainly not going to do that. Either you'll move back or I'll call the cops."

"Say, what is this, anyway?" Her voice rose. "How dare you speak to me that way? What do you take me for? Go ahead and call the cops. Do you think I'm afraid of their tin badges? . . ."

"Okay, we'll see." He turned quickly and officiously, pushing those at the door aside as he hurried out.

She was sitting up straight in her seat now and looking at those around her as if seeking some sign of support. The whites in front remained immobile. No one clucked, no one blew out his breath impatiently, no one turned to glare. No one was embarrassed—as yet—but only rendered actionless by the vigor and ferocity of this denial of the commonplace. The embarrassment and anger would come later. No doubt the clarity of the girl's sentence structure and the absence of an accent warned that this was no ordinary "Negro-gone-wrong." Both whites and blacks, though sensing the direction in which events might go, wished to hear a little more, anticipating perhaps a show which would terminate before the situation became so involved as to create a rising potency of racial feeling and antagonism.

"I can't understand this. I've never been treated this way before, and see no reason for it now." She shrugged her shoulders and waved her hands about with the palms up. "What does he take me for? I have my rights. I've paid my money, and good money, too. . . . Besides, I can't sit back there. I told him the seat is broken. The boy told him. I'm an ill woman and I cannot sit in that seat. I won't sit in that seat. He can call the whole police force. . . ." There was a long, silent pause. She sighed finally and sat back. The crowd outside had become still. The people stood without much movement, some tired, some resigned. The laughter in their faces had been replaced by sullen quiet, for by now it had become evident that "someone inside is makin' a fuss. Probably from up North."

The driver, who had been dashing in and out of the station in his search for aid, appeared from behind the cars parked outside the station. Two policemen were with him. All three walked very briskly, the driver preceding the others by a few nervous yards. In prearranged order they hopped into the bus, the young officer first, then the driver, and finally the older policeman, who remained standing on the lower step.

The young officer wore sergeant's chevrons. His uniform was tight-fitting and freshly pressed, and he wore freshly shined shoes and leather puttees. His fingers were hooked in a crisp Sam Browne belt from which dangled a new black leather holster, while two bright rows of copper-headed bullets and a gold-plated badge attested his right to speak with authority.

"All right," he muttered as he peered around for the source of the trouble. "Who is it?" The driver nodded in the direction of the couple. The girl was sitting back in her chair, her face drawn and her breath coming quickly.

He walked down to her seat, turning imperceptibly to allow for the narrowness of the passageway. Before speaking he looked long and hard at both of them.

"All right, now," he asked finally, "what's up?"

She did not answer or open her eyes, and the young man took it upon himself to explain.

"Nothing's wrong, officer. Nothing at all is wrong. We are simply sitting in these seats we paid to ride in. My friend here is ill. She can't ride over the wheel, and besides the seat back there is broken. . . ." His voice was just a bit too loud and too clear, an arrogant adolescent repeating by rote. Clearly he was not the one to deal with. The whites were not attracted to him because he was neither white nor black, spoke like neither, and threatened to upset a good fight.

"Why doesn't that guy shut up and let her do the talking?"

Before the youngster had finished his recital the officer had stepped back in order to get an uninterrupted view of the girl. "Aw, be quiet," he muttered. Under this impact the young man's chattering lurched, hesitated, petered out. By way of compensating for this humiliation the boy resorted to gaping up insolently, conspicuously, into the officer's face. The older man rendered this tactic ineffective by choosing to ignore it. He addressed the girl directly.

"Maybe you don't know it, but this bus is being held up just on accounta you two." He hooked one hand in his belt. "Let's not have any more trouble, is that clear? Now pick up your stuff . . ."

The girl was not to be so easily placated.

"Get out of here!" she cried. "Get out of here, do you hear me? You can't scare us. We're not animals. We're not dirt. Just because we're colored, you think you can push us around like sacks of meal! I'm not afraid of you, do you hear me. You don't frighten me one bit, not one tiny bit, with your gold-plated badge and your shiny bullets. Coming in here to bulldoze me with your bullets!"

The busload of people cringed under the pertinency of her observations as well as the force of her denunciation. Here was a situation far more complicated than the cop had figured on. The bus driver was due to catch hell for this. This girl was educated, and you had to handle them different. "Why didn't you tell me?" he complained to the driver as he swung out of the doorway. The girl continued.

"What does this mean? Why, you people on the bus, you saw! You heard! What does it mean? This shouldn't happen here. With his bullets and his patronizing tone. In America! Why don't you say something? Are you afraid? I'm right. I'm right. You know I'm right. All of you, all of you sitting there, you know I'm right."

The high-school senior sitting next to me was on his way to Duke University from Lansing, Pennsylvania, in order to see about the possibilities of a football scholarship. "What kind of hooey is this?" he mumbled, without looking up from the floor.

The driver was outside the door, calling to a helper across the yard. "Hey, Ed, you better pull out Number Two. I'm having some trouble here and it looks like we're not going to roll for some time yet. Load these on, willya?" He indicated the silent black group around him with a wave of his wrist. Then he climbed in. The fat cop followed him, and they both stood up front. Neither one moved. The bus was very silent.

Feeling behind him for the seat, the driver leaned against it, crossing his legs in front of him.

"Well, this is your trip, not mine. I don't care when we leave. I can wait all night."

No response. He stared at the girl absent-mindedly, sucking his tooth.

"I know this, though. We aren't moving out of this yard until you two move back."

"But look, driver," she was repeating it again just for him, because evidently it wasn't quite clear, and the trouble really was no trouble but only a failure of the two of them to reach a rational, common ground. "Look, driver, we aren't breaking the law. We aren't sitting up front there. When you let the others in, they'll fill in the back up to us and more. We wouldn't have moved otherwise. So why must we go back? I can't see the point. I can't." She began to cry. "Honestly, I can't see the point. I'm ill, besides, and can't sit back there. Won't you believe *that?"* She cried silently, slouched back in her seat, her head in her open hands.

The driver continued to stare at her. Silent until now, the older policeman pushed past him cautiously. In appearance he resembled the magazine-cover stereotype of "cop." Slow-moving, slow-thinking, soft-spoken, a half-popular man on the force, mild in manner, pleasant or nasty according to the orders of his superior; a frustrated mortal with a very large stomach.

Recognizing the possibilities of tact, he approached the girl. He was soft in his manner, though his face was very solemn. She wasn't so bad; the whole thing was about ready to break. With just a little proper treatment . . .

He leaned over and in a quiet, undisturbed voice advised her:

"Maybe you don't know it, miss, but there is a Virginia State Law that says that colored people must fill the bus startin' fum the rear. Now, I didn't make the law, but that's what it says, and there ain't much you or me can do about it."

No sign of response.

"It's just a law that way—the State Law of Virginia."

She looked straight up into his face for a long, uncomfortable moment. Taking a deep breath, she began to answer him, slowly at first, but then with increasing speed and mounting vehemence.

"You're not talking to *me* about the Virginia State Law. . . . I don't know a thing about the Virginia State Law. I never heard of it. I don't have to hear of it. This isn't Europe, you know. This isn't Europe! This is America! I'm not a Virginian, I'm a free American citizen. I can travel when and where I please and I don't need to give account to anyone. No one, do you understand? *No one.* At least," she protested, "at least I didn't *think* I had to give account to anyone. Why . . . why, there's a Constitution. Did you ever hear of the Constitution? Did you? Did your Virginia State Law ever hear of the Constitution?"

She was bold in her demand for an answer. The whites ahead of her smiled wryly, and a few shook their heads in embarrassed half laughter. "Oh-oh, we knew *that* was coming up."

"Where is she from?"

"New York."

"Uh-huh. . . . See?"

Disregarding the twisted heads, she continued. "I know my rights. I'm within my rights, and you just try to take them from me. I don't know about your law and I don't care. What *is* the difference between me and any other citizen? Is it my skin? My skin? *MY SKIN?* Is that it? Because I'm colored you think you are any better than I am?" She was hoarse with anger, and her throat muscles showed taut under the skin. She shrugged the boy's hand off her shoulder, where he had placed it by way of comfort.

Following this outburst there was a long period of inactivity. Adjusting his elbow on the baggage rack, the cop rested his head on the edge and peered down.

Certain blockages had presented themselves with which he felt insecure in dealing. A logical argument is a disturbing thing, especially when the answer comes out wrong. Maybe she had something, but he felt himself indisposed to debate. "It's still the law," he muttered, though he knew it was a waste of breath.

It was evident to all that an impasse had been reached; the cop was unable to debate with her, while at the same time he was loath to use coercion. Still, they just couldn't sit there all night. Besides, there was still a point of pride. Rights or no rights, logic or no logic, she was still a Negro and had talked too damn loud.

"I know what I would do if I was him."

"What would you do? What would you do? You'd do no more than he's done. He can't touch her because she's right and he knows it. According to plain common sense she's right, and don't think he wouldn't be glad to get out of the whole damn thing. What he's trying to figure out now is how he can get through with her and still be able to say to his boss or her lawyers, if she brings it to court, that he was acting in the name of common sense and the public trust. The poor flatfoot is having his own troubles. Right now he's thinking so hard his brain's like to pop from the strain. So what would you do? Better just shut up and listen, that's what you better do."

"We been in here almost three quarters of an hour. We'll be late for that nine-fifteen out of Danville. What are we gonna do if we miss that nine-fifteen out of Danville?"

"They prob'bly know . . ."

"I'm hungry. I didn't eat supper so's I could catch this bus. If I'd-a known this was going to happen, I'd-a gone inside and had me some supper. Seven-thirty. Am I hungry!"

"You'll find some candy in my coat pocket—up there on the rack."

"Look at what just pulled up."

"The wagon."

"Look at them lights on it. Square lights. Did you ever see square lights on a car? Not since the war you didn't. I remember square lights on cars, but you don't. I'll be damned, square lights. They ought to burn that boiler before it drops out from under them."

The conversation subsided and there was another long pause. The cop remained immobile. Once more he tried.

"Now look, miss," but it really was a waste of breath on his part, for he was only a day-to-day policeman who could not manipulate the fine points of law, and to the right people would have no compunctions in admitting it.

"I'm not sayin' anything about the Constitution, miss, because it's the Virginia Law which is what I'm here for, and that law says——"

The passengers, Negro and white, coughed and turned in embarrassment. The poor man had nothing fresh to contribute.

"Here's where it starts all over again."

The girl was quick to relieve everyone. "Now *you* look, mister," she interrupted. "I don't know what you take me for. I think I'm as good as anybody on this bus." A few heads in front turned slowly for the first time since the incident had begun. "What is more important, I'm ill. Ill! I'm sick! I can't ride over the wheel and I won't ride over the wheel. Besides, the seat is broken and I will not sit in a broken seat. . . . Say, look, mister, tell me, what is it that's wrong with me? Exactly what is it? Is there something wrong with my money?" And here her voice began to thin with tears. "I'm as good as any others. Because my skin is different from yours . . ."

The girl was saying things too bluntly. Who ever speaks these things out? Mention them to your priest; argue about them in class; a joke or two perhaps; but never, *never* shout. There are still some common decencies which white persons expect the educated Negro to observe. Granted that the word "equal" may be interpreted according to logical procedure to mean that educated Negroes and whites may ride side by side on the bus—is that any reason to take advantage of a good thing? Leave us a way out; cake dough whipped too hard will turn sour.

"Because I'm colored and you're white you think you can treat me like—like——" She burst into a long, sobbing wail, complaining finally through her tears that she had never been so embarrassed in her life. The boy next to me understood this. He settled back with a relieved "Hah."

The heavy crying broke the tension, and the policeman took the opportunity to leave. He picked a cautious way up the aisle, shaking his head as he went. Many turned to stare unkindly at the colored girl for her rudeness. Enough was enough. After all, she had made her point. Now "why don't she move back and let's get going?"

It was getting late and, seeing no further developments, the passengers began to grow impatient.

"Oh, sure we'll make that nine-fifteen, yeah, sure, oh yeah, like hell."

"Aw, stop crabbin'."

"Why don't they stop messin' with her or do something and let's get the hell outta here?"

The bus driver and the two policemen stood talking outside. Their conversation was inaudible, but that all three were very concerned was evident in the way they talked. Once the younger cop waved his hand as if in disgust.

A tall, well-dressed colored man sitting near the rear got up from his seat and, after mustering his poise, left the bus. Walking over to the three men, he was soon engaged in the argument. It was surprising to notice that he was quite firm and seemed to have something very definite to contribute. More than once his gestures indicated his unquestioned disapproval of what the other speakers were saying. All was quiet in the bus except for the gentle moaning of the girl and the whispered comfortings of her companion.

Then the colored man got on again, went straight to his seat, and sat down without saying a word. He was followed shortly by the bus driver, who began to distribute white cards such as are used in case of accident. Space was provided on the card for a brief description of the accident, a statement as to who was at fault, and an indication that the undersigned would be willing to act as a witness in court. Space was provided for the name, address, city, and state of the signer.

The card idea did not catch on.

"What do you want us to write?"

"Uh, just write down what you saw." The driver was flustered. He was an hour late, had been ill-advised, his job might well be in the balance, the Negroes were taunting him, and the whites didn't know what to do. Well, neither did he.

"Do you want us to sign our names?"

"Is this going to court?"

"There really was no accident. How can you answer it?"

"What did you write?"

"What did *you* write?"

"The hell with it. I left mine blank. I don't want no part of it."

"Look, look, he wrote 'nonsense' on his. Let me see again. Look, Cecelia, look what he wrote on his. 'Nonsense.' Isn't that cute? Here, lemme —— May I just borrow it a second? Thanks. See? . . . Are you going to sign your name? . . . Really?"

The driver had to say something while he waited for the cards. "I sure want to thank all you people for your help. . . ." Though that is not at all what he meant.

The colored girl did not know whether to laugh or cry. Over and over she repeated: "This is ridiculous. Ridiculous. This only happens in the movies. Why, I never . . . I . . . it's impossible . . ."

The fat policeman climbed into the bus again. In his hand were two warrants. The two men walked down the aisle to her seat and stood there a brief moment, looking first at her and then at each other, before the policeman began the dialogue.

"Do you want to swear out warrants for their arrest?"

"Of course I don't want to swear out——"

"Why not! Of course. Go ahead and make out warrants." She leaned toward them. "Are you still trying to frighten me? Are you really that simple? Don't you think I'll know what to do about it? Certainly I know. I'll take this case to court, and don't you think for one minute that I don't mean exactly what I'm saying. I'm not an ignoramus. I know my rights. If you think I'm not going to sue the bus company you're crazy. I'll sue the State of Virginia. I'll carry this case to the Supreme Court if I have to. I can do it, so go ahead and swear out your warrant because you don't scare me one bit. Not one bit.

"I've never in all my life been treated like this, and there are laws to prevent it from happening again. What do you take me for? I ask you. Why don't you answer me? Just what is it I *have* done? Is it the color of my skin, is that what it is? Well, can I help the color of my skin? Can I? *CAN I!*"

The bus driver pushed past the policeman and walked to the front of the bus.

She continued, but her voice was low and trembling, for she spoke with deep feeling, her stare fixed on the seat in front of her.

"Officer . . . officer, tell me, please, tell me what *is* the difference between me and any other woman in here?" The bus was very still and her voice carried to every ear. "If I were a white woman you couldn't do enough for me." Here she faltered and her lips trembled. "I'm colored and I'm sick. . . . Will you believe me?" She looked up at him. "Will you believe that I can be sick? Am I not human? Do I look any different from any other human being? My God, officer, don't I eat and sleep and talk just like any other human being? . . ."

The policeman tapped the papers with his pencil and peered around at the driver. The force of the outcry subsided and he poised his pencil.

"What's your name? Let's finish this up. What's your name?"

The answer was long in coming.

"Alice McBean."

The cop was indisposed to the task, and he wrote with difficulty because his mind was not on his duty.

"Alice . . . what?" He started, scratched it out, and started again. Without looking up, "Alice what?"

The weary answer came again.

"McBean. Capital M - c, capital B - e - a - n. Alice McBean. It's simple enough."

"Never mind that," he grumbled. "What's your address?"

"Four forty-one Wilmington Park West, New York City."

". . . Park . . . York City." He placed a dot after "City," glanced over the paper to see that it was in order, then slipped it under the other one and turned his attention to the boy.

"Yours?"

"Oliver Fleming, one thirty-five West One Hundred and Fortieth Street, New York City."

". . . easy, take it easy . . . Fleming. What else?"

The boy was very careful to see that the policeman had no further trouble understanding him.

After finishing with the names the policeman turned and went up the aisle, where the driver joined him. "Now, look, I've written the warrants out, but I don't think you'll need to serve them. Suppose I give them to you anyway and you hold them, and if you have any more trouble with them on the road, why, just stop the bus."

The younger officer stuck his head in the door. "They're no good beyond the city limits."

"Oh, that's right, I forgot. They're no good beyond the city limits."

The bus driver looked as perplexed as the cops looked embarrassed. The papers changed hands three times before the older policeman snatched them, glared down the aisle, snapped them against his palm, and pocketed them. A sign from the younger one and the meeting adjourned again to the outdoors.

The talk was muffled, but the tone indicated that everything was going to be all right because "we're willing to forgive and forget, but!—she'll have to meet us halfway." The two cops walked away from the bus, thereby carrying out their part of the bargain. The driver came aboard and approached the seat once more. This time he leaned his elbow on the back of a seat, his back almost parallel with the floor, and with a supplicating gesture put the proposition to her.

"Uh-h—look. There's really no reason for us having any trouble."

Though she made no answer, the girl rolled her eyes sideways to glance at him.

"Suppose we don't say anything more about it, only we'll meet each other halfway. Now that's fair enough, isn't it? I don't like this trouble any more than you do. Suppose we just compromise and we'll let it go like ladies and gentlemen. I realize you're new down here, and I don't blame you in a way. But you have to see our side too. Let's make it then that you move back one seat, just back here—and that's up further than you were before——"

The boy snapped him up.

"Oh no, it isn't! We were sitting just behind here. We moved up one seat. One seat, that's all."

"I don't like to contradict you——"

The girl spoke. "Of course there is no reason to contradict him, because I *was* sitting back there right in that broken seat."

The colored gentleman toward the rear nodded his head in relieved agreement. He reached out and touched the driver's arm.

"She's right, driver . . . right across there. She was sitting there."

The driver conceded the point.

"Okay, so you were sitting there. Well, it's a fair enough deal, isn't it?"

The young man with her revealed himself as the weaker of the two by the spirit of his acceptance. While speaking he glanced quickly from one face to the other. "Alice, that's fair enough. Isn't it? I think that's fair enough. Don't you? He's willing to meet us halfway, and I think we ought to do the same."

There was a slight pause before she looked up, smiling, and though many looked for it, there was no hint of malicious satisfaction, nothing to indicate that she was intending, subtly or not, to rub salt into an inviting wound.

She tossed her head slightly. "All right," she nodded, "I'm willing to compromise. What you ask is very fair, and I'll be more than glad to meet you halfway. That is all I ask, after all." She looked straight into his face and he nodded blankly in agreement. "Except that I still will not move back to a broken seat."

In one long stride the driver was beside the seat in question. He gave it a wrench, then a harder one. The ratchet caught with a loud click, and the seat fell into place.

"There you are." He returned graciously. "Fixed." He bounced the cushions with his palms. "Try it yourself and see. Nothing broken about it now. It just hadn't caught, that's all."

The two of them hitched themselves around to examine it over their shoulders. Putting his books down beside him, the younger one got up to try it.

"You know," the girl said to the driver, who was dusting off his hands, "you know, I don't like this any more than you do."

"I know. Well, I've tried to be as polite as I could about it. I want to be a gentleman if I can. . . ."

The boy brushed past him and plumped into the seat. "It's okay, Alice. I tried it and it's okay."

The bus driver dropped his head, his lips pressed together in annoyance.

"If that's the case, then I have no further objections." She turned in her seat to collect her purse and hat. The driver let out a long, slow breath and pushed his hat back from his forehead.

Rising from her place, she hesitated, glanced up at the driver, and, gnawing her lip, settled back. Before he could question this new development, she began.

"You have been very fair to me. You have been a gentleman. . . ." Again that smile.

The bus was a tomb of cold, puzzled silence.

"You're a gentleman, and I'm a lady . . ."

She sounded almost drunk.

". . . and therefore . . ."

Therefore!

". . . and therefore I think that as a gentleman to a lady you owe me an apology."

Good God in His everlasting mercy, did she realize what she was doing? The stillness pounded on the ears.

"Alice . . ." the young man behind her protested.

"Yes," she continued, "that strikes me as very fair."

Transfixed, the driver stared down at her. The smile remained in her face, and she nodded her head ever so slightly from side to side as if in nervous approbation of her idea.

"Apologize. Apologize for what?" His words were thick with effort.

"For the way you spoke to me." The smile vanished. "And, also, incidentally, I want it understood that I'm moving back to that seat only on the condition that it remains in perfect working order. . . ."

A few turned in their seats, visibly shocked.

Slowly the driver straightened up. This was the opening, here was something to understand; the fog had finally dissipated and the barriers were down.

He backed up with a snarl, "You black . . ." Growling and blind with rage, he was out of the bus in three clattering leaps. ". . . fool. . . ." He was yelling for the police even before he was out of earshot.

"Where did they go! Where did they go!" A brief glance around the yard, and he strode, almost ran, into the depot. The door had hardly slammed shut when it was flung out again; the three men emerged.

The driver jumped into the bus first and stood, arms akimbo, as the fat policeman walked down the aisle. The papers were in his hand as he approached them, and before he began to speak he cleared his throat.

"All right," he snapped, "now listen. You first." He indicated the boy by pointing his finger. He then proceeded to read the contents of the paper.

"Warrant for the arrest of Oliver Fleming, of one thirty-five West One Hundred Fortieth Street, in New York City, in the City of Petersburg, Virginia——"

"What did we do?"

"Shut up!" he rapped. "You're under arrest. I'll do the talking, you just shut up and listen. . . . In the City of Petersburg, Virginia, on the twenty-third day of March, nineteen hundred and forty, to wit: You are hereby charged with disorderly conduct and creating a public disturbance on a vehicle operating . . ." The voice droned on. The boy put his hand to the side of his head, registering amazement. When the charge had been read, the cop handed the warrant to the boy. "Here."

The boy took it.

The cop turned his body in, facing the girl, who by now was sitting upright, watching everything, at once fascinated and repelled by the performance. A lawsuit seemed a very definite thing now. The necessity for taking the right steps was impressed upon her consciousness. For many of the passengers it was the first time that they had witnessed the serving of a warrant, and now to be so close to the actual legal procedure proved intriguing. The linkage between the delicate, razor-edged wording of the document and the fat cop reading it was not clear; but one thing was certain, this was the law in action—albeit in slow motion.

"Warrant for the arrest of Alice McBean, of four forty-one Wilmington Park West, in New York City, in the City of Petersburg, Virginia, on this twenty-third day . . ." He read hers through without interruption. Finished, he handed her the paper with an abrupt movement and stepped back to let them precede him.

"You are both under arrest. Collect your stuff and get off this bus, and right now."

The two of them sat there looking at each other. Then they peered into the blank pink faces around them, at the driver, up at the cop, and finally back to each other.

"Come on, get up. *Get up!* Get your stuff, wherever it is, and get out."

The boy started to rise, was checked momentarily by the restraining hand of the girl.

"Don't make no fuss, there," the cop warned, "because I already give you the warrant, and I don't want no trouble outta you. You better come quiet and don't make no fuss."

The boy finally moved in his seat, stepped down to the aisle and began to load his arms—books, a coat, a battered yellow cardboard hatbox, a brief case, and a magazine. The box bounced against the seats as he made his way up the aisle so that his exit was not a graceful one.

The girl stayed where she was. Her face was drawn. "I'm ill. I'm ill," she said.

"Can't help that. You'll have to get up."

"Then you'll have to carry my typewriter. I'm too weak to carry my typewriter, and I won't get off without it."

"Where is it?" He searched the dark recesses of the baggage rack. "Okay, I'll carry your typewriter. Anything else?"

"No." Shifting over from the seat next to the window, she stepped out to the aisle while the cop backed up to give her room. She caught the seat for balance and stood swaying slightly, her hand pressed to her forehead, her eyes closed. A moment later she collapsed into the laps of the colored couple sitting across from her. Her arms flapped unnaturally as she fell.

With an awkward movement of his elbow and arm, the policeman tried to stop her.

"Here. None of that. None of—— Say what are you trying to pull?" She lay there while he looked around foolishly. If she weren't really unconscious, how was he to prove it to her? And if she were, how was he to get her out of there with his hands already full?

"Come on, cut it out. That's an old trick." He turned and addressed the people ahead, putting it to them. "That's an old trick." The girl remained motionless, however, and the couple in whose laps she lay were squirming and holding her head up with the ends of their fingers.

The cop put down the typewriter case and reached down to get a grip. A white man rose to help him but was pushed back by another sitting across the aisle. "Leave her."

He had the girl around the chest with his arms locked in front of her. She made a long, unwieldly bundle, resembling nothing so much as a seedy scarecrow, with her disheveled coarse black hair, homely flat features, head tipped mawkishly on one shoulder, arms hanging limply, though at a slight angle, away from her body. The cop shifted his awkward burden in order to keep her feet from dragging. Even so he had to shuffle up the aisle with his legs apart to keep from tripping.

At the door two pairs of arms extended into the bus's interior to grab the girl's legs. One step at a time the load was carried out, heavily and with much difficulty. The cop stepped full on his heels as he went down each step, and the impact could be felt throughout the bus. Once outside, two men were found sufficient to carry the limp burden. Once, however, they had to stop while the one holding her legs boosted her up with his knee, balancing her there until he was able to get a better hold.

A curious knot of people followed them to the patrol wagon, where it was a short moment's work to load the two of them in. After supervising this procedure, the young officer turned for a final word with the bus driver, who checked to see that everyone was aboard, and climbed in himself. The patrol wagon moved off slowly, almost reluctantly. The siren did not wail. The bell was silent. And the wagon waited patiently for the traffic to clear before getting into the line of cars going in its direction.

The driver watched the patrol wagon until it had became an inconspicuous part of the general stream of movement, and then he turned. Without a word he began to collect the cards which he had distributed earlier. He glanced at each one as it was handed to him, and looked up somewhat startled at one which read, "Nonsense. Bonehead playing all around." He reached the end of the aisle.

"Any more? Did I miss any?" A few shook their heads. "Okay." He walked absent-mindedly over to his seat, and sat down slowly, engrossed in reading the cards. At length he glanced abruptly up into the mirror, pocketed the cards hurriedly, cleared his throat, and leaning forward, flicked on the ignition. The motor spun hard and long before it caught, sputtered, caught again. He jazzed it up in a deafening crescendo and then waited for the roar to subside before putting in the clutch. The gears screamed, whined, dropped to a complaining moan, and with a dull resigned "clop" fell into place. The bus jerked as it started to roll.

"Eight-thirty."

A few seats tipped back as the passengers adjusted themselves for the night trip.

The boy next to me hoisted himself free of the seat by using his elbows and the seat arms for leverage, and as he settled slowly into a fresh position he plucked at the crease in his trousers.

"How far is it from Durham to Duke?"

"A mile, maybe."

"I hope they have buses. I bet I'll have to call him up now to meet me."

The student returning from vacation to Chapel Hill, the sociologist away from home, twisted in his seat in order to address the pretty girls sitting behind him. One leaned forward smiling when he opened his mouth to indicate that he wanted to say something.

"Well, there you have it. The next time someone speaks to you about our 'classless society,' you tell them about what you saw and ask them for an interpretation."

The girl looked properly impressed with this profound observation. The student smiled in a tired, knowing way. "Did you ever read *It Can't Happen Here?*"

She shook her head to indicate a negative answer. "Only the first few pages."

He twisted up further in order to get a clearer view of her. "Better read it." The driver took a curve hard, and, rather than risk losing the possible good impression that he had made, the student slid back into his seat.

The buzzer sounded and the bus slowed to a crunchy stop in order to discharge three Negro passengers. Hunched over in anticipation of the low doorway, the first one tapped the driver on the shoulder and waved his hand in friendly greeting as he clattered out. "Thankya, boss." The second did the same. The third said nothing. His hand on the door lever, the driver called after them.

"Boy, she sure didn't come from Virginia, did she?"

"Ah shood say not!" The answer drifted down the length of the bus as the group moved off.

He leaned toward the door, addressing the darkness. "Ain't you boys glad you live in Virginia?"

Again the answer, "You shoor said it, boss."

There was no echo to the driver's thin laughter.

"Good night."

"So long."

The door swung shut, the gears ground into place, and the bus pulled away. The driver glanced around quickly and turned back with a sniff of embarrassment. "A-h-h."

He punched out the lights. The bus picked up speed, slackening but imperceptibly as it jolted over a railroad crossing. According to any overt signs, the drama was over. . . .

Shall we applaud?

RUNAGATE NIGGERS

William March

With Company K, *written in the twenties, William March established himself as one of our most exciting contemporary writers. His short stories, formerly contained in several collections, will be merged in one volume to be published in the fall and called* Trial Balance. *Born in the South, he now lives in New York.*

LAFE ROCKETT'S WIFE began talking as soon as Uncle Elbert arrived and eased himself into the wicker chair on the porch: "I don't know what this country's coming to, when they put law-abiding citizens like Lafe in jail for no reason!"

Uncle Elbert rocked, rubbed his chin, and said: "If you want me to help Lafe out of his trouble, you'd better tell me what happened, Birdie."

"It really began last winter, Uncle Elbert, when Lafe put a nigger couple named Sam and Aphie to farm his cutover land near Milden, and no niggers ever got better treatment from a white man than those two did. Lafe advanced 'em their vittles and rented 'em a mule, but from the first those two niggers was always complaining. They said the land was so pore and stumpy that nobody could make a crop on it without some fertilizer. Sam said the only thing that growed well on that land was the squash and collards that Aphie raised.

"Well, things went on like that, with them niggers complaining that they didn't have enough to live on, and Lafe advancing meal and side meat now and then, until the cotton they'd planted was forming bolls. Lafe used to ride out regular to look at the cotton, and even though it was pindling, because of them niggers being so worthless, he figgered the crop would just about pay for the vittles he'd laid out and the rent owing to him.

"Uncle Elbert, Lafe treated them niggers as fair as anybody could, but they was just no-account. This'll give you some idea: Last spring Aphie wanted a dog for company, so Lafe gave her a hound puppy. Well, sir, when Lafe seen that hound three months ago, he said the sight of it made him want to cry. It was nothing but skin and bones. He said he couldn't understand how anybody could treat a dog like that. Sam said the reason was because they hadn't had nothing to eat all summer themselves, except collards and squash, and that a hound wouldn't eat squash or greens."

"I haven't got no use for folks that treat their dogs sorry," said Uncle Elbert. He shook his head.

"Things might have been all right," continued Birdie, "except for that rainy spell in September. It started just when the cotton was made and ready to be picked, and it lasted three weeks, nearabout. When it was over, Sam and Aphie's whole crop was soured and rotted in the bolls. After that, it looked like those two niggers was hanging around our kitchen all the time, begging for vittles. There wasn't much Lafe could do, but to show you how fair he acted, he said he'd let 'em stay on another year, if they found a way to feed themselves. By that time they'd have all the stumps out, and could make a better crop. He even said he might advance some fertilizer next spring if things worked out well."

Birdie laughed bitterly and wiped her mouth. "We found out later what a sly one that Aphie is, and how she was working behind Lafe's back all the time she was begging him for vittles. You see, Uncle Elbert, she had a sister cooking for some white folks in Chicago, so when Aphie got old Mrs. Todd to write a hard-luck letter to this here sister, she answered right off and sent what money she'd saved up, telling Sam and Aphie to come on to Chicago. That next day Mrs. Todd read the letter to Aphie and told her how to cash the money order.

"Well, Sam and Aphie must have had a guilty conscience, and when they ran away they didn't go to Milden to cash that money order or take the train there, because they knowed Lafe would hear about it, sure, and stop 'em. Instead, they lit out one night to walk to Lippincott, twenty miles away. It might have worked, at that, except the Pritchett boy seen 'em on the road, figgered out what was going on, and told Lafe. He also knowed about Aphie's letter, because Mrs. Todd was his aunt, so when Lafe found out about that, he did what anybody would: He wired the deputy sheriff at Lippincott to watch for two niggers carrying bundles and leading a hound and to hold them until he got there.

"Lafe said, when he got back from Lippincott, that he and the niggers and the sheriff all got to the depot about the same time. Sam and Aphie had already cashed the money order and were buying tickets when the sheriff put the handcuffs on 'em. It provoked Lafe right smart to see those niggers spending money they rightly owed him, so he lost his temper, like anybody would, and started hitting Sam and Aphie with a strap he happened to have with him at the time. But the story that he chained 'em to a tree when he got 'em home is a pure lie! He only *said* he'd do it, if they run off owing him money again, to show off before that woman at the depot. . . .

"You see, Uncle Elbert, when the trouble started, there was a young white woman standing on the platform who seen the whole thing, and when Lafe started hitting the niggers, she opened her camera and took pictures of it. She even followed the men back of the depot and talked with Lafe and the sheriff, laughing and joking. She asked Lafe how it happened, and he told her the whole story, just as I've told it to you; but the woman shook her head and said she didn't believe that part about sending the telegram. That was too smart to think of, she said, and she thought Lafe was making that part up.

"Well, sir, by that time she'd told her name and Lafe and the sheriff had told theirs, and they were all laughing and talking together in the friendliest way, so the sheriff took out the telegram and showed it to her, to prove Lafe was right. So this woman said she'd like to keep the telegram for a souvenir and put it in her purse. The train pulled in about that time and the woman shook hands and got on board. . . . Well, like you've already guessed, she went straight to Washington and turned the photos and the telegram over to the government, and yesterday two Federal men arrested Lafe and the deputy sheriff on a peonage charge and took 'em to jail."

Lafe's wife was quiet for a moment, rocking back and forth. "I declare," she said bitterly, "I don't see how any white woman could go back on her own race that-a-way! I don't see how anybody could be so low-down!"

Uncle Elbert spat over the rail and wiped his chin slowly.

"I been figgering things over all yesterday and today," continued Birdie, "and the more I think, the more disgusted I am with this here country and the way things are run. Things have come to a pretty pass when a man can't catch his own runagate niggers!"

Uncle Elbert spoke thoughtfully: "Lafe got him a lawyer yet?"

Birdie said: "For two cents I'd move out of this country and go some place where people still enjoy liberty. That's how disgusted I am with this here country, and I don't much keer who knows it, either!"

THE PEOPLE vs. ABE LATHAN, COLORED

Erskine Caldwell

Erskine Caldwell is the author of a novel called Tobacco Road, *which as a play threatened to outlive its creator. He is equally well known as a short-story writer, and recently all his stories were merged into a single volume titled* Jackpot.

UNCLE ABE was shucking corn in the crib when Luther Bolick came down from the big white house on the hill and told him to pack up his household goods and move off the farm. Uncle Abe had grown a little deaf and he did not hear what Luther said the first time.

"These old ears of mine is bothering me again, Mr. Luther," Uncle Abe said. "I just can't seem to hear as good as I used to."

Luther looked at the Negro and scowled. Uncle Abe had got up and was standing in the crib door where he could hear better.

"I said, I want you and your family to pack up your furniture and anything else that really belongs to you and move off."

Uncle Abe reached out and clutched at the crib door for support.

"Move off?" Uncle Abe said.

He looked into his landlord's face unbelievingly.

"Mr. Luther, you don't mean that, does you?" Uncle Abe asked, his voice shaking. "You must be joking, ain't you, Mr. Luther?"

"You heard me right, even if you do pretend to be half deaf," Luther said angrily, turning around and walking several steps. "I want you off the place by the end of the week. I'll give you that much time if you don't try to make any trouble. And when you pack up your things, take care you don't pick up anything that belongs to me. Or I'll have the law on you."

Uncle Abe grew weak so quickly that he barely managed to keep from falling. He turned a little and slid down the side of the door and sat on the crib floor. Luther looked around to see what he was doing.

"I'm past sixty," Uncle Abe said slowly, "but me and my family works hard for you, Mr. Luther. We work as hard as anybody on your whole place. You know that's true, Mr. Luther. I've lived here, working for you, and your daddy before you, for all of forty years. I never mentioned to you about the shares, no matter how big the crop was that I raised for you. I've never asked much, just enough to eat and a few clothes, that's all. I raised up a houseful of children to help work, and none of them ever made any trouble for you, did they, Mr. Luther?"

Luther waved his arm impatiently, indicating that he wanted the Negro to stop arguing. He shook his head, showing that he did not want to listen to anything Uncle Abe had to say.

"That's all true enough," Luther said, "but I've got to get rid of half the tenants on my place. I can't afford to keep eight or ten old people like you here any longer. All of you will have to move off and go somewhere else."

"Ain't you going to farm this year, and raise cotton, Mr. Luther?" Uncle Abe asked. "I can still work as good and hard as anybody else. It may take me a little longer sometimes, but I get the work done. Ain't I shucking this corn to feed the mules as good as anybody else could do?"

"I haven't got time to stand here and argue with you," Luther said nervously. "My mind is made up, and that's all there is to it. Now, you go on home as soon as you finish feeding the mules and start packing the things that belong to you, like I told you."

Luther turned away and started walking down the path towards the barn. When he got as far as the barnyard gate he turned around and looked back. Uncle Abe had followed him.

"Where can me and my family move to, Mr. Luther?" Uncle Abe said. "The boys is big enough to take care of themselves. But me and my wife has grown old. You know how hard it is for an old colored man like me to go out and find a house and land to work on shares. It don't cost you much to keep us, and me and my boys raise as much cotton as anybody else. The last time I mentioned the shares has been a long way in the past, thirty years or more. I'm just content to work like I do and get some rations and a few clothes. You know that's true, Mr. Luther. I've lived in my little shanty over there for all of forty years, and it's the only home I've got. Mr. Luther, me and my wife is both old now, and I can't hire out to work by the day, because I don't have the strength any more. But I can still grow cotton as good as any other colored man in the country."

Luther opened the barnyard gate and walked through it. He shook his head as though he was not even going to listen any longer. He turned his back on Uncle Abe and walked away.

Uncle Abe did not know what to say or do after that. When he saw Luther walk away, he became shaky all over. He clutched at the gate for something to hold on to.

"I just can't move away, Mr. Luther," he said desperately. "I just can't do that. This is the only place I've got to live in the world. I just can't move off, Mr. Luther."

Luther walked out of sight around the corner of the barn. He did not hear Uncle Abe after that.

The next day, at a little after two o'clock in the afternoon, a truck drove up to the door of the three-room house where Uncle Abe, his wife, and their three grown sons lived. Uncle Abe and his wife were sitting by the fire trying to keep warm in the winter cold. They were the only ones at home then.

Uncle Abe heard the truck drive up and stop, but he sat where he was, thinking it was his oldest boy, Henry, who drove a truck sometimes for Luther Bolick.

After several minutes had passed, somebody knocked on the door, and his wife got up right away and went to see who it was.

There were two strange white men on the porch when she opened the door. They did not say anything at first, but looked inside the room to see who was there. Still not saying anything, they came inside and walked to the fireplace where Uncle Abe sat hunched over the hearth.

"Are you Abe Lathan?" one of the men, the oldest, asked.

"Yes sir, I'm Abe Lathan," he answered, wondering who they were, because he had never seen them before. "Why do you want to know that?"

The man took a bright metal disk out of his pocket and held it in the palm of his hand before Uncle Abe's eyes.

"I'm serving a paper and a warrant on you," he said. "One is an eviction, and the other is for threatening to do bodily harm."

He unfolded the eviction notice and handed it to Uncle Abe. The Negro shook his head bewilderedly, looking first at the paper and finally up at the two strange white men.

"I'm a deputy," the older man said, "and I've come for two things—to evict you from this house and to put you under arrest."

"What does that mean—evict?" Uncle Abe asked.

The two men looked around the room for a moment. Uncle Abe's wife had come up behind his chair and put trembling hands on his shoulder.

"We are going to move your furniture out of this house and carry it off the property of Luther Bolick. Then, besides that," we're going to take you down to the county jail. Now, come on and hurry up, both of you."

Uncle Abe got up, and he and his wife stood on the hearth not knowing what to do.

The two men began gathering up the furniture and carrying it out of the house. They took the beds, tables, chairs, and everything else in the three rooms except the cookstove, which belonged to Luther Bolick. When they got all the things outside, they began piling them into the truck.

Uncle Abe went outside in front of the house as quickly as he could.

"White folks, please don't do that," he begged. "Just wait a minute while I go find Mr. Luther. He'll set things straight. Mr. Luther is my landlord, and he won't let you take all my furniture away like this. Please, sir, just wait while I go find him."

The two men looked at each other.

"Luther Bolick is the one who signed these papers," the deputy said, shaking his head. "He was the one who got these court orders to carry off the furniture and put you in jail. It wouldn't do you a bit of good to try to find him now."

"Put me in jail?" Uncle Abe said. "What did he say to do that for?"

"For threatening bodily harm," the deputy said. "That's for threatening to kill him. Hitting him with a stick or shooting him with a pistol."

The men threw the rest of the household goods into the truck and told Uncle Abe and his wife to climb in the back. When they made no effort to get in, the deputy pushed them to the rear and prodded them until they climbed into the truck.

While the younger man drove the truck, the deputy stood beside them in the body so they could not escape. They drove out the lane, past the other tenant houses, and then down the long road that went over the hill through Luther Bolick's land to the public highway. They passed the big white house where he lived, but he was not within sight.

"I never threatened to harm Mr. Luther," Uncle Abe protested. "I never did a thing like that in my whole life. I never said a mean thing about him, either. Mr. Luther is my boss, and I've worked for him ever since I was twenty years old. Yesterday he said he wanted me to move off his farm, and all I did was say that I thought he ought to let me stay. I won't have much longer to live, noway. I told him I didn't want to move off. That's all I said to Mr. Luther. I ain't never said I was going to try to kill him. Mr. Luther knows that as well as I do. You ask Mr. Luther if that ain't so."

They had left Luther Bolick's farm and had turned down the highway towards the county seat, eleven miles away.

"For forty years I has lived here and worked for Mr. Luther," Uncle Abe said, "and I ain't never said a mean thing to his face or behind his back in all that time. He furnishes me with rations for me and my family, and a few clothes, and me and my family raise cotton for him, and I been doing that ever since I was twenty years old. I moved here and started working on shares for his daddy first, and then when he died I kept right on like I have up to now. Mr. Luther knows I has worked hard and never answered him back, and only asked for rations and a few clothes all this time. You ask Mr. Luther."

The deputy listened to all that Uncle Abe said, but he did not say anything himself. He felt sorry for the old Negro and his wife, but there was nothing he could do about it. Luther Bolick had driven to the courthouse early that morning and secured the papers for eviction and arrest. It was his job to serve the papers and execute the court orders. But even if it was his job, he could not keep from feeling sorry for the Negroes. He didn't think that Luther Bolick ought to throw them off his farm just because they had grown old.

When they got within sight of town, the deputy told the driver to stop. He drew the truck up beside the highway when they reached the first row of houses. There were fifteen or eighteen Negro houses on both sides of the road.

After they had stopped, the two white men began unloading the furniture and stacking it beside the road. When it was all out of the truck, the deputy told Uncle Abe's wife to get out. Uncle Abe started to get out too, but the deputy told him to stay where he was. They drove off again, leaving Uncle Abe's wife standing in a dazed state of mind beside the furniture.

"What you going to do with me now?" Uncle Abe asked, looking back at his wife and furniture in the distance.

"Take you to the county jail and lock you up," the deputy said.

"What's my wife going to do?" he asked.

"The people in one of those houses will probably take her in."

"How long is you going to keep me in jail locked up?"

"Until your case comes up for trial."

They drove through the dusty streets of the town, around the courthouse square, and stopped in front of a brick building with iron bars across the windows.

"Here's where we get out," the deputy said.

Uncle Abe was almost too weak to walk by that time, but he managed to move along the path to the door. Another white man opened the door and told him to walk straight down the hall until he was told to stop.

Just before noon Saturday, Uncle Abe's oldest son, Henry, stood in Ramsey Clark's office, hat in hand. The lawyer looked at the Negro and frowned. He chewed his pencil for a while, then swung around in his chair and looked out the window into the courthouse square. Presently he turned around and looked at Uncle Abe's son.

"I don't want the case," he said. "I don't want to touch it."

The boy stared at him helplessly. It was the third lawyer he had gone to see that morning, and all of them had refused to take his father's case.

"There's no money in it," Ramsey Clark said, still frowning. "I'd never get a dime out of you niggers if I took this case. And, besides, I don't want to represent any more niggers at court. Better lawyers than me have been ruined that way. I don't want to get the reputation of being a 'nigger lawyer.'"

Henry shifted the weight of his body from one foot to the other and bit his lips. He did not know what to say. He stood in the middle of the room trying to think of a way to get help for his father.

"My father never said he was going to kill Mr. Luther," Henry protested. "He's always been on friendly terms with Mr. Luther. None of us ever gave Mr. Luther trouble. Anybody will tell you that. All the other tenants on Mr. Luther's place will tell you my father has always stood up for Mr. Luther. He never said he was going to try to hurt Mr. Luther."

The lawyer waved for him to stop. He had heard all he wanted to listen to.

"I told you I wouldn't touch the case," he said angrily, snatching up some papers and slamming them down on his desk. "I don't want to go into court and waste my time arguing a case that won't make any difference one way or the other anyway. It's a good thing for you niggers to get a turn on the 'gang every once in a while. It doesn't make any difference whether Abe Lathan threatened Mr. Bolick or whether he didn't threaten him. Abe Lathan said he wasn't going to move off the farm, didn't he? Well, that's enough to convict him in court. When the case comes up for trial, that's all the judge will want to hear. He'll be sent to the 'gang quicker than a flea can hop. No lawyer is going to spend a lot of time preparing a case when he knows how it's going to end. If there was money in it, it might be different. But you niggers don't have a thin dime to pay me with. No, I don't want the case. I wouldn't touch it with a ten-foot pole."

Henry backed out of Ramsey Clark's office and went to the jail. He secured permission to see his father for five minutes.

Uncle Abe was sitting on his bunk in the cage looking through the bars when Henry entered. The jailer came and stood behind him at the cage door.

"Did you see a lawyer and tell him I never said nothing like that to Mr. Luther?" Uncle Abe asked the first thing.

Henry looked at his father, but it was difficult for him to answer. He shook his head, dropping his gaze until he could see only the floor.

"You done tried, didn't you, Henry?" Uncle Abe asked.

Henry nodded.

"But when you told the lawyers how I ain't never said a mean thing about Mr. Luther, or his daddy before him, in all my whole life, didn't they say they was going to help me get out of jail?"

Henry shook his head.

"What did the lawyers say, Henry? When you told them how respectful I've always been to Mr. Luther, and how I've always worked hard for him all my life and never mentioned the shares, didn't they say they would help me then?"

Henry looked at his father, moving his head sideways in order to see him between the bars of the cage. He had to swallow hard several times before he could speak at all.

"I've already been to see three lawyers," he said finally. "All three of them said they couldn't do nothing about it, and to just go ahead and let it come up for trial. They said there wasn't nothing they could do, because the judge would give you a term on the 'gang anyway."

He stopped for a moment, looking down at his father's feet through the bars.

"If you want me to, I'll go see if I can try to find some other lawyers to take the case. But it won't do much good. They just won't do anything."

Uncle Abe sat down on his bunk and looked at the floor. He could not understand why none of the lawyers would help him. Presently he looked up through the bars at his son. His eyes were fast filling with tears that he could not control.

"Why did the lawyers say the judge would give me a term on the 'gang anyway, Henry?" he asked.

Henry gripped the bars, thinking about all the years he had seen his father and mother working in the cotton fields for Luther Bolick and being paid in rations, a few clothes, and a house to live in, and nothing more.

"Why did they say that for, Henry?" his father insisted.

"I reckon because we is just colored folks," Henry said at last. "I don't know why else they would say things like that."

The jailer moved up behind Henry, prodding him with his stick. Henry walked down the hall between the rows of cages towards the door that led to the street. He did not look back.

"—NEBER SAID A MUMBLIN' WORD"

Vernon Loggins

Vernon Loggins, a native Texan, was educated at the University of Chicago. He has taught at New York University and Columbia.

TOM WHITTLETON, his red face gleaming, his thick blue shirt splotched with patches dark in the wet of perspiration, stalked up his back-gallery steps. When he reached the top he kicked off his heavy brogans—hurled them bang against the wall, leaned his shotgun in the corner next to the kitchen door, and patted over to the wooden water bucket, which was hanging on a wire fastened to a rafter. "This stuff was drawed yestiddy mornin'!" Nevertheless, he drank three full gourds of it, dipping each time right down to the yellow slimy bottom of the bucket.

His thirst slackened, he slapped his hands against his breast, sent tiny squirts of perspiration darting out from between his fingers. He was satisfied with himself. Hunting rabbits on an April afternoon when the cotton was in the grass and needed plowing wasn't exactly work, and yet it was useful. The long-eared, white-tailed little pests were fine in corn dumplings, just the right sort of grub to make kids grow. It wasn't his fault if the Lord didn't scare up any of the animals for him to take a crack at. He had rambled down the gullies and in the woods looking for them—harder work than following a lazy mule along a furrow. "In the sweat of thy face shalt thou eat bread." God had said that to Adam; and he was Adam's son, sweating. Yes, he was satisfied with himself.

"Mama!" he called.

"I'm fixin' the boys' breeches, Papa. Come on out here an' blow a minute," reeled the whining reply of his wife, Maude, from the front gallery.

He slipped into the hall, his gray-stockinged feet dragging along the smooth pine floor, scoured that morning and still not dry in places. As he passed the parlor door, a nice inspiration came to him. Since he was an elder, blessed with the ceremony of the laying on of hands only the summer before, he could well give the rest of the afternoon to a reading of the Word. He turned and eased into the room, where there was bright-colored straw matting on the floor, over the windows long trailing lace curtains dotted with last year's Sunday-school Christmas-tree ornaments, and in the most prominent corner a golden-oak whatnot adorned with homemade paper flowers, more and more of them and brighter and gayer as he looked from the top to the bottom. Too fancy. He had always felt out of place here, ever since he was a boy and his oldest sister had threatened him with a spanking if he came prowling around where she was entertaining her beaux. Ugh. Hadn't all this been his own for years now, the pretty as well as the homely? Why, before very long beaux would come courting his own daughter. Addie Bird was thirteen her last birthday, and soon there would be plenty of boys setting their caps for her.

Reassured and proud and master-like, he strode over to the center table and picked up a much-worn Bible with a limp cover projecting into a skimpy ruffle around the edges. The touch of the Book in his hands gave him a feeling of righteousness, and he walked out on the front gallery and sat down in a rocking chair near his wife, who was in the act of putting the finishing touches to a neat pair of patches on the seat of their son Bob's pants.

"You needn' be readin' for prayer meetin' tonight, Papa. Alice was here right after dinner, an' she said that ol' Brother Cooke come ridin' up to her gate this mornin' 'bout leben o'clock. I 'low he'll be holdin' preachin' tonight."

"Ol' Brother Cooke? He ain't been in this neighborhood in fifteen year! What'd he go to Alice an' Ned's for? Why didn' he come here?"

"She didn' tell me that." Silence—during which Mrs. Whittleton took off her spectacles and looked down the road. "Them chillun's late gittin' from school." More silence—except for a nimble needle making little fine stitches in tough cotton cloth and Tom Whittleton's big gnarled thumb following clumsily the lines of the Forty-sixth Psalm. "Anyway, 'tain't any o' us what needs a preacher's company. An' as for Alice—she's lived a faithful Christian ever since she come through. But Ned, even if he is y'r brother—well, backslidin' like he does, I'd hate to be in his shoes when he gits up to the judgment house on the streets o' pearl."

She might have been saying, "Scat, Jack Robinson!" so far as her husband was concerned. "There is a river, the streams whereof shall make glad the city of God, the holy place of the tabernacle of the Most High." He was on the banks of that wondrous river, in company with a host of saints, all of them with their wings lowered in humble and comely manner. The waters were sparkling with the brilliance of the July sun, but his eyes, transfigured by the grace of Jesus Christ, were not dazzled. Transfigured by the grace of Jesus Christ, he had a pretty way of reasoning things out, even when his mind was in the ecstasy of a heavenly vision.

"Papa, here comes them two boys, an' Addie Bird ain't with 'em!" Maude Whittleton sighed, dropped her sewing in her lap, and looked up anxiously.

Bob and Marvin, aged fifteen and fourteen respectively, leaped over the board fence separating the yard from the open horse lot, wheeled around the flower beds—phlox and verbenas blooming—sprang up to the front gallery, and threw down their dirty oilcloth book satchels and dinner pails. They were in a feverish hurry about something.

"What's the matter with you two youngsters?" snarled their mother. "Ain't I done tol' you not to leave Addie Bird come home by herself, with all these black bucks doin' nothin' but traipse up an' down the road day an' night?"

"Augh—she had to stay in. She don't never know her spellin'," retorted Bob, who had inherited his mother's peculiar whine. "An' we couldn' wait. There's a crowd cuttin' a bee tree over in the Henson pasture, an' we're goin' to git some honey."

"Wanta come, Papa?" suggested Marvin, who had examined his father's expression and had decided that Bob was too sure.

"You ain't goin' to take a step to the Henson pasture," said Tom Whittleton, patriarchal. He had laid his Bible down on the floor by his chair and was standing up straight. "You're goin' with me to the cotton patch. Git y'r hoes."

His sons hung their heads, muttered something about "never havin' no fun," and moped around the house in the direction of the log crib where the farming tools were stored.

"You're too easy on them boys, Tom," explained Mrs. Whittleton, her apprehensive eyes fixed on the road. "They oughta be whipped. I don't have a minute's peace when Addie Bird is out of my sight. I've felt that way ever since what happened to that po' girl up in the Cedar Creek neighborhood las' fall."

"Ain't you never goin' to git through talkin' about that? The niggers aroun' here know their place. I ain't the deputy sheriff o' this beat for nothin'."

The sharp grinding noise of hoes being filed came from the back yard, and Mr. Whittleton, content that he was training his offspring to know the blessings of such honest toil as Moses had enjoined upon the children of Israel, started for his shoes. Just as he was entering the hall door, piercing shrieks, repeated screams, broke the afternoon stillness of the oak-bordered road.

"It's Addie Bird, Tom! My God!"

One glance at the anguish in his wife's ashen, stupefied face, and he dashed off the gallery, down the front walk, pushed the yard gate open with such force that a hinge was wrenched split, and ran madly towards the frenzied screams. Around the bend by the duckpond he rushed, and there was his little daughter flying up the middle of the sandy road, her long yellow hair in a straight stream behind her, her hands jerking furiously, her short skirt worked up above her knees by her fast-moving legs.

"Papa! Papa!" she cried, in a spasm of relief, as he sped on to meet her. Soon her palpitating body was folded in his arms.

"What's happen, my chil'? Tell me!"

But her breath was wheezing in quick nervous pants, and she was speechless. He nestled her hot head against his bosom and turned to retrace his steps back to the house, carrying her along as though she were still a baby.

"Tom! Tom! Is she dead?" called Mrs. Whittleton, just on the other side of the duckpond.

"No, Mama!" cried the girl, relaxed enough now to break into a fit of tears.

The dread-driven woman, followed by her two boys, appeared from around the bend. She came on desperately, clutched the sobbing child, and held her tightly.

"It's y'r kind ol' mother that's got you now, sweetie! Don' cry no mo'. Come, an' say what made the lil angel lamb holler like that!"

The father and sons looked on in a passive wonder. There was more coaxing, and soon Addie Bird was in condition to speak.

"I stopped at the bendin' oak," she said in a shambling voice, "an' put down my things to pull some violets. I heard somep'n in the woods, an' I was scared it was a mad dog, an' when I looked up a nigger was crawlin' through the fence. He come runnin' towards me, an' when I started away he whistled an' said for me to wait an' he wouldn' hurt me, jus' like that nigger done up on Cedar Creek."

"God protect us po' women! It's right in our own home at last! I knew it! I felt it comin'!"

"Where's he went, Addie Bird? Had you ever seen 'im befo'? Go on an' tell me everything. I'm y'r papa, an' have got to know!"

"I looked back once, an' he was wavin' his han' at me to foller 'im up the Gladish road, an'——"

The horrified faces of her mother and father and brothers threw the child into another terror, and her words were lost in a fresh paroxysm of screams.

Tom Whittleton, his brow stern and dreadful with determination, fixed his eyes on Bob and Marvin.

"Go to them fellows cuttin' that bee tree in the Henson pasture an' tell 'em what's happen. Run every step o' the way. Come on, Mama."

His sons darted into the woods to obey his command, and he snatched his daughter into his arms again and ran to the house with her. His wife, sobbing and crying more violently than the child, struggled along in the sand behind him.

He put Addie Bird down on his own bed, left her in the care of her frantic mother, and made for the telephone in the hall.

Four short rings—his brother's store, opposite Hopewell Church, where the Gladish and Rock Island bottom roads crossed. Curious ears, at least a dozen of them, followed the custom of the party line and clicked receivers off the hooks. "Stay on, all o' you. I wants you to hear what I got to say to Ned." "H'lo," came his brother's deep-bassed voice. "Ned, this is Tom. A nigger attacked Addie Bird when she was comin' home from school. He was last seen turnin' up the Gladish road. Stir everybody up. We've got to find 'im."

Without waiting for a word of reply, he thrust the receiver roughly on its resting place, hurried to the back gallery for his shoes and shotgun, came back to the trunk in the hall for his revolver—emblem of his distinction as an officer of the law—and rushed to the stables and threw a saddle on his red mule. God was on his side, for he had kept that mule from her pasture that afternoon with the vague feeling that he might take a notion to plow a little.

Twenty minutes later a crowd of men, forty or fifty in number, on foot, mounted on horses and mules, in automobiles, were gathered around the bending oak where Addie Bird had stopped to cull violets. It was a stately and magnificent tree, with its great deep trunk slanting gracefully towards the east. It had bowed before a hundred years of beautiful dawns, and yet it was youthful. Parasitic gray moss and white-berried mistletoe and sapping ivy had made no inroads on its vigorous vitality. Free and strong, it projected its straight rich branches out over the road, on the most shapely of which a long heavy rope was now strung.

One end of it was held in the hands of three men, Tom Whittleton's brother Ned among them; and the other end was being tied around the neck of a tall black Negro, perhaps twenty years old. He was straight and rigid, his bare feet imbedded in the sand, his head thrust back slightly by the knots in the rope under his chin. His awful rolling eyes seemed to stare without seeing the glowering faces about him. His fingers were twitching strangely, making little circles and figures, as though they would in some way exorcise the steel handcuffs that bound his wrists.

"For the las' time I asks you," fiercely rang the voice of Tom Whittleton, who was standing just at the foot of the tree, his two young sons near him, "to confess y'r crime."

The Negro remained fixed, a statue of terror. No movement, except in the twirling black fingers.

"This'll make 'im talk," growled Ned Whittleton, and straightway a pocketknife was stuck deep in the victim's leg. There was a faint moan of pain, and blood oozed through the rough denim trousers and trickled down. The sight of it set the gloating onlookers on fire. Grim oaths and hideous curses rumbled, thundered, and more pocketknives were whisked out and hurled into the body of the Negro.

Still he did not speak.

"He's guilty!" shouted Tom Whittleton above the passionate uproar. "He'd howl out if he was innocent. Pull 'im up, boys!"

Silence speaks in the affirmative—nothing declared is always yes. The officer of the law reasoned that since he had heard this saying so many times, it must be in the Bible, and therefore infallible. Yes, God was on his side, making the path of his duty clear to him.

The deed was done. The tall black body hung stiff and stark in the air. For a few moments there was stillness, broken only by the blood dripping down the dangling legs and sinking heavily into the loose sand below.

Then conversation arose, talk quiet and casual, about the wisdom of keeping niggers in their places, and crops, and mares that were going to foal, and the June elections. Contented, sated, the lynchers dispersed.

Tom Whittleton, leading his submissive red mule, walked slowly up the road in the company of his two boys. When they reached the open place, where his field began, the sun, no more than a half hour high, was shooting wide bands of yellow light right down the cotton rows.

"Didn' he never say a single word, Papa?" asked Marvin.

"Narry a word," answered the father. "He was shakin' like a ague when Ned an' them fellows found 'im runnin' through that hump o' woods at the crossroads. Nobody couldn' git nothin' out o' him, excep' a few grunts. They always acts like that when they's guilty."

"Didn' nobody know who he was?"

"No. He was a strange nigger. Musta come from across the river some'rs."

"Who's goin' to cut 'im down?"

"Ned's goin' to git ol' Uncle Jerry an' his boys to take 'im to the Rock Island bottom an' bury 'im."

"I thought he'd dance when they pulled 'im up," interposed Bob, who had the habit of going about with his head dropped and was not so inquisitive as his brother. "He didn' do nothin' but hang up there straight."

"I saw his neck gittin' longer. I bet it's more'n two feet by this time," added Marvin.

When they got into the house, they found Addie Bird and her mother in the parlor. The girl had all of her dolls sitting up in a row on the sofa and was pinning paper flowers on them, playing like a child of six, to the delight of her doting mama, who had listened over the telephone and had already heard in detail the relieving tidings of the hanging.

At supper, when a sweet-potato pudding was served because Addie Bird was very fond of it, Tom Whittleton reminded himself and his hungry family that old Brother Cooke would no doubt preach at the prayer meeting at Hopewell Church that night. It was out of the question to think of the baby girl leaving the house after the nerve-racking experience which she had undergone in the afternoon. Maude ought to stay with her. The boys must work their sums, for a man could never know too much arithmetic. Anyway, every blessed soul under Tom Whittleton's rooftree had confessed Jesus Christ as a personal saviour, and it wasn't a sin if a meeting was missed occasionally, when there was a real excuse. But, as for the father himself, he was an elder and must always go, rain or shine, sickness or health.

Thus the matter was beautifully reasoned out while he and his wife and children ate sweet-potato pudding. When the last morsel was devoured, he got up, emitted a puffed grunt of satisfaction, and then went to comb at his hair and put on a gray coat over his blue shirt, which had been wet with sweat twice that day and was still a little damp. Armed with his Bible and a lantern, he set out, with that sacred feeling which always came over him when he was going to church. The dew hadn't fallen yet, so he took the short cut through the cotton patch and the stretch of woods up by old Aunt Dora's house.

There was a waning glow of red in the west, but the stars were out in all their numbers and a full moon swung tranquilly against the milky sky over towards Gladish. Frogs had set up a merry questioning and answering in the duckpond, and whippoorwills called playfully to each other along the edge of the woods. The smell of growing April was in the air. The elder, unconscious of his surroundings, left the cotton field and entered the trail leading through the woods. He was thinking hard, trying to decide whether it really would be his duty to run for sheriff when Bill Perry did finally retire. There was nothing to do but trust to God to give him a sign. He passed on by Aunt Dora's house, a hundred yards in front of it, and saw the old woman sitting on her doorstep with the light of the moon falling directly on her round black face.

As he neared the church, the singing started, all the congregation, and a big one too, repeating lustily:

"When the roll is called up yonder I'll be there!"

He loved the songs that told about heaven—his inheritance as a child of God, and the inheritance of Maude and the three kids also. Listening intently, he stole up to the little porch at the entrance of the church and slipped his lantern, which he had not lighted, under the steps. He would not go in until the chorus was ended, since it was as bad to interrupt a hymn of praise as it was to walk into a sanctuary while a preacher or elder was leading a prayer.

"Tom," spoke his brother just behind him.

"Hello, Ned. You here?"

"Yep. I wanted to fin' out what ol' man Cooke had to say tonight. He's all shook up over what happened this evenin'. Alice said he come pretty near faintin' when he foun' out that there'd been a hangin' right under his nose. He went in the front room an' got down on his knees an' prayed for hours, didn' eat no supper."

"Well, I do declare. That's funny."

"I think the ol' man must be kinda crazy."

"He was a rip-roarin' soul-winner in his day. Let's go in befo' another song starts. There's Alice over next to the front window holdin' a place for you."

"Wait a minute. There's somep'n else I wanted to tell y'u. Uncle Jerry an' his boys cut down that nigger, an' the ol' man sent 'em on to Rock Island bottom with 'im an' come back home to do the feedin'. The blamed fools got it into their heads that it'd bring bad luck to touch a hangin' tree, an' they lef' the rope there. Couldn' you git it when you go by on your way home? We oughtn' not to leave it there."

"Sho, I'll git it. It'll make a good pair o' tetherin' ropes for the cows."

The two brothers entered the church. Ned did not join his wife, but slouched down in the first vacant seat he came to in the back. Tom, setting a good example by holding his Bible so that everybody could see it, made straight for his accustomed place in the amen corner.

If they expected anything exciting from the visiting preacher, they were to be disappointed. The old man might have come into the church with a special message, but now that he faced his hearers he was afraid to voice it. For an hour he talked vaguely and incomprehensibly about Christians keeping the peace of God in their hearts. The congregation, among whom Tom Whittleton counted twenty who had helped at the hanging, grew fidgety. Nobody seemed to be touched except Sister Henson, who kept putting her handkerchief to her eyes. It didn't take much to make that woman cry. Ned left before the sermon was half over, and Tom was disgusted that such a weak-voiced preacher was not put on the superannuated list. What sinners and backsliders needed was to be scared out of their skins by thundering stories of hell-fire and brimstone, like the tale of the jay bird and eternity.

But at the conclusion of the service something really did happen. "Let us lift our hearts to God in a prayer of silence, and go meditating on Him to our homes," said the old man, supporting himself on the pulpit. Tom Whittleton got on his knees and closed his eyes to pray. The church was still, like death. Then, across the fields and through the woods, came the sound of a ringing bell, intermittent peals, louder and clearer after each interval. It was in the direction of Rock Island bottom. God! Those dirty niggers were burying that black beast in the nighttime and were bold enough to toll a funeral knell for him. Every last one of the brutes ought to be wiped out of existence for the outrage.

The officer of the law straightened up from his knees, looked about, and saw that heads were being raised and necks craned all over the house. Then for one long moment his eyes were fixed on the unearthly, bowed face of the aged preacher. There was a look in that wizened countenance which he didn't understand, which all his reason couldn't for the time explain. It was like a ghost. With the image of it glaring clear in his mind, he broke up the prayer of silence by shuffling roughly out the back door. From there he rushed around to the front for his lantern and was gone before anyone else left the church. He must see Ned, for something had to be done about that infernal bell, the inevitable tolling of which was still sounding.

But the knell had ceased before he reached his brother's yard. Leaning up against the gatepost, he lighted his lantern and waited, terrified lest the frightful ringing would set in again. Voices came from the foot of the lane leading up to the house—Alice and the kids and old Brother Cooke. A cold shiver throbbed through him at the thought of looking upon that strange and ghastly countenance again. He ran across the vegetable garden and crawled through a barbed-wire fence out into the main road, and started rapidly towards the bending oak. He wanted to get that rope and be through with this business.

At last he reached the tree, looming up in the silent moonlight, with its great spreading limbs, and broad folding leaves, and new acorns sticking around like little balls. He had always liked this oak. When he and Ned were boys they used to race and see which one could climb it first. They would crawl up high, straddle their legs across a branch, take hickory nuts from their pockets, and crack them between two rocks, making believe that they were squirrels. Thank God that niggers thought there was a curse on it and would let it alone. But would it ever again be the same to him, now that his little daughter had happened to stop there to gather flowers?

He unwound the rope from the trunk of the tree, stepped back to pull down the end that was suspended above, and his foot struck something solid. It was Addie Bird's book satchel, buried in the sand, and on one side of it there was a splotch of dried blood as big as his hand. He would bury the things somewhere. No. Mama could wash off that satin and the satchel would be as good as new.

Burdened with the Bible, the lantern, the satchel, and the rope, now made into a neat roll, he trudged on towards home. When he reached the duckpond a strange, uncanny sound came to him from somewhere in the woods. That bell was tolling again. No, it was somebody singing—a nigger woman—old Aunt Dora. He stood still and listened. She must be on her doorstep, where he had seen her two hours before, with the moon shining right down on her black face. The words fell distinctly on his ears.

"Dey pierced Him in de side,
An' He neber said a mumblin' word.
Dey pierced Him in de side,
An' He neber said a mumblin' word—
Not a word—not a word—not a word.

"De blood come twinklin' down,
An' He neber said a mumblin' word.
De blood come twinklin' down,
An' He neber said a mumblin' word—
Not a word—not a word—not a word.

Held as though charmed, he heard the song to the end. Then, in no way aware of what he was doing, he impulsively hurled the book satchel and the bundle of rope into the pond. The loud splashes in the water brought him back to himself. That old woman had no right to make him destroy things. A farmer worth his salt never knew what it was to have too much rope, and it would take five dollars to replace those schoolbooks. He would show her who could pay for them. She mustn't forget that she was working a few acres of his land on halves, and that next fall when the year's profits were divided he would do the figuring. Her half wouldn't amount to more than a gourd.

He went on, and did not stop again until he reached his house, where everything was dark and silent. He flopped down in his rocking chair, set his lantern up on the arm of the swing, and opened his Bible to read. A few verses here and there would calm his mind, get him ready for a good night's sleep. "The heavens declare the glory of God: and the firmament showeth his handiwork." No. He could see nothing in the heavens but the yellowish sickly moon—like the countenance of old man Cooke, staring at him. And something was holding him down—the weight of that cursed rope and bloodstained book satchel. And there was a continual ringing in his ears—that funeral bell, and old Aunt Dora's song—

Dey pierced Him in de side,
An' He neber said a mumblin' word.

He turned the leaves, and a trembling terror gripped him as he read: "Thou shalt not kill." But a soldier who had fought in France had explained to him what that commandment really meant. The chaplains always read it, "Thou shalt do no murder," and that was the way God meant it when he handed it down to Moses. Germans had to be killed during the war, beeves and hogs had to be slaughtered, fryers had to have their necks wrung, rats had to be choked in traps, and sometimes niggers had to be hung. It was easy to see how clear that was.

But maybe the nigger whom he had sent to death that afternoon had meant no harm to Addie Bird and shouldn't have been killed. Could niggers possibly have souls? He would open the Bible just anywhere, and what his eyes fell upon would give him light on an answer to that question. God had helped him solve many a problem in this way. He turned the pages again, and saw: "Blessed are the meek, for they shall inherit the earth." The meek?

Dey pierced Him in de side,
An' He neber said a mumblin' word.

Cowering in horror, seeing the finger of a wrathful God pointed at him and directing him to that hell of flames which he had so many times warned sinners against, Tom Whittleton dropped his Bible to the floor and covered his face with his rough hands. He was aroused from his agonizing reverie by a horse galloping up the road towards his house. From the hind feet dragging in the sand, he recognized it as Ned's mare, and he was waiting at the gate when his brother arrived.

"Tom," began Ned, anxiety in his voice, "have you heard anything about Sheriff Perry resignin'? I think you'd better go to West Falls in the mornin' an' see 'im."

"Didn' I tell you about that?" replied Tom, somewhat relieved. "There ain't nothin' to it. He's jus' puttin' out that rumor in case anybody runs again' him in the primary. Then he could use it in his campaign that he wanted to quit an' the people wouldn' let 'im. I had dinner with 'im las' Sa'day, an' we talked it all over. He wants me to keep on as deputy in this beat."

"Well, that takes a load off'n my mind. I heard it from Luke Wallis tonight, an' if Perry'd git out an' the wrong sort o' man'd git in befo' the grand jury meets, you an' me an' some more fellows aroun' here might be in for it."

"What do yo' mean?"

"That nigger we hung this evenin' was innocent."

"Innocent? Don' say that! How do y'u know?"

"Ol' Jerry's boys foun' out who he was when they got down to Rock Island with 'im. He'd been plowin' for Luke Wallis a week or two, an' I rode down to see Luke to git things straight. He was a West Falls nigger, an' this evenin' a telephone message come for 'im that his mammy was sick, about to die. When we caught 'im he was hurryin' to Gladish to ketch the train to go to her."

"But why didn' he explain things to us?"

"There was a mighty good reason," Ned went on, half laughing. "He couldn', 'cause he was deaf and dumb."

"It's a lie! He hollered to Addie Bird to wait!"

"Augh—Maude has spoiled that kid so that she's scared o' her shadow an' is likely to imagine anything."

"You're jokin' with me! Tell me 'tain't so! Tell me that that nigger wasn' deaf an' dumb!" Tom Whittleton's whole body was shaking, and he had caught hold of the palings to steady himself. "Ned, do you believe niggers is got souls?"

"My God, Tom!" exclaimed Ned, disgusted. "Are you goin' crazy? Since you been an elder you ain't like yourself. I'm jus' as good a Christian as you, but I'll be damned if religion has made me a chicken-hearted fool. Of course niggers ain't got no souls! I'd rather hang a real brute any day, but one that's deaf an' dumb is better'n none at all. Here. Take a swig o' this white mule an' brace up."

Tom Whittleton took the opened bottle which his brother was holding out to him. "Look not upon the wine when it is red." But it wasn't red. It was watery. Color! He held the bottle to his lips and took a long draft of the fiery liquid. Color! Why, everything depended upon color! A mule often lost her hearing when she strained herself in pulling a heavy load up a hill, and he had a cow once so dumb she couldn't utter a sound. Her durned calf would see her shaking her head and wagging her tail and understand her just as though she were mooing. Color and souls and brutes. Why hadn't he used that head which God had given him? Things were so simple when a man reasoned a little.

"I don' like ol' man Cooke's way o' actin'," Ned was saying. "I'm goin' to give 'im a strong hint in the mornin' to be pushin' on. We want a preacher in here like that fellow Graham over in Montgomery County. By golly, he led a lynchin' hisself not long ago. What do y'u think about an intimidatin' raid? Luke Wallis says he'll see that there ain't no talk among his niggers about this hangin', but I think we ought to scare the res' of 'em up a little too. They didn' have no business to toll that bell tonight."

"Intimidatin' raid?" answered Tom, enthusiastic. "Sho. Make it to-morrow night. I'll tell all the fellows I see to meet at the bendin' oak at ten o'clock. We'll tackle ol' Dora first o' all. I wants to see that ol' woman shake till she coughs her gills up so's she can never sing no mo'. An' say, Ned. Bring along a quart or two o' that white mule if y'u got it to spare."

"All right. It's good stuff, ain't it? So long. See you tomorrow."

He rode away, and Tom Whittleton walked heavily upon his gallery. Since God had given him peace of heart, what would the Word say to him now? He picked up his Bible, opened it at random, and held it in the light of the lantern to read: "For rulers are not a terror to the good works, but to the evil." Rulers? That was simple enough. It was what he had been looking for, the sign, direct from heaven, that he should run for sheriff when Bill Perry retired. Yes, the Lord was on his side.

Glowing with satisfaction, he took his Bible into the fancy parlor, placed it reverently on the center table, and blundered into his bedroom without waking his wife. Ugh. Mama had Addie Bird in bed with her. He'd rather sleep on the cot in the boys' room anyway, for Maude's snoring was getting to be something terrible.

PART III

Today and Tomorrow

CITIZENS OF NEGRO BLOOD

Wendell L. Willkie

The whole world mourned the loss of Wendell Willkie, who spoke for all minorities and fought hard to make America realize what we owe them.

The political and economic status of our citizens of Negro blood assumes an importance in the election of 1944 which has not been equaled since the period immediately following the Civil War. The Negro people and their spokesmen both in the North and in the South know this; thoughtful Americans of whatever racial background know it; our enemies and our allies know it. Only those leaders of our two political parties who wrote and influenced the party platforms apparently have failed to grasp the import of this fact.

The war has given new opportunities to the Negro and at the same time has emphasized the injustices in our attitude toward him. More than that, it has made us conscious of the contradictions between our treatment of our Negro minority and the ideals for which we are fighting. The equitable treatment of racial minorities in America is basic to our chance for a just and lasting peace. For it cannot be too much emphasized that in the world today whatever we do *at home* affects our foreign policy and whatever we do *abroad* affects our domestic policy. The two are necessarily interrelated. On no single question is this truth so inescapable as in the repercussions all around the world that result from our treatment at home of our colored citizens.

One of the widespread consequences of this war is the growing determination among colonial, subject, and minority peoples everywhere to win for themselves a share of the freedom for which the Allied Nations are fighting. This is the great quest of our time. To future historians it may well overshadow all other aspects of the present conflict. We, as Americans, cannot be on one side abroad and the other at home. We cannot expect small nations and men of other races and colors to credit the good faith of our professed purposes and to join us in international collaboration for future peace if we continue to practice an ugly discrimination at home against our own minorities, the largest of which is our thirteen million Negro citizens.

The list of grievances of the Negro people is a long one. Not only is the Negro in many parts of the country denied his legal rights in violation of the Constitution, but he is denied the substance of freedom and opportunity in such matters as equal education, equal chance for economic advancement, and his just share of such public services as playgrounds, hospitals, and community provisions for health and welfare of all kinds. He is systematically housed in the worst sections of our large cities, and for his poor housing is frequently charged exorbitant rents. He is traditionally the "last hired" and the "first fired." He is too often denied protection under the law. But of all the indignities and injustices Negro men and women suffer today, the most bitter and ironic is the discrimination practiced by the Armed Forces of their country—the country for which they are being asked to give their lives.

In short, the Negro lives in our midst under discriminations which differ from the racial discrimination practiced by our enemies, the Nazis, only in that ours are illegal and that we are free—if we wish—to fight against them.

The deep patience of the colored people is nearing its end. The war has pointed the issues for them. They feel—and who can deny them?—that if they have the right to die with their white fellow citizens in the protection of liberty, they also have the right to live with them in the enjoyment of liberty.

We have granted them the first right. It is our obligation to see that they get the second. The most effective means at hand toward that end is political—effective as a bargaining point for the Negro whose vote at the moment is sought by both parties, and effective as an instrument of justice in the hands of all Americans who desire to redress wrongs of which most Americans are ashamed.

It must be said at once that both of the 1944 political platforms, in their pledges to the Negro and their programs for him, are tragically inadequate. It must also be said that the Republican platform is distinctly better than the Democratic. The latter, in a brief paragraph of generalities, gives lip service to the laws we already have and to the duties many of our elected representatives have systematically disregarded.

"We believe," reads the Democratic plank, "that racial and religious minorities have the right to live, develop, and vote equally with all citizens and share the rights that are guaranteed by our Constitution. Congress should exert its full constitutional powers to protect those rights."

Small wonder that the National Association for the Advancement of Colored People issued a statement after the Democratic Convention which said:

"To call the section on the Negro a plank is a misnomer. It is best characterized as a splinter. Badgered by professional bigots from the South and dictated to by Northern political machines more interested in votes than in principle, the Democratic mountain labored and brought forth a mouse of evasion by merely asserting that rights guaranteed by the Constitution exist and that Congress 'should exert its full constitutional powers to protect those rights.' When the Fourteenth Amendment was ratified in 1868, it said better what the Democratic platform of 1944 asserts."

This shocking and gigantic failure of the Democratic party was neither an accident nor an oversight. The Democrats yielded to the worst side of their split representation, and now their liberal Dr. Jekylls are telling us that they gained a "victory" over their reactionary Mr. Hydes. The victory, by their own confession, consists in having resisted pressure from the Hyde side of the party to adopt a "white supremacy" plank. In the name of party harmony the small but powerful group of reactionary party hacks—and they were not all from the South—was deferred to. No effort was made to mobilize the liberal Southerners and to give leadership to the increasingly large number of voters in all sections of the country who would have come to the support of a decent racial plank. Political expediency ruled.

The Republican platform condemns "unreservedly" the injection into American life of racial or religious prejudice. It calls for a congressional inquiry into "the extent to which mistreatment, segregation, and discrimination against Negroes who are in our Armed Forces are impairing morale and efficiency and the adoption of corrective legislation." It pledges the establishment by Federal legislation of a permanent Fair

Employment Practices Commission. It calls for the submission of a constitutional amendment for the abolition of the poll tax and "favors" legislation against lynching.

These are four outstanding evils in the present situation, and it is a step forward to have them concretely recognized. Of the four, however, only the forthright pledge of a permanent Federal Fair Employment Practices Commission can be said to meet realistically the need for action which the issues demand.

The plank in the Republican platform for a constitutional amendment to abolish state poll taxes in Federal elections presumably means that those who drafted the platform accepted the argument of the opponents of a Federal anti-poll-tax *law* that such a *law* would be unconstitutional. Certainly their motive cannot have been that they considered an amendment a practical means of achieving their end, for an amendment to the Constitution requires a two-thirds majority of both houses and ratification by three fourths of the states. There is no reason to believe the Southern die-hard senators would be less inclined to filibuster an amendment than they have been in the past to filibuster a bill. The only way to overcome a filibuster is cloture, which would meet the same arguments in the case of an amendment that it met this spring when an attempt was made to bring the anti-poll-tax bill to a vote.

But why did the drafters of the platform assume that a Federal anti-poll-tax bill was unconstitutional? There is excellent reason to believe that the Supreme Court would uphold its constitutionality. Certainly, in the interest of righting a great wrong as quickly and in as practicable a manner as possible, it would seem worth while to get the law passed and then, in our traditional procedure, let its constitutionality be tested. If the Supreme Court refuses to uphold it, that is the time to embark upon the very difficult course of attempting to amend the Constitution.

The leading constitutional argument of the opponents of congressional action to abolish the poll tax is that the poll tax is a *qualification* for voting, and the states have the right, under Article I, Section 2, of the Constitution, to determine the qualifications of voters.

But the legislatures of the states describe the poll-*tax* laws as tax laws and not as *election* laws. The Supreme Court has held that poll taxes are ordinary taxes, not qualifications for voting. Aliens, who cannot vote, are subject to it, and in some states persons over sixty are not required to pay it, though they are permitted to vote.

Since the right to vote in Federal elections is a constitutional right, Congress has the power to prohibit a state from taxing a Federal privilege and function. Article I, Section 2, which gives states the right to set qualifications, cannot be isolated from the rest of the Constitution.

The general power of Congress, under Article I, Section 8, Clause 18, "to make all laws which shall be necessary and proper for carrying into execution the foregoing powers," the privilege and immunity clauses of the Fourteenth Amendment, together with the general reservoir of powers of Congress with respect to impairment of Federal functions by the states, all taken together, outweigh the states' right to set qualifications.

Article IV, Section 4, is a well of comfort in itself to men and women who are concerned about discrimination: "The United States shall guarantee to every state in this Union a republican form of government." When a poll tax operates to deprive millions of citizens of the right to vote and when, because of it, only a tiny percentage of the eligible voters elect their representatives, a republican form of government is certainly being subverted.

Finally, Article I, Section 4: "The times, places, and manner of holding elections for senators and representatives shall be prescribed in each state by the legislature thereof; *but the Congress may at any time by law make or alter such regulations,* except as to the places of choosing senators," implemented by the "necessary and proper" clause, gives Congress the power to prohibit qualifications for voting which undermine the democratic foundations upon which our Federal government rests or which result in corruption or fraud in federal elections. (The poll tax, of course, often does. It is an old custom for politicians to pay poll taxes to get votes where needed.)

All of which goes to show that an excellent case can be made for the constitutionality of a Federal anti-poll-tax statute. Our constitutionalists are playing too safe; our politicians too wary.

There can be little doubt that the country as a whole is against the poll tax. An anti-poll-tax bill passed the House in 1942, and again in 1943 by a vote of 265 to 110. The threat of a filibuster on the part of a few senators kept it from reaching the floor in 1942 and from coming to a vote in 1943. It is a clear case of a minority—and a small one—obstructing the will of the majority.

The Republican plank for an amendment to the Constitution fails to say whether Republicans in the Senate will be more willing to vote for cloture in the case of an amendment than they were in the case of the Federal anti-poll-tax bill. Certainly the "white supremacy" Southern senators will be just as determined to filibuster.

Many Republican senators and a few Democratic ones insisted that they would have voted for the bill but were against cloture. The reluctance of the senators to invoke cloture seems to be at bottom more a concern with the prerogatives of the Senate than with any tenable argument that the right of unlimited debate is essential to the democratic process.

In 1789 the Senate rules provided for limiting the time of debate by putting the previous question which automatically terminated debate. In 1806 this rule was dropped, and the filibuster has been an American phenomenon ever since. The actual circumstances of the adoption of the cloture rule are revealing. In 1917 Senator LaFollette, the elder, and Senator George W. Norris talked the Armed Neutrality Bill to death.

President Wilson said at the time: "The Senate of the United States is the only legislative body in the world which cannot act when a majority is ready for action. A little group of willful men, representing no opinion but their own, have rendered the great government of the United States helpless and contemptible."

At the next session of Congress the cloture rule was adopted, 76 to 3. Under cloture, each senator is allowed one hour to debate—making ninety-six hours of debate in all on any given bill; hardly gag rule. Debate in the House is limited to one hour on any question for each representative.

Why is the poll tax so important?

The poll tax is one of the many devices which are used to keep Negroes from the polls in the South; but the disfranchisement it produces is not of Negroes only. Millions of poor whites are also disfranchised by poll taxes. Though one or two or three dollars may not seem a large tax, it must be remembered that in some of these states the average prewar cash income of sharecroppers and tenants—Negro and white alike—was two hundred dollars to three hundred dollars annually. Moreover, the poll tax is often cumulative; so that if a man does not pay his poll tax one year, he must, in order to vote the next year, pay back taxes as well as current taxes. In a few years this adds up to a sizable percentage of the total income of a very poor family—white or black.

A favorite contention of those Southerners who oppose Federal anti-poll-tax legislation is that it is a state matter which concerns only the people of the states and is no business of the rest of us. Nothing could be further from the truth. A study made by the National Opinion Research Center of Denver University in 1940 showed that 22 per cent of the eligible voters in the eight poll-tax states elected as many United States congressmen as 78 per cent of the eligible voters in the same number of free-voting states.

Furthermore, the South has only one real party. This fact, combined with the fact that only a small percentage of the people cast a vote at all, tends to make it easier than elsewhere in the country for individuals to perpetuate themselves in office. Since the important committee chairmanships and ranking positions go by seniority, these individuals, elected by a very small percentage of the eligible voters, wield a disproportionate power over the country's affairs. The political discrimination caused by the poll tax is not exclusively a state matter. It is a question which affects the government of the United States and hence all of us—wherever we live.

I think nothing more pertinent and more timely has ever been said on the poll-tax issue than was said in Congress last year when the poll tax was having its annual run-around in the House of Representatives. Rankin, Cox, and others of their way of thinking made speech after speech overflowing with ugly and unrestrained race hatred. Finally a young sailor in the gallery leaped to the railing and cried, "Mr. Speaker, I am a man from the Service. Do I have the right to be heard? I speak for thousands who cannot be here. Why does a man have to pay tribute for the right to vote? Why should a man be taxed to vote when he can fight without paying?"

The Democratic platform does not offer any remedy at all for the poll-tax evil—not even one so hard of attainment as a constitutional amendment. It expresses the pious belief that Congress should protect the right of minorities "to vote equally with all citizens." But in the face of decades of bad party record on the subject, it says nothing to indicate how its vague and generalized beliefs are to be made effective.

Neither does the Democratic party, to judge by its platform, recognize the need to protect our colored citizens against mob law.

The Republican party at least goes on record as being cognizant of the need. But its plank favoring anti-lynching legislation is unrealistic in detail. It even fails to specify whether state or Federal legislation is meant. But this is precisely the crux of the question. Here, too, the question of constitutionality has been raised again and again. Nevertheless the House of Representatives has passed three anti-lynching bills since 1922, all of which failed to become laws because of filibuster or threat of filibuster. The most recent, the Gavagan Bill, passed the House in January 1940 by a vote of 251 to 132. In 1937 a Gallup Poll showed that 72 per cent of the people in the whole United States and 57 per cent in the South favored making lynching a "federal crime."

The Gavagan Bill made it a felony, punishable in the Federal courts, for local or state officials to be guilty of negligence in lynch cases. The constitutionality of this bill was ably argued under the "due process" and "equal protection" clauses of the Fourteenth Amendment. If lynching isn't depriving a citizen of his life without "due process" and denying that citizen "equal protection" of the laws, it would be hard to say what is.

The 1940 bill was supported by a number of eminent Southerners and Southern organizations. Among the individuals supporting it were Mark Ethridge, of the Louisville *Courier-Journal,* and Douglas S. Freeman, distinguished biographer of Robert E. Lee and editor of the Richmond *News-Leader.*

Mr. Ethridge reminded us that: "America may consider herself a group of states, but in the eyes of other people we are a nation, and we must assume responsibility as a nation for whatever barbaric practices occur inside our borders."

Finally, there is the matter of discrimination against Negroes in the Armed Forces. Once more the Republicans are aware that something is wrong in our democracy, while the Democrats apparently haven't a disturbing thought on the subject. But once more the Republican remedy is inadequate. The Republican platform calls for a congressional inquiry into discrimination in the Armed Forces. Even the platform writers do not question the existence of discrimination. According to them, the purpose of such an inquiry would be to "ascertain the extent to which it is impairing morale." No informed person can doubt that it *is* impairing morale, not only of the colored soldier and his family, but of the thoughtful and sincerely democratic white soldier as well. The extent to which this is the case has been exhaustively documented in letters from servicemen, in discussions in the Negro and liberal press, and has had attention from such an authoritative publication as the *Infantry Journal.*

A congressional investigation is, in many circumstances, a most valuable mechanism of democracy. But it is a time-consuming one. Before any legislation could result, many months would pass, and the war in Europe—we may now legitimately hope—might be over. Under these circumstances it is inevitable that Negroes, in and out of the Armed

Forces, should interpret this plank as a device to delay, rather than to take effective action.

There is no question of the law. Section 4 (a) of the Selective Service Act reads: "In the selection and training of men under this Act, and in the interpretation and execution of the provisions of this Act, there shall be no discrimination against any person on account of race or color." All that was necessary was for the Republicans in their platform to call upon the Commander in Chief to enforce the law he is sworn to uphold, and to pledge that if the present Commander in Chief did not do so, their candidate—if elected—would.

While both the Democratic and the Republican platform writers in one degree or another shirked the responsibilities of their parties to the colored citizens of the United States and thereby lost a great opportunity, it would seem, under existing conditions, that the Negro should have a better chance for justice under a Republican administration than under a Democratic one. For despite the growing enlightened leadership in the South, the old-line, "white supremacy" Southern politician is still in the saddle and still powerfully affects all Democratic party policy and legislation; particularly in the case of the Negro, whom he regards as a special Southern problem. (The corresponding reactionary elements in the Republican party happen to cast their blight mainly in other directions.)

But the case for the Republicans is not too clear. They had a magnificent chance to state in modern terms a code of practice that would make real the very principle of freedom upon which the party was founded. However, apparently overanxious to obtain the support of the Southern delegates for the nomination of their favorite candidate, and fearing the loss in the election of racially smug Northern conservatives, they failed to measure up; they failed to gain the confidence of millions of the Negroes of America.

Furthermore, there is one point in Democratic policy and practice that weighs heavily in favor of the Democratic party with leaders of the Negro people. Negroes have benefited greatly under the Federal Farm Security Administration, Federal Social Security and labor legislation. The Republican party proposes to return to the states, as far as possible, such legislation.

Negroes know that under state legislation, even under state administration of Federal funds, in certain sections of the country they will be discriminated against. In such sections, whether under a Republican or a Democratic administration, their only hope of sharing fairly in social-security measures, in public spending for housing, health, and education, in unemployment benefits and all the human-welfare measures we have come to believe wise and necessary, lies in the Federal government. Under state laws they know that the so-called justice meted out to them will be uneven, uncertain, inadequate, and in some cases nil.

The 1944 election campaign is now in full swing. History cannot be erased or party platforms rewritten. But there is still the chance, the obligation, of interpretation. And undoubtedly, on the question of the status of our Negro citizens, the candidates, presidential, gubernatorial, congressional, all who make up the body of party opinion, will speak.

I write this article with the deliberate intent of helping to arouse an opinion that will require these candidates to put aside generalities, evasions, and pious platitudes, and deal in concise, concrete terms with this human, this national, this world problem.

THE NEGRO'S WAR

The Editors of Fortune

For many months Japanese radio propaganda aimed at the Americas has capitalized the Negro and the tough deal he gets in the United States. Take this English-language broadcast from Manchukuo (March 15, 1942) as recorded by American listening posts: "Democracy, as preached by the Anglo-Americans, may be an ideal and noble system of life, but democracy as practiced by Anglo-Americans is stained with the bloody guilt of racial persecution and exploitation." Last February the Detroit riot against Negro families who wanted to move into their lawful homes was a boon to the Japanese and, incidentally, also the German short-wave propagandists.

A specifically conditioned anti-Semitism has made certain inroads into Harlem; but so far the Nazis seem to realize how little chance the author of *Mein Kampf* has to be accepted as savior of Negroes and they do not address them openly. The Japanese, however, work hard. The clumsiness of their propaganda indicates the Japanese certainty of the Negro's readiness to turn against white America. They are making a mistake. As they are bound to find out, it makes no sense to apply Japan's strategy in Asia to the United States Negro—her gamble on the primitive thesis that peoples will choose sides in this world convulsion simply according to the color of their skins.

Although the American Negroes are undeniably in a critical state of mind, foreign agents still have pretty slim chances among them. America is all the American Negro knows. In fact, he is the isolationist par excellence; no other category of American has so few ties with the outside world. If nativity were really the measure of citizenship, the Negroes would excel any other national or racial stock in this country. Indeed, out of 12,865,500 Negroes (1940 census), 99.4 per cent are American-born and about 97 per cent are of purely native parentage. But of the United States white population nearly 10 per cent were born abroad and less than 70 per cent are of native parentage on both sides. Every attempt to revive for the American Negro alleged African allegiances has failed. Negro intellectuals, in a morose gesture of protest, may seek escape from frustration in an artificial nostalgia for an African civilization of their own; but, as a whole, the American Negro community is at home here in the United States, beyond any temptation from abroad, inextricably rooted into this country's soil.

The Negro has grown with America, though his was a different pace. He has seen members of his race achieve high academic and civic honors in contest with white people. In the North he has learned to use all the gadgets of American civilization and feels himself equal, if trained, to any job. He is molded by American patterns of life. He has shared everything with his American contemporaries, particularly their disillusionment. But his is a specific skepticism: the fierce, violent skepticism of a very young race. He lives in America, but then again he does not. Reminded every day of his color, sometimes he can't help thinking with his skin; worse even, sometimes his skin thinks for him. This is the irrational toll on his, and America's, rational way of life—an ever-present irritation, the steady denial of a normal American existence. The more hurdles he takes, the taller looms the last decisive one. His growing unrest is caused not by the lack but by the momentum of his progress. Being an offspring of America, he reacts as would any American in his position: he wants more.

The Negro wants more—but of America. He may occasionally find a gloomy sort of satisfaction when "the arrogant white folks" are taught a lesson about the efficiency of a colored people, any colored people; but even the most defiant and least astute American Negro senses that his fate is tied up with America's, and he realizes, with a minority's instinct for self-preservation, his selfish stake in an American victory. Defeated nations are neither generous nor rational. And no power on earth could save the Negro from the whiplash of a national catastrophe: it would scourge the least resourceful, most conspicuous minority with prompt and unabashed fury; it would destroy in one blow whatever the Negro has achieved or hopes for—and he knows it. That's why the Japanese gamble is a mistaken one.

Those colored people in Burma and Malaya who aided the Japanese invaders thought the white man to be the real intruder. But the American Negro certainly does not see himself as the native of a conquered colony. He is not disturbed by the principles of American government but by the fact that, as he feels, these principles are not fully applied to him. Sometimes these feelings explode violently in his press. Three months before the United States was attacked, *The Crisis,* a responsible and rather calmly edited Negro journal, stated: "We shall see what we shall see. Negro Americans might as well discover at the beginning whether they are to fight and die for democracy for the Lithuanians, the Greeks, and the Brazilians, or whether they had better fight and die for a little democracy for themselves." This vehement statement expresses a widespread attitude: The American Negro is agitated not because he is asked to fight for America but because full participation in the fight is denied him. He is humiliated as a Negro because he is not fully accepted as an American.

No serious review of the nation's status could ever overlook the contradiction between America's dream and the Negro reality. He has always been intimately involved in America's crises—sometimes retarding, sometimes accelerating the nation's march. This time America's battles for a fuller life have to be fought all over again, only on a higher and broader scale; and unavoidably the Negro takes the stage.

He is not the Southern white man's burden any more. True, in 1940 three quarters of our Negro population were still living south of the Mason and Dixon Line. But the South-North migration continues steadily. In Detroit the Negro community had grown from 5,700 in 1910 to about 150,000 by 1940; in New York City from 91,000 in 1910 to 152,000 in 1920 and 478,000 in 1940. The overwhelming majority found employment as unskilled laborers and in domestic or other service positions, only to lose it again in the depression of the thirties. Being Negroes as well as the most recently arrived labor group, they were marked for industrial decimation. During the thirties up to 70 per cent of the Negro communities in Philadelphia, Chicago, and New

York were on relief or WPA. In 1937, when Negroes were 6 per cent of New York's population, they constituted no less than 22 per cent of the city's relief load.

When after the lean years (and there were more than seven of them) prosperity came back, it pointedly avoided the colored unemployed. To illustrate: the Negro category on WPA rolls actually *rose* from 14.2 per cent in February 1939 to 17.6 per cent in February 1942. This was due not to any real growth of Negro unemployment, but to the fact that white workers enjoyed priority in re-employment by defense industries. Thus to be without a job during the defense boom was no longer an American fate, as it had been during the depression; it began to be a Negro fate.

Last September the United States Bureau of Employment Security inquired from selected defense industries the number of job openings the management expected to occur during the following six months; and for how many of them Negroes, if available, would be considered. The survey, concentrated on regions with considerable Negro labor, uncovered this fact: out of 282,245 prospective openings, 144,583 (51 per cent) were barred to Negroes, as a matter of policy. The answers were given at a time when labor shortage was beginning to make itself felt in many an industry, and to a Federal agency—two months after the President had called for the abolition of discrimination in war industries.

The survey revealed little difference between employment trends in the South and in the North. Out of Texas' announced 17,435 defense jobs, 9,117 were barred to Negroes—but in Michigan the figure was 22,042 out of 26,904; in Indiana, 9,331 out of 9,979; in Ohio, 29,242 out of 34,861. Moreover, the inquiry failed to support the assumption that the job-seeking Negro's frustration starts only when he seeks skilled work. No less than 35,000 out of 83,000 unskilled jobs were declared closed to colored applicants. There are even regions where a Negro would be hired for skilled rather than for unskilled work. Illinois, for instance, reported 72 per cent of the prospective skilled jobs open to Negroes but only 7 per cent of the unskilled jobs. Obviously, where demand for labor heavily outweighs the supply, the skin color miraculously lightens.

Not even the most essential defense industries have sufficiently lifted race barriers. Aircraft industries reported 37,659 out of 64,859 prospective jobs closed to Negroes; electrical machinery, 10,346 out of 20,792; chemicals, 5,561 out of 8,033; iron and steel, 20,397 out of 33,230. In general, the critical industries reported color restrictions rather above the average of 51 per cent. Shipbuilding is the one outstanding exception; out of 64,000 anticipated openings less than 28 per cent have been declared beyond the Negro's reach.

Management's actual experience with Negro labor has little to do with the habit of employment discrimination. Last December the National Industrial Conference Board presented in its management record the results of an extensive study of such experiences. One hundred and two selected managements of industries employing Negroes had been requested to rank colored and white employees on comparable skilled and semiskilled work. As to ability and skill, seventy managements graded Negro workers equal to their white colleagues, thirty-one poorer, one better than whites. As to production, eighty-five managements found Negroes equal to, twelve poorer, five better than white workers. As to regularity in attendance, sixty-four managements reported Negroes to be equal to, thirty-two poorer, five better than white labor. The Conference Board closed its report with a suggestion "that all firms having suitable work of any nature should make an honest effort to hire colored persons in proportion to the total population of the area."

The President had anticipated this advice on June 25, 1941, with Executive Order No. 8802, warning government, employers, and labor that discrimination in defense industries is contrary to the country's fundamental interests and must not be tolerated. In the history of the United States this was the second presidential executive order with a direct bearing on Negroes; the first one was the Emancipation Proclamation. Seventy-eight years after they had been freed, the American Negroes got another American President's pledge—on the brink of another war.

The President's proclamation would have caused more enthusiasm among the Negroes, and probably a quicker response throughout the country, had it not been so clearly the result of pressure. America's Negroes, headed by A. Philip Randolph of the Brotherhood of Sleeping Car Porters, had announced a general protest march on Washington for July first. A few weeks before the critical day, Fiorello La Guardia, then still in charge of the Office for Civilian Defense, requested them to call it off. When this was refused, the White House took the matter up officially. At a meeting with the President and ranking members of the Cabinet and the Office of Production Management, the suggestion of an executive order came from the Negro side of the conference table, and was coolly received on the other side. When only a few days were left for preventing an international embarrassment, the Negro leaders were shown a first draft, which committed defense industries but not government itself. The Negroes stood pat. Finally the President agreed to include an order to his own administration. And the march was canceled. But what could have been an inspiring demonstration of democracy at work came about as a compromise between hard-boiled pressure groups.

This genesis of a great document has hampered its effectiveness ever since. To realize the proclaimed policy, the President's Committee on Fair Employment Practice was created, equipped with little more power than that of investigating the field and holding public hearings on glaring cases of discrimination. True enough, the committee (whose jurisdiction includes all racial, national, and religious minorities) has somewhat accelerated the nation's adjustment to a critical situation, but the adjustment itself was caused by practical necessity rather than by political or industrial statesmanship.

The character of this necessity has been well defined by the Baltimore *Evening Sun,* an avowed supporter of conservative traditions. Baltimore's trained-labor supply is now virtually exhausted, and 35,000 more defense workers may be required by the end of 1942. There has already been heavy migration to the city. Sewer, water, highway, transport, police, fire, school facilities are overstrained and will have to be enlarged even if no more people come to Baltimore. How can the city digest an influx of another 35,000 families? So far no one has provided the answer. But Baltimore's Negro population of 167,000 could substantially lessen the pressure of labor need if an extensive training program were carried out in time. Concluded the Baltimore *Evening Sun:* "We are not here concerned with the long-range social consequences which might result from the removal of some of these barriers [against the use of Negroes for skilled work]. We are thinking simply of the ironic situation Baltimore finds itself in right now: on the one hand a desperate shortage of skilled and semiskilled workmen for our war industries, and on the other hand the existence of a large reservoir of labor which is rarely considered when there is need for skilled rather than unskilled workmen. It seems to us that in this emergency a dispassionate and objective examination of the situation of the Negro in Baltimore's industries is called for."

In varying degree this is the picture of each United States city with a war-production boom and Negro labor reserves. And management is not unaware of the critical situation. Last September 53,000 out of 184,000 additional jobs in both skilled and unskilled categories were declared open to Negro applicants by companies that had never before employed colored labor of any kind.

Theoretically, management should have fewer objections to hiring colored labor than any other part of the industrial team. The employer seldom has social contact with his workers anyway, and his primary concern is production efficiency and satisfactory investment return. This, and not a pedigree, is what management wants from labor—theoretically. In reality, a multitude of extra-economic motivations help to determine the employer's attitude. And nowhere are they stronger than in his dealings with men—in his employment policy.

Anything may happen, and sometimes does, when the first Negro workers enter a plant or an office—from a few minutes' slowdown to the walkout of aroused foremen, even to strikes of the entire personnel. If work is not directly disturbed, there may be in some cases the grievous problem of segregated cafeterias, washrooms, recreation facilities. Management is afraid of opening a formidable Pandora's box of troubles. And employers who, recoiling from the implications of a non-discriminatory hiring policy, tend to pass the buck to labor have some impressive facts on their side. Moreover, they argue that the same government that insists on such a policy for private industry has not exactly established a working model in Washington. Yet a conclusive answer to all that has been given by the Employers' Association of Chicago, in a memo to its members: "Some employers have raised the objection that the attitude of their own employees forces them to discriminate. However true this may have been in the past, it is now the job of employers to influence their employees toward sacrificing such prejudices as a matter of patriotic necessity. It is not going to be easy—nor is it going to be easy to train a whole new army of unskilled men and women—but both must be done, and the employer must do it."

And it can be done. Consider the example of Lockheed-Vega. Once the management had made up its mind to employ Negro labor, foremen and supervisors were advised to see that the plan succeeded; and they accepted the responsibility, since evidently the management was resolved to carry out its intent. Last August, after the internal machinery had been fully set up, each of Lockheed's thousands of employees was provided with a firm statement of the management's policy; even if they had wanted to, the local unions could not have resented Lockheed's compliance with the Commander in Chief's executive order, which was extensively quoted in the communication. And then one Negro worker after another was introduced into the plant—the one hundredth last November, by Joe Louis himself, cheered by the white workers. Today many hundreds of Negroes are working at Lockheed-Vega, mostly in production jobs, and the company reports no trouble.

Not every management in the United States has such elaborate industrial-relation devices at its disposal; nor are they indispensable. With different, though equally effective, methods the Wright Aeronautical Corporation in Cincinnati employed last April more than one thousand Negro workers without any friction. A year ago Western Electric hired Negroes for the first time in its Kearny, New Jersey, plant and put them to work side by side with skilled white people. The experiment was a full success. No separate cafeterias, no separate washrooms, and no move to get them. The plant is producing highly complicated instruments; neither the work nor its quality was even slightly disturbed. The navy shipyards increased the use of Negro labor extensively during the last year, and all over the country colored yardmen are working practically shoulder to shoulder with white colleagues. There is, however, not a single production region that cannot provide the President's Committee on Fair Employment Practice with documented complaints.

While experiences vary according to regional habits, local population structure, and type of work, they agree on one point: namely, that much depends on the management's own approach. Where management reluctantly yields to local Negro or governmental pressure, the result generally is trouble. Where management conceives the hiring of Negroes to be part of its own wartime labor policy and sticks to it, results are encouraging. They are exemplary where management and unions join forces against discrimination. In fact, the unions' responsibility for the Negro's economic fate equals, if it does not surpass, that of management.

For labor unions to turn against any group of men who have to work for a living contradicts their original aims but at least not the written constitutions of some of them. Nineteen international unions, ten of them affiliated with the A.F. of L., explicitly exclude Negroes from membership. Officially, the A.F. of L. advises its affiliated organizations not to retain a constitution discriminating against Negroes. So diplomats of those internationals long ago found an ingenious way out: the machinists, for example, exclude Negroes by a ritualistic oath. In America, and in the twentieth century, prospective union men must make a solemn promise that they will introduce into their union only "competent, white" men. To eliminate this hocus-pocus, the A.F. of L. leaders argue, is beyond their jurisdiction, since affiliated internationals and locals have jealously preserved their independence. Management usually accepts the situation, even where there is no closed shop, since most of the discriminating unions include highly skilled workers whom the employer cannot afford to lose to a competitor. Closed shop or no, in times of inflated demand for skilled labor no Negro can get into a machine plant if the worker aristocrats don't want him there.

In certain places and industries the congestion of war orders has been so heavy that discriminating unions could not totally obstruct Negro employment without endangering production and their own jobs. In some of these instances a peculiar device is used: the Negro is not accepted as a member, but purchases from the union a working permit—an interesting hybrid of tenant feudalism and industrial democracy.

The C.I.O., officially opposed to racial discrimination, is built on the principle of industrial, vertical organization and intends to embrace "all the workers." Furthermore, centralization is more strongly stressed in the C.I.O. than in the A.F. of L., so that headquarters have direct responsibility for the policy of a local. On both accounts Negroes have good reason to prefer the C.I.O. to the A.F. of L.

The inexhaustible variations of life, however, produce weird results in the struggle between the two organizations. In Birmingham, Alabama, of all places, the A.F. of L. acted as the advocate of the Negro ironworkers, merely because the local C.I.O. did not. Enjoying the bargaining rights in the two Birmingham plants of the Ingalls Iron Works, the C.I.O. had done little to improve the situation of the Negro workers (about a third of the personnel). The job classifications, they complained, were unfair, keeping Negroes in a low-paid wage stratum regardless of the job done. The part they played in union affairs was not commensurate with their numerical strength. Last year the Negroes offered to bolt the C.I.O. when and if the A.F. of L. would promise to right their grievances. Assured of a new deal from the A.F. of L., the Negroes shifted their votes and the C.I.O. lost its hold at Ingalls. In negotiating the next contract the A.F. of L. lived up to its promises: the Negroes' jobs have been reclassified and they are now paid for what they do; they serve on the shop grievance and contract committees; they share justly with white men the pay raise gained last year. Such miracles happen when two unions fight for jurisdiction—food for thought on the merits of competition in general and the closed-shop issue in particular.

Where organized labor indulges in ethnological double talk, industry is prevented from fully utilizing its potentialities. When Chrysler in Detroit tried to overcome the scarcity of skilled labor by upgrading and transferring able Negro workers, the C.I.O. personnel in a division of the Highland Park plant went on a sit-down strike. It took War Department intervention and a firm stand by both management and national union leadership to protect the Negroes and the country's claim on unhampered defense production. When Packard shifted two expert Negro metal finishers from work on automobiles to the polishing department of a new tank plant, 250 C.I.O. members staged a forty-minute sit-down strike, holding up the work of 600 persons. The Negroes were withdrawn; and for the following six months the United States Government, the Executive Committee of the United Automobile Workers-C.I.O., and the Packard company were interlocked with the personnel in a wrestling match over two American citizens' right to contribute their skill to the production of tanks. Fortunately, government, company, and union leaders did not back down but finally told the race-conscientious objectors either to work or to get out. Consequently, all usable labor is now harnessed smoothly to production.

The Labor Division of the War Production Board has a special Negro Employment and Training Branch, under Dr. Robert C. Weaver, which is attempting to secure the unions' co-operation. Improvements are slow but undeniable. In some regions C.I.O. and A.F. of L. officials have formed joint-action committees to speed the integration of Negroes into union shops. Usually C.I.O. headquarters is willing to put serious pressure on locals that are not yet impressed by the President's order. Although William Green of the A.F. of L., testifying before Representative Tolan's House Committee on National Defense Migration, was not particularly outspoken against the discriminatory practices of some of his unions, an increasing number of A.F. of L. organizations have put a damper on their racial feelings. But the unions still have a long way to go.

What America's Negro community resents as employment discrimination is in part due to the fact that the bulk of Negro labor is still unskilled. Every third gainfully working white American belongs to the skilled and semiskilled groups, but only one out of each eight working Negroes. In *Fortune's* manpower study of last April, training and upgrading of unskilled labor was shown to be a prime prerequisite for full mobilization of America's human resources. For the Negro it is more than that. He will march into a richer life through training schools or not at all.

On his initial steps along this road he has not exactly been encouraged. Here is an over-all picture of conditions in eighteen selected Southern and border states and the District of Columbia. Over 22 per cent of the population in this area is Negro; but in the pre-employment and refresher-training courses, supervised by the United States Office for Education, only 3,215 Negroes were enrolled last January—less than 4 per cent of the trainees. Out of 4,630 training courses only 194 accepted Negroes.

All these courses are financed out of the sixty-million-dollar fund appropriated by Congress in 1940 for the national-defense training program. The bill contains this amendment: "No trainee . . . shall be discriminated against because of sex, race, or color; and where separate schools are required by law for separate population groups, to the extent needed for trainees of each such group, equitable provisions shall be made for facilities and training of like quality."

For the strange execution of this program the training-school managers in the field have some plausible justification. In the South unions often refuse to supply instructors for Negro training schools. Also, it is indeed ironic to train workers who, after graduation, are almost sure to be denied the jobs they were schooled for: a year ago the records of the United States Employment Service showed that only one out of fifty Negro graduates of training schools could be placed.

Waste of training facilities is the result. Last February Texas was training 12,472 persons for defense production. These included exactly 206 Negroes. Yet more than 23,000 defense workers could have been trained with full use of the available equipment. If used to capacity, the state's courses for airplane-engine mechanics could have educated 749 specialists; they were producing 218. Classes for turret-lathe workers, capable of turning out 200 experts, were training 32. But many a trainable Negro was not admitted.

A New Orleans shipyard was recently reprimanded by the Maritime Commission for falling behind schedule. The company's defense: not enough local skilled labor; 700 or 800 additional trained workers would have made all the difference. But about 7,000 local Negroes had registered for defense training—unsuccessfully.

A plant is being built for Bell Aircraft near Atlanta, Georgia, which by the end of the year will employ many thousands of workers. In March 6,000 Negroes in the area had expressed their desire for training by registering with their Urban League. At that time forty-five defense courses were open for whites but only one for Negroes, and this was, unfortunately, a class in ship woodworking. When specific training for the Bell factory was first being planned, all these additional courses were confined to white applicants. Not until Washington intervened with the local and state vocational authorities in Georgia was training for the new plant finally promised to Negroes.

The Labor Division of WPB has estimated that 5,000 trained workers will be needed in the next few months in Mobile, Alabama, and ultimately more than 20,000 new workers will be required. As of April first, available Negroes were not being trained, although the local vocational centers for whites were running short of candidates. To take care of the stream of in-migrant workers 500 defense housing units have already been built and more are needed. But each new house for an imported worker whose job could be done by Mobile labor wastes around $3,000 and 2,330 pounds of critical metals.

There are other regions and an increasing number of them where all labor is used up, and still more must be imported; and there the construction of defense homes becomes a prerequisite for a thrifty investment of the nation's human resources. As for the Negro, it is another turn of the blind wheel.

In Denver, Colorado, Federal authorities were interested in a housing project for the three worst-housed local groups: Mexicans, Eastern-European immigrant workers, and Negroes. The plan miscarried. The Negroes resented the idea of living in close contact with Mexicans. In short, everybody is somebody else's Negro.

Just so, the spearhead of local opposition against Negro housing projects is nearly always one of the poorest, most recently arrived groups. The reasons are partly economic; i.e., fear of displacement by even cheaper labor; anxiety over their small real-estate holdings which may lose in value if close to a Negro settlement, the site of which is usually picked in the poorest section of a town. But the truly impelling motives are unmistakably psychological: the satisfaction of kicking someone who is socially even lower than oneself; the illusion that a potential target for xenophobia can escape being hunted by turning the heat on somebody else; the eagerness to belong—if only in sharing and outdoing a respectable community's prejudices. In recent months Negro housing projects have encountered especially vehement opposition in Detroit and in Buffalo, and in both cases primarily from Catholic Polish immigrants who thus had three rational reasons to appreciate tolerance.

The story of the Sojourner Truth project in Detroit has become a *cause célèbre* with repercussions high in the Federal bureaucracy. The riot hit not only bystanders in Detroit's streets but also the Director of Defense Housing in FWA, Clark Foreman. This scion of a leading Southern family lost his job, under some congressional pressure, because he supported too firmly the Negroes' insistence on their legal rights. But more revealing than the skirmish of Detroit, because more typical, is the stalemate of Buffalo.

Buffalo, having nearly exhausted the local labor pool, is in pressing need of homes for in-migrating defense workers. The Bethlehem Steel mills, which employ a great deal of colored labor, imported Negroes from New York State, Tennessee, Virginia—only to discover that four hundred of their men have to live under deplorable slum conditions. Last July, Federal authorities who then had five hundred million dollars for just such purposes decided to build a 200-unit housing project for Negro workers. As a matter of policy, defense-housing agencies decline to spend their funds for slum clearance. The money, after all, was earmarked for *additional* emergency housing, not for reform programs; besides, demolition and rehousing of the slum tenants waste labor and delay work. A desperate search for a site began. One selection after another had to be abandoned because of organized public pressure. After nine months of protests, petitions, and investigations, it now looks as if the Federal housing authorities must give in. The present plan, strictly contradicting a sound general policy, calls for the demolition of a slum area of one hundred existing homes. Therefore not two hundred but three hundred homes will have to be built—an excess expenditure of more than $400,000 and one hundred tons of strategic metals. Meantime the imported workers are still living under conditions that Bethlehem Steel considered impossible ten months ago.

However, when straightforward action of authorities has met calm co-operation of a township, experiments with Negro housing have been encouraging. In Chicago, in Stamford, in south Jamaica, Long Island, there are public projects where Negro and white tenants live in closest neighborhood. In industrial Elizabeth, New Jersey, 333 white families peaceably share the Pioneer Homes with seventy-two Negro families and have mixed clubs. The widely popular belief that Negro homes depreciate adjacent property values is not supported by the experience of Atlanta, Georgia. There the monthly rate of private construction in the vicinity of the John J. Eagan Homes showed a gain of 500 per cent, eight times the gain for the city as a whole. Nor is this an exceptional experience. Baltimore, Boston, Knoxville, Austin, Philadelphia, Detroit, Gary have learned that construction impetus and real-estate prosperity in connection with well-managed Negro housing projects is a country-wide phenomenon.

Socially, the Negro's place is not fully defined by the economic patterns of his life; nobody's is—particularly not in such times as these. What individuals or groups are aware of contributing to the collective endeavor determines their feelings more deeply than job, income, housing. Accordingly, the biggest single factor in shaping the American Negro's mind about this war and his part in it is his place in the United States Armed Forces.

In a communication to *Fortune* the War Department said: "The Army is extremely enthusiastic about the morale, the performance, and the re-enlistment rates of its existing Negro units, a number of which are outstanding on any basis." Last fall there were about 100,000 Negroes in the United States Armed Forces, but the pace of induction has been considerably stepped up since. The Army aims at reaching and preserving for the duration a ratio of 10 per cent. This, however, is an over-all ratio that does not necessarily apply to each of the various service branches, particularly not to the nation's pride and greatest single hope —the Army Air Corps.

There is only one training school for Negro combat pilots, the segregated establishment at Tuskegee, Alabama. Equipment, standards, instructors match anything the Army has elsewhere; so do the students, the first of whom got their wings in March. But at the present rate of training and graduation there will be only a few score Negro fighting pilots at the end of 1942. Inasmuch as the United States goal for 1943 is 200,000 combat fliers, the Negroes think their race could contribute much more to the air arm. In fact, they know it could. So do the white instructors at Tuskegee.

In 1918 all Negro officers were trained in a single segregated institution at Camp Dodge, Des Moines. Today Negro officer candidates are interspersed in almost all officer-training schools. The instructional part of the integration works perfectly. White and Negro candidates attend the same classes, get common physical exercise and common field practice. After they have been at school for two weeks, they rate one another for aggressiveness, loyalty, leadership, et cetera; and in Fort Benning, Georgia, Negroes rate whites above other Negroes, whites rate Negroes above other whites. As to achievement, one of the officers in charge of this training school thinks that white and black candidates shape up just about the same. Only one instance of a white candidate objecting to colored candidates sleeping in the same barracks was reported. If he did not like it, he was told, he could get out of the school and stay out. In training, housing, feeding, there is scrupulous impartiality. Outside of that, segregation continues in recreational and social affairs, but this applies to facilities and institutions that are not the camp's official business. To the Negro, however, who wears the United States officer's uniform and is told by a white enlisted man that he, an officer, is not wanted in the officers' movie house or club, the question of formal responsibility makes but little difference. And if the Negro officers have to journey nine miles for a haircut because there is no barbershop for Negro officers at Fort Benning, the blessings of integration appear somewhat limited.

Outside of the officer-training schools, segregation in the Army is total, except, of course, for white officers who are serving with Negro troops. But the Army, its leaders insist, did not create the problem and cannot undertake to change social views of the individual citizens who fill its ranks. Its sole objective is maximum success in training and using the country's men for military action; and, the army leaders point out candidly, that's why they are not going to indulge in experiments such as the establishment of a trial division including, on a voluntary basis, whites and Negroes alike.

The Navy insists even more strongly that it cannot take a chance on a social experiment. Since racial integration on naval units implies much more than in any other service, the Navy feels that it cannot justly be expected to be so far ahead of the nation's general habits in racial matters as the advocates of full integration wish. Still, these advocates (at the suggestion of Wendell Willkie, they now include the National Committee of the G.O.P.) retort that the Navy's argument is not watertight. The much-quoted "tradition of a white navy," they point out, is after all only twenty-odd years old and was preceded by a tradition of generations during which the United States accepted Negroes for every kind of naval service.

Last April the Navy announced its willingness to enlist Negro applicants in the United States Marine Corps and the United States Coast Guard, but to accept them as sailors only "for duty in District craft of various kinds, in maritime activities around shore establishments, in Navy Yards, and in the navy's construction crews and companies." This, the Negroes feel, is not necessarily more than a token payment on a pretty extensive debt. For the country it was reassuring evidence that the leadership of its armed forces is gradually living up to this war's unique, basically political nature.

For this is a war in which ideas weaken, enforce, and sometimes are even substitutes for armies. The Negro's fate in the United States affects the fate of white American soldiers in the Philippines, in the Caribbean, in Africa; bears on the solidity of our alliance with eight hundred million colored people in China and India; influences the feelings of countless neighbors in South America. In this shrunken world of ours a fracas in Detroit has an echo in Aden, and what a Southern congressman considers to be a small home-town affair can actually interfere with grand strategy.

At home, discrimination is too costly. To keep a minority "in its place" is a tough job. Germany, an old hand at efficient policing, had to profess the principle and to concentrate on it for many years, synchronizing all aspects of national life to that single purpose. Practiced apologetically, halfhearted discrimination is bound to damage the discriminators not less than those who are discriminated against. A perpetual irritation of the social tissues, it combines the discomfort of a troubled conscience with the high tax of inefficiency. In mellow times of peace our civilization could afford waste and inconsistency, but the raw climate of war forces upon society speedy, clean-cut decisions.

In the consciousness of all peoples in the world this war is being fought for and against the idea of racial superiority. America's Constitution, like Christianity, is based on the principle that every man is born with the inalienable right to equality of opportunity. Whether or not this assumption is "realistic"—we must either stick to it or change sides. Anything else would be not only immoral, it would be a military mistake. For men do not die for causes they are cynical about, and they cannot conquer on behalf of a principle they discount. That one tenth of our population may lack enthusiasm is bad enough, but not crucial. What counts in a war like this is whether the nine tenths feel at peace with themselves.

THE NEGRO: HIS FUTURE IN AMERICA

The Editors of the New Republic

ONCE AGAIN the race question is in a state of crisis. Within the space of a few war years we are making decisions, establishing policies, crystallizing our individual attitudes toward the issue in a manner that will determine whether America will witness a maximum or a minimum degree of racial turmoil in the coming decades. Whether as a people we proceed now in a moment of enlightenment, on a high level of humanism and intelligence, or whether we yield to the dark and primitive residues in our national spirit, attempting to ride roughshod over the Negro problem and over the Negro, is a decision which can bring to America a postwar era of internal healing and recovery, or a time of border fighting on the frontiers between the races, and involvement in an expanding conflict which might eventually precipitate the third world war.

The American race question is no longer a matter of domestic politics. Even in the middle years of the last century, when the controversy did assume this characteristic, it produced a destructive war. Then it was a two-part conflict between white Americans over the disposition of the Negro as property, but today the Negro is attempting to wrest the question of his own destiny from white hands, and only violence and main force will deter him in his efforts. Knowing this, American Negroes in recent years have begun to feel an *esprit de corps* with the other colored races whose numbers constitute an overwhelming majority, and the American race question has become an integral part of the colonial crisis throughout the world. The white majority in America must decide now what it intends to do about this crisis. Though the ultimate consequences of the decision will not confront them within the month or possibly even the decade, they belong inexorably to the future and someday they must be faced.

White America has two approaches to the problem: the first is an official approach through governmental acts and policies; the second approach is through the private acts and attitudes of citizens. An enlightened, courageous Federal program could go far in conditioning the attitudes of citizens. But, unfortunately, we live in a day of official expediency, and actually it has been the attitudes of private citizens and their pressure groups which have given direction to the government.

The history of the President's Fair Employment Practice Committee is a case in point. It was formed by presidential proclamation only after Negroes had threatened a march on Washington unless something were done to ameliorate widespread discrimination against them in war industries. Then a counterpressure was initiated by Southern industry and politicians, and the President permitted himself to be pushed in the other direction: the committee and its scheduled railroad hearings were abandoned. But now many white progressives joined with the Negro groups, and a still more persistent pressure was brought to bear on the President; the committee was re-established and the hearings opened.

In this respect it appears that initiative in the field of race relations has been defaulted by the administration and has passed to private citizens and pressure groups: to the Negro and his organizations on one hand, and to anti-Negro white groups on the other.

There is a third group which must interest itself in the problem, for its stake in the solution is as great as any. This is a large passive group of white Americans who consider themselves loyal supporters of the principles of American democracy and who have some actual sense of the meaning of the term. It is the reading, thinking, reasoning group in America who, though at present uneasy about the mounting race conflict, desires at least to understand it and to act with intelligence and fairness, and with effect. It is to these people primarily that this special supplement of the *New Republic* is addressed.

White America has a record of bad faith, ignorance, and cruelty toward the Negro, and, on the whole, the historic liberal movement shares this record. The antislavery agitation of the pre-Civil War era is tainted with economic implications. Though many of the agitators were sincere men, and some were even great men, it was not humanism that gave their movement its real weight so much as the greedy rivalry for the control of national policies which existed between Northern industrialism and Southern agrarianism. In the decades following the war, industrial exploitation became the beating heart and lifeblood of the Republican party. Continued strife with the South was now bad for business, and the South remained unyielding in its demand for political and economic debasement for the Negro. The North was now faced with the choice of Southern markets or continued interest in the Negro's welfare. Very quickly, and with thoroughness, the Negro's welfare was sacrificed. Under the inspiration of its industrial masters, rather than in a spirit of justice and sound law, the Supreme Court in the 1870s began a series of narrow and crippling interpretations of the Civil War amendments and the congressional acts which had been passed to ensure political suffrage for the Negro. The black man was turned back to his former masters, and in 1876 the deal was anointed forever. In this significant year the Northern Democrats, who were supporting Garfield in a close contest for the presidential candidacy, made a cold-blooded bargain with the Southern states by which, in return for their support of Garfield, they were assured a free hand for all time in their dealings with the Negro.

The most shameless aspect of this trading was the arrant hypocrisy of the liberals of that day. After 1876, in the words of Charles A. Beard, "agitation of the Negro question became bad form in the North." Most of the leading antislavery agitators who were still living—men of such stature as Carl Schurz, E. L. Godkin, James Bryce, and Thomas Wentworth Higginson—piously condoned the deal and began to express their belief that Southern Negroes were unworthy of political suffrage.

In this manner, throughout the history of the race question, the "Negro's friends" both North and South could be counted on eventually to take the path of least resistance; to pursue some policy that would create a minimum amount of inconvenience, and of fundamental readjustment, for the white race, and a minimum amount of progress for the black; and they could be counted on also to rationalize this betrayal of principle in whatever happened to be the current name for expediency—gradualism, realism, common sense. Militant women who could march in suffragette parades could also find it in themselves to accept customary or legal discrimination against Negroes without batting an eye; men who could write tracts in behalf of the eight-hour day could also fly with their neighbors to a city council for restrictive ordinances if a Negro residential section encroached upon their property; and labor unions, founded to resist the exploitation of the working classes, could be depended on to deny their communal fraternity to Negro workers, to aid and even insist upon their exploitation by the bosses.

The reason for this historic white faintheartedness grows out of the omnipresent, insistent anti-Negro propaganda inherent in every facet of our culture. Sometimes it sprang from a conscious and cynical intention to keep the Negro a peasant, an unskilled worker, a low-wage labor source open to exploitation by white ownership; but just as often it grew out of a deep psychological fear of a "strange" race, a race with superficial markings dramatically differing from the white norm; and deeply involved in this fear was a case of bad conscience. The white soul is saturated with fear; white culture embedded within itself, and perpetuated at all cost, every educational device that was possible to teach this fear of the stranger and buttress it through customs, myths, and old wives' tales. And white America as well as black America was victimized in the process.

There is not space in this supplement to bring to bear the resources of modern science against the vast and ramifying color prejudice. Modern studies in all fields which bear upon the subject—anthropology, psychology, sociology, history—have placed on endless rows of library shelves throughout the world (removed and burned for some years now in Germany) an impressive mass of data which demonstrate the mythical nature of these race beliefs. Scientists in each field have reinforced the findings of those in others.

In America no subject has been written on more prolifically than the race question. Much of it, unfortunately, has been bitter and violent exposition of the race myth; much of it is negative, hypocritical, and evasive. In the words of Carey McWilliams,[1] "there is actually something rather unwholesome about the accumulation of such a bulky literature on a particular problem when that writing is so barren, as it happens to be in the case of the Negro, of definite suggestions for social action." The best of the literature on the race question has appeared in very recent decades. Many good books are now being issued as a result of mounting crisis.

Under separate headings we shall discuss outstanding phases of the problem as it exists today. The discussion necessarily must deal primarily with current aspects rather than with history and anthropology, but a discussion of a few outstanding findings of the modern race scientists is properly first in order.

Race Science

A Jesuit priest who teaches a course in race relations in an American university, an authority in the field, asserted in a recent discussion of modern anthropological studies that "once you grasp the central idea you've got the whole thing." By central idea he meant the concept that, though races exhibit obvious and measurable physical differences, there are no inherited intellectual or moral superiorities. Leading anthropologists are overwhelmingly in agreement on this point.

A century ago it was the fashion of head measurers and anthropologists in Europe to cling to the theory of the master race, with a list of descending races who were graded, in most cases, by the colors of their skin. And almost without exception the particular anthropologist found that the master race happened to be his own. Count Arthur de Gobineau formulated and was the first great propagandist of the master-race theory—in a book called *Les Races Humaines*. It was copied by many others, among them Houston Chamberlain, a Germanophile who some fifty years ago was known as the Kaiser's private anthropologist. Gobineau's theory was the inspiration of Hitler's master-racism; and thus a

[1]*Brothers Under the Skin*. Little, Brown and Company.

piece of evil ignorance which is ridiculed by modern scientists—and rejected by most churches as heresy—inflamed the mind of a mean and thwarted psychopath and enabled him to drive a world to war largely through the manipulation of the latent prejudices and hatreds that exist in the masses of unthinking people.

This is a list of a few of the anthropologists, unquestioned leaders in this field, whose books and monographs through the years have taken the race myth apart piece by piece and laid it forever, like witchcraft, in the graveyard of primitive superstitions: Franz Boas, Ales Hrdlička, Melville Herskovits, Ruth Benedict, Earnest Hooton, Carlton Coon, Otto Klineberg, M. F. Ashley-Montagu. There are many others.

Climate, geographical background, diet, and breeding in isolation are most frequently advanced in theories concerning the explanation of physical racial differences. The folk belief of many whites that the Negro stands at a lower stage of development away from apes has long ago been brushed aside. To many intelligent people it may seem superficial even to bring this point into the discussion; but it is not, for these are the beliefs which still, at this late date, bolster the dark, subjective prejudices in many white minds, even those which have been exposed to education. The point is covered briefly in a pamphlet by Ashley-Montagu:

> If some of our racists would take the trouble to visit their local zoo, and for a moment drop their air of superiority and take a dispassionate look at either one of these apes [gorilla or chimpanzee], they would find that the hair of these creatures is lank, that their lips are thin, and that their body is profusely covered with hair. In these characters the white man stands nearer to the apes than does the Negro. Is the white man then, for this reason, to be judged inferior to the Negro? Surely not.

The proslavery literature of America is laden with the persistent tortuous argument that the Negro is a primitive—incapable of learning the white man's culture, incapable of appreciating it when he does make a show of learning it. Racists speak the same language: in *Mein Kampf* one runs across Hitler's violent resentment against the groups in Great Britain who give legal training to Negroes and then believe that they have actually made barristers out of "apes." Just as Hitler would have remained unconvinced by a citation of the brilliant legal work of the National Association for the Advancement of Colored People, the American racists who today couch the old slavery argument in current terms remain adamantly unconvinced in the face of abundant evidence of Negro achievement. One hears this argument frequently from old-

American Anglo-Saxon Southerners, whose forebears gave it currency in the beginning. There is a passage in a letter that Cicero wrote to Atticus which should come as a jolt to such people, for it reveals that once their own ancestors were considered the primitives of Europe, and Cicero's language is exactly their own. It is quoted by Ruth Benedict in *Race: Science and Politics:* "Do not obtain your slaves from Britain because they are so stupid and so utterly incapable of being taught that they are not fit to form a part of the household of Athens."

Environment has played a tragic part in retarding the Negro's progress in America. In the South this has been done with calculation, and the Negro's resultant ignorance has been offered as evidence of his unfitness—a trap from which there was no means of escape. In the North, anti-Negro prejudice has differed from that in the South only because of the fact that the fewer numbers of Negroes have kept this prejudice in a state of relative passivity. The Negro has been discriminated against and he has been subjected to customary, and sometimes to "legal," Jim Crow.

But one great advantage he has had in the North has been better schooling. In intelligence testing, when the Negro's environment has been related to the environment of the white children whose tests were used for comparison, the results have been similar. There is one brief table in Otto Klineberg's book, *Race Differences,* which shows in a penetrating manner the influence of environment on intelligence. It is based on army intelligence-testing records in the last war, which demonstrated the fact that Negroes who had been educated in the schools of progressive Northern states had higher intelligence scores than white recruits from a number of Southern states. The table is reproduced here:

SOUTHERN WHITES AND NORTHERN NEGROES, BY STATES, ARMY RECRUITS

Whites		*Negroes*	
State	*Median Score*	*State*	*Median Score*
Mississippi	41.25	Pennsylvania	42.00
Kentucky	41.50	New York	45.02
Arkansas	41.55	Illinois	47.35
Georgia	42.12	Ohio	49.50

The white intellect that will unshackle itself from a cultural residue of race myths can find abundant evidence in modern scientific literature of the equality of men; not equality between any two given men—the point on which little intellects are wont to quibble—but men in general, regardless of skin color, nose width, or eye slant. Even better evidence is available outside of libraries, for white people who can learn to look upon Negroes with a free and open mind, and with good will instead of fear or malice in their hearts.

The bugaboo of intermarriage, which lurks in even the most civilized white minds, could as well be forgotten. People are going to mate with whom they please, as they have in the past, and laws to prevent it are futile. For the white people who fear intermarriage, there is literally no problem; they will never be forced to submit to it. Marriages, to quote Henry Fielding, are made of "high and tender friendship," and such an emotion does not grow from a feeling of repulsion. Nor have the South's strict anti-miscegenation laws prevented a constant lightening of the Negro's skin. There have been many mixed couples, legally married in Northern states, whose lives would put to shame the clandestine carnality of the white men who have created the generations of mixed-blood Negroes—to whom they have repudiated all the obligations of parenthood.

Of the thirteen million Negroes in America, six million are light-skinned mulattoes. Melville Herskovits estimates that less than a quarter of all Negroes are pure-blooded. A good portion of the mixture comes from American Indian stock, but a considerable portion comes also from whites. It is ironic that those who cry loudest against "social equality," by which they mean intermarriage, hail from the states, counties, and townships where white blood, regardless of the law, flowed in the heaviest volume into Negro veins. These protestants should know, if anyone should, that people mate with whom they please; it is a very personal and private decision.

The Negro in Industry

In 1940 the Negro woke up to the fact that white America had just about decided not to give him a job in any of the profitable fields of employment. The story has been well told in a recent column by P. L. Prattis in the Pittsburgh *Courier:*

> Negroes did not know that they were being methodically and consciously driven out of industry. They knew that certain labor unions were excluding them, but they did not understand that management desired to get along without the black worker. Of course there had always been bars of a kind against the Negro worker. But this same worker had been hopeful that these

bars were relics of slavery and the Reconstruction period and that they would wear away. He had no idea that custom was going to depress his status with the same certitude as the infamous Black Codes. He had had some experience losing jobs after the World War. That period gave currency to the expression that "the Negro is the last hired, the first fired." The black worker always hoped to beat the tragic implications of that expression. He simply did not want to believe that a time might come when no Negroes would be hired.

Then came the depression, with millions of jobless Negroes. Even in the South, where certain classes of menial jobs had by custom been yielded to him, the Negro found himself displaced by the poor white who needed work. Closer and closer to the periphery of economic desperation the Negro was pushed. Some Negroes regarded their plight philosophically. There weren't enough jobs to go around. Whites needed jobs. Certainly the whites would get most of the jobs first. But, as more and more jobs became available in better times, the Negro would be given a fair share of them too. That is what the average black worker hoped.

Up until 1940 the black worker really had not sensed what had taken place. He didn't realize that there had been a sort of meeting of minds throughout America and that there existed a cold-blooded understanding not to use the hands and skills of Negroes in the vast majority of gainful pursuits. That only became apparent with the approach of the war emergency and the call for workers. Black workers thought they would be called too, but they weren't. Vast industrial enterprises went into operation, employing thousands and thousands of workers, but the doors were slammed hard in the face of the black man. . . .

In the years immediately preceding the First World War the United States was receiving annually about a million and a quarter immigrants, who supplied the bulk of the unskilled labor needed by industry. This tide was diminished, and then almost completely checked, as America closed the gates and as the countries of Europe kept their nationals home to work or fight. Mounting industrial production in America created a manpower vacuum, and into it eventually was sucked the surplus white and Negro labor of the fecund South. Nearly two million Negroes left Dixie during the war years. They were drawn not only by the lure of high wages but also by the greater freedom and educational opportunities offered in the North.

The Negro was hit severely in the depression of 1923, and the depression of 1929 brought him economic devastation. In the North he had been forced into run-down, overcrowded residential sections, and during the depression the rates for disease, crime, death, and delinquency began to soar. Desperate, the Negro sought escape from his problems in various ways. Some of these were gaudy and impractical, like the Marcus Garvey movement to found a "homeland" in Africa. During the days of mounting relief rolls—more than half the adult population of Harlem was on the dole—Negroes in large numbers began to follow the Communist party line. Communist exploitation of a number of celebrated issues like the Scottsboro case also proved effective propaganda. But an overwhelming majority of Negroes continued to cling stubbornly to a belief in the promise of America and a hope that sooner or later the great day would come when it would open to them.

It is difficult to determine exactly why the Negro found himself *persona non grata* when industry began to boom in 1940, even in many fields where before he had been accepted. Certainly he had not become a poorer worker in the interim. Perhaps he had become a different person. His race consciousness and militancy had been growing since the depression years. Probably the Negro had become identified in the thinking of industrial management as a point of focus for restlessness and agitation.

A brief listing of the FEPC's findings in Los Angeles in October 1941 illuminates the manner in which American industry had begun to freeze the Negro out: Douglas Aircraft employed 33,000 workers—ten of them Negroes. North American Aviation employed eight Negroes—all janitors; the company president announced publicly that Negroes were unacceptable in any other capacity. Bethlehem's San Pedro shipyard had two skilled Negroes working as common laborers, both hired on the morning of the hearing. Lockheed-Vega Aircraft had 54 Negroes out of 48,000—all hired in recent weeks, under threat of the hearing. Consolidated Aircraft of San Diego had 225 Negroes in custodial capacities out of 28,000, but claimed this was the fault of the International Association of Machinists (AFL). Boeing Aircraft had no Negroes among 41,000 at Seattle—and also blamed the Machinists.[2]

Negroes by their own efforts had forced the creation of the FEPC in Executive Order 8802, which prohibited racial discrimination in war industry. Picket lines, mass demonstrations, delegations to Washington had been organized all over the country. Fainthearted Negro leaders who cautioned "patience" were brushed aside as "Uncle Toms" and "handkerchief-heads" and "pussyfooters." For the first time an aggressive spiritual unity appeared in all sections of the country and in every stratum of Negro life. Under the leadership of A. Philip Randolph of the Brotherhood of Sleeping Car Porters, a leader with a reputation for

[2]John Beecher in the New York *Post,* February 2, 1943.

personal integrity and with a long history of effective militancy, a number of organizations united in a proposed "March-on-Washington" movement. The plan—probably too ambitious for actual realization—called for the march of 100,000 orderly Negroes down the streets of Washington.

At first it was derided by official Washington, and then taken seriously when it became apparent that the protestants were in earnest. It was not difficult to imagine what headlines such a demonstration would produce in Berlin or Tokyo. Under this sharp, persistent pressure—the Negro's own creation, it must be remembered—the administration acted, and the FEPC was created to ameliorate such flagrant discriminations as the first hearings uncovered on the West Coast.

So long as the committee confined itself to investigations in Northern and Western areas, it encountered only normal opposition. As soon as it scheduled hearings in Birmingham, Alabama, the Dixie bloc in Washington swung into action. A campaign of protest and propaganda—much of it inspired by Northern-owned subsidiaries in the South—swept through the Southern press and industries, and soon the inevitable charge that the committee was attempting to foster "social equality" was raised. Jew-baiting, Negro-baiting racists like Representative John Rankin of Mississippi, both behind the scenes and on the floor, assailed the committee savagely. Erstwhile Southern liberals, who in the past had been spokesmen for mild race reforms, made a complete about-face now that they were confronted with a decision that had more than superficial meaning. They began to speak and write about shelving all discussion of the race problem until after the war. Nevertheless the hearings were held, and they received sincere support by a number of Alabama newspapers and progressive citizens' groups.

The howl raised over the Birmingham session proved only the first stirring breeze to the storm that greeted the FEPC's scheduling of hearings into the firmly entrenched discriminatory practices employed by a number of railroads and railroad unions, particularly in the South. Skilled Negro railroad workers, the highest-paid Negroes in the country, were being systematically and brutally excluded from employment by an agreement between the railroads and the unions. The first victims of the exclusion were 2,400 Negro firemen. Very simple means provided for the exclusion. The Interstate Commerce Commission had ruled that steam engines must be replaced by Diesel or by stoker-fed engines by July 1, 1943. An agreement signed on February 28, 1941, by the Southeastern Carriers' Conference Committee and the Brotherhood of Locomotive Firemen and Enginemen, made it impossible for a Negro fireman working on a steam or stokerized engine to be switched to a Diesel engine. It limited these jobs only to "promotable men," which in an earlier agreement had been defined as white men only. Thus Negroes with long seniority, who had taken firemen's jobs on railroads twenty and thirty years ago when shoveling coal was hard and dirty work, at low pay, were now being summarily forced out because the work on Diesel engines was easy and comparatively pleasant, and desired by white men.

Negro railway employees had been completely deprived of any effective means of raising objections to this agreement. By the Railroad Labor Act, the Brotherhoods assumed the right to act as sole bargaining agent for Negro employees. But the same employees are excluded from membership in the "bargaining agent," which holds a closed-shop contract.[3]

Here was discrimination in a virulent form.

A delegation of six of the most reactionary Southern senators hastened to the White House and laid down an ultimatum that unless the hearings were canceled, the administration could not enact any of its legislation. The President, by now yielding to the Southern bloc almost through force of habit, yielded again. On the night before he left for the Casablanca conference he ordered "indefinite postponement" of the hearings.

The FEPC's budget was held up. Strangulation of the FEPC began, at first subtly, and then ruthlessly.

But the President had made a mistake. The committee had worked well during the months of its existence and had turned up malodorous discriminatory conditions that had affronted white noses as well as Negro. A nationwide protest of minority groups followed, and the March-on-Washington threat was again revived. But perhaps more effective than anything else in impelling the President to revive the committee and reissue an anti-discrimination proclamation was the bald and indisputable fact that for a signer of the Atlantic Charter and as the leader of world democracy, he had acted with extraordinary weakness in canceling the railroad hearings.

On September 15, under the guidance of a new FEPC headed by Monsignor Francis J. Haas, the hearings were resumed with a vigorous presentation of the case against the railroads. The results of this hearing are being watched closely by Negroes and white groups throughout the country. They will give a sign whether or not the administration,

[3] *America* Magazine, January 23, 1943.

after months of stumbling, appeasement, and indirection, now actually realizes that the question of Negro employment is a grave matter which requires an honest, capable program instead of vaccillation and expediency.

The railroad cases illustrate a widespread pattern of discrimination practiced by various unions, the great majority of them AFL. Another far-reaching case, now before the National Labor Relations Board, involves the Bethlehem Shipyard at Alameda, California, and the Bay Cities Metal Trades Council. The AFL Boilermakers' Union, principal member of the council, set up auxiliary locals for Chinese and Negro workers, collected dues, restricted them to the poorest jobs, but gave them no say in union affairs. The council's jurisdiction has been challenged by the CIO steelworkers' and welders' unions, which do not bar Negroes. The NLRB decision, which directly involves union discrimination, will have far-reaching effects.

It is true, however, that on the whole Negroes by now have been able to get work in wartime industry. They are still barred from most of the most desirable job classifications, and are denied upgrading according to their skills, largely through threats and resentful attitudes on the part of white workers. And, although the FEPC did unusually effective work on its meager budget, largely by bringing the pressure of publicity to bear upon industry, it is the cold, mathematical need for manpower which has been chiefly responsible for giving the Negro employment. And the Negro knows he faces one of the stiffest fights of his history to keep any appreciable amount of his gains.

In time of war and crisis he makes his gains. In depressions, and postwar eras of shrinking industry, he loses ground; the blows fall first and heaviest upon him. He remembers the First World War and what came after. The only answer he can have to "white friends" who enjoin him to put away any thoughts of race reforms until after the war is first to try to swallow his disillusionment and work with greater determination for his share of democracy—now.

The Negro has two means of preparing himself for the postwar crisis. One is to try to nail down every gain he has made by getting formal rulings from law courts and governmental agencies. This phase is important, but it is not enough. The Negro must also try by good work to fit so well into industry that management will see no economic advantage, and perhaps even disadvantage, in laying him off because of the color of his skin.

In driving this vital fact into the minds of Negro workers, the Negro press and a number of other organizations, hammering away week after week, logically, compellingly, are performing one of the most constructive educational tasks in American history. While the race press has been widely attacked for its militancy, white critics at the same time have consistently overlooked or failed to understand this important work.

While Negro leadership can accomplish much by attempting to create a prideful race consciousness on the part of poorly educated masses of workers—maintaining a constant din of propaganda against absenteeism, drinking, vulgarity, uncouthness in dress or manner—sermonizing alone cannot do it. Characteristics which grow up in any exploited peasantry or slum population, white or black, as a form of rebelliousness and release, cannot be completely eradicated by a period of momentary prosperity, especially when the prosperity is only relative. Oppression and discrimination must cease and slums must be obliterated before their effects upon a people can be obliterated as well.

Last July, in Detroit, Vice-President Wallace gave voice to a heart-lifting view of America's postwar assets; he described a world in which the Negro would have an excellent chance to hold his wartime gains, and to advance them, along with workers in general:

When the guns stop, America will find itself with the following assets:

1. Manpower by the million; skilled workers from war industries, military manpower, and young people coming of working age.

2. The largest industrial-plant capacity in the world.

3. The greatest resources, both natural and artificial, to make peacetime products and thousands of new inventions waiting to be converted to peacetime use.

4. The largest scientific arms plant in the world.

5. The largest backlog of requirements for housing, transportation, communications, and living comforts.

6. The greatest reserve of accumulated savings by individuals that any nation has ever known.

With such wealth, who says this nation is now bankrupt, if industrial management can bring the same wisdom for producing for peace that it has shown on many production fronts in the supply program for war?

The whole nation has a stake in bringing about full use of these assets. Most of the planning going on in Washington today is directed toward this end. But certainly a special and adequate type of planning is needed to assure the Negro's participation in this world on a broadening basis of equality. The Negro has aways had two strikes against him economically; if no special effort is made by the administration to prevent it, the first pitched ball of the postwar era once again will strike him out; the first postwar jolts to the full-employment war economy will result in nationwide layoffs of Negro workers, an inevitable reappearance of malcontent and unemployed slum populations, an inevitable heightening of race conflict, inevitable riots. This is a problem for the administration to think about. It is a problem too for industrial management, which certainly has much to lose in an America swept by race tension and rioting. And, of paramount importance, it is a problem that the individual white American must concern himself with and attempt to ameliorate through enlightened attitudes and deeds.

Negroes in the Armed Forces

Compared with his experience in the last war, the Negro soldier has a better time of it in this one. But one thing must be borne in mind in such comparisons: the Negro's maturing need for justice has outstripped his gains in all fields. This was an act of human nature, of intellects that learned, of eyes that observed, of native intelligence and manhood and human hungering rising over caution. There are a number of white men who try by tortuous, deceiving argument to attach some sort of blame to the Negro people for this development. In doing so, they reveal their own spiritual and intellectual inertia; no onus can be placed on a people for being alive and human and having the capacity to learn and hunger.

In the First World War less than a thousand Negroes were trained as officers, in a segregated camp at Des Moines, Iowa. The training given them seemed at times as though it were designed to ensure their failure as officers. After he had received his commission the Negro officer found himself subjected to a disheartening variety of humiliations. When he reached France he found that official United States Army orders and advices had been issued warning the French people not to associate with Negro officers or soldiers and barring Negroes from restaurants and public places. Yet despite all this, Negro troops exhibited an ironclad resistance to German propaganda which sought to capitalize on their experiences in the Army and at home.

Many of the Negro regiments distinguished themselves. One of them, the 369th of New York, served under fire longer than any other regiment and achieved the distinction of never having yielded an inch of ground. Because it was brigaded with French troops, who treated its soldiers more decently, the 369th was given opportunity to show its mettle as was no other Negro unit.

But the experience of Negro troops on the whole was humiliating:

To the Service of Supply regiments [writes Carter G. Woodson] most Negro draftees were sent. Not less than three fourths of the 200,000 of the Negroes sent to France were reduced to laborers. It resulted that one tenth of the population of the nation was compelled, by a country fighting for democracy abroad, to supply three fourths of the labor of the expeditionary force. They were commanded moreover largely by illiterate, prejudiced white men, and finally all but enslaved in the Service of Supply divisions abroad by unsympathetic whites, the majority of whom were Southerners on the order of slave drivers.

Abolition of segregated officer training has been the most liberal advance in army race policy between the wars. During the present war, without difficulty or conflict, Negroes in considerably larger numbers have been trained with white soldiers in officer-candidate schools, the majority of which are in the South. But after training, the officers return to duty with segregated troops—not all, it is hoped, to forget the lessons of democracy and mutual respect learned through association in the schools.

Large numbers of Negro troops still go to labor battalions, but here too, by comparison with his First World War experience, he is getting a better break.

The Air Forces at first refused to accept Negroes in any capacity, but after the appeals and criticism of Negro and white groups had been focused on the War Department, the Air Forces established a training school for a limited number of pursuit pilots at Tuskegee Institute in Alabama. These pilots have been in action since the Sicilian campaign. The War Department, apparently convinced that Negroes make satisfactory airmen, has announced that Negroes will be trained for bombers also, as pilots, navigators, and bombardiers, in an unsegregated school at Del Rio, Texas.

The Navy, in which the Negro had served almost exclusively as a mess attendant, held out for a long time against enlisting Negroes as general seamen, but it announced last year that Negroes would now be used in this classification and assigned to navy yards and shore installations. The Coast Guard and Marine Corps, also initially prejudiced against Negroes, finally let down the bars and manifested an encouraging willingness to admit Negroes and to permit their advancement as combat personnel.

In their comparative effects upon Negro morale, these relative gains in military status have been more than invalidated by the constant humiliations suffered by Negro soldiers at the hands of sheriffs, police, bus drivers, railway conductors, shopkeepers, and, to a lesser extent, by white commanding officers and military police. There have been about a score of race riots, ranging from small localized outbreaks to pitched battles in which a number of lives were lost. These involved Negro and white troops, and sometimes white municipal police. A growing number of Negro soldiers have been beaten or murdered in the vicinity of Southern training camps. The inflexible pattern of local authorities has been to put the blame for aggressiveness on the victims. The record of the War and Justice departments in these cases has been one of constant evasion of their democratic responsibilities and surrender to Southern racial patterns. It must be remembered that in almost all of these cases, regardless of how the blame has been fixed officially, it is inconceivable that a white soldier could have been shot for the same reasons or that wanton slayings of white personnel would be ignored by the Federal government as they have been ignored in the case of Negro troops.

It is true that the Army (like America) has been confronted with an extraordinarily difficult dilemma. At the beginning of the war in Europe we were caught with probably less than 100,000 fully equipped troops. The General Staff faced staggering tasks: of creating divisions literally overnight; of transforming America from a comatose peacetime nation into a great military power. Draft machinery had to be set up. Cantonments and other centers by the hundreds had to be planned, ordered, and built in a matter of weeks and months. The Army's task was enormously complicated by the confusion in domestic politics, by habitual obstruction and an incredible lack of realism—or worse—on the part of men who seemed almost willing to see America eventually humiliated and defeated. To top it all, the Army was forced to maintain our fiction of neutrality and to train men for hypothetical battles with unnamed enemies, rather than for a certain death struggle with Germans, Italians, and Japanese.

No necessity was as urgent as the necessity for speed. One decision made instantly was that a large proportion of the camps had to be built in the South. The milder climate afforded more days for outdoor physical work by green civilians in uniform. The open spaces, the forests, the cutover pinelands afforded room for maneuvers, resulting in the least damage and delays for farming and other civilian pursuits. In the milder climate camps could be built with a smaller proportion of vital building materials, such as heating equipment and insulation.

In the face of these monumental tasks, the Army apparently decided that it must accept the Southern Jim Crow patterns for the Negro troops which would be trained in the South. The Army itself, furthermore, was built of America's components, and the principle of segregation was embedded in it. There were large proportions of Southern officers of all ranks, from top to bottom; as military resources the Army relied heavily on them. Southern states had the highest rates of enlistments. Because of the relative poverty of the South, a greater proportion of its young men had been trained in the state-supported institutions which conducted reserve-officer-training programs as a function of their land-grant charters, in return for state and Federal support. Huge Texas A and M, for example, has sent more officers to the war than has West Point. Because of all these factors, the student of contemporary America, even though deploring the tragic national background which produced it, must nevertheless understand the inevitability of the Army's decision not to buck the Southern race pattern or comparable biracial patterns wherever they manifested themselves, North or South.

By now it must have become apparent to the Army that a mistake has been made, a mistake judged not on the basis of ethics but on the basis of military logistics. The mistake was not in its failure to choose completely to override the South's Jim Crow patterns—for that could not be done—but in the excessive degree in which they have been observed. As a result, the morale of Negro soldiers is one of the major background problems which confront the Army—probably the most important; and the morale of Negro civilians—who number a tenth of the nation—has suffered its severest damage through the experiences of Negroes in the Army.

For three years now the letters of Negro soldiers have flowed homeward; month by month the volume has mounted; year by year the information which they contained has been digested and disseminated through the Negro population; until at last, in this brief space, they have created an actual *folkway,* to use the term of social scientists, among the Negro people. It is an ominous folkway.[4] Its basis is a belief

[4]This fact is recommended to the attention of those sociologists, most of whom are Southerners, who argue that the South can be expected to make no rapid readjustment in its archaic relationships with Negroes because these relationships are rooted in folkways, which by their slow growth and inertia cannot be altered except through continuance of the slow evolutionary process. A counter-folkway has grown up in the Negro people; on the side of this folkway reposes elemental justice and the weight of modern world history. Intransigeance on the part of white Southerners breeds intransigeance on the part of Negroes; a genuine and meaningful effort to adjust the Southern pattern would greatly diminish the ominous and fatalistic element in the Negro attitude. Only in this way can the present tragic attrition and mounting clashes be brought to a halt and a period of actual interracial progress be ushered in.

that sons and husbands and loved ones are subjected to humiliation and injustice in the army of American democracy. It is a belief also that Negroes in army camps, particularly in the South, are in constant physical danger at the hands of white authorities, principally civilian.

The Negro press has disseminated much of this information. A number of white critics, with utter disregard for elemental considerations of justice, have accused the press of reckless and hysterical agitation. It is fallacious to accuse the Negro's newspapers and his leaders of having created this folkway; they have done no more than report and react—with indignation, it is true—to actual instances of cruelty and brutality to Negro soldiers by civilians, or discriminatory treatment of them in the Army. The folkway has been created by the Negro soldier's experiences.

Anyone who has had access to large numbers of the letters of Negro soldiers knows their tone: bitterness and disillusionment, often accompanied by macabre humor. Their experiences have an impressive uniformity. They are put off buses to give white soldiers or civilians a seat; they are beaten, or their friends are beaten, for speaking out sullenly or bitterly to bus drivers; merchants insult them and keep them out of their stores; townsmen refer to them commonly as "nigger"; white policemen threaten them or beat them with little provocation; the Army refuses to stand up for them in controversies with local authorities; there is little to do when they go into the towns on passes but walk around aimlessly trying to keep out of trouble—feeling like unwanted pariahs even though clothed in the uniform of a soldier. There are many other complaints; sometimes bloody violence figures in them.

There is no use quoting these letters or raking over the details of riots and shootings. This supplement is not intended as an exposé but as exposition and analysis of the problem.

It must be observed also that the morale of many white troops, many who have an actual philosophical understanding of the principles of a democracy, and a belief in them, and a desire to fight for them but not for fascist principles, has been damaged by observing the undemocratic indignities suffered by Negro soldiers. It is significant that at least three fourths of the articles and letters sent to the *New Republic* by soldiers deal with the problem. This does not mean that three fourths of the white personnel of the Army is concerned about it—far from it; soldiers who read journals of opinion in preference to magazines with pin-up girls must be in a very small minority. But it is nevertheless a fact of significance; it argues that there must certainly be elements of native democracy and decency in the Army on which a more enlightened, and less dangerous, race policy could be built by the commanding generals.

A reading of Southern newspapers discloses the fact that the South is laboring under the illusion that race clashes are caused almost exclusively by "uppity" Negroes in Northern units who don't know their place like Southern Negroes. A study of the facts of these clashes disproves this. A listing of the home towns of Negro soldiers involved in riots discloses a large number of them, probably a majority, to be from Southern states. And it is also true that the folkway of discontent is firmly embedded in Southern Negro civilians whose men are in the Army. This forebodes a tragic day for the South when white troops and Negro troops are mustered out and return home. It is impossible for the Army to take a Negro youth and make a soldier out of him, teach him how to kill on a battlefield, how to defend himself, how to sustain himself in crisis through courage, daring, and skill, and then expect him to slip back easily into his former role of complacency, servility, and caution. Clearly the only way to avoid the tragic results that are looming in Southern history is for the South to learn—for the South's leaders to teach it—that the Negro, by all the rights of democracy, by all the ethics of Christianity, by all the arguments of prudence and common sense, must be accorded a greater measure of freedom and respect than he has known before. For the South to develop some techniques of actual co-operation with Negroes would be a way out; but co-operation does not mean patronizing—the subtle, dictatorial arrogance which has often passed by this name in the past. The only other answer is to hold the Negro to the old pattern by force and violence. The South's history stands proof that it can be done, for a time at least; but it also suggests what the ghastly cost will be.

It is a known fact that the Army is gravely concerned with its race problem as a military factor. Some of the top command are convinced that segregation is uneconomical, militarily wasteful, and harmful. Much attention is being given to the problem—but, unfortunately, with the field of remedial action always limited, perhaps in the long run fatally so, by the swollen power of Southern politicians.

The single, dramatic, sound, and clear-cut act by which the Army could give an incalculable lift of spirit to its Negro troops, to thousands of white troops, to Negro civilians and to millions of white ones, is the creation of a voluntarily mixed division of white and Negro soldiers. Responsible Americans in great numbers have petitioned the War Department to take this step. The division could undoubtedly be filled instantly with volunteers; many soldiers, including numbers of liberal Southerners, have already made known their wishes to serve. Undoubtedly the division would draw an intelligent, high-type personnel. But the Army will probably not take this step (in the American race question it often seems that the right steps are the ones which must be summarily ruled out). From the Army's point of view there are two obstacles: the inevitable opposition from the South, even though the enrollment would be on a voluntary basis; and second, the Army's own innately reactionary wish to keep enlightened liberal white troops and Negroes far apart, lest they give one another "subversive" ideas. The consideration that a division motivated by intelligence and a creative ideal would probably be a splendid division for hazardous fighting will hardly enter into the matter.[5]

A mixed division would be the best thing; the next-best things are remedies of limited nature. Yet it is important to try them. The Army shows signs of making some progress. Thus far, however, the emphasis

[5]There is a forgotten Civil War story in the Army's archives which is timely today and which would have been well worth study by the ranking officers who laid down the Army's race policies in the present war.

It concerns General Benjamin F. Butler and his use of Negro troops in defense of the Mississippi Valley in 1862. Butler, commanding general at New Orleans following the city's capture, was at first contemptuous of the Negro's military potentialities. A congressional resolution furthermore had restricted Negro service to labor battalions "for the purpose of constructing entrenchments, performing camp service, or any other labor in the military or naval service for which they may be found competent." But eventually, having been denied reinforcements from Washington and proceeding under orders to hold New Orleans "by all means and hazards," he mustered into service a self-drilled corps of Native Guards numbering about five thousand Negroes. In the course of time his prejudice moved to another extreme and he wrote of his Negro troops that "better soldiers never shouldered a musket." Later he wrote a report excoriating General Nathaniel P. Banks, who succeeded him at New Orleans, and reinstituted retrogressive policies toward the black troops. While Butler's personal character has been discredited, this following opinion of the service of Negro troops (a clear foreshadowing of the Army's race problem today) cannot be deprived of its military significance:

"After I left New Orleans, General Banks enlisted many more of them [Negroes] but was weak enough to take away from them the great object of their ambition, under the spur of which they were ready to fight to the death, namely, equality with the white soldiers. He was also unmanly enough to add injustices to that folly by taking the commissions from their line officers, which I had given them, and to brand their organization with the stigma of a designation as the Corps d' Afrique. Yet in spite of this unwisdom, they did equal service and laid down their lives at Port Hudson in equal numbers comparatively with their white brothers in arms."

Today, eighty years later, the progressive attitude toward the conditions of Negro service, which General Butler found militarily sound policy and for which he argued, is still denied by the Army.

This material is quoted from an article by Enoc P. Waters in the Chicago *Defender,* based on an unpublished study by James La Fourche of New Orleans.

has been on minimizing race prejudice among troops in foreign service among dark peoples. The Office of Special Services of the War Department has prepared excellently written guides for troops in countries where skin color, traditions, history, language, clothing, and religion are markedly different. They include valuable instructions on what to do and what not to do, among them injunctions concerning race prejudice itself. But the point is not labeled, and in some of the guides the issue is treated so delicately as to be of doubtful efficacy. Some passages, however, offer arguments which the Army might well present to its own white troops training in America, and to civilians in cantonment areas. Here is one from the guide to West Africa:

> Race prejudice against the African or against American Negro troops in Africa would be a good way to turn the African against us. Everyone is entitled to his own prejudices, but it would be only sensible for those who have them to keep them under cover when such high stakes as the war and men's lives are on the table. None of us wants to aid Hitler.

After a regrettable and costly delay, the Army apparently has begun to realize the necessity for some sort of domestic program. In September the Army War College made excerpts of a clear-cut military analysis of race prejudice from the August issue of the highly respected *Infantry Journal.* These excerpts, and others from the *Journal,* were supplied to officers along with a selected reading list of articles and books dealing with the race problem. A few queer books like the racist tract *The Rising Tide of Color,* by Lothrop Stoddard, were included, perhaps through an ill-considered effort to give a rounded picture. But on the whole the material was excellent. It is also rumored that the War Department is planning to include courses of instruction in all army camps—presumably illuminating the military cost of aggressive racism—under the direction of Lieutenant Commander Herbert Agar.

If passages from the *Infantry Journal* article could be impressed upon all commanding officers, and if these would thereby stand up for the human dignity of their troops in uniform, Negro as well as white, in the face of frequently wanton aggression and brutality on the part of civilian authorities and occasionally white military police, they would go a long way toward solving the mounting problem of Negro morale, on the home front as well as in the Army. One passage reads:

> Sometimes the prejudice against the Negroes flares up in the Army. It is not a problem, however, in a camp where it is well understood that a soldier in the United States uniform is a *soldier,* not a white or Negro,

Christian or Jew, rich man or poor, but a soldier, and as such is worthy of respect.

And not everyone feels race prejudice. There are plenty of white men who are constantly meeting and working with black, brown, and yellow men of brains, education, culture, and ability. These white men know that skin color is not a sign of inferiority or superiority, and they tend to forget about it. . . . Those white men are numerous in Europe, South America, Asia, and Africa, where the races are mixed up in business and politics.

In the United States we are more used to seeing large numbers of men with dark skins who are uneducated. We do not often meet the scholars among the Chinese, Negroes, and other dark-skinned peoples. The two oceans have in the past prevented most of us from becoming acquainted with the more able and successful men of Africa and Asia. So we keep our prejudices. Nowadays, with the great American enthusiasm for the bravery of our Chinese allies, this prejudice is less than it was, but it is still very strong.

Now, however, the American soldier is going among people who do not share his prejudices. These unprejudiced white men may find it hard to understand if he shows antagonism toward other Americans or our allies on account of their color, just as the Americans may be surprised at these more liberal attitudes.

If, however, the American soldier understands the basis for his own feelings, as well as those of the men he meets, he can avoid friction and embarrassment to America.

And he must come to understand and learn to respect their manners. Only then will he realize that national differences in manners and customs are mostly due to differences of tradition, climate, and religion.

"A soldier in the United States uniform is a *soldier,* not a white or Negro, Christian or Jew, rich man or poor, but a soldier, and as such is worthy of respect." Here is the mandate of common sense, of morality, of history, to the army of American democracy.

The Negro and Politics

Legal and extralegal disfranchisement of some nine million Negroes—and millions of whites—who live in Southern states is one of the chief pieces of unfinished business before American democracy. Among progressive Americans everywhere a priority must be given to all efforts to broaden the basis of suffrage. This must be done through the support of Federal measures like the perennial anti-poll-tax bill, which sooner or later will be passed, and through educational programs to bring home to the understanding of the white masses that the Negro is a potential ally and not an enemy. It is only through broadening the base of suffrage that the South can escape from its long and costly imprisonment by the industrial and agrarian plutocracy. Once, in an access of enlightenment and affirmation, white men rose in a populist political rebellion against their masters. Fear of the Negro in the long run proved their fatal weakness, for it was manipulated with skill and ruthlessness by the plutocracy; it was used to divide and confuse, and eventually to crush the movement. The impetus which moved them half a century ago must be again awakened by organized labor and other progressive groups in the South, and this time the Negro must be an ally. History teaches this lesson.

Over and over again one hears in the wartime declarations of Southern politicians a curiously twisted argument, an argument which is not without grim humor. "While our boys are fighting and dying for democracy on Guadalcanal," one Southern legislator said some months ago, "democracy is being betrayed at home by these anti-poll-tax agitators, who are trying to destroy our principle of white supremacy." In one version or another this statement has been made many times. One runs across it in a recent one-man declaration of secession from the Democratic party by Governor Sam Jones of Louisiana, who conducted his unilateral revolt in the pages of the *Saturday Evening Post:*

> White Southern boys in the armed services, who perhaps have an understanding and affection for the Negro race not shared by their comrades from other sections, do not improve in morale when they are told that one of the things they are fighting for is social equality of the Negro. They would renounce any such war aim, rightly or wrongly.

For "social equality" it is more accurate to read "political equality." This is the real fear of Southern reaction for which Governor Jones in recent months has been a confused but active spokesman. It is true that most white Southerners in the Army would renounce such a war aim, for they are heirs to the prejudice against the Negro and have had little opportunity to learn its cost to their impoverished land and exploited people. But wars wrench men out of their backgrounds and jolt their thinking, and white soldiers and others in the postwar South are going to have a chance to learn some of the political facts of life. For one thing, the labor movement has made significant inroads into the growing industrial populations of a number of the states. On the water front of New Orleans, in the mines and mills of Alabama, in the war plants of

Tennessee and Texas and Georgia, progressive groups of organized labor are growing. There has been a long and significant list of NLRB elections in Southern industry. Those centers of the growing labor movement are proving invaluable bases of operation in the agitation for broadened suffrage. These are the realities which have the plutocracy's spokesmen, like Governor Jones, musing in a disquieted frame of mind about domestic war aims and democracy.

Here is a paragraph from an interesting letter sent some months ago to the *New Republic* which suggests the strong labor undercurrent in the South today:

> When last I was in Birmingham I talked to a Negro named ——, and though it was a brief conversation, I will not forget it. He was an officer of one of the mine-union locals, a local with white and Negro membership. He had a lot of servile mannerisms like "yassuh" in his talk still, but the words that came out of his mouth were pure militant trade-unionism. It was a curious thing to see this ideology matched up with this soft-spoken cornfield Negro, to use the old term. He had a pleasant, humorous, direct manner—and he gave the impression that there was plenty of guts below the surface. If there are very many more Negroes like him in the South today—and the number must be growing—I know some white folks who are going to be in for a rude awakening when they try to continue with the old line about "we know what the nigger wants; he wants the white man to tell him what to do."

Elimination of the poll tax will not, of course, assure the Negro suffrage; other techniques, ranging from discriminatingly administered qualification tests to threats of violence, will continue for the time being to keep him from the polls. But the poll tax is the principal buttress between the Southern Negro and the ballot, and its removal will bring him pressing ever nearer to political emancipation. One by one these buttresses will go down. Four states already have repealed the tax: Louisiana, North Carolina, Florida, and Kentucky. Tennessee would have made the fifth, but the repealing act of the legislature was ruled unconstitutonal by a state supreme court which took the all-but-incredible position that a legislature could not repeal its own act. The seven other states in which the tax remains are: Alabama, Arkansas, Georgia, Mississippi, South Carolina, Texas, and Virginia.

The poll tax is badly on the defensive. It has important and influential enemies among Southern people of prestige. The most effective argument against it, in the South, is that it disfranchises more white people than it does Negroes. The statistics of this disfranchisement are startling and effective. Southern senators and representatives are elected by proportions of voters commonly ranging from 2 to 7 or 8 per cent of the potential voters; outside the South the average ranges from 45 to 60 per cent. In comparable states like Wisconsin and Georgia, each with a population of three million, 1,500,000 vote in Wisconsin compared with 300,000 in Georgia. Representative Martin Dies of Texas and Representative Warren G. Magnuson of Washington come from districts about equal in population. Dies was elected by 12,824 voters, Magnuson by 147,061.

Huey Long, who was supported by the common people of Louisiana with a fanatical loyalty, abolished the poll tax to enable more of them to go to the polls and swell the margins of his victories. Ironically, it was this very expansion of the electorate that resulted in the defeat of the Long ring after his death; it no longer could hold the masses enthralled and, though a mighty effort was made, it could no longer steal enough votes to turn the tide of reform sentiment.

Under a rotten-borough political system which deprives nine people in ten of the ballot, a congressman can get elected term after term with monotonous ease; a coalition of a few plantation owners, or factory owners and the business cliques in the towns, can make him a political invincible. He is their tool for the duration of the arrangement, which is commonly twenty to thirty years in many Southern districts. Under the antiquated seniority rules of Congress, Southern members—almost inevitably reactionary—win their ways to the all-important chairmanships of more than half of the powerful committees, although they represent scarcely a quarter of the population.

There is little wonder, in the light of this record, that legislation desired by minority groups such as the Negro and labor face almost hopeless obstacles. This is the unanswerable argument for Southern electoral reform. It is the argument that the expanding labor movement and other progressive forces in the South will be making with increasing effectiveness in the years immediately ahead.

It would be idle to deny that many Negroes at present are deeply dissatisfied with President Roosevelt. Probably some of them will vote for the Republican candidate next year, whoever that candidate may be. It is regrettable, of course, that any Negro should vote on a single issue, that of race equality; that he should not consider all the elements in the situation, including the kind of America the Republican party wants to make if it gets into power. It is indicative, however, of the seriousness with which the Negroes take the race issue that many of them will vote on a basis of this matter alone.

The growing power of former Mr. Justice Byrnes in his capacity as "assistant President" is a manifestation which Negroes consider ominous. There has obviously been an amount of serious consideration on the President's part of the possibility of running Byrnes as vice-president in 1944. Negroes remember him for his hostility when he was a high-grade political trader in the Senate. They recall and cite the fact that when he was a representative from South Carolina he consistently fought appropriations for Howard University. Negroes would deny their vote to any ticket which placed Byrnes and others like him in power. Negro leaders point out that the migratory shift of some three million Southern Negroes, in the past quarter century, has built up Negro populations which all but hold the political balance of power in states like New York, New Jersey, Pennsylvania, Ohio, Illinois, and Indiana.

The two most clever and aggressive Republican hopefuls, Willkie and Dewey, have been cruising around with hungry eyes on the Negro vote. Willkie's outspoken liberal views of the race issue have made him an object of sincere appreciation and even affection. Like white progressives, Negroes have been suspicious of Dewey on the whole; but Dewey not only is hopeful but smart, and his recent nomination of a Negro attorney for a $17,500 judgeship—the most remunerative public office ever given a Negro—is an indication that he will make an effective bid for Negro votes.

Negro Progress

Negroes have gained much in America, and, though race reform is still the great lag in our democracy, the story of Negro progress does not give cause for despair.

Negro gains in the field of higher education have been impressive. In 1916 all the Negro colleges in the country showed a total enrollment of only 2,637. Six years later the figure had doubled; by 1927 it had more than doubled again. In 1932 the figure reached 22,000; in 1938, 34,000; in 1941, more than 45,000.[6] In the eighty-odd years since emancipation, literacy has risen from 5 to 85 per cent. Negro ownership of property has risen in the same time to $2,500,000,000; annual purchasing power in the last normal year before the war was $2,000,000,000.

Fifty years ago, the annual death rate was 33 per 1,000—comparable to the death rates in the worst sections of China and India. Great improvement in health facilities and modes of living have cut the rate to an estimated

[6]*Below the Potomac*, by Virginius Dabney. New York: Appleton-Century.

14 per 1,000—32 per cent above the annual death rate of 10.6 for the country as a whole.[7]

These gains are important and impressive. They are proof of a fact which Negroes understand even in a mood of agitation and spiritual revolt, that it is in America where their hope of greatest progress lies.

But lest these statistics become a cause for complacency and an argument for the status quo in race reform, they must be compared with comparable white statistics rather than with what the Negro had fifty or eighty years ago. Eighty years ago he had nothing. The real question is not how much freedom or education or food the Negro has, but what are America's resources and does he get his share. In the ideal democracy, health and education are not largess to be doled out benevolently through the years, but rights and privileges shared in equally by all.

There are many more agencies at work educating public opinion than there were at the close of the last war. Few churches do not make some form of educational effort on the race problem. Increasingly, leading magazines open their pages to thoughtful treatment of the problem of race. Many colleges, universities, high schools, and even grammar schools give it consideration today. A gradually improving treatment of the Negro in movies and radio will help to destroy the old stereotype of the Negro as a comic or menial figure exclusively and picture him as he really is.

Fortunately, the United States Supreme Court in recent years has consistently handed down decisions in cases brought before it dealing with the Negro which have enormously improved his status. Among these have been the Negro's and any other citizen's right to a trial in a court not dominated by mob violence; the right to a trial before a jury from which members of his race have not been excluded; the right of equal pay for equal work by teachers; and various other rights dealing with the franchise. These are decisions which, more than being merely preventive, have given pause to those who would depress the Negro's status still further.

To individuals the *New Republic* recommends that they join at least one of the various organizations which are tackling this question directly or indirectly. To those who are church members and would prefer working through these organizations, there are several departments, such as the Race Relations Department of the Federal Council of Churches of Christ in America, and the Catholic Interracial Council, which are doing effective work on this question. Those who are con-

[7] *American Negroes,* by Edwin R. Embree. New York: John Day.

nected with the labor movement can work through their local and international units. It is particularly important that members of the Railroad Brotherhoods and of those AFL unions which, by constitutional provision, ritualistic practice, or custom, bar Negroes from membership should work within the ranks to change these policies. There are many other organizations, such as the National Association for the Advancement of Colored People, the National Urban League, the Council Against Intolerance in America, the March-on-Washington Movement, the Union for Democratic Action, and others, which are tackling the problem.

Readers of newspapers and magazines can help by challenging biased or inaccurate news or editorial treatment of the Negro question. It is especially important to express approval when newspapers or magazines carry thoughtful and intelligent articles or editorials. Moviegoers should express disapproval of ridicule or biased treatment of the Negro or other minorities in the moving pictures, and express approval and support of films which depict the Negro and other minorities in normal and decent fashion.

Particularly important to the solution of the race question is the necessity for the American electorate to beat back reaction, especially in the 1944 election. It is unfortunate that today many liberals are either disheartened or weary. To them we repeat a passage from a recent issue of the *New Republic:*

> . . . The vote which put Mr. Roosevelt into power and has kept him there . . . is not the Solid South, which will support any Democratic nominee but falls far short of a majority. It is not the Republican conservative backbone, which will vote the Republican ticket come hell or high water, and also fall short of a majority. It is the Northern industrial workers, the dissatisfied or progressive farmers, the lower- or middle-income classes, the Negroes and the independent progressives who find natural allies in these groups, and have done much to provide leadership of their opinions. These voters also would fall short of a majority if they voted alone, but they can pile up an overwhelming majority if they vote together for any Democratic or Republican candidate.

In race persecution, white America has learned to play a dangerous game, and must unlearn it. Two can play at any game, races as well as individuals.

This supplement, and all such writing like it, will be accepted by the racists of America as an attempt to whitewash the Negro's rebelliousness. By any enduring standards of truth and ethics, the Negro's cause is just. Justice cannot be whitewashed. It is a tragedy that a vast number of

Caucasians have learned to live by the lie of racism; it is true that inherited beliefs cannot be changed overnight; it is true that an amount of understanding, of pity, of commiseration must be placed in the scales in favor of even white oppressors who are suffering today beneath the weight of their own tragic folkways. But this cannot halt the expression of extreme criticism of these folkways; it cannot invalidate the obvious fact that extreme reforms are needed. Everything the white man suffers because of his tragic racial folkways the Negro suffers a hundredfold; everything the white man gains in privilege, prestige, laborious services, material wealth, the Negro loses. Who will justify this?

There is something pitiable in the folly of white men who issue fiats and moratoriums and unilateral prohibitions against race reform. It seems a very simple thing to them to slam the door of white America in the Negro's face. They are quick with accusations of blindness, while in their own blind arrogance they attempt the impossible and believe that they carry it off. Humanity has its shoulder in that door. No door can be slammed against its weight.

COUNT US IN

Sterling A. Brown

Sterling A. Brown, the well-known poet, was also one of the editors of the recent Negro Caravan. *He has degrees from Williams College and Harvard and teaches at Howard University in Washington.*

Counted Out

A YOUNG EUROPEAN SCHOLAR, back from a swift trip through the South, picked up from my desk a copy of Hal Steed's *Georgia: Unfinished State*. A passage on the last page confused him. It read: "I would not say that the Anglo-Saxon is superior to other races, but that this race makes up nearly one hundred per cent of the population of the South augurs well for unity—unity in political beliefs, in religion, in social problems."[1] The European was amazed at the figure—nearly one hundred per cent Anglo-Saxon. "But I saw so many Negroes there," he said.

I could have mentoned other oddities in the enumerating of the Negro, from the adoption of the Constitution when a Negro slave counted as three fifths of a man, to the present when a Negro is counted as a unit, a fraction, or a zero, according to the purpose of the counter. Instead I assured him that the evidence of his eyes could be trusted: the gatherings at one side of the depot to see the train go through, the hordes in the ramshackly slums of the cities, the crammed Jim Crow waiting rooms and coaches. Negroes were there all right. Even the publicists who excluded Negroes as part of the population would admit that they were there. Too much so, some might say ruefully, pointing out the large numbers of Negroes as the cause of the poverty and backwardness of the South, apologizing for the belt of swarming cabins engirdling the cities, hoping that the stranger might soften his verdict on the town until the business section around the depot slowly came into view. Too numerous, therefore Negroes had to be kept in their places, the argument might run. Such spokesmen would have a glib reply to reconcile the statistics of "nearly one hundred per cent Anglo-Saxon" with the patent reality: "Oh, that's easy to understand. By population we mean the people that count."

I knew that longer study of the South would convince the visitor that in certain respects Negroes definitely counted. He might learn how it was that one scholar called them "the central theme of southern history" running constantly through the record of the section. It would be easy for him to see how the presence of Negroes was chiefly responsible for the political "solidifying" of a region so far from solid in many other respects. Fear of Negroes' voting had been the primary cause for a poll tax peculiar to the region, resulting in the disfranchisement of ten millions of American citizens, half again as many whites as Negroes. This disfranchisement, he might learn, exerts more than a sectional influence, since it has been estimated that one poll-tax vote is worth more than five votes in states with no poll tax. Many poll-tax congressmen seem to have a permanent tenure on their seats in Congress, and their resulting seniority gives them a power disproportionate to the number of people who voted them into office, to say the least. The European might learn that the Federal ballot for soldiers was most forcefully opposed by those who feared that Negro soldiers might vote; that Federal aid to education was defeated because the race issue was raised; that the "G.I. Bill of

[1] Hal Steed, *Georgia: Unfinished State* (New York, 1942), p. 336.

Rights," providing unemployment insurance for returning soldiers, was jeopardized because of what the senator in charge of the bill calls the "hatred of certain congressmen for the colored portion of our armed forces." He might learn how a program of social reform—the Farm Security Administration—though it aided Southern whites as much as Negroes, was in danger of being scuttled by those who feared it meant that the Negro would "get out of his place."

Just how the Negro counted might be clarified should the visitor read Lillian Smith's "Two Men and a Bargain: A Parable of the Solid South," in which the rich white man says to the poor white man:

> There's two big jobs down here that need doing: Somebody's got to tend to the living and somebody's got to tend to the nigger. Now, I've learned a few things about making a living you're too no-count to learn (else you'd be making money same way I make it): things about jobs and credit, prices, hours, wages, votes, and so on. But one thing you can learn easy, any white man can, is how to handle the black man. Suppose now you take over the thing you can do and let me take over the thing I can do. What I mean is, you boss the nigger, and I'll boss the money.[2]

The visitor would thus learn that the Negro counted, and still counts, in this "Anglo-Saxon" section. But he would learn also what the Southern spokesmen mean by "people that count."

Negroes have lived too long with this paradox, as with so many others, to be confused by it; they understand the reality behind it. They have been counted out for so long a time.

"Sure, the Negro is all out for the war," my friend the sociologist told me. "He's 72 per cent all out for it." Some might consider this estimate to be cynicism, others optimism. The general conclusion is hardly to be disputed: that for all of its high promise, this war has not summoned 100 per cent of the Negro's enthusiasm and energies.

Before attacking this apathy as shortsighted, it might be wise to look for its causes. They are unfortunately too ready at hand to require much searching. On a six months' stay in the Deep South of wartime I saw my fill of them; even casual observations in a border city and on trips to the North have heaped the measure to overflowing.

Documentation of the refusal to count the Negro in the war effort is hardly needed. Discrimination in industry was so flagrant, North and South, East and West, that Executive Order 8802 was issued to ban discrimination in wartime industrial jobs, and the President's Committee on

[2]Lillian Smith, "Two Men and a Bargain," *South Today,* VII (Spring, 1943), p. 6.

Fair Employment Practice was set up to investigate cases of alleged discrimination. While Negro employment was definitely aided, progress has not been in a straight line. All sorts of obstacles have been in the way: congressmen and pressure groups continue to snipe and blast at the committee; the governor of a Southern state openly violated the Executive Order; the railroads have defiantly challenged a showdown. The integration of Negroes into industry has been opposed even with violence; strikes have been called because Negro workers were upgraded; and one of the causes of the Detroit riot is said to be the influx of Negro workers. In spite of welcome gains, Negroes are far from convinced that fullest use is being made of Negro manpower, North or South.

A powerful symbol to the Negro of his "not belonging" was the refusal of the Red Cross to accept Negro donors to the blood bank. Against the medical authorities who stated that there was no such thing as Negro blood, that blood from the veins of whites and Negroes could not be told apart, the Red Cross sided officially with Congressman Rankin, who saw, in the proposal that Negroes too might contribute much-needed blood, a communist plot to "mongrelize America": "They wanted to pump Negro or Japanese blood into the veins of our wounded white boys regardless of the dire effect it might have on their children." The establishment of a segregated blood bank—needless, complicated, and irrational—did not help matters much. Nor did the fact, publicized by the recent Spingarn Award, that one of the most important men in the successful establishment of the blood bank was Dr. Charles Drew, a Negro.

In the armed forces, advances have certainly been made over World War I. Drafted to their full quota, Negroes are supposed to be serving in all branches of the Army. Only recently it was reported that Negro paratroopers in Atlanta proved to white paratroopers that they really belonged to the daredevil's branch. Except in training for pursuit piloting, Negro officers are trained along with white. There are more Negro officers than in the last war, several officers of the rank of colonel and one brigadier general. Negro airmen are now being trained as bombardiers and navigators. Negro squadrons have seen action in the hot fighting in the Mediterranean theater and have been highly commended by military authorities. The long-closed ranks of the Marine Corps are now open, and marine officers praised Negro marines as "good marines," to be used everywhere and exactly as other marines. In the Navy, Negroes have finally been admitted to other capacities than mess boys. Some are to serve as seamen on patrol boats and destroyer escorts. The first ensigns have been commissioned. The record of the Coast Guard toward Negroes has been a good one, and the Merchant Marine, with its Negro officers and mixed crews, is looked upon as an achievement in democracy.

Advances have been made, but the Negro was so far behind in opportunity that he does not let his glance linger on the gains; he looks ahead along the road to full participation. This is good Americanism rather than ingratitude. The gains are not unmixed: there still seem to be, for instance, a ceiling on Negro officers and an opposition to having white officers serve under Negro officers. Negroes are dubious about the large number of Negro troops in the service and non-combat units; when the famous Tenth Cavalry, a source of historic pride, was assigned to service duties, Negroes were disturbed in spite of the assurance that military necessity required the transfer. And the Negro still looks askance at the Navy.

In the South I met on every hand the sense of not belonging. On a bus near Baton Rouge conversation had hardly started with my seat mate, a little fellow who looked like a black Frenchman, when he offered me a sure way of staying out of the Army: I was to roll a piece of "actican" (Octogon) soap in a pellet of bread and eat it just before the physical examination. He himself knew it would work, he said in his patois. He didn't have nothing against the Germans or Japs, neither one, but he did know some enemies over here. I found the same embittered spirit in a young Negro lieutenant who wanted to get overseas, anywhere, where he could find an enemy *to shoot at.* At the Negro section of an air base, segregated from the rest by a marker reading Beale Street, I found the men not proud of belonging to the Air Corps, but disgruntled at the type of menial labor they were called on to perform. I talked with a well-educated young Negro corporal, who had felt that some meaning might be given to his work in the Army when he learned that he was to be sent to an "area and language" school, but who on the eve of going was told that the school had suddenly been closed to Negroes. I talked with Negro pilots, who in the long hours of the day were learning the intricacies of high-powered P-40s, reading the involved instrument boards, soaring into the "wild blue yonder," with their lives and planes dependent on split-second judgments, developing the aggressiveness and self-reliance necessary for combat pilots. At night these men were forbidden by curfew to be seen in the downtown section of Tuskegee. This kind of thing, and so much else, rankled.

With a few honorable exceptions, newspapers, radio programs, and motion pictures (omitting, of course, Negro newspapers and newsreels for Negro theaters only) have done little to convince Negro soldiers of belonging. Some Northern periodicals, *PM* outstandingly, may publicize Negro military service. But in practically all Southern newspapers the daily row on row of native sons with the armed forces never showed a dark face. I should have known better, perhaps, than to look for one: pictures of Negroes in these papers were traditionally confined to those of prize fighters or recently deceased ex-slaves. In the North the practice is little better. In a Northern railroad station a picture, "blown up" by marvelous photographic technique, showed departing soldiers what they were fighting for: a sea of American faces looking out, anxiously, proudly. All were white. An observer saw a contingent of Negro troops entraining; they gave the eye-catching picture a swift glance and then snapped their heads away, almost as if by command. He wondered, he told me, what thoughts coursed through their minds.

"The Negro Soldier" is a first-class picture, wisely aimed at offsetting some of this indifference and ignorance concerning one tenth of our armed forces. But only when the picture reaches American white people will Negroes believe its real service to be achieved.

The situation that I found in the South was not solely that of whites refusing to count Negroes in, and of Negroes sensing that they did not and could not belong. It would be inaccurate to omit the friendliness that undoubtedly exists in the South between many whites and many Negroes. Though exaggerated by sentimentalists into a mystical cult of mutual affection instead of a human attachment, certain Southern whites have for a long time protected "their Negroes" and have cherished them with a fondness that has been gratefully received. But, as is frequently pointed out, this has generally been on a basis of master and underling. It has been affection rather than friendship, patronage returned by gratefulness, not the meeting of friends on a plane of mutual respect. It has been Santa Claus and the child. In certain phases—in the courts, for instance—when a white man protects *his* Negro regardless of innocence or guilt, the relationship is dangerous. Kindness can kill as well as cruelty, and it can never take the place of genuine respect. Those who boast of the affection between the races below the Mason-Dixon Line must be brought up sharp when they realize that one of the worst insults to a Southern white is to be called "nigger-lover," and one of the worst to a Negro is to be called "white-folks nigger."

Genuine respect between whites and Negroes can be found in the South, though to a smaller degree than paternalistic affection and dependent gratefulness. It would be serious omission to fail to recognize undoubted services rendered by many white people, not in the spirit of "Christmas gift," but at the price of social ostracism, loss of preferment, and even physical violence. Sheriffs have braved mobs to protect their prisoners; women have leagued against lynching; preachers, editors, professional men, scholars, and authors have spoken and acted against flagrant abuses; trade-union organizers have risked life and limb in efforts to establish industrial democracy. Many people, less dramatically, have been generous and courageous in treating Negroes in the spirit of brotherhood. People like Frank Graham, Arthur Raper, Thomas Sancton, Lillian Smith, and Paula Snelling, to name a conspicuous few, are warrants that there are white Southerners who believe that a New South of justice is attainable, or, at the least, worth fighting for.

These exceptions must be noted. Yet what I found most apparent among Southern Negroes—civilians and military men, upper and lower class, conservatives and radicals—was a sense of not belonging, and protest, sometimes not loud but always deeply felt. It is a mistake to believe that this protest in the South is instigated by Negroes from the North, or other "furriners," as Eugene Talmadge called them. I found a large degree of militancy in Negroes who were Southern born and bred, some of whom have never been out of the South. I talked with sharecroppers, union organizers, preachers, schoolteachers, newspapermen, and bankers who spoke with bitter desperation and daring. Clinton Clark, certainly among the sturdiest fighters, was born in one of the back-country parishes of Louisiana; when he was arrested for organizing in a parish near by, the planters refused to believe him a native of the section. The protest I heard ranged from the quietly spoken aside, through twisted humor and sarcasm, to stridency. Time and time again I heard the anecdote, which spread like a folk tale, of the new sort of hero—the Negro soldier who, having taken all he could stand, shed his coat, faced his persecutors, and said: "If I've got to die for democracy, I might as well die for some of it right here and now." Some of the protest, undoubtedly, is chip-on-the-shoulder aggression, like that of the Negro woman who in a jammed bus lumbering through the Louisiana night suddenly raised her voice, seemingly apropos of nothing, to say: "I had my Texas jack with me, and I told that white man I would cut him as long as I could see him."

At Columbus, Georgia, buses marked "K.O. for Tokyo" roared past Negro soldiers, who had to wait for special buses to take them to Fort

Benning. It was not only the boys from Harlem or Jersey who griped. The Negro train passengers who, standing in the aisle, wisecracked at the flushed conductor seated in his "office" in the Jim Crow coach, and then belabored the Negro porter for being a good man Friday, were not Northerners. It was not a Northern waiter who told the Negro sitting in the diner after lavish and ostentatious service: "Man, I was afraid you weren't coming back here." They were not Northern Negroes who repeated the refrain, whether called for or not, "That ain't no way to win the war."

I found this protest natural, since the Southern Negro is where the grip is tightest and the bite goes deepest and most often. The legend of Negro docility was always exaggerated. The novelists and poets, "befo' de war," wrote soothingly of contented slaves, but many of their readers lived in dread of insurrections and applauded the politicians who, fuming about the loss of their property via the Underground Railroad, sought anxiously to put teeth into the fugitive-slave bill and to set up a code of *verbotens* to prevent slave uprisings. Printers, whose presses busily ran off stories of docile Mose and Dinah, kept handy the stereotype of a Negro with a bundle on a stick, loping towards free land. The image of docility was cherished as a dream, but the hard actuality of furtiveness, truculence, rebelliousness, and desperation gave other images to the nightmares. The praises of old massa that white men wrote in "Negro" speech and "Negro" melody ring falsely when set beside "I been rebuked and I been scorned," "Go down Moses, tell old Pharoah, let my people go," and "I thank God, I'm free at last."

"When a man's got a gun in your face, ain't much to do but take low or die," a sharecropper in Macon County told Charles S. Johnson. In that setting he was talking sense, not docility. Southern Negroes too often have seen the gun in their faces; but many, all along, have asserted their manhood as far as they were able, walking as close to the danger line as they could and still survive. Some edged over, some were dragged over, and some found the line a shifting one; many of these last paid the penalty. This has been true through the long years, and now, when fine-sounding talk of freedom and democracy comes to them from the newspapers and sermons, tales swapped around the cracker barrels of country stores, letters from their boys in camps, and speeches over the radio, Negroes begin putting in stronger, though still modest, claims. Talk about freedom did not reveal a new discovery; true freedom was something they had long been hankering for. I do not believe that they were so naïve that they expected full values for all of the promissory notes.

Freedom was a hard-bought thing, their tradition warned them; the great day of "jubilo" had been followed by gloomy days; but the talk sounded good and right, and perhaps a little more freedom *was* on its way. Through the radios—many of them the battery sets which fill needs in small shacks once filled only by phonographs and guitars—booming voices told them of the plans for a new world. Over the air waves came the spark, lighting and nursing small fires of hope; the glow and the warmth were good in the darkness. "One of the worst things making for all this trouble," a Mississippi planter told me with frank honesty, "is the radio. Those people up in Washington don't know what they're doing down here. They ought to shut up talking so much."

Evidence of the Negro's not belonging is readier at hand in the South. But the North is by no means blameless in its race relations. According to an alleged folk anecdote, a Negro said he would prefer to be in a race riot in Detroit than in a camp meeting in Georgia. And orators repeatedly urge, "Come North, young man," as the only solution. Nevertheless, the folklore that the North is a refuge, a haven, has met up with the hard facts of unemployment, discrimination, and tension. Paradise Valley, Detroit, is as badly misnamed as Ideal, Georgia. The mobs that wrecked that Negro section of Detroit showed a crazed lust for bloodshed and destruction that was no Southern monopoly. Harlem has been fondly spoken of as a Mecca for Negroes; but the rioting Negroes who smashed the windows and looted the stores reveal that Negroes have found causes there for desperation and fury. In Northern cities that cradled abolitionism Negroes are to be found cramped in ghettos, still denied a chance to earn decent livelihoods, to make use of their training, to develop into full men and women.

Though convinced that the Negro is "thoroughly Jim Crowed all over the North—considering Jim Crow in its deepest aspects," Thomas Sancton writes:

> And yet it is true that the main body of the race problem lies within the boundaries of the Southern states, because some three fourths of America's 13,000,000 Negroes live there. . . . The Negro is oppressed in many ways in the North, and certainly economically, but the long antislavery tradition has at least given him some basic civil and social rights which the white South continues to deny him and would like to deny him forever.[3]

Since the problem of the Negro in America is of national scope, steps to integrate the Negro into American democracy must be taken every-

[3]Thomas Sancton, "The South Needs Help," *Common Ground,* III (Winter, 1943), p. 12.

where. Nevertheless, it remains true that the gravest denial of democracy and the greatest opposition to it are in the South. It goes without saying that what happens to the Negro in the South has great bearing on what participation the Negro will attain in American democracy. If a Negro is allowed only second- or third-class citizenship in Tupelo, Mississippi, his Harlem brother's citizenship is less than first class. And if America has more than one class of citizenship, it is less than a first-class democracy.

No Trespassing

What are the chances that freedom is really on its way; that the Negro may finally be "counted in"? Some signs are none too propitious. For instance, Negro soldiers are indoctrinated to believe that they are to fight for the four freedoms, but what they run up against daily is confusing, rather than reassuring. Fraternization between Negro soldiers and white soldiers is largely discouraged; it seems to be considered un-American for soldiers of different color, though fighting for the same cause, to be brothers-in-arms. A bulletin from headquarters may attack the subversiveness of race hostility, but part of the bulletin will warn Negro soldiers that dissatisfaction with Jim Crow is tantamount to subversiveness. Democracy to many seems to be symbolized by this message, printed under a large red V on a bus in Charleston, South Carolina:

> Victory Demands Your Co-operation
>
> If the peoples of this country's races do not pull together, Victory is lost. We, therefore, respectfully direct your attention to the laws and customs of the state in regard to segregation. Your co-operation in carrying them out will make the war shorter and Victory sooner. Avoid friction. Be patriotic. White passengers will be seated from front to rear; colored passengers from rear to front.

Looking about them, especially in the South but also in the North, Negroes see convincing proof of these implications: that patriotism means satisfaction with the *status quo ante* Pearl Harbor, that co-operation really does not mean pulling together but rather the Negro's acceptance of the subservient role; that otherwise friction threatens.

A current anecdote tells of a white officer who, seeing a Negro officer eating in the diner, exclaimed: "I'd rather see Hitler win the war than for niggers to get out of their place like that!" Negroes do not believe the attitude to be exceptional.

With all of the commendable efforts of the Army to improve the morale of Negro troops and to investigate and iron out the difficulties, Negro soldiers still find too many violations of democracy, ranging from petty irritations to rank injustices. Negroes may lose precious hours of leave because they can find no place to ride on the buses. Negro officers may find a studied refusal on the part of white soldiers to salute. Negro soldiers may be manhandled, cursed, and even killed by civilian officers of the law. Living the rough, exacting life on maneuvers, driving a jeep, manning a tank or machine gun, servicing or flying a fighter plane, the Negro soldier is expected to be a man doing a man-size job. In contact with civilian life, however, the Negro soldier is expected to be something else again.

There are signs elsewhere that do not reassure. That Negroes were given jobs at a steel plant "that have always been filled by white men," that Negro veterans of World War I were filing legal action "to force the American Legion in Alabama to charter Negro posts," that Tuskegee officials were demanding that pistols be restored to Negro military police in Tuskegee—these frightened and angered Horace Wilkinson of Bessemer, Alabama, into urging the foundation of a "League to Maintain White Supremacy." He was shocked at the impertinence of the Fair Employment Practice Committee in coming to Birmingham and recording proof that Southern industrialists and labor unions discriminated against Negro labor and thereby hampered the war effort. Mr. Wilkinson's efforts have reached some success; the "League to Maintain White Supremacy" has been set up. A race-baiting sheet, the *Alabama Sun,* is being published. The first issue has a picture of Mrs. Roosevelt greeting a Negro Red Cross Worker, back from service in England, with the caption "Mrs. Roosevelt Greets Another Nigger."

Mr. Wilkinson is playing an old game, of course, and is a member of a large squad. Mrs. Roosevelt, because of her genuine and gracious democracy, has long been the target of abuse in the South. Years ago, in order to aid the election of Eugene Talmadge, the Georgia *Woman's World* published a picture of the first lady escorted by two Negro cadet officers on her visit to a Negro university. Recent rumormongering has built up a folklore of mythical Eleanor Clubs, dedicated to getting Negro women out of the kitchens and white women into them. The smear campaign was indecently climaxed when a Mississippi editor, hardly concealing his satisfaction at the Detroit riots, blamed Mrs. Roosevelt for the massacre. The editorial impressed Representative Boykin of Alabama so favorably that he had it inserted in the *Congressional Record*. It closed:

In Detroit, a city noted for the growing impudence and insolence of the Negro population, an attempt was made to put your preachments into practice . . . Blood on your hands, Mrs. Roosevelt, and the damned spots won't wash out, either.[4]

According to a Gallup Poll, many white Southerners believe that the Negro has been made "unruly and unmanageable" because "large-scale reforms have been undertaken too swiftly."[5] Writing from his winter home in Florida, Roger Babson lectured his friends—"the several millions of colored people"—about their "lazy, wasteful, saucy moods." White workers may "strike when they shouldn't, but they are not lazy nor do they throw away money."

In all likelihood "sauciness," rather than laziness or wastefulness, is the chief cause of the present wide race baiting. Any symbol of the Negro's getting out of "his place"—a lieutenant's shoulder bars, or even a buck private's uniform; a Negro worker at a machine, or a Negro girl at a typewriter, or a cook's throwing up her job—these can be as unbearable as an impudent retort, or a quarrel on a bus, or a fight.

The demagogues have had and are having a field day. Running for re-election as governor in 1942 against strong opposition, Eugene Talmadge of Georgia preached race prejudice from Rabun Gap to Tybee's shining light. He ordered his state constabulary to be viligant against Northern Negroes and other "furriners" and warned Southern womanhood to arm. His opponent was not above race baiting himself; it seemed that he had to do it to win. In neighboring states in the Deep South the demagogues may have been less spectacular, but they were busy. Results were soon forthcoming. Three Negroes, two of them boys, were lynched within a week in Mississippi. Negroes were beaten and thrown off buses and trains in all sections of the South. Crises have followed close on crises. A riot stopped work in a Mobile shipyard because Negroes were upgraded; a pogrom laid waste the Negro section of Beaumont, Texas, because of a rape charge, later discredited; and murder ran wild in Detroit.

Any concessions to Negroes—any guaranteeing of democratic rights—set the demagogues off full steam. Sometimes they cry "wolf," as in the instance of the voluminous report of the Office of Education which, among other recommendations, urged co-operation between Negro and white colleges "in the interest of national welfare." Congressman Brooks

[4] The *Congressional Record,* June 28, 1943.

[5] George Gallup, "The Gallup Poll," the Washington *Post,* August 28, 1943.

of Louisiana equated this co-operation to "forcible co-mingling of students of the two races in the South . . . unthinkable . . . leading to the producing of a mongrel race in the United States."

When two anthropologists published a pamphlet, *The Races of Mankind,* to give wide circulation to the scientific proof of the brotherhood of man, and to help bring it about that "victory in this war will be in the name, not of one race or another, but of the universal Human Race," Congressman May of Kentucky was enraged. He was especially irked to read that Northern Negroes scored higher on the A.E.F. intelligence test than Southern whites (of his native state, for instance), although the authors advised that the statistics meant only that "Negroes with better luck after they were born got higher scores than whites with less luck." As chairman of the House Military Affairs Committee, Congressman May decided that these scientific facts had "no place in the army program," and promised to keep his eyes open lest the soldiers be contaminated with such doctrine. The pamphlets went to an army warehouse.

Coincidental with the fight waged by the National Association for the Advancement of Colored People to equalize teachers' salaries in South Carolina, the South Carolina House of Representatives resolved:

> We reaffirm our belief in and our allegiance to establish white supremacy as now prevailing in the South and we solemnly pledge our lives and our sacred honor to maintaining it. Insofar as racial relations are concerned, we firmly and unequivocally demand that henceforth the damned agitators of the North leave the South alone.[6]

Shortly after the Negro teachers of South Carolina won the fight to equalize salaries, a Charleston judge stated that many Negroes "would be better off carrying a load of fertilizer rather than a bunch of schoolbooks. . . . I am going to break up some of this education."

The perennial demagogues of Mississippi, Senator Bilbo and Representative Rankin, hold the limelight. Senator Bilbo recently held up for the admiration of his constituents his old scheme for deporting Negroes to Africa. One of the first steps he planned as chairman of the Senate Committee for the District of Columbia was clearing Negroes out of the alleys of Washington. "I want them to get into the habit of moving so as to be ready for my movement to West Africa." Until the day of that migration, Senator Bilbo promises alley dwellers of Washington that they can find places to stay in the basements of city

[6]The Washington *Post,* March 7, 1944.

homes, and on farms in neighboring states, where the need for cooks and farm hands is acute. Senator Bilbo also threatens to repeat his record-making filibuster against the repeal of the poll tax.

Representative Rankin also stays busy: attacking the President's Committee on Fair Employment Practice as subversive of democracy, since white and Negro sailors in the National Maritime Union are assigned to the same ship; threatening with lynching "that gang of communistic Jews and Negroes that . . . tried to storm the House restaurants, and went around arm in arm with each other";[7] attacking the Federal ballot for soldiers; and raging at every specter of "social equality."

Both Senator Bilbo and Congressman Rankin, as so many other demagogues, protest that they act in the interests of the Negro. Senator Bilbo says, "I am the best friend the Negro has." And Representative Rankin blames "communistic Jews" for causing "the deaths of many good Negroes who never would have got into trouble if they had been left alone."

So run the warnings from the demagogues. But it is not only among the demagogues and their Gestapos—the frontier thugs, the state constabularies, the goon squads, and the lynchers—that violent aversion to change is found. Many of the intellectuals speak lines that sound like Talmadge and Rankin. A decade ago the *American Review,* now defunct, published their ideas. Donald Davidson viewed with dire misgivings "a general maneuver, the object of which is apparently to set the Negro up as an equal, or at least more than a subordinate member of society. The second, or unavowed, program was the new form of abolitionism, again proposing to emancipate the Negro from the handicap of race, color, and previous condition of servitude."[8] Mr. Davidson considered this program (he was talking chiefly of a program of ownership of small farms by Negroes) to be "unattainable as long as the South remains the South," and its sponsors he called ruthless. The only possible solution, he thought, is "to define a place for the American Negro as special as that which they [the American people] defined for the American Indian." Allen Tate, condemning the reformers "who are anxious to have Negroes sit by them on streetcars," wrote:

I argue it this way: the white race seems determined to rule the Negro race in its midst; I belong to the white race; therefore I intend to support the

[7]The *Congressional Record,* July 1, 1943.

[8]Donald Davidson, "A Sociologist in Eden," the *American Review,* VIII (December, 1936), p. 200ff.

white rule. Lynching is a symptom of weak, inefficient rule; but you can't destroy lynching by *fiat* or social agitation; lynching will disappear when the white race is satisfied that its supremacy will not be questioned in social crises.[9]

Tempting the Negro to question this supremacy, he believes, is irresponsible behavior.

Frank Owsley called the agitation to free the Scottsboro boys the "third crusade."[10] More important to him than the defendants' innocence or guilt was the fact that some Negroes were going to get hurt: "The outside interference with the relationship of the whites and blacks in the South can result in nothing but organizations like the Ku Klux Klan and in violent retaliation against the Negroes—themselves often innocent."

It is to be expected that the die-hards should interpret Negro aspirations to democracy as incendiarism. But there are Southern liberals who do the same. Some congressmen, noted for their support of New Deal reforms, have been recently forced into race baiting, in order to prove that they are not "nigger-lovers." Some of the liberals protest with David Cohn that they view the position of the American Negro with "a sore heart, a troubled conscience, and a deep compassion." A few of these have shown genuine sympathy with the Negro's progress. Nevertheless, by and large, they are defeatists. Mark Ethridge, one of the leaders of Southern white liberals, stated flatly: "There is no power in the world—not even in all the mechanized armies of the earth, Allied and Axis—which could now force the Southern white people to the abandonment of the principle of social segregation."[11]

Since the Negro hardly would count upon the armies of the Axis as friends in any case, the prophecy is all the more direful. Mr. Ethridge warns that "cruel disillusionment, bearing the germs of strife and perhaps tragedy" will result from exacting the abolition of social segregation as the price of participation in the war. It is inaccurate to say that the Negroes were exacting this: Negroes at the time of Mr. Ethridge's prophecy were in all likelihood participating as fully as they were allowed to participate.

It is the gravity of the fear, however, rather than the accurate description of its cause, that concerns us here. Howard Odum also sees the net

[9]Allen Tate, "A View of the Whole South," ibid., II (February, 1934), p. 424.

[10]Frank L. Owsley, "Scottsboro: The Third Crusade," ibid., I (Summer, 1933), p. 285.

[11]John Temple Graves, *The Fighting South* (New York, 1943), p. 125f.

results of outside agitation in the affairs of the South to be "tragedy of the highest order, tragedy of the Greek, as it were, because it was the innocent Negro who suffered."[12] Virginius Dabney sees the two races edging nearer and nearer "to the precipice," if the Negro continues his demands.

David Cohn echoes Mr. Ethridge. As so many Southern intellectuals do, he finds comfort in William Graham Sumner's adage that you cannot change the mores of a people by law. Segregation is "the most deep-seated and pervasive of the Southern mores"; Negroes and whites who would break it down by Federal fiat had therefore better beware. "I have no doubt," Mr. Cohn writes, "that in such an event every Southern white man would spring to arms and the country would be swept by civil war." Patience, good will, and wisdom (wisdom meaning acceptance of segregation without protest) are needful, otherwise the question will be delivered out of the hands of decent whites and Negroes "into the talons of demagogues, fascists, and the Ku Kluxers, to the irreparable harm of the Negro."[13]

It is significant that Southern spokesmen, reactionaries and liberals alike, are exercised over the harm that may come to Negroes. Watch out, the warning goes, or *Negroes* will get hurt. This is an old refrain; over a century ago the first proslavery novelist threatened, when Garrison's blasts were sounding off from Boston, that the "mischievous interference of abolitionists would involve the negro in the rigor which it provokes." And the latest demagogue expresses this threat and this tenderness.

The whites and Negroes who hope for a democratic solution to the problem must learn that the problem is insoluble, warns Mr. Cohn: "It is at bottom a blood or sexual question." Southern whites are determined that "no white in their legal jurisdiction shall marry a Negro" and "white women shall not have physical relations with Negro men except, when discovered, upon pain of death or banishment inflicted upon one or both parties to the act."[14] And John Temple Graves takes his stand on two bedrock "facts": "The unshakable belief of southern whites that the problem was peculiarly their own and that attempts to force settlement from outside were hateful and incompetent. The absolute deter-

[12]Howard W. Odum, *Race and Rumors of Race* (Chapel Hill, 1943), p. 155.

[13]David L. Cohn, "How the South Feels," the *Atlantic Monthly,* CLXXIII (January, 1944), p. 50f.

[14]Ibid., p. 49.

mination that the blood of the two races should not be confused and a mulatto population emerge."[15]

Negroes have long recognized this as the hub of the argument opposing change in their status. A chief recruiting slogan for the Ku Klux Klan of Reconstruction, when Negroes were "getting out of their place" by voting, buying farms and homes, and attending schools, was that Southern white womanhood must be protected. "The closer the Negro got to the ballot box, the more he looked like a rapist," is the quip of a Negro who has studied the period closely. Thomas Nelson Page wrote that the barbarities of Reconstruction were based upon "the determination to put an end to the ravishing of their women by an inferior race, or by any race, no matter what the consequence."[16] Though a later Southern student, W. J. Cash, has estimated that "the chance [of the Southern white woman's being violated by a Negro] was much less . . . than the chance that she would be struck by lightning,"[17] it is Page rather than Cash whose opinions are most followed. Political campaigns still seem to be waged not so much to get into office as to protect women. In his last campaign Eugene Talmadge reported "an usual number of assault cases and attempts to assault white ladies" (though newspaper reporters could not find them), and he denounced the Rosenwald Fund, noted for its benefactions to the South, as being determined to make a "mulatto South." Senator Ellender, in one of his attacks on an antilynching bill, revealed the train of thought of so many filibusters when he promised that if the bill should pass he would propose three amendments all prohibiting intermarriage. If mobs were forbidden by Federal law to lynch Negroes, white people were at least not going to be allowed to marry Negroes. Instances of such reasoning make up a sorry tale.

For all of their protesting of decency and good will, the intellectuals do not talk very differently from Gerald L. K. Smith, a spellbinder generally considered to be of the native fascist variety. The Reverend Smith inherited one of Huey Long's mantles; he is certain that he knows what people want or at least that he can rouse them into wanting what he wants. Immediately after the Detroit riot the Reverend Smith wrote in *The Cross and the Flag* that most white people would not agree to any of the following: intermarriage of blacks and whites; mixture of blacks and whites in hotels, restaurants; "intimate relationships" be-

[15]Graves, op. cit., p. 239.

[16]Thomas Nelson Page, *The Negro: the Southerner's Problem* (New York, 1904), p. 100.

[17] W. J. Cash, *The Mind of the South* (New York, 1941), p. 115.

tween blacks and whites in the school system; "wholesale mixture of blacks and whites in residential sections"; "promiscuous mixture" of blacks and whites in streetcars and on trains, "especially when black men are permitted to sit down and crowd in close to white women and vice versa." The Reverend Smith added generously, "I have every reason to believe black women resent being crowded by white men." Mixture in factories was also offensive, "especially when black men are mixed with white women closely in daily work."

It is true that the Reverend Smith is no longer tilling Southern fields, but he learned his demagoguery in the South, and many of his audience were transplanted Southerners. It is also undeniable that his words struck responsive chords in many Northerners. But he expresses a cardinal tenet of the Southern creed that social mixture must be forbidden, or else, as John Temple Graves puts it, "a mulatto population will emerge."

Negroes know well that that horse has been out of the stable too long a time for the lock to be put on the door now. Even the race purists must realize the large amount of mixture in the American Negro, that hybrid of African, Indian, and Caucasian stock. And though, as the anthropologist Montague Cobb says, the Caucasian component is "the most apparent and the least documented," race purists must realize how the Negro got that way.

Fears that lowering the barriers of segregation will lower the level of civilization are often expressed. If these fears are not liars, one consequence might be that civilization in such Southern cities as Atlanta, Birmingham, Memphis, and Vicksburg will decline to the level of that in unsegregated Boston, New York, Iowa City, and Seattle. According to these fears, intermarriage will result when Negroes and whites eat in the same restaurants or in a diner without a little green curtain; when they stop in the same hotels and ride the same streetcars and buses without wooden screens or other separating devices. Negroes laugh at the suggestion that crowded buses and streetcars and cafeterias are marriage bureaus. They know that intermarriage is not widespread in the states where there are no segregation laws and no laws forbidding intermarriage. They believe with great reason that there is more illicit sexual relationship between the races in the states whose laws forbid intermarriage than there are mixed marriages elsewhere.

Intermarriage is hardly a goal that Negroes are contending for openly or yearning for secretly. It is certainly not a mental preoccupation with them and scarcely a matter of special concern. Nevertheless, they do not want laws on the statute books branding them as outcasts. They do not want governmental sanction of caste, however long they have seen it hardened about them. They know how prophetic were the words of the anguished heroine of George Washington Cable's story of the last century: "A lie, Père Jerome! Separate! No! They do not want to keep us [white men: colored women] separate: no, no! But they *do* want to keep us despised!"

It is likely, of course, that friendships will develop where Negroes and whites meet on a basis of respect and where people can be drawn together by kindred interests. It is likely that some of these friendships might ripen into love and marriage. That certainly should be left as a private matter, the affair of the persons involved, as it is now in most civilized lands. An individual's choice of a mate should hardly be considered as a chief cause of the downfall of Western, or American, or even Southern civilization. A more grievous cause for alarm, a more dangerous omen of ruin, is the contempt for personality based on skin color and hair texture. Negroes laugh a bit ruefully at the dread that one tenth of a nation's population will corner the marital market of the nine tenths. They know to what a degree in the past the opposite has prevailed, though the market could not with accuracy be termed marital. They could scarcely consider laws banning intermarriage to be protective of their own women. And they do not share the Southern white man's fear that the white women of the South are so weak and easily misled that they cannot be trusted to select their own husbands. They agree instead with the numerous white women of the South who have publicly stated that they do not need lynching or special legislation to protect them.

The black herring of intermarriage has been dragged too often across the trail to justice. "Would you want your sister to marry a nigger?" is still the question that is supposed to stun any white man who sponsors rights for Negroes. It stirs Negroes to ironic laughter, although on all levels they recognize the white man's fear of intermarriage as deep-seated. From the jokes of the people—of Negroes talking to Negroes, where "Miss Annie's" name is changed to "Miss Rope" or "Miss Hemp" —to the satire of the publicists, this awareness is to be found. A Negro editor, fighting a covenant restricting housing, was asked point blank: "Do you believe in intermarriage?" to stop his guns of logic and facts. Some Negro public speakers, faced with the question, dodge behind statements like "Well, I'm married already myself." Some take refuge in Kipling's line, "Never the twain shall meet," without sharing

Kipling's assurance or hope. The twain have met and the twain will meet. But Negroes are not convinced thereby that they must give up their struggle to share in American democracy.

Though David Cohn warns that irony and reason cannot answer what he calls "blood-thinking," the "biological" fear of "a chocolate-colored American people," Negroes wonder if that fear is as real among Southerners as the determination to keep the Negro in his place economically. Certain Southern liberals have stated their willingness for Negroes to have the rights of voting, good schools, sanitation, paved and lighted streets, justice in the courts, and equitable employment. But Negroes wonder if the possibilities of these—merely these without intermarriage—do not stir great and widespread fears, real instead of spectral. They wonder if the smoke screen of intermarriage is not raised to frighten Southerners from conceding any of these rights, which are fraught with more danger to privilege and exploitation. Some Negroes wonder if maintaining a cheap labor reservoir is not as important a motive as preventing Negroes from crowding whites on buses and proposing marriage to them. Pointing to a group of poor whites and poor Negroes, a planter said to Ira Reid and Arthur Raper: "As long as these whites keep those Negroes humble, we'll keep them both poor."[18]

Many Negroes are sardonic about the oddities of segregation. The white patron, who is willing to eat soup prepared in the kitchen by black hands and served by a black waiter who may get his thumb in it, but who nearly faints when he discovers a Negro eating at another table in the same restaurant; a man's fulsome worship of the black nurse in whose lap he was rocked to sleep, and his horror at sitting next to a black man on a streetcar (it might be the nurse's son); the preservation of white supremacy on a diner by a little green curtain, or on a streetcar by a screen or a rope, in a Jim Crow coach by a chalk line beyond which the overflow from the white coach may not roll, in a government office by setting a Negro's desk cater-cornered, slightly off the line of the other desks; these afford ribald amusement. They do not make sense; they do not add to respect for the rationality of Southern whites. Such instances are recognized as sprouting from deep roots, certainly; but other superstitions have been uprooted. Maybe these can be.

Some Negroes, of course, realize that a logic does lie behind the apparent oddities. This is the time-hallowed logic of dividing and ruling—the playing off of underprivileged whites against Negroes to prevent a real democratic union—a practice that has paid the oligarchs

[18]Arthur Raper and Ira De A. Reid, *Sharecroppers All* (Chapel Hill, 1941), p. 78.

well. Northern industrialists in the South have done their full share of capitalizing on race hostility, exciting it by talk of Negroes "getting out of their places." Some Negroes, therefore, see segregation as more than a superstition; but they are convinced that it can and must be uprooted.

Negroes are not contending for wholesale entree into drawing rooms. They see no contradiction in democracy that people shall select their own friends, cliques, husbands, and wives. They do see as contradictory that false fears of social intermingling should be raised to jeopardize honest aspirations to full citizenship. What segregationists denounce as "wanting to be with white folks," Negroes think of as participating in the duties and enjoying the privileges of democracy. This means being with white folks, undoubtedly, since whites have nearly monopolized these duties and privileges. But it means being with them in fields and factories, in the armed forces, at the voting booths, in schools and colleges, in all the areas of service to democracy.

Count Us In

Negroes want to be counted in. They want to belong. They want what other men have wanted deeply enough to fight and suffer for it. They want democracy. Wanting it so much, they disregard more and more the warnings: "This is not the time." "The time isn't ripe." "Take your time, take your time." Nearly a hundred years ago, in desperation at the plight of the slaves, Herman Melville wrote, "Time must befriend these thralls." And in crucial moments since, time has been pointed to as the solvent. Patience, urges David Cohn, rule out the emotional and irrational, and then the burden will rest "upon the whites to do for the Negro what they have not done at all, or only in part." But the Negro has difficulty in finding the guaranties of this hope that so many Negro and white spokesmen have promised to him. Southern Negroes are not of one mind with Southern whites that "outside interference is hateful and incompetent." They do not see democracy as a commodity to be quarantined at the Potomac and Ohio rivers; as a sort of a Japanese beetle to be hunted for in the luggage before travelers are allowed to go on. Negroes are glad whenever democratic ideas circulate through the South, whether by means of liberal weeklies, *PM,* the speeches of labor organizers, pamphlets, sermons, radio forums, books, Negro newspapers and magazines, or letters from the boys in service. They know, of course, that if democracy is to be achieved in the South, where it is least found, the greatest work must be done by Southerners, whites and Negroes together. But they welcome whatever help they can get from any sources.

And they know, furthermore, that the agencies working for democracy are not necessarily "outside agitators." The National Association for the Advancement of Colored People may have its headquarters in New York, but, as its name suggests, it is a *national* association. Many of its leaders are Southerners by birth and training. Many of its courageous workers are living in the South. The Negro teachers who risk their jobs and even worse in the struggle for equalization of salaries are Southern born and bred. Negro journalists in the Deep South generally speak out uncompromisingly for justice. Southern Negroes have not needed Northern agitators to stir up dissatisfaction with discrimination and abuse. As pointed out earlier, they have learned the hard way, and the lessons have sunk in deeply.

They have heard the threats. Against their democratic aspirations they see a concerted line-up: college professors as well as hoodlums; congressmen as well as vigilantes; Rotarians as well as manual laborers; cotton planters as well as cotton hands. Negroes expect that some of them are going to get hurt before they get what they want. This is no new experience for them; they have been getting hurt in this country since 1619. But getting hurt in a stand-up struggle for justice is one thing; getting hurt merely because of the color of your skin, while lying down, is quite another.

On trips through the South I have talked with several who had been hurt. With Roland Hayes, for example, shortly after he had been savagely beaten by the policemen of Rome, Georgia. With Hugh Gloster, a young college professor, who had been thrown off a train in Tupelo, Mississippi, because he asked the conductor to let Negroes who were standing in the aisles of the Jim Crow coach overflow into a white coach, only partly filled. With Clinton Clark, who had been beaten, arrested, jailed, and threatened with the rope time and time again for organizing the cane cutters and cotton hands of Louisiana into a union. Roland Hayes talked broodingly; Hugh Gloster, sardonically; Clinton Clark, stoically, without any surprise: "You try to organize people to get out of slavery, may as well expect the big planters and their boys—the sheriffs and deputies—to get tough." But all of these, and others who told me their stories of abuse, knew the shock of the sudden oath, the blow, the murderous look in the eye.

They had been hurt, no doubt of that. But it is unlikely that they, or many other Negroes, merely because of the violence, will become reconciled to what caused it. Many Negroes are still going to protest rough language to their wives, as Roland Hayes did; or unfair travel accommodations, as Hugh Gloster did; or exploitation in the cane and cotton fields, as Clinton Clark did. "Get out and stay out of this parish," the jailer in Natchitoches told Clark. "I'll be back," said Clark. "I'll have a stronger organization behind me the next time."

Some of the victims do not forget the lessons that the rubber hose, the fist, the long black hours in the smelly cell fix so deeply. But from as many other victims comes this: "And if I had it to do all over, I'd do the same thing again."

Negroes who profess faith, whether real or not, in passive waiting for decent whites to take up their burden are losing that faith. Negroes who feared that asking for democracy would lead to some Negroes' getting hurt are losing that fear. But losing the passive faith is not defeatism, and losing the fear is not bravado.

There are many Negroes who are not convinced, as some forlorn liberals are, that democracy is a doomed hope in the South. They see heart-warming signs. They see the opponents of the poll tax gathering strength. The filibusters may rant so long or maneuver so craftily that the repeal may not pass this year, but the struggle against the poll tax will continue. Negroes applaud the Supreme Court decisions outlawing the white primary as a private club's election. They see the FEPC holding on, a symbol of the hope to abolish discrimination in industry, though challenged on many sides, flouted occasionally, and hard beset. They hear native white South Carolinians disclaim the "white supremacy" resolution of their House of Representatives in humiliation "because it is white people who have thus held up the state to scorn. . . . The only white supremacy which is worthy of the name is that which exists because of virtue, not power." White supremacy is not the issue, they say, but that Negroes should serve on juries, that they should be allowed representation on boards which administer affairs involving Negro citizens and their property; that Negro policemen should be provided in Negro residential districts; that the disfranchisement of all Negroes in South Carolina cannot endure indefinitely; these are some of the pressing issues. Negroes are aware of the importance of such words from representative citizens, neither interracialists nor "radicals," in Cotton Ed Smith's bailiwick.

Of course many Negroes keep their fingers crossed. They expected Congressman Rankin's blast at the Supreme Court vote, which ran true to form: "I see that the parlor pinks in the Department of Justice are already starting to harass the Southern states as a result of the blunder of the Supreme Court. The Negroes of the South are having their hope of peace and harmony with their white neighbors destroyed by these pinks." Canny through long experience with the politicos, Negroes realize that the road from outlawing white primaries and the poll tax to widespread voting may be long and rocky. "Let 'em try it," said the Jackson *Daily News;* "There are other ways of preserving southern tradition," the Birmingham *Post* said; "We will maintain white supremacy, let the chips fall where they may," said the governor of South Carolina.

It may be a long and rocky road. But it is the right road. Some Negroes may remain lethargic about their rights and duties as citizens. Some Negroes may get hurt; some may be timorous; the overpraised "harmony" may go off key. As a sign that they are being "counted in" Negroes see several Southern editors applauding the decision. One called it "a much-needed political safety valve" instead of a threat. Virginius Dabney writes that Tennessee, Kentucky, North Carolina, and Virginia, all of them without the white primary, have never seen white supremacy endangered. More significantly, he writes: "No society . . . is truly democratic . . . which shuts out anywhere from a quarter to a half of its people from all part in the choice of the officials under whom they must live and work."

Another cheering signpost, indicating that some mileage has been covered on the long journey, is the work of certain Southern white liberals. Virginius Dabney performed a historic act in advocating the abolition of Jim Crow on Virginia streetcars and buses. It is true that he had to surrender his proposal; though numerous white Virginians applauded it, Mr. Dabney became convinced that the time was not right. But it was a first step that may count, and the proof that Virginia white opinion was not unanimous for Jim Crow is worth recording. Hoping that Negro leadership will rest in Atlanta (not so coincidentally Walter White's native city) rather than in New York, Mr. Dabney realizes that steps toward democracy must be taken *in the South*. This realization is quite as honest as his fear of trouble.

Southern white liberals deplore the demands of outsiders and then come out themselves for many of the same reforms. The Atlanta Conference of representative white Southerners praised the Southern Negro Conference at Durham for frankness and courage. Among so much else the Atlanta Conference conclusions stated: "No Southerner can logically dispute the fact that the Negro, as an American citizen, is entitled to his civil rights and economic opportunities"; and "we agree . . . that it is 'unfortunate that the simple efforts to correct obvious social and economic injustices continue, with such considerable popular support, to be interpreted as the predatory ambition of irresponsible Negroes to invade the privacy of family life. . . .' We agree also that 'it is a wicked notion that the struggle by the Negro for citizenship is a struggle against the best interest of the nation.'"[19]

Negroes look with hope to the continuing conference, composed of several Southern Negro leaders who met in Durham and Southern whites who met in Atlanta. The conference is "to convenant together for better co-operation, more positive and specific action, and for enduring ways and means for carrying out the recommendations." They have reason for confidence in the two co-chairmen, Guy Johnson of the University of North Carolina and Ira Reid of Atlanta University. Many Negroes deplore the isolation of the problem as a Southern regional affair, but they want the results that such a conference may achieve. They notice the stress on good manners and good will and on the absence of "any suggestion of threat and ultimatum," and may wonder just how these terms are defined; but they suspect that this forward step would not have been taken without the activity of organizations like the N.A.A.C.P. "We want those fellows to keep the heat on," a quiet Southern Negro preacher said to me.

On the national scene, wherever significant work is done to integrate the Negro into the war effort: in industry, in agriculture, in community planning, in the armed services, Negroes are cheered, and their morale rises accordingly. Sometimes discounted as drops in the bucket, these instances of integration might also be considered leaks in the levee, straws in the wind, or as the signposts I have frequently called them. If signposts, Negroes know that the longer, perhaps rougher journey lies ahead. They are therefore not in the mood for stopping, for laying over, for slowing up, or for detouring. And they do not want to be mere passengers, a sort of supercargo, hitchhikers being given a lift, guests being sped along. They want to do some of the map reading and some of the driving. Thomas Sancton, a white Southerner who recognizes this truth, writes: "The real liberal knows that the Negro is never going to win any right he doesn't win for himself, by his own organization, courage, and articulation."[20]

The sticking point in the co-operation of Negro and Southern white

[19]Odum, op. cit., p. 199.

[20]Sancton, op. cit., p. 15.

liberals is segregation. The Atlanta Conference stepped gingerly about it: "We do not attempt to make here anything like a complete reply to the questions raised. . . . The only justification offered for [segregation] laws . . . is that they are intended to minister to the welfare and integrity of both races."[21]

However segregation may be rationalized, it is essentially the denial of belonging. I believe that Negroes want segregation abolished. I realize that here, as so often elsewhere, it is presumptuous to talk of what *the* Negro wants. I understand that Negroes differ in their viewpoints toward segregation: the half-hand on a back-county farm, the lost people on Arkansas plantations, the stevedore on Savannah docks, the coal miner in Birmingham, the cook-waitress-nurse in Charleston, the man-on-the-street in Waco, Los Angeles, New York, Boston, the government workers, the newspaper editors, the professional men, the spokesmen for pressure groups—all see segregation from different angles. An illiterate couple on Red River may differ greatly in attitude from their children on River Rouge. On the part of many there has been a long accommodation to segregation, but I believe that satisfaction with it has always been short.

An old railroad man in Birmingham, directing me to the FEPC hearings in the Federal Building, told me that whites and Negroes entered the courtroom by the same door (there was only one), but that they did not sit together. "No," he said. "They sits separate; whites on one side, the colored on the yother." Then he added, "And that's the way I'd ruther have it, too, ef'n I had my druthers. Of course I don't believe in scorning nobody, but——" He might have had memories of whites and Negroes "mixing socially," where the gains had all fallen to the whites or where insult or violence had followed. But he knew, in spite of his "druthers," that segregation and scorn were bedfellows.

During Mr. Talmadge's campaign against the co-education of the races, one Georgia Negro college president gave white folks the assurance that "Negroes didn't want to attend the University of Georgia; all they wanted was a little school of their own." I found a young Negro army doctor who sharply opposed the setting up of mixed military units, especially a mixed hospital. Only in an all-Negro hospital, according to his experience, could a Negro physician function to the best of his ability, realize his full development, and be free from insult. He was nevertheless violently opposed to Jim Crow in transportation and public services.

I heard varying defenses of segregation, but I still did not find many supporters of it, even in the South. Of the many who had gained from it

[21]Odum, op. cit., p. 197.

in safety, comfort, wealth, and prestige, I found some who were candid enough to admit that in segregated schools, churches, lodges, banks, and businesses, they had risen higher than they might have risen in competition with whites. Many were fighting to improve their side of the biracial fence, to equalize teachers' salaries, to obtain buses for students, and for similar ends. But the fighting was not to buttress biracialism, but to make the most of a bad thing, to lessen the inferiority that segregation always seemed to mean. The young fliers at the segregated Tuskegee base trained rigorously to become first-rate fighting men, to prove that Negroes should be piloting planes; but their most fervent admirers, however proud of their achievement, would not say that they would have made a poorer record at an unsegregated base. And they would not deny that there were indignities at the segregated base.

A sign in Atlanta read: "This line marks the separation of the races which were [*sic*] mutually agreed to by both." My friend, certainly no hothead but long "accommodated," interpreted it: "Mutual agreement. You know: a man puts his gun in your ribs and you put your pocketbook in his hands."

When the conference in Durham excluded Northern Negroes, many white Southerners (and Negroes, for that matter) were led to expect a conservative set of principles. As Benjamin Mays, an important member of the conference, states: "They were Negroes the whites of the South knew. They were not radicals. They were Negroes the South says it believes in and can trust." Yet the Durham charter went on record as fundamentally opposed to segregation, and Walter White considered the recommendations to be almost identical in language and spirit with those of the N.A.A.C.P. and the March-on-Washington movement.

A chief difference between Southern and Northern Negro spokesmen is not that one group defends and the other condemns segregation, but that Southern leaders, in daily contact with it, see it as deeply rooted; Northern leaders, not seeing it to be so widespread and knowing that occasionally it can be ripped out, do not see the long, sturdy tentacles. The dangers are that Southern Negroes will believe it ineradicable and that Northern Negroes will believe it can be easily uprooted by speeches and governmental decree.

At Negro mass meetings in the North, demands that racial segregation should be abolished, "that the Negro and the white must be placed on a plane of absolute political and social equality," have been roundly applauded. It is doubtful if even the orators themselves envisaged that their demands would be immediately or even soon forthcoming. Delegates from the South knew that on the return trip home, at St. Louis or Cincinnati or Washington, they would be herded into the inferior Jim Crow coach; that if they wished to travel by bus they would be lucky even to get on, into the rear seats; that once home, Jim Crow would be all about them wherever they turned. Even Northern delegates knew where Jim Crow had caught hold in their communities.

Negroes know that more than stirring speeches will be needed to remove Jim Crow. But they also know another thing, on all levels and in all callings—whether an illiterate sharecropper comparing the one-room ramshackly school for his children with the brick consolidated school for the white children, or a college president who knows, in spite of the new brick buildings, how unequal a proportion of state funds has come to his school—Negroes recognize that Jim Crow, even under such high-sounding names as "biracial parallelism," means inferiority for Negroes. And most American whites know this too, and that is the way that many prefer it. As the beginning of one kind of wisdom, Negroes recognize that the phrase "equal but separate accommodations" is a myth. They have known Jim Crow a long time, and they know Jim Crow means scorn and not belonging.

What Negroes applauded from their orators, many recognized as a vision, the vision of a good thing. Though a dream, and difficult of achieving, it still was not wild and illogical. It made more sense than the reality: that in the world's leading democracy, democratic rights were withheld from one man out of every ten, not because he had forfeited his right to them, but because his skin was darker and his hair of a different texture from those of the other nine. The reality was that in a war against an enemy whose greatest crimes are based on spurious race thinking, this democracy indulged in injustice based on race thinking just as spurious.

This war is the Negro's war as much as it is anybody's. If the Axis were victorious, Negroes would be forced from the present second-class citizenship to slavery. Hitler's contempt for Negroes as apes and his sadistic treatment of Jews and all the conquered peoples, and Japan's brown Aryanism, similarly ruthless and arrogant, offer far less hope than America's system of democracy, bumbling though it may be, but still offering opportunity for protest and change. Even at the cost of the preservation of the *status quo,* this is still the Negro's war.

These are truisms. But they do not incite high morale. Indeed, they are somewhat like telling a man with a toothache that he should consider himself fortunate, since he might have a broken back. True, but his tooth still aches, and he wants something done for it.

This is even more the Negro's war, if it is truly a people's war, a war of liberation, aimed at establishing the Four Freedoms, ushering in the century of the common man, as the fine slogans have it. The Negro could do well with the Four Freedoms, especially the freedoms from want and fear, for these two freedoms have long been strangers to him. This is all the more the Negro's war if, as Michael Straight hopes, the peace will "guarantee to all of its citizens the right to constructive work at fair wages; to good low-cost housing; to minimum standards of nutrition, clothing, and medical care; to full opportunities for training and adult education; to real social security."

There is more cleverness than wisdom in the remark of John Temple Graves that asking for complete democracy at home is as logical as saying "that because America's house was on fire America must take the occasion for renovating the kitchen or putting Venetian blinds in the parlor." The trouble with the house is more serious than that; it really has much to do with the foundations. Wendell Willkie warns that:

> We cannot fight the forces and ideas of imperialism abroad and maintain any form of imperialism at home . . . We must mean freedom for others as well as ourselves, and we must mean freedom for everyone inside our frontiers as well as outside.[22]

Pearl Buck points out:

> Our democracy does not allow for the present division between a white ruler race and a subject colored race. If the United States is to include subject and ruler peoples, then let us be honest about it and change the Constitution and make it plain that Negroes cannot share the privileges of the white people. True, we would then be totalitarian rather than democratic.[23]

Daily reports of the violations of democracy crowd upon the Negro, breeding cynicism. Nevertheless, while denouncing them, he does so in the framework of democracy. He continually relies on America's professions of democracy as having some validity; he has not yet descended to the hopeless view that America prefers totalitarianism.

As has been so often stated: If America is to indoctrinate the rest of the world with democracy, it is logical to expect that the American Negro will share it at home. It may take a long time, but segregation must be abolished before there will be true democracy at home. True democracy will mean the right and opportunity to win respect for human worth.

[22]Wendell Willkie, *One World* (New York, 1943), p. 190ff.

[23]Pearl Buck, *American Unity and Asia* (New York, 1942), p. 15.

It can have no truck with Nazi concepts of race supremacy, with Nazi contempt for people because of race. Democracy will mean equal pay for equal labor, equal employment opportunities, opportunities to learn and use technical skills and to advance according to mastery of them, and the right to join and participate fully in trade-unions. The tentative beginning made by FEPC must be developed. Democracy will mean equal educational opportunities, equalized salaries for teachers, equalized facilities in the schools. The spread of the segregated system of education must be checked and eventually abolished as wasteful and unjust. Democracy will mean that the Federal government will go on record against mob violence, for, in spite of the decline in lynching, threats of mob violence are still powerfully coercive. Democracy will mean the discouraging of police brutality, will mean justice in the courts rather than patronizing clemency or cruel intolerance. Negroes will serve on the police force, at the lawyers' bar, in the jury docks, and on the judges' bench. Democracy will mean the franchise, with elimination of the poll tax and the subterfuges and intimidations that keep qualified Negroes from the polls. It will mean training Negroes to fulfill the duties of free citizens. Democracy will mean the strengthening and extension of the social legislation begun by the New Deal in such agencies as the Farm Security Administration and the Federal Housing Authority, and the opportunity not only to share in the benefits of such agencies but also in their planning and operation. Democracy will mean the opportunity to qualify for service in the armed forces in all its branches, the opportunity for whites and Negroes to fight side by side in mixed commands. Democracy will mean simply the opportunities for all Americans to share to the full extent of their capacities in the defense of America in war and the development of America in peace.

This is not much to ask for, since it is essentially what America guarantees to every white citizen. Only when viewed from the angle that these opportunities are to be extended to Negro citizens does the list seem staggering, outrageous to some, foolishly idealistic and unattainable to many.

I think that most Negroes are not so optimistic that they foresee the overnight arrival of these opportunities. No group should know better that perfectly functioning democracy in the United States has always been a hope, rather than an actuality. Even in those sections where one undemocratic practice—legal segregation—has been missing, democracy—to whites as well as to Negroes—has not been simon-pure. The poverty of the South would be oppressive on both whites and Negroes even if segregation laws were stricken from the books, and discrimination from the practices, tomorrow. The Negro's plight in the South will be lightened substantially only when the plight of the poor white is enlightened; when these cannot be pitted against each other in contempt and hatred; when genuine democracy replaces the fictitious (and fictitious not only in the matter of race relations). Nevertheless, however herculean the task, Negroes are not so defeatist that they think democracy to be unattainable. They are good Americans in nothing more than in their faith that "democracy *can* happen here." Worth fighting for in Europe, it is worth working for here. But since time does not stand still, all America—black and white—had better start to work for it. President Roosevelt, speaking of the Four Freedoms, has said: "Magna Carta, the Declaration of Independence, the Constitution of the United States, the Emancipation Proclamation, and every other milestone in human progress—all were ideals which seemed impossible of attainment—yet they were attained."[24]

Negroes should not want fundamental rights of citizenship donated to them as largesse, and should not consider them as barter for loyalty or service. American whites should not consider Negroes as beneficiaries, being accorded gifts that to men of different complexion are rights. Nor should they think of Negroes as passive objects of humanitarianism, since Negroes can really be allies in a common struggle for democracy. Even after Hitler and Tojo are defeated, democracy is going to need all of its strength to solve grave problems. The strength of the Negro will be as much needed and as useful in the coming economic and political crises as it is needed and should be useful now.

I believe that many Negroes realize this and wish to be allowed to share in the sacrifice and travail and danger necessary to attain genuine democracy. Wendell Willkie's world trip excited him with "fresh proof of the enormous power within human beings to change their environment, to fight for freedom with an instinctive awakened confidence that with freedom they can achieve anything."[25] In times of frustration Negroes would do well to recognize that power and to understand that it fights on their side.

Negroes know they have allies. There are the numerous colored peoples of the world, the millions of yellow, brown, and black men in China, India, the Philippines, Malaysia, Africa, South America, the Caribbean, all over the globe, where hope for democracy is stirring a mighty fer-

[24]Franklin D. Roosevelt, "The Four Freedoms," in Clayton Wheat, ed., *The Democratic Tradition in America* (Boston, 1943), p. 291.

[25]Willkie, op. cit., p. 163.

ment. Almost all are concerned with their own perplexities, but they agree in their fight against color prejudice. The success of the Soviet Union in destroying race prejudice gives hope and courage. And there are other allies abroad, in the smaller as well as the larger, the conquered as well as the unconquered nations, who are tied, not by a common urge to abolish race prejudice, but by the determination to be free. And in America there are allies too. It does not seem overoptimistic to believe them on the increase, although still outnumbered by the indifferent or the hostile. Negroes must join with these American allies, in the North and in the South, in a truly interracial program, or, better, a democratic program. The minority must work with the men of good will in the majority. Negroes recognize their allies here without difficulty, and their affection for them runs strong and deep.

Americans, Negroes and whites, may believe that to achieve full democracy is arduous. It may well take a slow pull for a long haul. But it can no longer be postponed. American dreams have been realized before this, however difficult they seemed to the fainthearted and skeptical. Americans, Negro and white, have mustered the doggedness and courage and intelligence needed. I have confidence in my own people that they will help achieve and preserve democracy and will prove worthy of sharing it. But we must be counted in.

REPORT FROM ENGLAND

Roi Ottley

Roi Ottley started his career as a newspaper reporter in New York. After the publication of his book New World A-Coming *he went abroad as a correspondent for the newspaper* PM *and* Liberty *magazine. He is now in the CBI theater of war gathering material for a new book.*

LONDON, Sept. 21.—The noose of prejudice is slowly tightening around the necks of American Negro soldiers, and tending to cut off their recreation and associations with the British people. For—to be frank—relations between Negro and white troops have reached grave proportions. There are, of course, hopeful aspects.

This is my considered opinion after a careful survey in which I interviewed British men and women in all walks of life, as well as white and Negro American officers and soldiers. To get an over-all picture I visited the key cities of Glasgow, Belfast, Manchester, Liverpool, Bristol, and many small villages that do not even appear on the average map.

Because the problem is of vital importance, not only to military morale but also to Anglo-American amity and to a peaceful transition from war to peace in America when the soldiers return, I feel the facts should be reported—not for inflamatory purposes, but in order to serve as a basis for a fruitful discussion of the issue.

The racial situation in England is a vast contrast to that in France, where I found few had the time or inclination for racial discrimination and insult. The reasons for its acuteness in England is complex. Much of it lies deep in the American way of life. For in essence there are those here who are still fighting the Civil War—this time on British soil.

American observers who were here in 1942 when the first contingents arrived from America saw amicable and smooth relations develop between the Negro troops and their British hosts. Some were even lionized—so much so that certain white American soldiers became openly resentful. And they lost no time in attempting to discipline the British people. For—and this is perhaps the crucial issue—in back of the minds of some Southerners here is the belief that on his return the Negro will be mighty difficult to remold into the Jim Crow pattern.

Many thousands of American Negro troops are in Britain. They represent a larger Negro population than the British Isles has ever known. For most Britons it is the first time that they have seen Negroes in relatively large groups. For most of the Negroes it is the first time they have been away from their homes and communities.

But the people here have a racial tolerance which gives them a social lever. They are inclined to accept a man for his personal worth. Thus the Negro has social equality here in more ways than theory. To put it in the language of a Negro soldier, "I'm treated so, a man don't know he's colored until he looks in the mirror."

The fact is, the British do draw racial distinctions, but not within the doors of the British Isles—at least not until the arrival of the white American soldiers. This is not to say the British are without racial prejudice. They do have it in a subtle form. But, in the main, it is confined to colonial and military officials who have spent their lives administering affairs in the colored colonies and derive their incomes from them.

What contact the British people had with Negroes before the arrival of the American troops was on the whole very good. Paul Robeson and many other Negro artists and entertainers made quite an impression on the British. In the ten years he resided in England, Robeson created a good opinion of the American Negro.

By and large Negro troops have been billeted in the country sections of England, Scotland, and Ireland. The British people in the country are naturally hospitable. They warmly greeted the Negro troops. Soon Negroes were invited to British homes, churches, and trade-union meetings. Easy and friendly associations developed between the races.

This was a great shock to many white Americans, particularly some from the deep South. At Highton in northern England—to illustrate—a Negro soldier had an appointment with a British girl to meet him in front of his camp. When he got outside she was engaged in conversation with two white American soldiers. The Negro soldier walked over and greeted the girl. "I've been waiting about fifteen minutes for you," she scolded cheerfully. They smiled, locked hands, and walked down the road. One of the white soldiers snatched off his hat and flung it to the ground. He broke into tears and kept repeating over and over, "I'm from Georgia and I just can't take that!"

There are some white commanders who, when they arrive in an area with their unit, restrict passes to Negroes until after inspection has been made of the nearest town or city. The best cafés, restaurants, theaters, and hotels are chosen for the white personnel and the proprietors are informed that they are to bar Negro soldiers.

This has proved an effective strong-arm instrument for establishing the Jim Crow pattern in public places, and, incidentally, relegates Negroes to the worst sections on the outskirts of town or along the water front.

A Negro Red Cross worker, J. Clarice Brooks, former New York social worker, was alone late one night at a Belfast Red Cross club waiting for transportation home when in walked five white American soldiers. This is what transpired:

"There's the bitch that's runnin' the club for niggers," one shouted as they strode toward her.

"This is a Red Cross club for American soldiers if they behave themselves," she replied.

"What do you mean? Niggers are better behaved than we are?"

His companions interjected, "You going to let her talk to you like that?"

"Let's beat her up," another said.

"Yeah, we know how to treat niggers!"

They were about to assault her when luckily a white officer happened along and intervened. Miss Brooks told me that although she attempted to press charges against them, that was the last she heard of the affair.

Negro Red Cross workers in England have been known to go home nights armed with baseball bats to fight off prejudiced white soldiers.

In some areas "gangs" have been formed by white soldiers to terrorize Negroes. When such groups arrive in a town they immediately declare it "their" territory.

There are many cities, towns, or villages that have witnessed race rioting. The most infamous of these clashes is called "The Battle of Bamber Bridge"—an area in Lancaster. Negroes billeted here complained of unfair restrictions. They were burning with resentment. One night a white MP regarded by Negroes as their mortal enemy shot a Negro soldier in the back following a fracas. News of the killing soon reached camp. The Negro soldiers felt they had reached the limit of their endurance. So they broke into the arsenal, took arms, and barricaded themselves for battle.

When the first white officers approached, they were met by a volley of gunfire. Four of them went down. The other officers sought cover and called for armored cars. A great tragedy was averted by Lieutenant Edmund Jones, a Negro popular with the troops.

Well aware that these desperate Negroes were prepared to fight to the death, he persuaded his white commander to give him authority to end the affair without further bloodshed. He was made a provost general for three days and was successful in having the Negroes end the futile battle. He assured them by radio that reforms would follow and in the future they would be dealt with fairly.

This distressing racial situation must be laid squarely on the doorstep of the white officers. Certainly, if they wished to do something concrete about the problem, there are sufficient memorandums, directives, and orders to bolster them.

Tons of such literature has been published. I have seen much of it. Most is forthright in explaining, and even insisting, on mutual respect among soldiers. Many are masterpieces of clarity. The declared policy of the American Army in relation to the Negro soldier is absolutely clear:

"He is to receive the same treatment, wages, rations as the white troops. He is to have equal opportunities for recreation."

Unhappily, certain of the officers whose tasks it becomes to implement these instructions violate them where the Negro is concerned. Some of them never bother to read the instructions. They well know that in practice there is no penalty for any show of racial hostility. The fact is, there is ample evidence to prove that racial prejudice is encouraged by such officers, a group often dominated by a few Southerners.

An RAF flier told me of an indoctrination course he attended, conducted by an American lieutenant. His whole lecture was devoted to explaining to the British the reasons why they should not associate with Negro soldiers. He made no bones about the fact that not to conform with the American view of race was to be the victim of actual physical violence.

These roughhouse tactics have, of course, been augmented by word-of-mouth propaganda. At every turn attempts are being made to discredit the Negro. The catalogue of lies and misinformation is well known in America. But new twists have been given old clichés. A Negro major told me of being surprised when he visited a British home by the concern for his comfort. The mistress of the house had placed a number of soft pillows in his chair. Every so often she would anxiously look in his direction. Before the evening was over he learned the reason: His hosts had been told by American soldiers that Negroes have tails!

Perhaps much of the propaganda would stick if so many white American soldiers did not abuse the feelings of the British people. Some of them stride about the city streets with the look, "We came to save you dopes."

The English people are acutely sensitive to their dilemma after Dunkirk. But some Americans not only mention it but are noisy about it, even boastful. Much of their behavior would never be countenanced in America. It has embarrassed many Americans—for bad manners are bad whether at home or abroad.

London, Sept. 22.—Two weeks of sporadic fighting took place between white and Negro American soldiers at Leicester in the Midlands. Four white soldiers and one MP were killed. Many whites were hospitalized. Numbers of Negroes were hurt and wounded. Following these incidents signs appeared in public places with variations of the following theme:

FOR BRITISH CIVILIANS AND
U.S.A. NEGRO FORCES ONLY

The British are aggressively resisting the prejudice which certain white United States soldiers are intent upon imposing. This seems to have been the case when United States soldiers boarded a bus in London and tried to eject two Negro soldiers from seats they already occupied.

"You can't do that sort of thing here," a woman conductor protested. "We won't have it. Either you stand or off you go."

They stood. But the seeds of prejudice are easily scattered. Even some white troops who shared no feeling of prejudice in the United States have accepted the anti-Negro attitudes held by certain Americans. Inevitably, in their contact with the British, some have sought to transfer these attitudes.

What's true of the United States seems equally true in England: The customer is always right. When the manager of a restaurant was questioned recently about refusing service to a Negro soldier, he had a ready answer: "White Americans say they will not patronize my place if Negroes were served."

Nevertheless, the Negro soldier has appealed to the British heart.

The Negro has brought along his gifts. I was quite surprised to find British girls in Manchester, Liverpool, Glasgow, and London dancing the lindy hop. Every Monday morning the newspapers are filled with reports of Negro activity with the British—such as hikes and picnics. Negroes are seen at churches, groups of them even taking over the choir loft on occasion.

In England Negroes are on their very best behavior. They are fully aware of what is at stake. Their Negro officers and Negro Red Cross directors have done a splendid job of making them conscious that they are the guests of the British people, and as such they must prove themselves worthy of their hospitality.

Negro troops stationed near Manchester originated the idea of entertaining the local children to repay some of the hospitality which they had received in that city. I attended the second of a series of six weekly parties. About twenty Negro soldiers sung and danced. Then they distributed chewing gum and candy from their rations. Five hundred children attended the party given at the Red Cross club. The Lord Mayor was present.

Hardly a day passes that there is not newspaper comment about the race problem in England and the United States. Here are a few heads chosen at random to illustrate the manner in which this topic is being handled:

LAW IS SAME FOR WHITE OR COLORED.—Gloucestershire *Echo*.

BECAUSE THEIR SKINS ARE BROWN.—London *News Chronicle*.

RECORDER HITS AT COLOR BAR.—London *Daily Mirror*.

COLOR BAR IS "SHAMEFUL."—London *Daily Mail*.

National attention was recently focused on a case which came before a Liverpool court. A West Indian Negro, George Alexander McGuire, charged that he was refused admission to a public dance because of his race. The judge used this incident to strike out at American race prejudice in England. He said:

"I am told that the position of colored people in this country has somewhat changed since the nationals of another of our allies joined us in this country.

"When people come here to risk their lives they are entitled to think that they are coming to conditions of decency and order fit for a country that claims the title imperial in its best sense.

"I think it is impertinence for any country to accept the aid of colored people from any part of the world and then to say: 'Our laws don't enable us to deal with you on terms of complete equality.' "

Mounting opinion has not ended here. The newspapers have been deluged with letters-to-the-editor from British people protesting the imposition of American racial attitudes. A typical one appeared in the *News Chronicle* signed by a Reverend J. Giles. It said:

"The impression our Negro guests made on Nuneaton was one of natural and profound culture. Their courtesy, their politeness, their manly bearing, their frankness, and, above all, their unfailing cheerfulness and good humor quickly endeared them to the inhabitants."

The *Tribune*, a popular weekly, received a letter from a British soldier complaining that his detachment had been given a list of "suggestions" advising the adoption of an "attitude not unfriendly toward Negro troops, but not too friendly." To members of ATS it forbade associations with Negro soldiers.

Three months ago two Negro soldiers were charged with rape and were sentenced to death by court-martial in Gloucestershire. A dispute arose as to whether these soldiers were guilty. Thirty-three thousand people protested. Workers in a local factory immediately sent a protest to the American authorities and copies to the newspapers. They charged that the men were sentenced to death because of their color.

The formal statement went on to say, "In England we have learned the meaning of equality and freedom and we are revolted by the unjustness of American laws concerning Negroes."

The Negro soldiers feel keenly about the frequent show of racial animosity. Voicing a fairly typical attitude of troops who have recently arrived in England, Pfc. William B. Brown, Newark, N.J., told me how he felt:

"Since my arrival I've been constantly reminded that I'm a Negro. The pattern seems more pronounced here than in the Deep South."

Sergeant Charles Brown, Indiana, expressed it in pithy language: "We feel misused."

Traveling between London and Manchester, I met a soldier who gave me a slant which I've heard often enough to make me believe it can be chalked up as what every Negro soldier thinks:

"What I want to see is a real struggle to overcome this race question, which—as it stands today—threatens to make this war quite useless in relation to the great aims for which we are said to be fighting.

"I want to see some organization really trying to reach a solution."

The fact is, numbers of people are scrambling around for a solution. I talked quite extensively with British officials. They are frankly embarrassed and even alarmed by the race situation provoked by certain Americans. None will talk for the record. Lend-lease makes them keep their official mouths closed, for they are well aware of the spitefulness of some Southern politicians. Moreover, they feel that Americans are creating a vast amount of antiwhite feeling throughout the world, which will make the dealings of the British with colored colonials pretty difficult.

Many of them feel Americans presumptuous to talk of freedom for India in the face of the unsolved race problem in America.

Perhaps no one here is more disturbed than Americans. But individuals cannot stand up alone. Friends, whom I knew in the U.S.A., admit they are helpless. Yet white officers are daily sticking their necks out to make democracy vibrant and living within the Army. Such army publications as *Yank* and *Stars and Stripes* are dramatizing the Negro soldier's vital role in the war. Several white American seamen signed a petition protesting the barring of Negroes from a ballroom they visited.

The one hopeful aspect of this situation is the fact that the noose of prejudice has not closed. The reason may be found in the fact that many of the most rabid anti-Negro American soldiers are now not so sure of their position. They do not have wide public support for any show of racial hostility.

S. L. Solon, an American reporter working for a London paper, relates a conversation which he overheard. It sums up the situation, tying it in a nice tight knot.

"Personally," a town councilor said, "I have no feeling of race prejudice. I've been led to believe, however, that our relations with American white troops will be better if we conform to what I understand to be American practices of discrimination."

The answer to that came from a white American officer. "Discrimination is not American," he said. "Even less so today, when we are fighting a war to preserve and extend democratic values in the world."

THE RACES OF MANKIND

Professor Ruth Benedict and *Dr. Gene Weltfish*

Ruth Benedict and Gene Weltfish both teach at Columbia University in the department of anthropology.

THIRTY-FOUR NATIONS are now united in a common cause—victory over Axis aggression, the military destruction of fascism. This is the greatest fighting alliance of nations in history. These United Nations include the most different physical types of men, the most unlike beliefs, the most varied ways of life. White men, yellow men, black men, and the so-called "red men" of America, peoples of the East and the West, of the tropics and the arctic, are fighting together against one enemy.

Every morning in the newspapers and on the bulletin boards we read of yesterday's battles in Russia, in China, in Italy, in the Solomon Islands, and in New Guinea. One day's hop in a plane can carry us across the oceans. Our supply ships go to every corner of the globe. On the radio we hear men reporting on the spot from Cairo and Australia. Burma is much closer to us today than New Orleans was to Washington at the time of the War of 1812. Distance then was a hard fact; it had not been scaled down by the triumphs of human invention.

This war, for the first time, has brought home to Americans the fact that the whole world has been made one neighborhood. All races of man are shoulder to shoulder. Our armed forces are in North Africa with its Negro, Berber, and Near-East peoples. They are in India. They are in China. They are in the Solomons with its dark-skinned, "strong"-haired Melanesians. Our neighbors now are peoples of all the races of the earth.

For Americans this is not so new an experience as it is to people of most nations. In our country men of different color, hair texture, and head shape have lived together since the founding of our nation. They are citizens of the United States. Negroes and whites, Indians, Mexicans, Chinese, and people from the European nations are all taxable, subject to the draft and to the other laws of the land. They are part of our great national community. History today is only bringing together on a world scale races which have been brought together on a smaller scale here in America.

Americans know better than most how much hard feeling there can be when people of different races and nationalities have to live together and be part of one community. They know that there is often conflict. Today, when what we all want more than anything else is to win this war, most Americans are confident that, whatever our origins, we shall be able to pull together to a final victory. Hitler, though, has always believed we were wrong; he has believed that hard feeling would break out and leave us defeated. He has been sure that he could "divide and conquer." He has believed that he could convince non-white races in Asia and Africa that this is a "white man's war." He has believed especially that America was a no man's land, where peoples of all origins were ready to fall to fighting among themselves. He believes that this is a front on which we are doomed to lose the battle. It is certainly a front no less important in this war than the Production Front and the Inflation Front.

In any great issue that concerns this war we turn to science. When we need new fuels, substitutes for rubber, lighter metals, or new plastics, we ask scientists to tell us what is possible and what is impossible. The chemists tell us how to make the plastics we need, and the physicists tell us how to detect and locate an approaching airplane, and the engineers tell us how to build a better fighting plane. When we are faced with war shortages, they tell us what essential materials we have been throwing out on the dump heap.

We need the scientist just as much on the race front. Scientists have studied race. Historians have studied the history of all nations and peoples. Sociologists have studied the way in which peoples band together. Biologists have studied how man's physical traits are passed down from one generation to the next. Anthropologists have studied man's bodily measurements and his cultural achievements. Psychologists have studied intelligence among different races. All that the scientists have learned is important to us at this crucial moment of history. They can tell us: "This is so," "This is not so," "This occurs under certain conditions," or "This occurs under opposite conditions."

This booklet cannot tell you all that science has learned about the races of mankind, but it states facts that have been learned and verified. We need them.

The Bible story of Adam and Eve, father and mother of the whole human race, told centuries ago the same truth that science has shown today: that all the peoples of the earth are a single family and have a common origin. Science describes the intricate make-up of the human body: all its different organs co-operating in keeping us alive, its curious anatomy that couldn't possibly have "just happened" to be the same in all men if they did not have a common origin. Take the structure of the human foot, for instance. When you list all the little bones and muscles and the joints of the toes, it is impossible to imagine that that would all have happened twice. Or take our teeth: so many front teeth, so many canines, so many molars. Who can imagine finding the same arrangements in two human species if they weren't one family?

The fact of the unity of the human race is proved, therefore, in its anatomy. It is proved also by the close similarity in what all races are physically fitted for. No difference among human races has affected limbs and teeth and relative strength so that one race is biologically outfitted like a lion and another biologically outfitted like a lamb. All races of men can either plow or fight, and all the racial differences among them are in non-essentials such as texture of head hair, amount of body hair, shape of the nose or head, or color of the eyes and the skin. The white race is the hairiest, but a white man's hair isn't thick enough to keep him warm in cold climates. The Negro's dark skin gives him some protection against strong sunlight in the tropics, and white men often have to take precautions against sunstroke. But the war has shown that white men can work and fight even in a tropical desert. Today white men in hot countries wear sun helmets and protect themselves with clothes and rub their skin with sun-tan oil. Very dark-skinned people in the North, too, can add cod-liver oil and orange juice to their diet, and, if they need to, take a vitamin pill or two. The shape of the head, too, is a racial trait; but whether it is round or long, it can house a good brain.

The races of mankind are what the Bible says they are—brothers. In their bodies is the record of their brotherhood.

What Are Race Differences?

The greatest adventure story in the history of the world is the spread of early man to all corners of the globe. With crude tools, without agriculture, without domesticated animals except the dog, he pressed on, from somewhere in Asia to the tip of Africa, to the British Isles, across Bering Strait into America and down to Cape Horn. He occupied the islands of the Pacific and the continent of Australia. The world had a small population then, and many of these pioneers were for centuries as separated from other peoples as if they lived on another planet. Slowly they developed physical differences.

Those who settled nearer the equator, whether in Europe, Asia, or in the Americas, developed a darker skin color than those who settled to the north of them. People's hair is often the same over great areas: frizzly hair, lank hair, wavy hair. Europeans remained quite hairy, but in some parts of the world body hair almost disappeared. Blue eyes appeared in the north. In some places in Asia a fold of skin developed over the inner corner of the eye and produced what we call a slant eye.

All these distinctive traits made it easy to recognize people as belonging to different parts of the world. In each place the people got used to looking at one another. They said, "Our men are really men. Our women are beautiful. This is the way people should look." Sometimes they liked the appearance of their close neighbors. But strangers seemed odd and queer. Strangers wore funny clothes and their manners were bad. Even more important, strangers did not look the way people should. Their noses were too flat or too pointed. Their skin was "a sickly white" or "a dirty black." They were too fat or too short. Everywhere in the world men and women used the standard of their own people to judge others and thought that people who differed from this standard looked funny or ugly.

After the discovery of America by Columbus, Europeans began traveling to every quarter of the globe, and all the new peoples they met were complete strangers to them. For one thing, the Europeans couldn't understand their languages. They looked and acted strange. Europeans thought they were different creatures and named a lot of different "races." Gradually the Europeans described each one as having a skin color, kind of hair, kind of lips, height, and head shape that was peculiar to that "race." Nowadays we know that this was a false impression.

Take height, for example. There are tall and short people almost everywhere in the world. Near the sources of the Nile the Shilluk Negroes are six feet two inches; their neighbors, the brown pygmies, are four feet eight inches. In Italy a six-footer and a five-footer could both be native Italians for generations back. Among the Arizona Indians the Hopi Pueblos are five feet four inches; their Mohave neighbors are nearly six feet.

A report of the Selective Service System of November 10, 1941, showed that registrants examined for the United States Army varied in height from four feet six inches to seven feet four inches. This represents the extremes of height anywhere in the world. The Army's limits for acceptance, from five feet to six feet six inches, would include most men the world over.

Take the shape of the head as another example. In West Africa there are more long heads; in the Congo, more round. Among the American Indians, as well as in the population of Europe, both the longest and the roundest heads are to be found, and in Asia Minor long heads and round heads appear among very close relatives.

Or let us take the brain itself. Because the brain is the thinking organ, some scientists have tried to find differences in the size and structure of the brain among different groups of people. In spite of these efforts, using the finest microscopes, the best scientists cannot tell from examining a brain to what group of people its owner belonged. The *average* size of the brain is different in different groups, but it has been proved over and over again that the size of the brain has nothing to do with intelligence. Some of the most brilliant men in the world have had very small brains. On the other hand, the world's largest brain belongs to an imbecile.

For ages men have spoken of "blood relations" as if different peoples had different blood. Some people have shouted that if we got into our veins the blood of someone with a different head shape, eye color, hair texture, or skin color, we should get some of that person's physical and mental characteristics.

Modern science has revealed this to be pure superstition. All human blood is the same, whether it is the blood of an Eskimo or a Frenchman, of the "purest" German "Aryan" or an African pygmy—except for one medically important difference. This medical difference was discovered when doctors first began to use blood transfusion in order to save life. In early attempts at transfusion it was discovered that "agglutination," or clumping together, of the red cells sometimes occurred and caused death. Gradually investigators learned that there are four types of blood, called O, A, B, and AB, and that although blood typed O can be mixed successfully with the other three, none of these can be mixed with one another without clumping.

These four types of blood are inherited by each child from its forebears. But whites, Negroes, Mongols, and all races of man have all these blood types. The color of their skin does not tell at all which blood type they have. You and an Australian bushman may have the same blood type. Because you inherit your bodily traits from your many different ancestors, you may have a different blood type from your mother or your father or your brothers and sisters. You may have eyes like your mother's, teeth and hair like your father's, feet like your grandfather's, and a blood type like your great-grandmother's.

Today doctors do not "type" blood for transfusion at all. The red and white cells or corpuscles are removed, and the remainder is the same whatever race it comes from. The Blood Bank calls it plasma. It is dried and kept indefinitely. When needed for emergency transfusions, it is mixed with water and can save the life of any man or woman in the world. The same blood plasma is used to restore any man of any color who has been wounded in battle.

Finally, let us take skin color, the most noticeable of the differences between peoples. Few traits have been used as widely to classify people. We all talk about black, white, and yellow races of man.

In the world today the darkest people are in West Africa, the lightest people in northwest Europe, while in southeast Asia are men with yellowish-tan skins. Most people in the world, however, are not of these extremes but are in-betweens. These in-betweens probably have the skin shades that were once most common, the white, yellow, and dark brown or black being extreme varieties.

Recently scientists found that skin color is determined by two special chemicals. One of these, *carotene,* gives a yellow tinge; the other, *melanin,* contributes the brown. These colors, along with the pinkish tinge that comes when the blood vessels show through, give various shades to the human skin. Every person, however light or dark his skin may appear, has some of each of these materials in his skin. The one exception is the albino, who lacks coloring substances—and albinos appear among dark- and light-skinned peoples alike. People of browner complexions simply have more *melanin* in their skin, people of yellowish color more *carotene*. It is not an all-or-nothing difference; it is a difference in proportion. Your skin color is due to the amount of these chemicals present in the skin.

How Are Races Classified?

The three primary races of the world are the Caucasian Race, the Mongoloid Race, and the Negroid Race.

The Caucasian Race inhabits Europe and a great part of the Near East and India. It is subdivided in broad bands that run east and west: Nordics (fair-skinned, blue-eyed, tall and long-headed) are most common in the north; Alpines (in-between skin color, often stocky, broad-headed) in the middle; Mediterraneans (slenderer, often darker than Alpines, long-headed) in the south. The distribution of racial subtypes is just about the same in Germany and in France; both are mostly Alpine and both have Nordics in their northern districts. Racially, France and Germany are made up of the same stocks in just about equal proportions.

American Indians are Mongoloid, though they differ physically both among themselves and from the Mongols of China.

The natives of Australia are sometimes called a fourth primary race. They are as hairy as Europeans, and yet they live in an area where other peoples have very little body hair.

Aryans, Jews, Italians are *not* races. Aryans are people who speak Indo-European, "Aryan" languages. Hitler uses the term in many ways —sometimes for blond Europeans, including the Scandinavian; sometimes for Germans, whether blond or brunet; sometimes for all who agree with him politically, including the Japanese. As Hitler uses it, the term "Aryan" has no meaning, racial, linguistic, or otherwise.

Jews are people who practice the Jewish religion. They are of all races, even Negro and Mongolian. European Jews are of many different biological types; physically they resemble the populations among whom they live. The so-called "Jewish type" is a Mediterranean type, and no more "Jewish" than the South Italian. Wherever Jews are persecuted or discriminated against, they cling to their old ways and keep apart from the rest of the population and develop so-called "Jewish" traits. But these are not racial or "Jewish"; they disappear under conditions where assimilation is easy.

Italians are a nationality. Italians are of many different racial strains; the "typical" South Italian is a Mediterranean, more like the Spaniard or the Greek or the Levantine Jew than the blond North Italian. The Germans, the Russians, and all other nations of Europe are *nations,* not races. They are bound together, not by their head shape and their coloring, but by their national pride, their love of their farms, their local customs, their language, and the like.

As far back in time as the scientist can go he finds proof that animals and men moved about in the world. There were different kinds of animals, and many of them went great distances. But wherever they went, the different kinds could not breed together. A tiger cannot mate with an elephant. Even a fox and a wolf cannot mate with each other. But whenever groups of people have traveled from one place to another and met other people, some of them have married and had children.

At first men had to travel by foot. It took them a long time, but they got almost all over the world that way. Long ago, when people knew only how to make tools out of stone, the Cro-Magnons lived in Europe. Waves of migration came in from the east and the southeast. These new people settled down, bred with the Cro-Magnons, and their children were the ancestors of modern Europeans. Since then there have been many migrations from Asia and northern Africa.

Later men tamed the horse. They built carts and rode horseback. They built great boats, which were rowed by hundreds of men. They could go faster and travel farther than ever before. The Phoenicians went on trading expeditions through the Mediterannean. The Romans went to Spain and up along the coast to the British Isles. Then the Huns swept in from Asia through central Europe and destroyed the Roman Empire. The Tartars came in from the east. They threatened to conquer all of Europe but were defeated in one of the greatest cavalry engagements of all time. The Mohammedans captured all of North Africa; they took Spain and went on up into France across the Pyrenees. Thousands of Negro slaves have been brought into Europe at various times. Where are they now? Peoples have come and gone in Europe for centuries. Wherever they went, some of them settled down and left children. Small groups were absorbed into the total population. Always the different races moved about and intermarried.

We are used to thinking of Americans as mixed. All of us have ancestors who came from regions far apart. But we think that the English are English and the French are French. This is true for their nationality, just as we are all Americans. But it is not true for their *race*. The Germans have claimed to be a pure German race, but no European is a pure anything. A country has a population. It does not have a race. If you go far enough back in the populations of Europe you are apt to find all kinds of ancestors: Cro-Magnons, Slavs, Mongols, Africans, Celts, Saxons, and Teutons.

It is true, though, that people who live closer together intermarry more frequently. This is why there are places like Alsace-Lorraine, where Germans and French have intermarried so much that the children cannot tell whether they are German or French and so call themselves Alsatians. Czechoslovakia included old Bohemia, which had a population of Nordics and semi-Asiatics and Slavs. After World War I the Germans and the Czechs along the border between the two countries intermarried so often that the Germans of this section got to look like Czechs and the Czechs began to speak German. But this did not make the two countries love each other.

People of every European nation have racial brothers in other countries, often ones with which they are at war. If at any one moment you could sort into one camp all the people in the world who were most Mediterranean, no mystic sense of brotherhood would unite them. Neither camp would have language or nationality or mode of life to unite them. The old fights would break out again unless social conditions were changed—the old hatred between national groups, the old antagonisms between ruler and ruled and between the exploiter and the exploited.

The movements of peoples over the face of the earth inevitably produce race mixture and have produced it since before history began. No one has been able to show that this is necessarily bad. It has sometimes been a social advantage, sometimes a running sore threatening the health of the whole society. It can obviously be made a social evil, and, where it is so, sensible people will avoid contributing to it by grieving if their children make such alliances. We must live in the world as it is. But, as far as we know, there are no immutable laws of nature that make racial intermixture harmful.

When they study racial differences, scientists investigate the way by which particular traits are passed on from parents to children. They measure head form and identify skin color on a color chart. They map out the distribution of different kinds of hair or noses in the world. Scientists recognize that these differences do not themselves show better or worse qualities in peoples, any more than bay horses are better than black ones. They knew that to prove that a bay horse is superior to a black one you have to do more than identify its skin color on a color chart; you have to test its abilities.

Science therefore treats human racial differences as facts to be studied and mapped. It treats racial superiorities as a separate field of investigation; it looks for evidence. When a Nazi says, "I am a blue-eyed Aryan and you are non-Aryan," he means, "I am superior and you are inferior." The scientist says: "Of course. You are a fair-haired, long-headed, tall North European (the anthropological term is Nordics, not Aryans), and I am a dark-haired, round-headed, less tall South European. But on what evidence do you base your claim to be superior? That is quite different."

Race prejudice turns on this point of inferiority and superiority. The man with race prejudice says of a man of another race, "No matter who he is, I don't have to compare myself with him. I'm superior anyway. I was born that way."

It is the study of racial superiorities and inferiorities, therefore, which is most important in race relations. This investigation, to have any meaning at all, must get evidence for and against the man who says, "I was *born* that way. My race is proof that I am the better man." It must be an investigation of what is better and what is worse in traits passed down by inheritance. Such traits are, by definition, racial. The first thing we want to know scientifically is what traits a man is born with and what things happen to him after he is born. If he is lucky after he is born, he will have good food, good care, good education, and a good start in life; these are not things of which he can boast: "I was *born* that way."

A man learns the language he speaks. If he'd been born of Nordic parents and brought up from infancy in China, he'd speak Chinese like a native and have as much difficulty learning Swedish when he was grown as if he'd been born of Chinese parents. He wasn't "born" to speak cockney English or to speak with a Brooklyn accent; he speaks the way people around him speak. It's not a racial trait; he didn't inherit it.

Differences in customs among peoples of the world are not a matter of race either. One race is not "born" to marry in church after a boy-and-girl courtship and another race to marry "blind" with a bride the groom has never seen carried veiled to his father's house. One race is not "born" equipped to build skyscrapers and put plumbing in their houses and another to run up flimsy shelters and carry their water from the river. All these things are "learned behavior," and even in the white race there are many millions who don't have our forms of courtship and marriage and who live in shacks. When a man boasts of his racial superiority and says that he was "born that way," perhaps what he's really saying is that he had a lot of luck after he was born. A man of another race might have been his equal if he'd had the same luck in his life. Science insists that race does not account for all human achievements.

The most careful investigations of intelligence have been made in America among Negroes and whites. The scientist realizes that every time he measures intelligence in any man, black or white, his results show the intelligence that man was born with *plus* what happened to him since he was born. The scientist has a lot of proof of this. For instance, in the First World War intelligence tests were given to the American Expeditionary Forces; they showed that Negroes made a lower score on intelligence tests than whites. But the tests also showed that Northerners, *black and white,* had higher scores than Southerners, *black and white*. Everyone knows that Southerners are inborn equals of Northerners, but in 1917 many Southern states' per capita expenditures for schools were only fractions of those in Northern states, and housing and diet and income were far below average too. Since the vast majority of Negroes lived in the South, their score on the intelligence test was a score they got not only as Negroes, but as Americans who had grown up under poor conditions in the South. Scientists therefore compared the scores of Southern whites and Northern Negroes.

Median Scores on A.E.F. Intelligence Tests

Southern Whites:	
Mississippi	41.25
Kentucky	41.50
Arkansas	41.55
Northern Negroes:	
New York	45.02
Illinois	47.35
Ohio	49.50

Negroes with better luck after they were born got higher scores than whites with less luck. The white race did badly where economic conditions were bad and schooling was not provided, and Negroes living under better conditions surpassed them. The differences did not arise because people were from the North or the South, or because they were white or black, but because of differences in income, education, cultural advantages, and other opportunities.

Scientists then studied gifted children. They found that children with top scores turn up among Negroes, Mexicans, and Orientals. Then they went to European countries to study the intelligence of children in homelands from which our immigrants come. Children from some of these countries got poor scores in America, but in their homeland children got good scores. Evidently the poor scores here were due to being uprooted, speaking a foreign language, and living in tenements; the children were not unintelligent *by heredity*.

The second superiority which a man claims when he says, "I was born a member of a superior race," is that his race has better *character*. The Nazis boast of their racial soul. But when they wanted to make a whole new generation into Nazis they didn't trust to "racial soul"; they made certain kinds of teaching compulsory in the schools, they broke up homes where the parents were anti-Nazi, they required boys to join certain Nazi youth organizations. By these means they got the kind of national character they wanted. But it was a planned and deliberately trained character, not an inborn "racial soul." In just the same way the Japanese have bred a generation of ruthless fighters. Fifty years ago Europeans who lived in Japan used to describe them as "butterflies flitting from flower to flower," incapable of "the stern drives" of Western civilization. Since 1900 the "butterflies" have fought six times overseas, and they are desperate and ruthless fighters. In a generation the butterflies have become gamecocks. But their *race* has not changed. The same blood still flows in their veins. But spiritually they are more like the Germans than they are like their racial brothers, the peace-loving Chinese.

It can go the other way too. In 1520 the ancient Mexicans were like the Germans. They talked like Nazis, thought like them, in many ways felt like them. They, too, believed war to be man's highest mission. They, too, trained their children for it, placing their boys in great state schools where they learned little else but the glories of battle and the rituals of their caste. They, too, believed themselves invincible, and against small, defenseless villages they were. But they were defeated in battle by the Spaniards with the help of the peoples whom the Aztecs had oppressed; their leaders were killed, their temples destroyed, their wealth pillaged, and their power broken. The Mexican peasant, who still speaks the Aztec language and in whose veins still runs the blood of Aztec conquerors, no longer dreams of glorious death in battle and eternal life in an Indian

Valhalla. He no longer goes on the warpath, no longer provokes war with peaceful villages. He is a humble peon, wishing only to be left in peace to cultivate his little field, go to church, dance, sing, and make love. These simple things endure.

Americans deny that the Nazis have produced a national character superior to that of Goethe's and Schiller's day, and that the ruthless Japanese of today are finer human beings than in those generations when they preferred to write poetry and paint pictures. Race prejudice is, after all, a determination to keep a people down, and it misuses the label "inferior" to justify unfairness and injustice. Race prejudice makes people ruthless; it invites violence. It is the opposite of "good character" as it is defined in the Christian religion—or in the Confucian religion, or in the Buddhist religion, or the Hindu religion, for that matter.

History proves that progress in civilization is not the monopoly of one race or subrace. When our white forebears in Europe were rude stone-age primitives, the civilizations of the Babylonians and the Egyptians had already flourished and been eclipsed. There were great Negro states in Africa when Europe was a sparsely settled forest. Negroes made iron tools and wove fine cloth for their clothing when fair-skinned Europeans wore skins and knew nothing of iron.

When Europe was just emerging from the Middle Ages, Marco Polo visited China and found there a great civilization, the like of which he had never imagined. Europe was a frontier country in those days compared with China.

Since the beginning of history an unusual collection of fortunate circumstances have been present among one race, sometimes among another. Up to now every great center of civilization has had its day and has given place to others. The proud rulers of yesterday become the simple peasants of another era. The crude people who once threatened the great cities become later the kings and emperors in the same country. The peoples change, but the old arts of life are, for the most part, not permanently lost. They pass into the common heritage of mankind.

Inventions pass, too, from one continent to another when people trade with each other. This has happened since the dawn of history. About five thousand years ago, when Europe was on the frontiers of the civilized world, Asiatics came to trade in Europe and North Africa in great caravans. They followed the main rivers—the Nile into North Africa, the Danube into Europe, and the Tigris and Euphrates rivers out of Asia. People from all over came in contact with one another and compared notes on what they knew. In this way they pooled their knowledge, and out of this combined knowledge came the great inventions of civilization—massive building and the arts of metallurgy, chemistry, writing, medicine, and mathematics; transportation on wheels. The idea of printing and the use of movable type is an old Chinese invention, and our power engines depend upon a knowledge of explosives that the Chinese worked out with firecrackers.

When Columbus discovered America, corn, "Irish" potatoes, tobacco, and "Boston" beans were unknown in Europe. They had been developed by American Indians. Within ten years corn was being planted in Central Asia and in the interior of Africa, and African tribes today think that corn was given them by their own gods "in the beginning."

All races have made their contributions to human knowledge. Those who have lived at the crossroads of the world have invented most; those who have lived isolated on islands or at the tip ends of continents have been content to earn their livelihoods by old traditional methods. There was, for them, no "necessity" to be "the mother of invention" after they had devised a way to live on the land.

Peoples who came into contact with strangers, however, gave what arts of life they had and took what the strangers had. These contributions to civilization accumulated over the centuries, and on this accumulation new discoveries are based. We are all the gainers.

The United States is the greatest crossroads of the world in all history. People have come here from every race and nation, and almost every race in the world is represented among our citizens. They have brought with them their own ways of cooking food, so that our "American" diet is indebted to a dozen peoples. Our turkey, corn, and cranberries come from the Indians. Our salads we borrowed from the French and Italians. Increasingly in recent years we have enriched our tables with soups from Russia, vegetables from Italy, appetizers from the Scandinavian countries, sea foods from the Mediterranean lands, chili and tortillas from Mexico, and so on almost endlessly. At the same time, everywhere we have gone in the world, we have popularized ice cream, beefsteak, breakfast cereals, corn on the cob, and other foods that are called "American."

Industry in the United States has taken the hand skills of our immigrants and made machines to do the work; without their skills we should not have known how. Our music, our buildings have developed from patterns brought to our shores or learned from every quarter of the world. Our country would be poorer in every phase of its culture if different cultures had not come together here, sharing and learning the special contributions each had to offer.

The Future of Race Prejudice

Nevertheless there is race prejudice in America and in the world. Race prejudice isn't an old universal "instinct." It is hardly a hundred years old. Before that, people persecuted Jews because of their religion—not their "blood"; they enslaved Negroes because they were pagans—not for being black.

Looking back now, moderns are horrified at all the blood that was shed for centuries in religious conflicts. It is not our custom any more to torture and kill a man because he has a different religion. The twenty-first century may well look back on our generation and be just as horrified. If that century builds its way of life on the Atlantic Charter—for the whole world—our era will seem a nightmare from which they have awakened. They will think we were crazy. "Why should race prejudice have swept the Western world," they will say, "where no nation was anything but a mixture of all kinds of racial groups? Why did nations just at that moment begin talking about 'the racial purity' of their blood? Why did they talk of their wars as racial wars? Why did they make people suffer, not because they were criminals or double-crossers, but because they were Jews or Negroes or non-Nordic?"

We who are living in these troubled times can tell them why. Today weak nations are afraid of the strong nations; the poor are afraid of the rich; the rich are afraid they will lose their riches. People are afraid of one another's political or economic power, they are afraid of revenge for past injuries, they are afraid of social rejection. Conflict grows fat on fear. And the slogans against "inferior races" lead us to pick on them as scapegoats. We pin on them the reason for all our fears.

Freedom from fear is the way to cure race prejudice. When aggressions like those of the Axis are made impossible by guarantees of collective security, those guarantees must cover countries of all races. Then Nazi race tactics will be outmoded. In any country every legal decision that upholds equal citizenship rights without regard to race or color, every labor decision that lessens the terror of being "laid off" and gives a man self-respect in his employment, every arrangement that secures the little farmer against losing his acres to the bank—all these and many more can free people from fear. They need not look for scapegoats.

The Russian nation has for a generation shown what can be done to outlaw race prejudice in a country with many kinds of people. They did not wait for people's minds to change. They made racial discrimination and persecution illegal. They welcomed and honored the different dress, different customs, different arts of the many tribes and countries that live as part of their nation. The more backward groups were given special aid to help them catch up with the more advanced. Each people was helped to develop its own cultural forms, its own written language, theater, music, dance, and so on. At the same time that each people was encouraged in its national self-development, the greatest possible interchange of customs was fostered, so that each group became more distinctively itself and at the same time more a part of the whole.

The Russians have welcomed cultural *differences* and they have refused to treat them as *inferiorities*. No part of the Russian program has had greater success than their racial program.

In the United States a considerable number of organizations are working for democratic race equality. To mention only a few: The East-West Association has done some splendid work in emphasizing the importance of racial understanding, especially between Asiatic and Western peoples. The China Institute is active in promoting the work of Chinese students in America, and the Phelps-Stokes Foundation has brought many African students here, cementing the relation between the two continents.

The Council Against Intolerance in America has a continuous program in the schools. The Council on Intercultural Relations has done much to emphasize the Negro's contribution to American culture. The Bureau for Intercultural Education interprets the contributions made to America by many different races and nationalities. The Rosenwald Foundation has sponsored Southern Negro schools, elementary, high school, and college, in order to make up for the deficiencies of Southern Negro education. They have also pressed for Negro housing and health projects in the North. The National Association for the Advancement of Colored People arranges publicity and fosters public education through periodicals, the radio, and special publications. It fights cases of discrimination in the courts and tries to get effective laws passed for the protection of Negro rights. The National Urban League helps Negroes who move from rural districts to the cities to find industrial work and proper living conditions.

Many church bodies have done much to help people realize that ideas of race superiority or inferiority are un-Christian. The Department of Race Relations of the Federal Council of the Churches of Christ in America and the National Conference of Christians and Jews have encouraged collaboration among church leaders interested in interracial co-operation. During World War II the Executive Committee of the Council called on all local churches to eliminate racial discrimination in their own practices. Church bodies of all faiths have encouraged education for tolerance.

For some twenty years white and Negro leaders of the South have cooperated actively through the Commission on Interracial Co-operation in establishing local committees of both whites and Negroes. This commission has promoted mutual respect and understanding. In many local areas small groups have worked patiently to increase interracial cooperation.

Among the unions we find that the National Maritime Union has fought and won the right of Negroes to serve as skilled workers instead of in menial jobs only. Today mixed crews on freighters, tankers, and merchant ships are doing a magnificent job without friction. The *Booker T. Washington,* with its Negro captain, Hugh Mulzac, is a notable example. The United Auto Workers has an interracial committee with Walter Hardin, a veteran Negro official, as its chairman. At first white workers resisted the right of Negroes to do more skilled kinds of work. For example, when Negroes were first placed on machines previously manned by white operators, a work stoppage shut down a whole section of the Packard plant. R. J. Thomas, the president of the union, ordered the white strikers to return to work or suffer loss of union membership and employment. Within a few hours the strikers were back, with the recently promoted Negroes still at their machines.

Besides the National Maritime Union and the Auto Workers, a number of other unions have taken the lead in promoting interracial understanding. They include the International Ladies Garment Workers, the Amalgamated Clothing Workers, the United Electrical Radio and Machine Workers, the Marine Shipbuilding Workers, and the United Rubber Workers. In the Birmingham, Alabama, area there are more than a hundred union locals with both white and Negro members, and the Southern Tenant Farmers Union has a mixed membership.

From the time of Lincoln's Emancipation Proclamation to the present day, the national and state governments have passed laws to carry forward the principles of our Declaration of Independence and our Constitution. In June 1941, President Roosevelt took direct action in his

Executive Order No. 8802 toward eliminating discrimination in employment in plants with war contracts. The Fair Employment Practice Committee was set up and held public hearings in Los Angeles, Chicago, New York, and Birmingham. When an individual applied for a job in a plant doing war work and was refused for reasons of prejudice—because he was a Negro, a Jew, or a naturalized citizen—he could bring his case before the committee, who then called the company to a public hearing. This committee is now part of the War Manpower Commission.

The Negro Manpower Commission of this same body is headed by an able Negro economist and maintains a staff of Negro field representatives attached to the United States Employment Service. They also work through the regional offices of the Social Security Board to detect cases of racial discrimination.

The Bureau of Indian Affairs, under Commissioner Collier, should be mentioned here as a government bureau with a long record of successful effort for the adjustment of a racial minority.

But at best the government can act only as a policeman, finding a wrongdoer here and there. Only the people themselves can really end racial discrimination, through understanding, sympathy, and public action. But there is evidence that the American people as individuals are beginning to think and to act. One hundred thousand Americans have petitioned the War Department to have at least one division in the Army containing both Negroes and whites. A separate petition was signed by American white men of draft age who asked to be assigned to such a division—many of these were Southerners.

In Houston, Texas, the mayor and a group of prominent citizens advertised in the local papers that no disturbance would be tolerated that would blacken the reputation of Houston when the Negroes of that city celebrated Juneteenth Day in honor of the emancipation of the slaves. It began with the statement, "Don't do Hitler's work," and warned citizens not to repeat rumors. The celebration was peacefully carried out. It is unfortunate that in Beaumont, Texas, similar effective action was not undertaken and a serious riot occurred.

In the most disastrous of recent riots in Detroit, a number of obscure bystanders performed heroic actions.

A white passenger on a streetcar spoke to the mob and dissuaded them from searching the car.

Two women, a mother and daughter, realizing that the Negro passenger was in danger, sheltered him so that when the rioters looked into the car he was effectively hidden.

In a bus going South recently the white passengers all remained standing rather than occupy the "white" seats of a Jim Crow bus.

During the recent disturbances in New York's Harlem, a group of Negroes stood in front of the restaurant of a white proprietor who had been their friend and in this way protected it from being broken into and destroyed by the mob.

In the last analysis these homely incidents tell the real story. They tell us that the conscience of America is aroused, that there is work to be done, and that some of us are already trying to do it.

With America's great tradition of democracy, the United States should clean its own house and get ready for a better twenty-first century. Then it could stand unashamed before the Nazis and condemn, without confusion, their doctrines of a Master Race. Then it could put its hand to the building of the United Nations, sure of support from all the yellow and the black races where the war is being fought, sure that victory in this war will be in the name, not of one race or of another, but of the universal Human Race.

THE TRUTH ABOUT THE DETROIT RIOT

Earl Brown

Earl Brown is well known for his magazine articles. He is a special feature writer for Life *magazine.*

ON SUNDAY, JUNE 20, 1943, a common fist fight between a white man and a colored man precipitated a race riot in Detroit. Twenty-five Negroes and nine white persons were killed in the riot, the worst of its kind since the one in East St. Louis in 1917. The most remarkable thing about the Detroit riot is this: the possibility of such an outbreak had been foreseen for more than a year before it occurred; feeling in the city became more inflamed as months went by. All this was going on in what is really the munitions capital of the United Nations, a center where unimpeded war production is absolutely essential in making the munitions that go up to every battle line in the world—Italy, the Solomons, Russia, Australia, everywhere. Why was no action taken to prevent the riot?

When, in August 1942, *Life* said that Detroit was dynamite there were outraged denials from local officials. When a Detroit newspaperman wrote to Attorney General Biddle about the critical state of affairs in Detroit in March 1943, Mr. Biddle replied: "Your letter has received careful consideration, although it does not appear that there is sufficient evidence of violation of any Federal statute to warrant action by this department at this time." What action the Federal government was not able to take in March it took with Federal troops three months later.

The causes of the riot are both complicated and simple. In a city swollen with a mushroomed population, where shelter was almost unobtainable, the Negro population had become steadily more resolute in the determination to overcome discrimination; this determination provoked opposition in a large segment of the white population, an opposition that was egged on day and night by demagogues and exhorters. This state of feeling was further complicated by the fact that there was an intense distrust and suspicion between the automotive manufacturers and their employees, following a short and remarkable campaign in which the city had been turned into the strongest union town in the country. The atmosphere in Detroit was such that almost any incident would provide the spark to blow it up. The fist fight provided the incident.

The effect of the riot was as damaging to morale as a major bombing raid would have been. Though a recurrence of the riot is not expected, Detroit continues to seethe with hatred between the races. Nothing is being done about housing; some dwellings are labeled with signs that say "Nigger Keep Out." The day before I wrote this I saw three young white sailors and their girl friends yelling, "Nigger! Nigger! Nigger!" at some Negroes going by in a Woodward Avenue streetcar. Negro night clubs have been receiving regular visitations from the police, who line up the customers, frisk them, and in general shove them round. The mayor holds conference after conference which result in no action. I attended a meeting of his Interracial Committee set up to determine the causes of the riot and to make recommendations as to how to remedy them. Every member, black and white, all but fell asleep. When the chairman announced that he was going on a vacation for the month of August everybody perked up and voted him a pleasant trip. As for the commissioner of police, he has undertaken to curb juvenile delinquency among the colored youth of Detroit with a policeman-ventriloquist, whose performances are designed to encourage virtue.

II

Though the fact is not widely recognized, Detroit to a considerable extent is a city of transplanted Southerners. It is an old town, the oldest in the country west of the original colonies. In the nineties it was still a self-contained, closely knit city of carriage builders and furniture makers, noted for its brick mansions, parks, and trees. All this was changed with the coming of automobile manufacture. The little factories of Robert Olds and Henry Ford and Henry Leland in the cow pastures on the edge of town eventually swallowed up the countryside. Since the turn of the century the city has proliferated; now it is urban yet broken up into a multitude of neighborhoods and centers.

Henry Ford set his minimum wage at five dollars in 1914. The great migration, both black and white, from the South began in that year. Boomed by the First World War, it continued through the twenties, dried up during the thirties, and boomed again once the "defense effort" began. Here have come Willie Washington from the cotton fields of the Black Belt, John Thomas fresh from Tennessee and eager to draw down big pay at Ford's, the hillbillies from Arkansas and the Allegheny ridges, the rednecks and the crackers. With them came the crossroads preachers, white and Negro, the shouters and the exhorters, the tent-show camp-meeting gospel men, damnation Baptist and Methodist clerics from Southern small towns and the back country. These migrants moved in along with a stream of foreign born, of whom the Poles furnished the largest contingent.

In 1940 the population of the city was 1,623,000. The figure has shot up since then because of the demand for war workers. In the town and spilling over its edges there are now estimated to be about 210,000 Negroes, nearly half a million Southern whites, and perhaps 350,000 Poles (who are mostly Catholic). There are about 70,000 Jews.

Negroes live in practically every part of Detroit, but most of them live on the west side and in an east-side district called Paradise Valley. Paradise Valley, near Cadillac Square, is a belt of cheap, jerry-built two-story brick and wooden stores and houses, littered with gin mills, poolrooms, Poro System hair-straightening parlors, grimy eating joints, and dives of every description. To this district came the young Alabama farm hand, Joe Louis, with his mother and sisters and brothers; here

John Roxborough, with the assistance of crooked city officials and policemen, laid the foundations of his fortune in the numbers racket.

These people lived in a town in which the well-being of everybody, white and black, depended absolutely on automobiles. The reputation of the town was fabulous, for enormous fortunes had been made there. The crash after 1929 was even more resounding. It was in Michigan that the bank holidays began, and some of the greatest bank scandals were in Detroit itself. Accustomed to the doctrine of everlasting prosperity, Detroit became a desolate place during the depression. Only those who saw the town in the early thirties can conceive of the atmosphere of paralysis and despair that pervaded the place. For long periods the auto plants were shut down, and the dependent industries with them. The fringes of Detroit were littered with Hoovervilles, and in many dreary suburbs it was a common practice in winter to get up parties to wreck houses for firewood. The greatest boom town on earth was flat on its back.

Detroit had been an open-shop town. Henry Ford, the great genius and monument of the community, not only had no union in his plant, but abominated Wall Street as well and refused to be a member of the Automobile Manufacturers Association. The city is now, and for a generation has been, a great ant heap of newcomers and strangers, to which more newcomers and strangers are forever being added.

So it was at the beginning of the depression, when the first attempts were made to start a union in the auto industry. In February 1931 the Union League of Detroit, which included many of the most prominent industrialists of the city in its membership, began fulminating against Communists and what they judged to be criminal syndicalism.

These philippics from the Union League helped to inaugurate an era of demagoguery and exhortation in Detroit the like of which America has never seen. Los Angeles has been pale in comparison. Scarcely any segment of the population was left untouched. Chronologically, the first comer was Father Charles Coughlin of Royal Oak. He attracted no particular attention until he began his excoriations of Hoover and Wall Street after the crash in '29. By temperament an agitator and exhorter, he accumulated a tremendous following through the Middle West. He had not been agitating long when the Black Legion appeared on the scene in Detroit. This organization, an offshoot of the Ku Klux Klan, was organized in 1931 or 1932, and went in for hoods, grips, and passwords. It was a "poor white" organization from the start, and violent against Catholics, Jews, Negroes, and "radicals." The exposure of the order followed the arrest of the murderers of a Catholic named Charles Poole in May 1936, and gave the police clues to a long list of unsolved crimes—including several murders, burnings of houses, and the bombing of Coughlin's house and the Workers Book Store, as well as the homes of a number of labor organizers. A grand-jury investigation resulted in the naming of eighty-six persons as members of the Legion. These included a member of the legislature, the manager of the state sales tax, a city treasurer, sheriffs, and other officials.

By the time Coughlin's Social Justice was booming, Detroit was sizzling with every sort of panacea, agitation, and political nostrum. The Townsendites were present in force; voodooism flourished among a number of Negro groups; the Anglo-Saxon Federation was a local movement, and there were many others.

But the most continuous and red-hot exhortations came from the Bible Belt pulpiteers. The two most spectacular of these were and are the Reverend J. Frank Norris and the Reverend Gerald L. K. Smith. Norris, a native of Alabama and a vociferous Baptist, was the editor of the *Fundamentalist* and the pastor of a church in Fort Worth that claimed a membership of ten thousand. In 1926, in most sensational circumstances, Norris shot and killed a man in the study of his church in Fort Worth. In 1935 he came to Detroit and became the pastor of the Temple Church, commuting to Fort Worth by plane in order to shepherd both flocks. His is the standard sulphurous gospel thunder of Southern tradition, but in excelsis.

Gerald Smith has been showier in his politics than Norris, though it would be impossible to be more stentorian. Smith was a minister of the Disciples of Christ and had a reputation as a go-getting preacher in Indiana and Wisconsin. By 1935 he was so busy with Huey Long that he abandoned his Shreveport congregation. He was what Harnett Kane called one of Huey's strongest "air conditioners." Eventually, after Huey's death, Gerald showed up in Detroit after a long and lonesome wandering among the Townsendites and other outfits of the discontented. By the time he reached Detroit he had organized the Committee of One Million, which was to serve as a background to his spellbinding. He was and is a skillful demagogue. After Coughlin's *Social Justice* had been denied the mails, it wasn't long before Gerald had a periodical called *The Cross and the Flag*. Last year he ran for the Republican senatorial nomination on a "Tires for Everybody" platform and found himself at the tail of the ticket; now he is doing his best to galvanize the fragments of the old Detroit America First contingent into an America First party.

These three men—Coughlin, Norris, and Smith—are the best known of the Detroit religious-political-agitational crowd, but behind them are thousands of others. It is estimated that there are more than twenty-five hundred Southern-born evangelists in Detroit alone. Some have gospel tents, some have regular churches, some are radio exhorters, some work in war plants and preach in their spare time. Their doctrine is red hot. A local Presbyterian preacher described them this way: "Their forerunners for generations preached from the crossroads and schoolhouses that 'Christ came to His Own and His Own received Him not.' His Own being the Jews." Many of these preachers are members of the Ku Klux Klan or its front organizations. They argue that the Jew is dangerous, that Russia is a menace, and as for the colored man, that he is not only a hewer of wood and a drawer of water, but must be kept firmly in his place so long as the Lord God Jehovah reigneth. The advertisements of these exhorters fill a page and more in the Detroit Saturday papers. The sermon topics—"Hell's Own Razzle Dazzle," "Increased Commotion Among Nations," and "God Spared a Wicked City"—are as hot as the sermons. For more than ten years emotional hard cider of this character has been pouring in a flood over Detroit. It contributed in no small degree to the feeling that produced the riot.

After 1933, when economic recovery, the New Deal, and Relief blew some breath of life back into the town, the automobile business began to recover. The sporadic attempts to organize the automobile workers became more frequent; after Section 7a got into the statute books the effort never stopped. In October 1936, Chrysler recognized the United Automobile Workers. In November 1936 came the sit-down strikes at Flint, followed by the General Motors strike in January and February 1937. The capitulation of General Motors was followed by the establishment of the union throughout practically the whole industry.

Ford alone held out. The union could never be sure of itself until Ford was organized, and one of the crucial factors was Ford's Negro employees. Not only were many of them anti-union but practically all of them were profoundly loyal to "Uncle Henry" because he was the only big manufacturer who gave Negroes jobs. Before the advent of the UAW-CIO the Negroes were systematically excluded from the craft unions in the automobile industry.

In the past, when a colored man arrived in Detroit with his heart set on a Ford job and five dollars a day wages, he had found that it would help to get a letter from one of the various Negro preachers who were in Ford's good graces before he applied for a job. The result was obvious. The colored boy made a beeline for the preacher, joined the church, secured a letter, and got a job. The church had saved another soul, the pastor had gained another follower, and Mr. Ford had hired another "safe" worker.

Company vigilance over this boy did not cease when he punched the time clock and went home. Company investigators went to picnics, scrutinized his marital life, and kept an eye on his politics. More than half the Negro automobile workers worked for "Uncle Henry," the man who first paid five dollars a day. If these men were to be organized, the union had not only to overcome the influence of Harry Bennett, Ford's powerful personnel director, and the Ford police; it would have to circumvent the traditional personal attachment of the colored people for Ford himself.

The CIO had made considerable capital originally out of its announced intention to obliterate race and religious lines in its organization. This was the theme of many a resounding speech. In Detroit the United Auto Workers had no choice. They had to include the Negroes or run the risk of losing the whole game. This was the situation in 1940, when a campaign was undertaken on a grand scale to bring Ford into camp.

III

During these years the political organization of Detroit blindly followed in the wake of the city's mushroom growth. Local government has seldom been efficient, clean, or good. Following a graft scandal a quarter century earlier, the old board of aldermen had been abolished and a non-partisan system put in its place. The councilmen are usually elected on a popularity basis, and the council meetings are not unlike the bedlam that reigns on any Sunday in Plaza Square in Los Angeles. Among the current incumbents of the council are Billy Rogell, former star shortstop of the Detroit Tigers baseball team, and Gus Dorais, coach of the Detroit Lions professional football team. If the Tigers win a pennant, local acid tongues say that any nine of them could be elected to the city council with ease. Edward Jeffries, the present mayor, is an American who was educated in England. The riot has not made him a happier man, but neither housing nor any other ameliorative move gets forward any faster because of his anxiety.

The management of police graft is as trying a job in Detroit as it is anywhere else, but in 1939 the distribution of gravy got out of hand. The wife of a Detroit gambler committed suicide. Before doing so she wrote letters to the mayor, the police commissioner, and the newspapers, saying that her life had been wrecked by the sort of life she had to live as a gambler's wife. These letters blew up the works. The Detroit *Free Press* started a crusade against gambling; and after several months' rummaging had satisfied the paper and others that the city officials were knee-deep in a variety of rackets, a one-man grand jury was called to investigate the matter. Former Circuit Judge Homer Ferguson of Detroit, who was later elected to the United States Senate because of his work in this investigation, found enough evidence to lead to the conviction of a former mayor, prosecuting attorney, superintendent of police, sheriff, three city councilmen, and a whole crop of minor police officials. All went to jail except Mayor Reading, who, along with John Roxborough, Joe Louis' manager, and Everett Watson, a numbers banker, is still out on appeal.

The investigation showed that the policy racket was dominated by Negroes and operated with the connivance of city officials. Rackets among Negroes, however, do not flourish in very lush pastures. The gravy comes from the nickels and dimes of both blacks and whites—of a population at the bottom of the heap. But policy playing is popular, and the morning gamble is a fling toward a golden fortune by sundown. Because it is as popular with whites as with Negroes, the total take of this five-and-dime racket is enormous. If it is to operate, the police must be cut in on the melon. In Detroit the cops not only gave the Negro racketeers free rein but protected them from white gambling competition. There was a reason for this: the Negro gamblers were not as likely to resort to gunplay to settle their differences. They were easier to exploit.

Though city officials were happy to let the Negro racketeers flourish, along with their white brethren (Roxborough's numbers racket is said to have been going full blast at the time he was on trial), they were not especially concerned with the fact that, as usual, the Negroes had the worst Detroit slums to live in. This is not to say that the white slums were attractive. Housing hasn't been a popular issue in Detroit. Real-estate interests were against government housing and rent control; and once when private capital dabbled in a housing project the result was the conviction of three city councilmen on graft charges.

Paradise Valley is one of the most intensely crowded urban districts in the United States. Filthy, smelly, dive-ridden, whore-infested Hastings Street is as crowded as Coney Island on a hot Sunday. Men and women with their pockets full of war wages live with their children, packed like sardines, in the horribly dirty one- and two-family houses and apartment buildings on Hastings and other streets of the Valley. Four and five families live in space where one or two were crowded before. At the corner of Adam Street a small group of Negro businessmen have built a sumptuous bowling alley and a beautifully appointed air-conditioned night club called the Three Sixes. Here the night-lifers of Detroit, both white and black, listen to the best Negro bands and pay feverish prices for liquor while a hundred yards away Negro children, jammed in lousy bedrooms, can scarcely breathe.

As always, the more resolute Negroes who accumulate a competence seek to escape segregated districts. Detroit is speckled with little islands of middle-class, prosperous Negroes who have got out. The establishment of these islands has frequently caused ructions. In 1925 a Negro doctor, Dr. Ossian Sweet, moved into a house in a white district. When a mob of four hundred persons stoned his house and then rushed it, Dr. Sweet fired into the crowd and killed a man. Sweet was defended by Clarence Darrow at a sensational trial and was released. There have been other incidents of this character, including the agitation to prevent tenants from moving into the Sojourner Truth housing project for Negroes. It finally took troops to get them in. Three white men were indicted by a Federal jury for inciting riot at the time of the Sojourner Truth riot, but they have never been brought to trial.

Intermittent race disputes of this character did not prevent the Negro population from getting some political preferment. They represent a large and desired block of votes. The practice of voting at large for councilmen in the city prevents Negroes from being elected to that body, but there are two Negro assistant prosecuting attorneys. The State Labor Commissioner is a Negro, and one of the state senators is a Negro. The city-owned Detroit Street Railway Company employs about a thousand Negroes as motormen, bus drivers, and workers of other sorts. With the police it is another matter. Out of thirty-six hundred cops only forty are Negroes; there are two Negro firemen in the city.

IV

The inauguration of what was first called "the defense effort" plunged Detroit into confusion. The division of opinion in the country over foreign policy was reflected in the city. The automobile manufacturers were in a tremendous run of prosperity; the notion of converting the plants to war production was vehemently opposed, and this opposition was not weakened by the tactics of William S. Knudsen of General

Motors, who had been made head of OPM. The vigorous promotion of the Reuther Plan by the Auto Workers Union was balked both in Detroit and in Washington. War contracts were accepted, work on the Chrysler Tank Arsenal, built with government money, went ahead, and plans were made for Willow Run; but there was little feeling of common enterprise.

In the spring of 1940 the union went ahead with its campaign to organize Ford. It was a long job, but finally, in April 1941, a group of workers started a strike without the permission or knowledge of the union officials, and the die was cast. Although a few thousand of Ford's loyal Negro workers stayed on their jobs when the strike broke, many of them later signed up with the union and joined the strikers in picketing the plant, because the union officials went out of their way to prove to them that it accepted them as equals. Today the largest union local in the world is UAW-CIO Local 600, the River Rouge Ford plant local. It has about ninety thousand members, and about eighteen thousand of them are Negroes.

The Auto Workers Union had now swept the board in Detroit, and many an oration from union rostrums declared that the color line was no more. There are 450,000 members of the UAW-CIO in Detroit, and about 55,000 of them are Negroes. These are truly gigantic figures. Negroes have prominent and influential positions in the union. At Ford's, for example, the recording secretaries at the River Rouge, Willow Run, and Highland Park plants—jobs paying up to forty-five hundred dollars a year—are all Negroes.

But union membership, while it can accomplish extraordinary things, won't do everything. This huge contingent of men almost defied discipline and organization. Here were whites and blacks, Jews and Christians, hard-shelled Southern Baptists, Polish Catholics, Full Gospel men, Socialists, Communists, followers of Coughlin and Smith. Factionalism has been rampant in the union ever since it was organized. The stakes for which the factions jockey are far from inconsiderable. There is money—in the shape of well-paid jobs—and there is real power. Internal conflict first came to a head in 1938, when the union's first president, the Reverend Homer Martin, a firebrand Baptist preacher from Kansas City, was thrown out. The Communist issue, always on the stove, continued to sizzle. Finally there are the race and religious issues, and they began to burn fiercely two years ago. There are thousands of union men who are members of the Ku Klux Klan or the organizations that follow in its wake—the Dixie Voters League, the United Sons of America, the Southern Society, and the Mantle Club. There are thousands of Catholic union men who revere Coughlin; thousands who belong to the Association of Catholic Trade Unionists. Judophobia, Negrophobia, and a dozen other phobias heave and bubble in the union, and these hates are sometimes employed by adroit maneuverers to further their own ends.

The union now divides into two principal wings. The right wing, led by Walter Reuther, international vice-president and author of the Reuther Plan, has the support of the Socialists. The left wing, which has the Communist support, is headed by George Addes, the international secretary and treasurer. Above these two wings is the president, R. J. Thomas, who sweats blood in the effort to keep to the middle of the road. Negroes appear in both the right and the left wings, and so do the other race and religious groups.

By the time Ford was organized, this great, floundering trade-union, riven with discord, was the biggest single influence in Detroit. It vociferously backed the war and was incessant in its demand for labor-management committees. War production, though it had managed to achieve remarkable records, was still moving by jerks. By the summer of '42 there was an acute labor shortage. Some manufacturers were hoarding labor while others clamored for men. Skilled workers, not needed at the moment, were put to work sweeping floors at big wages to prevent their going elsewhere. Workers in the Chrysler Tank Arsenal struck because they couldn't smoke during work hours; spectacular publicity was talking about production at Willow Run when not a single plane had been turned out; a worker told a reporter: "I'm going to stay home tonight and go fishing; we're not getting anything done here."

V

In the midst of all this there was a steadily increasing tension over the race question. An editor of a Polish paper told of anti-Negro handbills being distributed on the steps of St. Florian's Church in Hamtramck during the Sojourner Truth riots. At the same time the Negro population was becoming more determined to get rid of some of the color bars. The Negro press was plugging a "Double V" campaign for victory at home as well as abroad, arguing that a war against the fascists didn't mean much when there was intense race discrimination at home. This resolution among the Negroes was manifest from top to bottom. At the bottom, the Negro tough element was constantly having brushes with the white toughs. Fist fights were common. Farther up the scale, Negroes who had finally got skilled jobs were determined to hold them and not to be ousted by whites. These efforts were viewed with alarm by many of the brimstone exhorters, who urged the white man to stand fast.

Meantime the Jews were shivering in their shoes, for they too were getting their share of abuse. This was true inside the union, where despite official statements of policy the race issue was rampant. The declared intent of the union was to insist upon the "upgrading" of Negroes to better jobs, to which by skill and merit they were entitled. This policy the War Manpower Commission and the Federal Fair Employment Practice Committee had been trying feebly to promote. These efforts provoked bitter contentions both inside the union and out.

That there were the makings of an upheaval was now clear to everybody in the city. As Mayor Jeffries subsequently admitted, a riot was expected. The only question was—when? It is a singular fact that in face of this expectation neither the city government nor Washington made any positive moves.

Shortly after the turn of this year there began a series of anti-Negro "hate strikes" in the plants. It is remarkable that, aside from a number of individual fist fights, there was never any rioting in the plants. This led to the suspicion that the race strikes were being planned and engineered. The incitements were all familiar from the old Klan days. On the twenty-fifth of March there was a strike at Vickers when two Negroes were upgraded. Other such strikes followed, including one at the Ford River Rouge plant. In the first six months of this year more than three million man-hours were lost in hate strikes of this character. Officers of the union held their breath at every strike, fearing that feeling would boil over, a riot would start, and the union members would get completely out of hand.

On May 27, 1943, came a strike at Packard when twenty thousand white workers walked off their jobs in protest against the upgrading of three Negroes. The situation bordered on the fantastic. In the Packard local union hall a white worker and a Negro, who were both opposed to the strike, sat on the banister listening to a wild harangue from a Southerner. "I don't wanta work nex' to no nigger. They all got syphilis. If one of 'em touches you, you'll sure get it." Having delivered this noble thought, the speaker walked over to the Negro on the banister and said: "Gimme a cigarette, will ya, Joe?"

A feature of these hate strikes was the appearance of anti-Jewish scrawls in plant toilets. Max Chait, an axle builder at River Rouge since

1934, said: "I caught a big Irish shop committeeman typing a filthy poem about Jews in the plant. I took the poem to our local's president. He promised to investigate, but I haven't heard anything since. An Arkansas hillbilly passed round a cartoon strip in the plant called 'History of America.' It showed an Englishman shoving an Indian off a cliff, an American shoving the Englishman off, and finally a Jew, with hooknose and all, shoving the American off."

Shortly after this Mayor Jeffries called together the editors of the three local dailies, the *Free Press,* the *News,* and the *Times,* to take counsel. The consultation over, nothing was done. A procession of Negro leaders and a few white leaders constantly visited City Hall beseeching the mayor to take heed and do something about the impending upheaval. The mayor listened, but appeared to be more confused after these visitations than before. Then all hands relaxed to await the inevitable. It came on the evening of June 20.

VI

Belle Isle Park is on an island in the Detroit River, connected with the city and Grand Boulevard by a bridge. There may have been a hundred thousand people in the park that humid Sunday afternoon, the greater number of them Negroes. It was anything but peaceful; tension had been screwed up to the breaking point. An altercation between a Negro and a white man became a fist fight, and the fighting spread.

By the time the police arrived a party of some two hundred white sailors had pitched in and were attacking the Negroes. By this time it was a riot, and fighting spread across the bridge into a riverside park on the mainland near the Naval Armory. Small fighting units had got going in the city itself when, at about eleven-thirty, a Negro named Leo Tipton was said to have grabbed a microphone in a Negro night club and urged the five hundred customers present to get busy and "take care of a bunch of whites who had killed a colored woman and her baby at Belle Isle Park." This false rumor had a twin that was circulated among white crowds: that Negroes had raped and killed a white woman on the park bridge. By midnight the fight had spread north, east, south, and west, and Paradise Valley was going crazy. By three in the morning store looting was in full swing, and at daybreak both black and white mobs were attacking streetcars crowded with war-plant workers on their way to and from work.

An elaborately detailed time sequence of events is given in *Race Riot,* a report on the riot by the Messrs. Lee and Humphrey of Wayne University.

At four that morning (Monday, June 21) there was a meeting in the office of Police Commissioner Witherspoon to determine action. Mayor Jeffries, Colonel Krech (the United States Army Commander of the Detroit area), Captain Leonard of the Michigan State Police, John Bugas (in charge of the local office of the FBI), and Sheriff Baird were present. Colonel Krech told the mayor that the military police could be on duty in Detroit forty-nine minutes after a request had been cleared from the mayor through the governor to the proper United States Army officials. Nothing was done about this at the time, and by six-thirty Commissioner Witherspoon decided that there was a letup in "serious rioting."

At eight-thirty in the morning (June 21) a Negro delegation called on the mayor and asked him to send for troops. At nine o'clock Commissioner Witherspoon asked the mayor for troops. Jeffries telephoned to the governor, who transmitted the request by telephone to the Sixth Service Command Headquarters at Chicago. By eleven o'clock it was known that troops could not come unless martial law was declared. Governor Kelly hesitated to do this. By this time gangs of white hoodlums were roaming the streets, burning Negro cars.

At noon Mayor Jeffries attended a meeting of the Detroit Citizens' Committee, an interracial body, where President Thomas of the UAW-CIO demanded action to stop bloodshed. More requests were made for martial law, though the move was opposed by a local colored preacher, the Reverend Horace White, who wanted the job done by the police and Negro auxiliaries.

The police proved uncertain. Mr. Humphrey gives this firsthand story:

> There was an automobile burning on Woodward, and up a side street a Negro was being horribly beaten. Eventually the mob let the Negro go, and he staggered down the car tracks and tried to get a streetcar. The car wouldn't stop for him.
>
> The Negro was punch-drunk. There were policemen down the street, but they didn't pay any attention to him.
>
> I started shouting, "Hey, copper," and pointed to the Negro in the middle of the street. The policeman finally took notice of me, but instead of going in the direction in which I was pointing he walked over to his parked scout car. Then two huge hoodlums began to slug the Negro, and he hung there

on the side of the safety zone, taking the punches as if he were a bag of sand. That infuriated me, and I yelled even louder to the cops, all the time gesturing toward the Negro.

Finally the policeman started walking toward the fight, which in the meantime had moved down the street. Then the crowd started pushing me around, but I kept moving and kept my fists up near my chest, and the crowd moved after the much tastier and more permissible Negro game.

At four o'clock that afternoon Major General Aurand arrived from Chicago. By that time high school was out and bands of sixteen-year-old white and colored boys had joined the fighting, while a mile from City Hall a crowd of white and colored students peacefully and noisily watched a ball game that would decide the city high-school championship.

At six-thirty, just as Mayor Jeffries was going on the air with a plea for a return to sanity, four white boys, aged sixteen to twenty, shot down Moses Kiska, a middle-aged Negro, who was waiting for a streetcar, "just for the hell of it" and because "we didn't have anything to do." A few minutes later the governor proclaimed "modified martial law," forbade the sale of liquor (almost twenty-four hours after the riot had started!), shut amusement places, and told the people to stay at home. But still no troops.

At seven-thirty Mayor Jeffries, according to the Detroit *News,* made an inspection trip and watched men stopping streetcars, pulling Negroes off the cars, and beating them up. At eight-thirty the mayor returned to the police commissioner's office and agreed that the situation was out of control. At nine twenty-five the governor formally requested Federal troops, and the 701st Military Police Battalion was sent to Woodward Avenue to disperse the crowd. At 11 P.M., informed that a proclamation from the President would be necessary before he could get Federal troops, Governor Kelly telephoned to President Roosevelt, and at eleven fifty-five the President issued the proclamation. By morning six thousand troops in trucks and jeeps were patrolling the city. It took the United States Army to assure protection to the twenty-nine Negro members of the graduating class as they left Northeastern High School after the closing exercises!

VII

By Thursday Governor Kelly decided to ease the curfew restrictions. Congressman Martin Dies, apparently having come to the conclusion that the riots had been fomented by Japanese-Americans legally released from internment in the West, announced that he was going to Detroit to investigate. He was urged to stay away.

On Monday, June 28, Commissioner Witherspoon made a report to the City Council justifying his conduct and that of the police. "This was not believed to be a proper time," he said, "to attempt to solve a racial conflict and a basic antagonism which had been growing and festering for years. Such a policy could well have precipitated a race riot at a much earlier date and one of much more serious proportions. The fact remains that this department did not precipitate the riot." The proposal of Councilman Edwards that a county grand jury be called to investigate fifteen unsolved riot murders was rejected by both Council and police commissioner in a hurry. No more grand juries, please.

"Don't get the impression that I'm afraid of a grand jury," said the police commissioner, "but it would be an unfair position to put any judge in." The upshot of the Council session was the chloroforming of any grand-jury notions and the appointment of a five-man committee to plan and finance new housing and recreation facilities.

As the city began breathing more freely, officials began casting about to assess what seemed to them proper responsibility for the riot. On the thirtieth of June, Mayor Jeffries stated that he was "rapidly losing . . . patience with those Negro leaders who insisted that their people do not and will not trust policemen and the Police Department. After what happened I am certain that some of these leaders are more vocal in their caustic criticism of the Police Department than they are in educating their own people to their responsibilities as citizens." This showed which way the wind was blowing. Less than a month later, on Monday, July 26, a subcommittee of the mayor's Interracial Committee visited Prosecutor Dowling and asked that he appoint a grand jury to investigate the riot. The prosecutor, apparently unaware that a reporter from the *Free Press* was in the room, not only declared that he was against a grand jury but also took the opportunity to charge the National Association for the Advancement of Colored People and the Michigan *Chronicle,* the local colored weekly, with being responsible for the riot. When his statement was published in the *Free Press* the next day, the effect among the Negro population of Detroit was as if a bomb had been dropped. Instantly tension was heightened again.

When I interviewed Mr. Dowling a few days later he denied that he had accused the NAACP and the Michigan *Chronicle* with being responsible for the riot. "Why, I like Negroes," he said. "I know what it is to be a member of a minority group. I am an Irish Catholic myself."

Then, as if to find a scapegoat to assuage the feelings of the Negroes, the prosecutor continued: "It's a pity the way the Negroes are treated in the Valley. Why, the Jews have them living on top of one another. The Jews own all the food and liquor stores. They own all the pawnshops and get a profit of 42 per cent out of their business in the Valley. The Negroes in the Valley don't have a chance under such a setup."

The report of the governor, issued August 11, took a line not very different from that of the local prosecutor. (Of course the report did not accuse the Jews of robbing the Negroes.) The net result of the various statements was to put the blame on the Negro population and their various organizations; the bungled management of the crisis by the city officials was ignored and, as Mayor Jeffries put it, "We'll know what to do next time." Neither before the riot nor since has there been any real effort to deal directly with the more obvious and glaring reasons for the outbreak.

Perhaps the most remarkable statement came from Attorney General Biddle who, in March, had found no way to act in Detroit. It was a long statement made in the form of a letter to the President on July 15, and contained a number of recommendations. Among other things he suggested "that careful consideration be given to limiting, and in some instances putting an end to, Negro migrations into communities which cannot absorb them, either on account of their physical limitations or cultural background. This needs immediate and careful consideration. . . . It would seem pretty clear that no more Negroes should move to Detroit. Yet I know of no controls being considered or exercised. You might wish to have the recommendations of Mr. McNutt as to what could and should be done."

When this proposal by an attorney general was challenged as being obviously unconstitutional, Mr. Biddle replied that he could not comment on his "strictly confidential" letter to the President—the President who had issued Executive Order 8802 against discrimination. But it is remarkable that in the entire document there is not a word that suggests that joint action between responsible blacks and whites is essential if any real progress is to be made. The last thing in the world that American Negroes will consent to is any compromise in their status as citizens. Meanwhile, what should be done in Detroit?

1. Call a grand jury to investigate the riot. One probable result would be the indictment and conviction of many rioters, black and white, who other-

wise might go free. It would certainly restore some confidence to Detroit citizens, especially the Negroes.

2. Set up a bona-fide working committee of colored and white citizens representing all groups in the community. Let the city government give this committee solid backing in working out and putting into practice a real and not a window-dressing program for dealing with race relations. The mayor's present Interracial Committee is a sham.

3. Let the Auto Workers Union really put on the heat in stopping hate strikes. In every instance strikes to prevent the upgrading of Negroes have been defeated. Why not stop them?

4. Let the Detroit papers quit playing up crimes committed by Negroes, and stop giving the untrue impression that Negroes are more lawless than whites. The papers themselves know what the truth is.

5. Freedom of speech is a constitutional right, and there's small chance that the anti-Negro exhorters will reform. But local papers and radio stations could put in some real effort to tell the people of Detroit some constructive news about the local Negro population.

6. The police should give up their habit of intimidating Negroes as a matter of routine. They have been doing this in Detroit because they regard it as an easy way to keep the Negroes in line. Such tactics build hate.

7. The police should crack down hard on every black or white thug in town. Let it be known that equal justice is being handed out. The tonic effect will be remarkable.

8. Appoint more Negro policemen. Detroit badly needs more policemen anyway. The Negroes will be inclined to step lively with a little more alacrity if it's a colored man that's carrying the club in Paradise Valley. During the riot the Detroit Negro cops (about forty) are said to have been kept in the station houses. At any rate, Commissioner Witherspoon was unable to tell me where they were when the riot was on.

9. There are a number of anti-Negro schoolteachers in the Detroit public schools. Investigation would uncover them; they should be ousted. Let black and white school children get their instruction on the level.

10. The shelter and recreation situation has been described until the people of Detroit know it by heart. Do something.

There are other American cities where the local government is apprehensive and half expects a riot. Most of the suggestions enumerated above would hold good anywhere. Why not get busy?

THE NEGRO COMES OF AGE IN INDUSTRY

Robert C. Weaver

Robert C. Weaver was, until his resignation, chief of the Negro Training and Employment Branch of the War Production Board. His articles have appeared in numerous magazines.

34 DEAD, OVER 500 INJURED IN BLOODY DETROIT RACE RIOT
MOB SLAYS 2, WRECKS BUSINESS SECTION IN NEGRO AREA OF BEAUMONT
TWO FORT BLISS SOLDIERS SLAIN AS FAKE RIOT RUMORS CAUSE OUTBREAK
MILLION MAN-HOURS LOST IN DETROIT RIOTING

THESE HEADLINES startled the nation. They announced violent eruptions in areas of racial tension. In each instance the outbreak followed a familiar pattern of dissemination of false rumors, the occurrence of a provocative incident, and the development of mob psychology and hysteria. Beneath these outward manifestations there are fundamental social and economic maladjustments breeding race hatred. They have existed for generations.

Although the recent wave of interracial violence was unmistakably foretold by a series of smaller conflicts, an attempt has been made to ignore or to minimize the dangers of the situation. Specific outbreaks have been interpreted as isolated "incidents," and peculiar local irritants have been presented as the occasion for them.

Racial conflict has been brewing for the past three years. Huge concentrations of white and colored troops in areas contiguous to small urban and semirural communities have taxed existing housing, transportation, and recreational facilities. Traditional attitudes and methods of local law enforcement have often increased or incited racial discord. In centers of industrial activity there have been and continue to be—especially for Negroes—inadequate housing, woefully deficient recreational facilities, and overcrowded transportation lines.

These community defects, under the strain of wartime living, result in short tempers and fights. Local police, on many occasions, have been most inept in handling potentially explosive situations involving Negroes, and the press has often stressed inflammatory material. But more important than any of these has been the reaction of the community to the changes in the economic status of the Negro which were inevitable at the outbreak of the war—changes which are becoming imperative as we face a serious shortage of manpower.

During the First World War, Negroes were introduced as unskilled workers in many new industries and areas. Problems of housing, transportation, and recreation arose. Racial tensions grew and ultimately found expression in postwar riots essentially similar to those of 1943. Now areas of Negro employment are again expanding. The black worker is entering new industries and, more important, he is going into new and higher types of occupations. He is being introduced in many places as a semiskilled and skilled production worker. Not only has economic necessity required this development, but the Negro himself has constantly pressed for wider job opportunities. These trends and the opposition to them are underlying factors in the current racial tension which faces America.

The arbitrary assumption that Axis agents manufactured the recent riots may appear to relieve the nation of a grave responsibility, but actually it is only a convenient avoidance of the facts. The fundamental cause of these conflicts has not been "zoot suits," the acts of hoodlums of any race, the migration of prejudiced Southern whites, or the rise of native racialists. Although each of these elements played an important part, the primary cause of the outbreaks was the existence of long-neglected issues in interracial relations.

We face the rise of racial disturbances because we have not taken preventive measures to avoid them. An immediate program for relieving the tension would begin by ameliorating situations which cause the Negro to be acutely resentful of a position outside the main stream of American life. It would establish fair employment practices offering the Negro a chance to participate freely and fully in the war-production program; it would permit him to serve in the armed forces on the same terms as white citizens; it would make him feel that he is an important part of the nation and that his contribution is wanted and appreciated by his fellow citizens.

Simultaneously steps should be taken to interpret the cost of racial tension and conflict to the nation, to direct management and labor in methods for successfully introducing new sources of labor, to secure the effective co-operation of national, state, and local officials in carrying out programs for dealing with the basic causes of race conflict, and to direct community pressures upon those who encourage race prejudice and bigotry.

These steps will be effective as emergency wartime measures, but they are only temporary palliatives. A long-run national program for combating racialism in the United States must dig down to the basic causes. One of the most important of these is economic. It stems from the fear of job insecurity and competition. The black worker has become a symbol of a potential threat to the white worker, and the Negro's occupational advancement is consciously or unconsciously feared.

This fear has been bred in the economic realities of America. Its origins lie in the unfavorable position of the "poor white" in the slave era and under the intense competition for employment in the South during Reconstruction. The repeated introduction of the Negro as a strikebreaker, particularly in the industrial North and West, was instrumental in spreading the fear geographically and infecting organized labor with its germ. It has grown out of the American worker's experience with an economy which has seldom had enough jobs to absorb the labor supply. In such an economy its development was an inevitable consequence of a caste system which perpetuated the concept of white men's jobs and black men's jobs; while, at the same time, it was used to secure the support of the white worker for such a system.

Resistance to advances in the economic and occupational status of the Negro persists even in periods of full employment, such as the present, because better jobs for him represent a direct challenge to the accepted color-caste system. To some the changes represent a loss of Negro servants and laborers; by others they are interpreted as a threat to the white man's job in the postwar economy. Also, in recent months, the higher earnings of the Negro have made him an effective competitor for limited available supplies of housing, transportation, food, clothing, and other goods and services.

At the same time the entrance of the Negro into new spheres of activity has brought the "race problem" into the experience of hundreds of thousands of Americans who never before had any real contact with it. These citizens are poorly prepared to meet the situation. Most of them accept the popular misconceptions about race; many of them have been conditioned to look for undesirable racial characteristics; almost all of them have been disturbed about the so-called militancy of the Negro, who has often been described as their potential economic competitor.

II

This summer more than a million Negroes were in war plants. The vast majority entered war work during the latter half of 1942 and the first quarter of 1943. Unemployment among Negroes has reached a new low, and occupational progress has been steady. Signs are already in the air that the black worker may emerge from this war with significant footholds in semiskilled production jobs. The tradition of white men's jobs and black men's jobs is being challenged and actually broken down in a score of tight labor markets outside the South. In the South itself there are unmistakable evidences of economic advances among Negroes, and this fact has been dramatically and unpalatably brought to the attention of the white community by the scarcity of Negro domestics.

Although unemployment among Negroes has been materially reduced, there is far from effective utilization of this source of labor. *Fortune's* survey of five thousand leading business executives in February of this year revealed that fewer than 30 per cent of them employed as much as 10 per cent Negro labor, and over a third did not believe that Negroes could be effectively used in their plants.

Colored workers in war industries are still, for the most part, employed below their maximum or potential skills. Few of them participate in in-plant training and upgrading programs. They are poorly represented in industries where most of the jobs require semiskilled and skilled production workers. Their female labor reserves remain essentially untapped by war industries, and the bulk of Negro workers are still in nonessential employment. Many are concentrated in areas of labor surpluses and are not being trained or recruited for essential war work.

The job ahead is primarily one of effective utilization of labor. It involves securing acceptance of Negro women in industrial employment, transferring Negro men and women from nonessential to war production, moving Negroes from areas of labor surpluses to tight labor markets, and facilitating vastly wider participation of Negroes in in-plant training and upgrading programs. There has been progress in Negro employment, but it has been uneven and spotty. The continuation of this progress, necessary to the war effort, involves a definite break with the situation at the beginning of the war. It will occasion changes which have been interpreted in the past as economic threats to the white worker and inconveniences to the normal economy.

Many sincere and well-meaning people counsel retreat from the current trend toward new and better jobs for Negroes. Such employment, they say, inevitably results in conflict; therefore the Negro should not press for industrial diversification and occupational advancement but accept more employment in traditional jobs. Such action, they think, will reduce racial friction and thereby increase production.

Persons indulging in this type of thinking have neglected two all-important factors: the manpower requirements of war production and the nature of the Negro community.

It is reliably estimated that 75 per cent of war jobs are skilled and semiskilled. One tenth of the population cannot make its maximum contribution to the war effort if it is generally restricted to the remaining unskilled and service jobs. This is particularly true in areas where colored labor forms an appreciable segment of the unused manpower reserves. In many tight labor markets, segments of industry have already recognized this fact.

Accordingly, even in regions where there has been the firmest adherence to occupational caste lines, relaxations are painfully but slowly appearing. In a shipyard in Brunswick, Georgia, for example, skilled Negroes are being recruited. In the area of Hampton Roads, Virginia, as of February, four government establishments and the largest private contractor employed two thousand skilled and seven thousand semiskilled Negroes. Shipyards in Mobile, Alabama, are recruiting Negro welders—and that occupation, from its inception in the industry, has traditionally been a white man's job.

Outside the Deep South, the relaxation of occupational limitations has been more rapid and extensive. In Baltimore, Maryland, a leading shipyard employed some ten thousand Negroes in June. Of these, over two thousand were skilled men in a wide variety of occupations. Two years ago this yard employed only a few colored workers and restricted them to unskilled work. In the aircraft industry, where at the beginning of the defense program there was an announced and pronounced exclusionist policy toward Negroes, over sixty-five thousand colored men and women had found employment by the summer of 1943. Thousands of these were in production jobs.

Large industrial corporations have inaugurated company-wide programs for inducting and upgrading Negroes. A good example of this trend is offered by the Western Electric Company, which used few colored workers prior to Pearl Harbor and restricted them to unskilled and service jobs. From the fall of 1941 to January 1943, Western Electric increased its Negro employees in its New Jersey plants from none to over twelve hundred. A large proportion of these were women, and colored workers were employed in technical, clerical, skilled, and semi-skilled capacities. In the Baltimore plant Negro employment grew from ten unskilled workers in January 1942 to over seven hundred employees in March 1943. During the same period the company's Chicago plant increased its colored labor force from approximately thirty to over seven hundred.

Truly, management is beginning to realize the validity of the conclusion of the American Management Association: "Today's urgent need for manpower effectively removes Negro employment in industry from the realm of social reform." Labor unions outside the railroad industry are also responding to this urgent need for manpower through relaxations of the remaining exclusionist policies of certain organizations. For in some tight labor markets closed-shop agreements often break down when the union is unable to recruit workers through its machinery; work permits, second-class membership, and full acceptance of Negroes are resulting.

In the months to come these trends will continue, probably at an increasing tempo. America's job is to recognize their necessity and to plan to direct them in an orderly manner.

In considering the Negro community, the important factor to remember is that Negroes are the objects of discrimination and segregation. In almost every instance there are certain phases of the colored man's life in which he finds himself, his home, his amusements, or his thinking separated from the main stream of the nation.

The Negro in the United States has developed more rapidly than his opportunities for participation in American life. Although he has been and is conditioned through exposure to education and propaganda to seek the goals of Americans, he is denied these goals and accused of being impatient and unduly militant when he exerts pressures to achieve them. As a matter of fact, in demanding fully recognized citizenship, the Negro is being a typical American, seeking accepted American objectives in characteristic American ways. He is demanding for American citizens more of those freedoms which the nation is dedicated to secure for peoples all over the world.

When, in his quest for more of the rights of American citizenship, the Negro encounters occupational limitations, he is again reminded of his inferior status in America. He realizes that job discrimination is a part of a general picture which emphasizes that he does not belong—that his position is outside the main stream of American living.

At the outset of the defense program Negro leaders viewed with alarm the long-run economic implications of tying the Negro to restricted occupational and industrial patterns. They knew the immediate dangers of having WPA become almost exclusively a group of Negro projects. They were apprehensive of the apathy of Negroes toward the war. Experience had taught them that such results would haunt colored Americans in the future and become justification for extending patterns of discrimination.

They remembered World War I, when Negroes were brought into industrial areas and introduced into industrial employment only to be generally dismissed in the depression of the thirties. They united in pressing for training, employment, and upgrading in all war industries, and today the Negro community is no less dedicated to such a program. The fight for equal job opportunities is not the agitation of a few Negro radicals; it is the will of the Negro people.

III

When the Negro worker leaves his job he returns to a world of which it is difficult for the average white American to conceive. It is so similar to the rest of American life and yet so different. It is a world in which the same radio programs, daily newspapers, schoolbooks, Bible, and motion pictures enter. Yet it is a world in which most of the members are poor. Most of them work long hours. Most of them are held together by one bond—their status as Negroes. This in its fundamental features cuts across cultural levels, class lines, and economic position.

Negro status makes theirs a world apart; a world in which there are definite limitations based on color affecting all who live in it; a world in which the professional man, the white-collar worker, the skilled artisan, the common laborer, and the service worker all know that certain opportunities are closed to them. It is a world in which the fortunate few—a Joe Louis or a Marian Anderson—who get to the top are idols of the group. In this city within a city, where the majority of Negroes live, there are constant reminders that there is a "race problem" and that it affects and limits the inhabitants.

It is this separation and this feeling of being apart, supported by a multitude of individual experiences of being excluded, that have promoted certain characteristics which are often termed racial traits. Negro workers are said to be too aggressive, while in the next breath they are damned for being too submissive. Modern psychology has, of course, a valid explanation for aggressiveness. Usually it is a reaction to frustration. It appears in any group which is underprivileged and disadvantaged. It is not racial; it is human.

It should be unnecessary to reiterate the fact that colored people vary as much as white people. Years ago, when the matter of educating Negroes was a controversial issue, a leading white Southerner, when asked if he believed "in educating *the* Negro," replied, "Which one?" There are Negroes with bad work habits. There are other Negroes with good ones. But *the* Negro is seldom judged by this latter group. Those who constitute it are considered the rare exceptions since they don't fit the stereotyped conception which the press, radio, and moving pictures perpetuate.

The important thing in a war economy, however, is the fact that most of the undesirable traits which are attributed to Negroes—laziness and irresponsibility, tardiness and absenteeism, body odor and the like—are environmental and occupational rather than ethnological. Today, as all groups of workers face problems of inadequate housing and transportation—chronic ills of the Negro—the incidence of tardiness, absenteeism, and lack of interest in jobs transcends racial lines. It is a national problem. Workers of any race who are in heavy, dirty work have body odor. Any man or woman who has no hope of ever rising above common labor will not be so industrious as his fellow employee who can get advancement. Habitual low wages, uncertain income, and general economic insecurity breed irresponsibility. Tardiness and absenteeism, too, are often the result of industrial inexperience, hopelessness of promotion, and certain physical transportation difficulties.

Much has been written about the supposed undesirable work habits of Negroes. We know today that these are not racial characteristics and that they can be modified through fair employment practices. Lack of responsibility and laziness are most effectively counteracted when a worker, regardless of his race or color, is given a job for which he is qualified and has an opportunity for advancement in accordance with his abilities. Men and women who have prepared themselves for skilled or technical work cannot be expected to be vitally interested in a janitor's or maid's job—especially at a time when the radio and the press are full of appeals for trained people to enter war production.

Workers who, because of the color line, cannot rise to production or skilled jobs regardless of their regularity, punctuality, or affability will hardly manifest these characteristics. Groups, such as the Negro, which have systematically been let out of jobs when the peak of labor demand has passed, can make their maximum efforts for war production only if they believe that the contribution which they now make will assure them a chance for equal job opportunities in the postwar economy. In a word, the causes of undesirable work habits must be known and understood, and handled by recognized methods of good personnel administration.

The American Management Association conducted an "off-the-record" panel discussion on the Negro worker at its Production Conference on November 10, 1942. Shortly after that meeting it published a Special Research Report, *The Negro Worker*. Some of the conclusions of this report, reflecting as they do the experience of enlightened personnel officers, are pertinent. They are:

1. Negro workers have great potentialities: they . . . have responded to training for industrial employment.
2. Regardless of race or color, *where accepted, good personnel procedures are employed, workers respond and satisfactory production may be expected.*
3. *There is some evidence of a relationship between the rate of absenteeism among Negroes and the character of the work assigned to them.* The Association did not find any case in which absenteeism among Negroes was so high as to constitute a real handicap to their employment.

IV

There is, of course, another side of the picture. Absenteeism, regardless of its cause, is an enemy to production. Tardiness is a deadly slow-up factor in modern production. And fellow workers do not stop to analyze why a person is overaggressive; they resent him. Excessive fraternizing on the job and lack of cleanliness are objectionable both to management and to serious employees.

When the offender in any of these particulars is an easily identified member of a minority group, his action is usually considered a "racial characteristic," and the other members of the group are judged by him. It is not too much to ask that intelligent management analyze the situation carefully and take steps to deal with it effectively. Some managements—though by far too few—are doing so today. It is, however, impractical to assume that the mass of white workers will delve into the social institutions which have created certain habits in individuals.

A large section of Negro leadership and the Negro press realize these things. They see the immediate dangers incident to the display of undesirable work habits by some Negroes. They know, also, that to stress, even in Negro circles, the existence of these situations and give what some would call "constructive leadership" is to forge another weapon which will be used to justify the status quo in racial employment patterns. For it has long been the habit of those who would defend the exclusion of Negroes from many types of work to cite the failings of some Negroes as the reason for all racial limitations.

To meet this danger the colored weekly papers are devoting an increasing number of editorials and news stories to the matter. Negroes who have significant followings have discussed it in their speeches and writings. As there is marked improvement in the integration of Negroes in war industries, the Negro will within his own ranks turn more attention to this *second* phase of his fight to enter and to stay on the production lines of American industry.

To have stressed this side of the picture when a vast majority of Negroes, regardless of training and work habits, were being turned away from the gates of defense plants would have been most unfortunate. It would have fallen upon deaf ears and have been interpreted by the Negro people as an appeasement policy. Such an eventuality would have made subsequent appeals for self-improvement suspect. Today, however, it is possible and desirable to press government, management, and labor for more work opportunities for Negroes and at the same time to warn colored workers that they have a grave responsibility to prove their worth.

This is a project which demands the joint action of management and the Negro community. If Negroes are convinced that management is sincere in its efforts to establish fair employment policies and equal opportunities for advancement, there are many persons of influence who will join with management in improving the performance of colored workers. If the Negro community is sure that in this war, in contrast to World War I, the colored worker will not be relegated principally to the hot, the dirty, and the least secure jobs, and that this time he will have equal job security in peacetime employment, it will have a real incentive to plug for maximum efficiency from its members.

The interests of the Negro community and those of enlightened management are identical. Both want to make of the colored worker a successful and efficient producer. Working together, they can do much to accomplish this end. Neither can succeed in this objective unless it has the confidence and support of the other.

The influence of group pressure upon efficiency is shown by a recent occurrence in Indianapolis. Although there is much machine work in that area, Negroes have participated little in it. One of the first companies to engage colored machine operators made a careful selection of a crew of ten Negroes for this training. Upon the completion of their course these men were assigned to machines. One of the group was unsatisfactory. His production was below the standard and showed little improvement as time went on.

The other nine operators called the matter to the attention of the management and requested that the inefficient worker be assigned to other duties. The management hesitated to take this action, but the crew was adamant. At the third conference on the matter they stated their case simply and forcefully. The crew, they said, was on trial. They were being watched by the company and their fellow workers. The one slow and inefficient colored worker endangered their record and tended to destroy the respect of other workers which they hoped to build up. They insisted that management act—and they won their point.

The co-operation of the Negro community is necessary if we are to achieve full utilization of all labor. Such co-operation, however, cannot be effective unless it is met with understanding and is welcome. Negroes, by themselves, cannot secure full use of their labor resources; desirable work and behavior habits will not evolve or grow in a community which is continually discriminated against. Nor will such habits alone prevent racial tensions.

The immediate wartime necessity is to learn, community by community and as a nation, how to take rapid strides towards achieving equal economic opportunity for the Negro and, at the same time, to avoid the racial conflicts we have recently seen. Our whole tradition as a nation has been one of doing new things when we realized the necessity for taking the step. Making effective adjustments incident to the expansion of Negro employment in war production is but a part of a successful program for meeting the over-all manpower problem. Both will require conviction and resolution.

One of the primary needs to meet the immediate necessities of wartime production and secure the full co-operation of the Negro community is to present the problem to the people of the nation in its true light. The upgrading of Negroes and the industrial employment of Negro women are not social experiments. They are wartime economic necessities. Every delay in the production of the vital instruments needed to carry on this war means unnecessary loss of American lives. It is not white men's work we have to do—it is war work, and there is more than enough of it. These truths must be told and retold until they become a part of the average citizen's thinking.

But what of the Negro worker after the war? Two principal factors will determine his economic status: the degree to which he is integrated into a wide variety of occupations, industries, firms, and labor unions at the close of hostilities and the type of postwar economy we are to have. A depressed economy has always meant but one thing for the Negro worker—widespread unemployment. If, however, he has a significant degree of occupational status, his chances are good for retaining a higher proportion of the more desirable jobs and suffering a lower intensity of job displacement than in the past. If we have an economy of full employment, it will establish a framework favorable to the continuing occupational advancement of the black worker and to the removal of the white worker's fear of him as an economic rival.

Full employment in the postwar period will not remove racial tensions. It will set the economic stage for effective programs designed to reduce the frequency and intensity of *one* of the basic causes for race conflict. In such an economy trade-unions can, as some of them have so well done in the past few years, take the lead in establishing co-operation between white and black workers. Other agencies, both governmental and private, will find conditions more favorable for developing racial understanding and national unity.

And there will be important secondary results. Such an economy should provide better housing for all the people, better educational and recreational facilities, and more adequate transportation. Thus it would ease situations which are often serious irritants in areas of interracial contacts. Most important, however, is the fact that economic success will offer practical experience in relaxing the caste system which limits the Negro in America.

WHAT SHALL WE DO ABOUT THE SOUTH?

Langston Hughes

Langston Hughes is a short-story writer, novelist, poet, and playwright. His best-known books are The Ways of White Folks, Without Laughter, *and several collections of poetry, the latest,* Shakespeare in Harlem.

For a New Yorker of color, the South begins at Newark. A half hour by tube from the Hudson Terminal and one comes across street-corner hamburger stands that will not serve a hamburger to a Negro customer wishing to sit on a stool. For the same dime a white pays, a Negro must take his hamburger elsewhere in a paper bag and eat it, minus a plate, a napkin, and a glass of water. Jim Crow always means less for the one Jim Crowed and an unequal value for his money—no stool, no shelter, merely the hamburger, in Newark.

As the colored traveler goes further south by train, Jim Crow increases. Philadelphia is ninety minutes from Manhattan. There the all-colored grammar school begins, the separate education of the races that Talmadge of Georgia so highly approves. An hour or so further down the line is Baltimore, where segregation laws are written in the state and city codes. Another hour by train, Washington. There the conductor tells the Negro traveler to go into the Jim Crow coach behind the engine, usually half a baggage car, next to trunks and dogs.

That this change to complete Jim Crow happens at Washington is highly significant of the state of American democracy in relation to colored peoples today. Washington, as the capital of this nation, is one of the great centers of the Allied war effort toward the achievement of the Four Freedoms. Yet to a South-bound Negro citizen told at Washington to change into a segregated coach, the Four Freedoms have a hollow sound, like distant lies not meant to be the truth in the land of the Jim Crow car.

The train crosses the Potomac into Virginia, and from there on throughout the South life for the Negro, by state law and custom, is a hamburger in a sack without a plate, water, napkin, or stool—but at the same price as the whites pay—to be eaten apart from the others without shelter. The Negro can do little about this because the law is against him, he has no vote, the police are brutal, and the citizens think it is as it should be. For his seat in the half coach of the crowded Jim Crow car, a colored man must pay the same fare as those who ride in the air-cooled coaches further back and are privileged to use the diner when they wish. For his hamburger in a sack, served without courtesy, the Southern Negro must pay taxes but refrain from going to the polls, must patriotically accept conscription to work, fight, and perhaps die to regain or maintain freedom for people off in Europe or Australia when he hasn't it himself at home. To his ears most of the war speeches about freedom sound perfectly foolish, unreal, high-flown, and false. To many Southern whites, too, it must all seem like play-acting—the grand talk so nobly delivered, so poorly executed.

Liberals and persons of good will, North and South, including, no doubt, our President himself, are puzzled as to what on earth to do about the South—the poll-tax South, the Jim Crow South—that so effectively and openly gives the lie to democracy. With the brazen frankness of Hitler's *Mein Kampf,* Dixie speaks through Talmadge, Rankin, Dixon, Arnall, and Mark Ethridge.

In a public speech in Birmingham, Mr. Ethridge said, "All the armies of the world, both of the United States and the Axis, could not force upon the South an abandonment of racial segregation." Governor Dixon of Alabama refused a government war contract offered Alabama State Prison because it contained an antidiscrimination clause which in his eyes was an "attempt to abolish segregation of races in the South. . . . We will not place ourselves in a position to be attacked by those who seek to foster their own pet social reforms," said he. In other words, Alabama will not reform. It is as bullheaded as England in India, and its governor is not ashamed to say so.

As a proof of Southern intolerance, almost daily the press reports some new occurrence of physical brutality against Negroes. Governor Talmadge was "too busy" to investigate when Roland Hayes and his wife were thrown into jail and the great tenor beaten on complaint of a shoe salesman over a dispute as to what seat in his shop a Negro should occupy when buying shoes. Nor did the governor of Mississippi bother when Hugh Gloster, professor of English at Morehouse College, riding as an interstate passenger, was illegally ejected from a train in his state, beaten, arrested, and fined because, being in an overcrowded Jim Crow coach, he asked for a seat in an adjacent car which contained only two white passengers. Legally, the Jim Crow laws do not apply to interstate travelers, but the FBI has not yet got around to enforcing that Supreme Court ruling. Recently, en route from San Francisco to Oklahoma City, Fred Wright, a county probation officer of color, was beaten and forced into the Texas Jim Crow coach on a transcontinental train by order of the conductor, in defiance of Federal law. A seventy-six-year-old clergyman, Dr. Jackson of Hartford, Connecticut, going into the South for the National Baptist Convention in September, was set upon by white passengers for merely passing through a white coach on the way to his own seat. There have been similar attacks upon colored soldiers in uniform on public carriers. One such attack resulted in death for the soldier, dragged from a bus and killed by civilian police. Every day now Negro soldiers from the North, returning home on furlough from Southern camps, report incident after incident of humiliating travel treatment below the Mason-Dixon Line.

It seems obvious that the South does not yet know what this war is about.

As answer Number One to the question "What Shall We Do About the South?" I would suggest an immediate and intensive federally directed program of pro-democratic education, to be put into all schools of the South from the first grade to the universities. As a part of the war effort, this is urgently needed. The Spanish Loyalist Government had trench schools for its soldiers and night schools for civilians even in Madrid under siege. We are not yet under siege. We still have time (but not too much) to teach our people what we are fighting for, and to begin to apply these teachings to race relations at home. You see, it would be too bad for an emissary of color from one of the Latin-American countries, say Cuba or Brazil, to arrive at Miami Airport and board a train for Washington, only to get beaten up and thrown off by white Southerners who do not yet realize how many colored allies we have—nor how badly we need them—and that it is inconsiderate and impolite to beat colored people anyway. Education as to the real meaning of this war might help the South a little in this respect.

Because transportation is so symbolic of the whole racial problem in the South, the Number Two thing for us to do is evolve a way out of the Jim Crow car dilemma at once. Would a system of first-, second-, and third-class coaches help? In Europe, formerly, if one did not wish to ride with peasants and tradespeople, one could pay a little more and solve that problem by having a first-class coach almost entirely to himself. Most Negroes can hardly afford parlor-car seats. Why not abolish Jim Crow entirely and let the whites who wish to do so ride in coaches where few Negroes have the funds to be? In any case, our Chinese, Latin-American, and Russian allies are not going to think any too much of our democratic pronunciamentos as long as we keep compulsory Jim Crow cars on Southern rails.

Since most people learn a little through education, albeit slowly, as Number Three I would suggest that the government draft all the leading Negro intellectuals, sociologists, writers, and concert singers, from Alain Locke of Oxford and W. E. B. DuBois of Harvard to Dorothy Maynor and Paul Robeson of Carnegie Hall, and send them into the South to appear before white audiences, carrying messages of culture and democracy, thus offsetting the old stereotypes of the Southern mind and the Hollywood movie, and explaining to the people, without dialect, what the war aims are about. With each, send on tour a liberal white Southerner like Paul Green, Erskine Caldwell, Pearl Buck, or William Seabrook. And, of course, include soldiers to protect them.

Number Four, as to the Army—draftees are in sore need of education on how to behave toward darker peoples. Just as a set of government suggestions has lately been issued to our soldiers on how to act in England, so a similar set should be given them on how to act in Alabama, Georgia, Texas, India, China, Africa, Brazil—wherever there are colored peoples. Not only printed words, but intensive training in the reasons for being decent to everybody. Classes in democracy and the war aims should be set up in every training camp in America and every unit of our military forces already abroad. These forces should be armed with understanding as well as armament.

I go on the premise that Southerns are reasonable people, but that they just simply do not know nowadays what they are doing, nor how bad their racial attitudes look to the rest of the civilized world. I know their politicians, their schools, and the Hollywood movies have done their best to uphold prevailing reactionary viewpoints. Heretofore nobody in America, really, except a few radicals, liberals, and a handful of true religionists, has cared much about either the Negroes or the South. Their sincere efforts to effect a change have been but a drop in a muddy bucket.

Basically, of course, the South needs universal suffrage, economic stabilization, a balanced diet, vitamins for children. But until those things are achieved, a few mild but helpful steps might be taken on a lesser front, to ameliorate—not solve—the Negro problem.

It might be pointed out to the South, for instance, that the old bugaboo of sex and social equality doesn't mean a thing. Nobody as a rule sleeps with or eats with or dances with or marries anybody else except by mutual consent. Millions of people in New York, Chicago, and Seattle go to the same polls and vote without ever cohabiting together. Why does the South think it would be otherwise with Negroes were they permitted to vote there? Or have a decent education? Or sit on a stool in a public place and eat a hamburger? Why they think simple civil rights would force a Southerner's daughter to marry a Negro in spite of herself, I have never been able to understand. It must be due to some lack somewhere in their schooling.

A federally sponsored educational program of racial decency could, furthermore, point out to its students that co-operation in labor would be to the advantage of all—rather than to the disadvantage of anyone, white or black. It could show quite clearly that a million unused colored hands barred from war industries might mean a million weapons lacking in the hands of our soldiers on some foreign front—and a million extra deaths—including Southern white boys needlessly dying under Axis fire—because Governor Dixon of Alabama and others of like mentality need a little education. It might also be pointed out that when peace comes and the Southerners go to the peace table, if they take there with them the traditional Dixie racial attitudes, there is no possible way for them to aid in forming any peace at all that will last. China, India, Brazil, and Free French Africa, Soviet Asia, and the whole Middle East will not believe a word they say.

Peace only to breed other wars is a sorry peace, one we must plan now to avoid. Not only in order to win the war but to create a peace along decent lines, we had best start now to educate the South. That education cannot be left to well-meaning but numerically weak civilian organizations. Government itself should take over—and vigorously. After all, Washington is the place where the conductor comes through every South-bound train and says, "Colored people, change to the Jim Crow car ahead."

That car, in these days and times, has no business being "ahead." War's freedom train can hardly trail along with glory behind a Jim Crow coach. No matter how streamlined the other cars may be, that coach endangers all humanity's hopes for a peaceful tomorrow.

THE SOUTH NEEDS HELP

Thomas Sancton

Thomas Sancton came to New York from New Orleans via a Nieman Fellowship at Harvard. His short stories and articles have appeared in many magazines. Until his recent return to the South to work on a novel he was the managing editor of the New Republic.

ANY SOUTHERNER who has read the true history of his section—the whole story and not alone the heart-lifting tales of battles and generals—knows that it is the long shadow of slavery which hangs upon his land today and confuses and maddens his people, which withers the spiritual values of their lives and institutions, and every day, in every hamlet, town, and city, visits a tragic penalty upon the sons of the generations who first thought that they could build a green and fruitful society on the stolen labor of black slaves. Stealing these people from their own continent was a violation of a profound natural law, and we are paying for it. Not all the high-flown moral tracts of ante-bellum ministers and college presidents of the South could explain away the truth, that white men went blackbirding to another continent and stole a race of people; or justify one cotton dollar earned by the churchgoing planters who turned these people into their fields by the threat of the lash and violence, and said work for us, because God made you beasts. And not all the flaming words of abolitionists could burn away the guilt of New England slave trading or the Yankee's hypocrisy that *he* had not sinned against the Negro.

And so here we are today. Can this be last century's tragedy still upon the boards? Can this poll-tax oratory in Washington, and these black boys swinging from the bridge at Meridian, and mass meetings in the

North, and defiance in the South, and that solitary, symbolic Negro there walking down the country road—can these be the actors and these be the situations that had begun to grip the nation by 1842? Yes, here they are, incredible though it seems. Here is Mr. Rankin speaking the lines which men who have been dust for a century once spoke in Congress. Here is the new abolitionism in the North, in character, indignant and angry at the South and never realizing that Jim Crow lives in the Yankee's heart as it always did, and that a Harlem tenement is a hundred delta cabins, plus tuberculosis. And here is the Eastern businessman, outgrowth of the tariff system, who wants a poverty-stricken section to educate its masses and who lobbies to death any program that will cost a dollar or, like adjustment of freight rates, enable the South to earn one. Yes, and here is that lonesome Negro on a Southern road, the same dark symbol, disfranchised, working in another man's fields, as he did in another century, walking on down to the furnish merchant's for half a sack of potatoes. Seventy-five years ago if someone could have told a Yankee soldier—or a Confederate—that he had fought for four bloody years to settle an issue which would still be alive to plague his great-grandchildren, he could not possibly have believed it.

But the issue is alive today, and it will be alive forever unless the problem of race relations becomes once more a matter of major national interest and we learn finally how to face it. It will stay with us, and we will find the tragedy in the North scarcely less than in the South. Relatively few white people as yet realize that this is a smoldering and explosive problem which needs a frontal approach and an intelligent and courageous national effort to solve it: mere pamphlets printed by sociological or government agencies which ask for better treatment for the Negro are utterly inadequate. It seems to me that most white Northerners have a vague impression that when the Civil War was fought and the Emancipation Proclamation signed, the race question was officially over so far as the North was concerned. When they think at all on the subject, their thoughts generally revolve about lynchings and Jim Crow in the South. Few seem aware that the Negro is thoroughly Jim Crowed all over the North—considering Jim Crow in its deepest aspects and not just the fact of the Negro's being able to sit where he chooses in a subway train. Any Northerner who is inclined to think of the "race problem" as exclusively Southern, the sure solution for which is repeal of the poll tax, might do well to get in touch with some Negroes themselves and listen for a while. He will find that the Negro faces some of his worst conditions in ghettos like Harlem, where, for example, one finds the most overcrowded city block in the country, one square containing more than four thousand inhabitants, packed into rows of shabby, high-rent tenements.

And yet it is true that the main body of the race problem lies within the boundaries of the Southern states, because some three fourths of America's thirteen million Negroes live there. And it is also true that the problem is far more serious in the South, not only in the matter of quantity, but in degree. The Negro is oppressed in many ways in the North, and certainly economically, but the long antislavery tradition has at least given him some basic civil and social rights which the white South continues to deny him and would like to deny him forever.

The white South has been paying an increasingly heavy cost for this denial, both materially and in the spiritual values that make for a healthy and developing society. For if you isolate a third of your population, hammer and din into their heads that they are "niggers," ignorant, irresponsible, and barbaric; if you deny them any opportunity to better themselves and to escape from this shabby destiny, they can only reward you by filling the role into which you force them. When the white South holds a third of its population in the "nigger" role, it places inexorable limits on its own total progress, for the standards of any great mass of an area's population influence the standards of the rest. If the Negro must do a day's work in a cotton field for seventy-five cents because he is black, a white worker won't get better pay because he is white.

There is then a heavy cost that Southern white society pays for demanding that "the nigger keep his place." As a result, the Negro has a tremendous incidence of diseases like tuberculosis and syphilis; and bacilli can't read the white man's Jim Crow signs. Moreover, the Negro's dreary, hopeless surroundings have a blighting influence on his personality, just as they would have upon the white man's if destiny had reversed the roles. The product of these combined circumstances is the Negro as the Southern white man sees him: poorly dressed, ignorant, aimless, superstitious, eager to flee the dreary routine of doing the white man's dirty work for a Saturday-night fling at high life and perhaps drunken oblivion. The Southern system of race relations produces the "nigger," and then the white man points to the product to justify the system. His mind is closed on the subject. It cannot understand that the white man himself could not beat such a system.

Spiritually, also, the cost is great. For no matter how firmly or how bitterly the Southern white believes in the philosophic justification for the

Negro's continued debasement, he cannot escape the sense that something, somehow, is wrong with the picture. "To keep the Negro in the gutter, you've got to jump down there with him," a white Southern legislator once told me, paraphrasing the words of a great Negro leader. But he saw no way out of it, because a Negro is a Negro and therefore his place is the gutter. That philosophy was good enough for the legislator's father and it was good enough for his grandfather, and even though he could see that something was wrong about the whole concept, it was good enough for him.

The fact that it is the South's unshakable custom to accept what its fathers regarded as holy is close to the heart of its deep social tragedy now. For if, suddenly, on a given day, the whole young college generation of the South would throw off the spell of their fathers' thinking and set about to read through a small list of first-rate historical and sociological studies of their own background, I have no doubt that a century's progress in race relations could be telescoped to ten years. (And if any young Southerner should read this and want to take me seriously, the books I should advise him to begin with are *The South Looks at Its Past* by Kendrick and Arnett, *Human Geography of the South* by Vance, *Southern Regionalism* by Odum, *The Mind of the South* by Cash, *Liberalism in the South* and *Below the Potomac* by Dabney, and *Culture in the South,* edited by Couch.)

With sensitive individuals this feeling that something is wrong may trouble the conscience, and many are given to idealizing the traditional humanity of the master-and-servant relationships. Negroes are children, they say. With coarser people, the sense that something is wrong is sublimated in a sort of cruel, Nazi bravado about "the lowest white man being better than the best nigger." This was something which, as a reporter in New Orleans, I used to see in many brutal cops. It is the wellspring of the lynch spirit. It is the spirit which results in the beating of Roland Hayes because his wife, suddenly disgusted, spoke her mind to a shoe clerk about Jim Crow restrictions in a democracy at war. I have often wondered how clergymen and the sincerely religious people of the South reconcile in their own minds the sermons on brotherly love and other noble teachings of the New Testament with the flagrant debasement of the Negro. I have never heard one sermon in my life on the race issue.

Now suddenly the white man finds that the symbolic Negro in the old cast of characters is, well, the same, and yet different. In the South at least he still speaks the same servile lines: yes, boss, sure, boss, dass right, white man; but a new tone has come into his voice, a grim sneer, and he is beginning to ad-lib such lines as "I want democracy and I want it now." To meet this development, the white man has been shifting his own character accordingly, and once more, instead of the old massuh, he is becoming the brutal overseer. He has picked up the lynch rope again, and he has used it three times in a week in Mississippi. The real tragedy is that, unless the Federal government really *does* something, the white man's part will become more and more brutalized.

In the face of this showdown, the small group of newspapermen and editors who have generally been considered spokesmen for the liberal element in the South have hit the trail to compromise and caution. They speak of real danger for the Negroes. They warn the Negroes and their leaders that this is no time to raise hell for democracy at home because we have first got to win the war for democracy abroad. It is Toryism, exactly as we have seen it in India. It always sounds sensible, and it never accomplishes anything.

Any white man who has come out of the South knows that the Dabneys and Ethridges are speaking the truth when they say it will take a period of intensive education, the book kind and the political kind, to prepare the deeply prejudiced white masses of the South for economic co-operation with Negroes. But here is where a real liberal and a Tory must part company. For these solutions are so fundamental, and the speed at which they are approached so glacial, that the real white friend of the Negro cannot ask him to refrain from his indignant and bitter agitation for democracy now, to sit by waiting meekly through long decades for his position to improve: to ask him to forego his own agitation and his own leadership toward these ends and heed only the temporizing warnings of his "white friends." The real liberal knows that the Negro is never going to win any right he doesn't win for himself, by his own organization, courage, and articulation.

It is the Southern white man who must realize that the Tory spirit, wherever it is found, is the spirit of death and defeat in this war, which must be fought as a people's war or be lost. In the South the white man has got to realize that the race issue has profound new internal forces at work; that these are going to demand major adjustments, in white attitudes toward the Negro and in white economic treatment of the Negro. This is something that has been coming, although the white South has hardly realized it until now with the outbreak of the war.

For Southern Negroes, as a group, in spite of the dearth of educational advantages, have matured with the slowly passing decades. They are not the simple, docile, ignorant people they were fifty years ago. For one thing, since emancipation, their illiteracy figure has dropped from 95 per cent to 10. Southern Negroes are reading and writing and swapping their own ideas today about the order of things. For some time they have been growing aware and resentful of the anomaly of their position in a nation which is vociferously proud of its Constitution and its dedication to the rights of man.

The war has sharply accelerated this development. The fact that we are fighting as a democracy against totalitarian aggression has shed harsh, revealing light on our treatment of the Negro at home. The Southerner who insists that it is only the Northern Negro press which is excited and indignant about the Negro's anomalous position is kidding himself. For even in the rural back country Negroes have sensed the general meaning of this situation. In the field of economics the Negro has partaken to some extent in the wartime industrial boom. There are tremendous new plants and consequently new labor markets in many parts of the South where they never existed before. This has placed a higher value on the Negro's labor, awakened his dormant self-respect and independence, encouraged him to speak out more openly for his rights; and finally—and this is the development which the white South has noticed above all others—the war has inclined the Negro to turn openly sullen and bitter against white employers and old Jim Crow restrictions to which, not so long ago, he seemed both accustomed and resigned.

The white man can go on forever fighting the old war to hold the Negro to his "place" of servility, or he can try to act like an inhabitant of the twentieth century and try to accustom himself to living beside, rather than on top of, another race.

But the South by itself is not going to solve the problem. It needs the help of the nation. The Federal government has got to approach the issue directly and sincerely, and as a war emergency. The first step should be to tell the FBI investigating the Mississippi lynchings that this time evidence and indictments, not a whitewash, are needed. For few things in recent months have embittered Negroes as deeply as the perfunctory investigation conducted after the brutal Sikeston, Missouri, lynching. Then Northern and Western congressmen have got to stop using the Negro issue for swaps and trades with Southern members, and get through a strong antilynching bill and abolition of the poll tax. In addition, there should be evolved a broad program of legislative relief for the Negro that will accomplish material benefits and relieve his rightful bitterness as well. This should include the Federal purchase of land for resale on long-term contracts to tenants and croppers, white and black, in order to raise these people to the class of self-respecting yeoman farmers who will not be afraid to respect one another.

But legislation alone cannot bring the solution, no more than it did in the Reconstruction. The Federal government must also undertake, as Langston Hughes suggests earlier in these pages, a broad program of federally financed education.

Illiterate the South is—and poor. Through all its old history of the tariff laws and the belabored freight-rate differentials, and by all the faults of its agricultural methods, the South has become for America, and particularly for the industrial and capitalistic East, a land very much like India—a backward land with little capital of its own and no particular commercial talent, but with great riches of minerals, agriculture, and labor only waiting to be garnered by the utilities or oil or chain-store corporations controlled by Northern capital. It is one thing to deplore the blind ignorance of the Southern cracker who keeps the Negro in a state of submissiveness by violence and the threat of violence, and who despises any suggestion of co-operation between the white and Negro races or any effort to help the Negro improve his own position. It is another to realize that the cracker himself is the native of a poor South which spends about one fourth as much in actual dollars for education per capita as do the wealthier regions, although even this little represents a greater proportion of his tax revenues; and that the money which is available for education must be spent on duplicating school systems for white and black (with the Negro getting the short end of it). The birth rate and the percentage of children in the country's population is highest in the South, and this in spite of the fact that in the last thirty years 3,500,000 more people have left it for the factories of Detroit and other areas than have entered it. The South, with pitiful resources, is thus educating a large proportion of the future residents of other sections. The situation is not fair to the South, not fair to the other states, not fair to the individuals concerned.

Education, even a system aided by heavy Federal grants, cannot give the Negro overnight the unqualified democracy that his militant and articulate leaders are asking. But it is the thing which above all else can begin to dissolve the dull, flinty ignorance which is the mainstay of prejudice and bad race relations. Unless we unite on some such far-reaching and frontal assault on the problem, the new internal forces at work in it may explode in our faces. And unless we attack it now, courageously and intelligently, we give the lie to our professions of fighting a "people's war."

OUR CONFLICTING RACIAL POLICIES

Will W. Alexander

Will W. Alexander, vice-president of the Julius Rosenwald Fund, is well known for his work in the field of race relations.

WHILE THERE IS NOWHERE any official statement of the policy of this country as to its Negro citizens, an examination of our actual dealing with Negroes indicates that over the years unofficial policies have been developed. In fact, there have been two well-defined policies in race relations and only two.

The first of these is the policy that Negroes shall be educated. Negro education had its beginnings in the activities of Northern churches when, immediately following the Civil War, they established schools for Negroes in the South. These schools have had a profound influence. Their establishment was followed by the inauguration of separate state-supported schools for Negroes in the South, and by the opening to Negroes of schools in the rest of the country. So firmly has the idea of educating Negroes taken hold that today the annual expenditure in the Southern states for the higher education of Negroes exceeds the total income of all private schools for Negroes. The increase in educational opportunity has caused the Negro illiteracy rate to drop from 95 per cent at Emancipation to less than 10 per cent today. And the Southern states are showing a tendency to move toward equalization of educational funds for Negro and white schools.

Everywhere the idea of education for Negroes is accepted as part of our American way. Howard, Fisk, and Atlanta universities have come to take their place as institutions of higher learning which are making an important contribution not only to Negro life but to national life.

In the great graduate schools of the North, wherever knowledge is pursued, increasingly Negro scholars are doing creditable work. In many cases these men and women are doing superior work in fields that have nothing to do with Negroes as such; they are contributing to the enrichment of American culture. The superior quality of the educated American Negroes always impresses foreigners as a striking aspect of American life.

Foreigners are also puzzled by America's second policy regarding her Negro population: segregation. Segregation is not only Southern, but national—it varies not so much in degree as in method in different sections of the country. In the South segregation in schools, transportation, entertainment, and community services is maintained by law and by custom. In the North segregation is maintained by social pressure and by such quasi-legal arrangements as restrictive covenants. In connection with many public services, such as hotels and restaurants, segregation is as rigid in the North as in the South. Thus segregation is accepted in all sections of the country to about the same degree that education is provided and accepted.

Much of the uncertainty and tension in connection with our American race relations grows out of the conflict in these policies. Education is the most hopeful aspect of American race relations. Segregation is one of the most puzzling aspects of American life and one of the most difficult questions in American race relations. It is generally recognized by Negroes as their number-one problem and is insisted upon by many whites as the one thing in the American race scene that can never be modified or dispensed with. Here we have the greatest conflict between our professed democratic doctrines and our actual practice in day-by-day living. Segregation tends to defeat the inspiring work of Negro education. Unless the problem of segregation can be solved, there is no hope of any alleviation of the race problem in America.

II

The fact that segregation exists is bad enough. To make matters worse, the patterns of segregation are so inconsistent as to be completely bewildering to Negroes. Often they cannot tell just what *is* expected of them. For example, in one railroad station in the South, Negro and white passengers have to board the railroad trains through separate gates; but leaving the trains in this station, they use the same gate.

In some Southern communities Negroes are supposed to sit in the front of the streetcar or bus in order to maintain racial separation; in others, they must be seated in the rear of the car.

In some office buildings in the South, Negroes have access to the general elevator service. In other buildings a special elevator is provided which carries both white and colored passengers. Occasionally special elevators marked "Negroes and Freight" are provided.

In the past the use of Pullmans by Negroes has been usually confined to "Lower 13"—which means that an influential Negro traveler could occupy the drawing room for the price of a lower. Now, in some cities, Negroes can secure Pullman reservations.

Both North and South, Negroes are usually denied service by hotels and restaurants that serve the general public. Occasionally, however, if sponsored by some white person with sufficient influence, they are admitted as a special privilege to limited service. This lack of consistency and uniformity occurs all the way through the pattern of American Negro segregation and is very confusing and irritating to Negroes and to white persons who are with them.

Much more important than these vagaries is the fact that segregation has meant inferior service to Negroes. The constitutions of most Southern states require that there shall be equal, but separate, schools for Negroes. But an examination of the expenditures for Negro and white education in those same states, and the cities within the states, indicates that segregation in education has meant not equal but inferior service to Negroes. Studies of nine Southern states in 1940 showed average annual expenditures of $58.69 per white student and only $18.82 per Negro. In Mississippi the discrepancy was much greater—$52.01 compared to $7.36.

In cities North and South, housing is far poorer for Negroes than for whites. Colored people are largely forced to live in slum areas which have been abandoned by other groups. And Negroes who are financially able to secure better accommodations find it almost impossible to do so outside the segregated areas. Residential segregation has forced Negroes to pay higher rents and higher purchase prices for inferior accommodations in every city where they seek housing. Residential segregation, as well as administrative arrangement, has led to a definite tendency in Northern cities toward segregated Negro schools. Since Negroes are usually required to live in the overcrowded sections of these cities, separate schools for Negroes in Northern cities are usually housed in run-down buildings and are similarly overcrowded. In Chicago sixteen public schools have double shifts—all of them Negro schools.

Where segregation has been enforced in transportation, Negro travelers have had less space per traveler, older and less sanitary cars, less safety, and less courtesy and consideration from the servants of the railroads—not only the ticket sellers but the brakemen and flagmen, who usually occupy much of the space set aside for Negro travelers.

In many ways the most subtle and most damaging form of segregation results from the fact that while educating Negroes for participation in American life, we have denied them free participation in the economic life of the country. Consciously and unconsciously we have developed, both North and South, so-called Negro jobs which tend to freeze Negro employment in the lower-income brackets and to exclude Negroes from an opportunity to acquire skills in other than the poorer jobs. This has tended to lead to segregation within the labor movement; this, until the coming of the CIO with its new patterns of organization, was a means of excluding Negroes permanently from large areas of employment in organized industries. It left Negroes little choice but to become strikebreakers, divided the ranks of labor, and weakened the labor movement in America perceptibly. Even when labor unions were friendly, qualified Negroes were often turned away by employers.

There are some white people who assume that we can have two economic systems—one for Negroes and another for whites. A very charming lady, in a discussion of the problems of Negro employment, said, "Why don't Negroes employ each other?" When it was called to her attention that there were great difficulties as to capital and organization, she said, "Why, Marian Anderson makes lots of money. She could use that to set up business concerns to meet the economic needs of Negroes." This is quoted because it is typical of much of the thinking on this question.

In an effort to solve their economic problems, Negroes have established some business concerns that employ Negroes and serve the Negro community. The Negro insurance companies are the most successful of these enterprises, and the best of them have made large contributions to sustaining the economic life of the American Negroes. But to adopt economic segregation as a means of solving the economic problems of Negroes bears on its very face the stamp of futility. There can be no adequate provision for the economic life of these thirteen million Americans except as they share in the general economic life of the country.

III

The segregation of Negroes in jobs, their exclusion from free access to the ways in which other citizens earn their living, has meant permanent poverty, degradation, and defeat—not only for the majority of Negroes, but for other large sections of the American people. One of the causes for the general poverty of the South is the failure to develop the economic potentialities of Southern Negroes. By allowing the Negro to remain at a low economic level, the South has kept itself on the bottom rung of the economic ladder. Slavery was responsible for the plight of the poor white in the South, and the low wages and generally low standards of living for Negroes since Emancipation have added greatly to the difficulty of improving the status of the Southern white worker. He is perhaps the poorest and least-skilled white man in the world. He will remain so until better economic advantages are available both for him and his Negro neighbor. Poverty cannot be segregated—North or South. Economic realists in the South admit privately that if the South is to succeed, something must be done about the economic status of Negroes. An effort to deal realistically with the question of Southern poverty will reveal that segregation is wasteful, expensive, and economically unsound.

Segregation has impeded the nation in the use of its manpower in the war effort. When the manpower shortage developed it was discovered that, because they had been denied free access to work experience, many of our Negro workers were lacking in the required skills. But a greater handicap was the fact that in many plants even qualified workers were not accepted, or were accepted only in the lower, unskilled brackets. Their employment and advancement were opposed by other workers and by many employers who, despite the long and creditable history of Negro workers in this country, insisted that Negroes could not build ships and planes and guns. Finally the President, in order to meet the emergency, was forced to issue Executive Order 8802, requiring that all war contracts should provide that there should be no discrimination in employment "because of race, creed, or national origin," and that an agency—the Fair Employment Practice Committee—should be set up to enforce this provision. While this has resulted in wider and more intelligent use of Negro labor, much time and manpower had already been wasted by the time the order was issued. And the new arrangement has been only partially successful because of continued opposition and the limited authority of the committee.

Our American policy of segregating Negroes has created an almost impossible task for the armed forces. Because of this, in the past the Navy has used Negroes only in the most limited way. The Army has, on the other hand, used Negroes as enlisted men and, to a limited degree, as officers—but always in segregated units. This arrangement has been expensive and difficult to administer, and has limited the use which the Army could make of Negro troops.

Because of the special conditions under which the Negro soldier serves and the attitudes which he encounters outside the army camps, it is difficult for him to develop a high morale. He feels that he is being asked to give his service and perhaps his life for a country that guarantees him only second-class citizenship. His segregation in the Army symbolizes the limitations he suffers as a citizen. He often feels that he is a limited kind of a soldier—outside military reservations his uniform does not secure for him the respect and consideration given to other men in uniform. In World War II it has been reported that in some unusual cases prisoners of war have been admitted to eating places in which Negro men in the uniform of their country have been denied service because of their color. If American Negro soldiers could fight in this war in voluntary, unsegregated units of Americans or with the French or Russians, the question of their morale would be less of a problem. They have already made excellent records in combat, and on today's battlefields are proving themselves able fighting men. But our discriminatory policies—our refusal to use them as widely as their capabilities deserve—are handicapping the war effort. The Negro contribution to it would be much greater if we would only allow it to be.

There is no better evidence of our conflicting racial policies than in the churches which have been the champions of Negro education. Certainly what the church has done for Negroes has been largely within the pattern of segregation. This is especially true of the Protestant churches. It seems to be less true of the Catholic church. The difference is to be found in the fact that, in most cases, a Protestant church is to some extent a social organization as well as a place of worship; the Catholic church, with its emphasis on worship, is more nearly an altar before which all men are equal.

On many Protestant churches are announcements to the effect that "all are welcome." A Negro reading this announcement knows that, in most cases, if he turned up at any of the activities he would not be welcome or the embarrassment on the part of the preacher and the congregation would be such as to destroy any sense of spiritual fellowship. These churches give money for the support of Negro schools, hospitals, and orphanages, but would be embarrassed at accepting Negro Christians into full fellowship in their church activities. In most Southern Protestant churches Negro worshipers would be seated in the gallery or otherwise segregated.

In many American cities Negro communities have grown by infiltration into old communities formerly occupied by whites. In spite of the fact that Negroes are Protestants and speak the same language as the old congregations, the churches in these areas do not, as a rule, offer any service to the incoming Negroes. The advent of Negroes is not looked upon as an opportunity for service, but as a reason for moving on.

In institutions owned and operated by the church, the segregation pattern is usually accepted—at least in a modified form. One of the largest church-controlled universities in the country, while accepting Negro students, does not allow them to live in its dormitories. Church-controlled hospitals do not, as a rule, admit Negro physicians for practice or train Negro nurses. Many of these church-controlled institutions own real estate, held in the form of endowment. Restrictive covenants as to Negro occupancy usually cover such property.

One of the great inconveniences to Negroes is the general denial of service by hotels and public eating places, in violation of the civil-rights laws. The American population is mobile. Our type of life necessitates travel. The result is our remarkable hotel system, upon which large sections of our population depend for comfort and health. In being denied access to this public service, Negroes are greatly handicapped. Anyone who knows the facts wonders how even so distinguished a person as Marian Anderson can stand up under the hardships of travel which she encounters because of the lack of hotel service.

Segregation carried to its logical conclusion is often dramatized by cruel and inhuman aspects. A few years ago a graduate of Fisk University, Miss Julie Dericott, a young woman of charm and culture, was seriously injured in an automobile accident in north Georgia. She was taken to the near-by hospital, where emergency treatment was requested. She was very fair, but when it was discovered that she was classified as a Negro, she was refused emergency treatment. She died on the long journey to Atlanta attempting to reach the nearest hospital known to give emergency treatment to colored people.

Recently in Atlanta a Negro girl stepped off the streetcar on one of the wider streets. A speeding driver knocked her down and left her lying unconscious. A crowd gathered, and one white woman who had seen the accident requested that an ambulance be called. The ambulance came, but the driver, seeing that the victim was a Negro girl, said, "We can't haul a nigger," and drove away, leaving the victim of the accident by the roadside. Such incidents are not isolated. They happen frequently and seem to be an inevitable consequence of segregation as it works out in practice in many sections of America. Most white people are not aware of them.

IV

Segregation in the South not only separates the races but symbolizes the idea of the inevitable inferiority of Negroes. It "keeps the Negro in his place," not only on the streetcars and buses, but in the social and economic system. It is more effective as a symbol than as a means of preventing contact between the races. In fact, racial contacts are more intimate in the South than in any other section of the country. Southerners as a rule do not object to contact with Negroes so long as the idea of Negro inferiority is maintained. Segregation does this. This fact explains why the South has never claimed that under segregation there are equal services for the races.

Under the new pressures that have come with the war to save democracy and the stronger pressures that will come when the war is won, the South will probably attempt to attain equal services within the framework of segregation. There are two reasons why this will not be possible—one psychological and the other practical. There will be resistance in the South to any modification of the symbol of the Negro's inferiority. When a person speaks of the Negro "getting out of hand," he usually means getting out of his inferior status. Therefore, equal service would destroy to some extent one of the chief functions of segregation. If Negroes in the South had equal service under segregation, they would have gone a long way toward "getting out of hand," because the symbolic function of segregation would have lost much of its meaning.

As a practical matter, separate but equal service under segregation cannot be rendered. Such service would require, for example, the duplication of the present most expensive phases of transportation and the duplication of the state university systems, already poorly supported. Separate and equal services for the races in the South, or any other section, are a luxury which cannot be afforded.

It is generally accepted that human beings behave better in the long run when they enjoy a maximum of freedom. Human relations are certainly more satisfactory when they are a result of free choice. Left with the maximum amount of freedom, white and colored Americans would probably adjust amicably most of the difficulties that arose between them. Under the denial of freedom which segregation enforces, there is constant and increasing friction. An examination of incidents where tension has become acute will indicate that most of the tensions are involved in and aggravated by segregation. Rioting is less frequent in mixed residential neighborhoods than elsewhere. Segregation accentuates unduly the racial factors in our civilization and obscures the wide cultural differences that exist within the racial groups. To many white people every Negro looks like every other Negro and any white man, no matter how unworthy, is better than any Negro, however distinguished. Segregation tends to make every row between a white man and a Negro, whatever the initial cause may have been, a race quarrel.

Left free, human beings group themselves according to their tastes, interests, and cultural backgrounds. American Negroes are not seeking an opportunity to mingle with whites. They desire freedom and opportunity to live as Americans. If there were no arbitrary segregation, common interests and common backgrounds would probably lead most American Negroes to develop their own way of living and find much of their association among themselves as other groups do.

Whenever the matter of freedom or equal opportunity for Negroes is discussed, the question of intermarriage usually arises. It will probably be sufficient to point out that miscegenation in this country has already gone a long way—chiefly in those very sections where the relations between whites and Negroes have been "least free" and where segregation has been most deeply rooted in law and custom. The majority of our colored people in America today are the result of racial intermixture which has taken place under segregation.

There are some evidences of changes in the pattern of American segregation—small but significant. There are evidences of dissatisfaction with it. One such evidence is the very vehement declaration by some that segregation must not and cannot be modified in any way. The advocates of segregation protest too much. In the very loudness and continuousness of their protests is one of the best evidences that the country is not satisfied and that segregation is not succeeding.

The change in government attitude is especially significant. In the past the Federal authorities, on the whole, accepted the segregated pattern of employment in government. Government work was open to Negroes only in the lower service brackets. There were many Negro messengers, porters, charwomen, but outside of the postal service no Negroes were employed in positions that required education or technical training. Negroes were excluded from restaurants in government buildings. Since the beginning of World War II this has changed, and today there are in government departments large numbers of Negro clerical workers and an increasing number of Negroes doing technical work. Here the educated Negroes are finding an opportunity for work in which they can use the training they have acquired. The Federal government will continue to be one of the large employers in the country, and its employment patterns should have real influence on other employers.

In the long run it may turn out that the new attitude of labor toward Negro workers, as expressed by the CIO, will have more significance than the changes that have taken place in government employment patterns. Officially, the CIO has abolished the color line as to opportunity and privileges for Negroes in its unions. An educational division has been created in part for the purpose of bringing the rank and file of the CIO to accept the idea of the essential unity of all American workers without regard to race. Negro workers are finding in the CIO a champion where they most need it, among the masses of workers to which most Negroes belong. The CIO is, at the moment, the most promising force for correcting the inconsistencies in our racial patterns. Furthermore, its policy is already having an effect upon older, more conservative unions and is giving support to many liberal-minded employers who are willing to give Negro workers a chance.

Another source of encouragement is the growing pressure within and without the South for some kind of change. This will probably lead to an effort to furnish equal but separate services to the races. While such an effort cannot succeed, it will certainly result in some improvement of service to Negroes under segregation. In the long run it may lead to the modification of the present patterns of segregation in the South. How rapidly and how far these changes will go depends upon many factors, chief of which are the strength of the growing liberal movement in the South and the amount of political influence Southern Negroes acquire.

V

In the acquisition of political power lies one of the Negro's great hopes for improving his status. Certainly the Negro's vote in border and Northern states will hold for him the gains made in government employment. The organized political power of the CIO is on his side; through its affiliation with Negro political groups and its fight in behalf of all liberal movements, it gives the Negro real help in obtaining the things all citizens want. By the strength of their votes and increasing political representation, Negroes could get better schools, housing, health facilities—all the public services. And they could use their influence to assure the enforcement of the civil-rights statutes that are already enacted.

For example, New York is America's most liberal city. Negroes in New York have more political influence than in any other city in America. New York is a city of hotels which deny service to Negroes. New York State has good civil-rights laws. It would seem reasonable to expect that before much longer New York hotels may find themselves liberalizing their service to Negro travelers. Such a thing—if it could be brought about—would have an influence that would be far-reaching. To achieve it would be a good use of the power of New York's able Negro political leadership.

Under the Constitution, as liberally interpreted by our present Supreme Court, many of the legal devices by which segregation is protected could no doubt be declared unconstitutional if properly presented to the court. This has already been done in important fields. Even though the Gaines decision has not yet put any colored students in the University of Missouri, the fact that prevailing systems of segregation in higher education are unconstitutional has caused uneasiness in the states where such systems prevail. Since the Supreme Court decision declaring the "white" Texas primary unconstitutional, it is apparent that political participation of Negroes in the South has been greatly accelerated.

There is no doubt that the Negro vote, the power of labor, and government attitudes can profoundly affect our racial practices. If the church, with its strong influence, also took a firm stand, the process could be accelerated. And there are some indications that church leaders are becoming aware of the feebleness of their position. One well-known theological seminary in the South has seriously considered service to Negroes. Opposition was so strong that the idea had to be given up. The American Protestant church has ambitions for extension into Africa and Asia. Its racial policies at home stand in the way. Increasing numbers of American church leaders realize the far-reaching effect of American racial segregation on the influence of the church abroad. Because of this, within the next few years the patterns of segregation within the church and church institutions in America may be greatly modified in the direction of a more democratic and more Christian practice. The church has wide contacts with many classes and kinds of people in this country. Whatever it might do in the interest of a policy of non-segregation within the local churches and church institutions would be leaven widely placed in American life.

Most white Americans are puzzled and alarmed by the impatience and bitterness of large sections of our Negro population. They feel that Negroes are no longer pleasant to live with. Whites are inclined to charge this to some subversive influence from the outside. Many Southerners say that agitators from the North are responsible for stirring up Negroes in the South. In other sections of the country Negro resentment and unrest are usually charged to Communists or whatever bogy happens to be current in the mind of the community.

That there is unrest and bitterness among our Negro population is a fact. This unrest is to be found not just among Negro intellectuals; it exists also in the alleys of our Negro ghettos and among the remote and inarticulate Negro sharecroppers and common laborers. It will not pass with the war. Negroes were probably never so docile as they seemed. The trouble is that they behave like other human beings. In subjecting Negroes to American education we have made them Americans. So completely American are they that they will not submit passively to being pushed around as they are under segregation. Educational opportunity for the common man is a part of the American way of life. In giving it to Negroes, we have let them in on the meaning of democracy. Their unrest under their special limitations is the result not of sinister influence from the outside but of our education, which, with all its faults, is the best thing in our democracy.

The education of Negroes in America has not been a mistake. Here we see American faith and American idealism at their best. Segregation, on the other hand, is rooted in fear and in doubt as to whether our democratic principles will really work. It remains to be seen whether or not our faith in democracy is strong enough to overcome our fears as to what may be some of its consequences.

MEMORANDUM TO JUNIOR HOSTESSES

Margaret Halsey

Margaret Halsey first hit the best-seller list with a little bombshell called With Malice toward Some. *Her recent* Some of My Best Friends Are Soldiers *has had the same sort of success. She wrote this memo while serving as a hostess at the Stage Door Canteen.*

QUITE A FEW OF YOU have asked me questions recently having to do with the Negroes at the Stage Door Canteen, so I think I had better explain the matter in its entirety.

The Canteen's policy about Negroes is based on a quotation which runs as follows: "We hold these truths to be self-evident: That all men are created equal. . . ." I'm sure all of you know where that comes from.

The Canteen's policy about Negroes is also based on the Fourteenth and Fifteenth amendments to the Constitution of the United States, in which it is specifically stated that nobody is to be denied the rights, privileges, and immunities of American citizenship on account of race, creed, or color.

One hears a good deal of talk, in some circles, about the reds and long-haired radicals who want to tear down the Constitution. The reds and long-haired radicals only *want* to tear it down. The people who deny Negroes democratic equality actually *are* tearing it down.

I know that some of you on our shift are very deeply prejudiced against accepting Negroes as your social equals. You can't be blamed for having that prejudice in the first place. It was taught to you when you were too young and helpless to be critical. But you certainly can be blamed for hanging on to the prejudice when (a) you are now old enough to know better; (b) you are being given, in the Canteen, a golden opportunity to come into contact with Negroes under the best possible circumstances and find out what they are really like.

Let's examine the feeling that some of you have against, for instance, dancing with Negro servicemen and see what it really amounts to.

There is no scientific basis for the notion that Negroes are inferior to white people. A scientist, given a collection of human brains pickled in alcohol, cannot tell which ones belonged to Negroes and which to white people. You can check this statement in any good reference library. Intelligence depends on the number and fineness of the convolutions in the brain. It has absolutely nothing to do with the amount of pigment in the skin. If it had, you would all be much stupider when you are sunburned.

Actually, I don't believe any of you are very deeply concerned with Negro intelligence. What worries you more is the fear of rape. You unconsciously, but very arrogantly, assume that no male Negro can so much as glance at you without wanting to get you with child. The truth is, that while you are an extremely attractive group of young women, there isn't one single one of you who's *that* good. Negro males react to you no more and no less than white males. As women, you know in your hearts that men of any description respond to you pretty much as you intend them to respond. This is especially true in the Canteen, which has hardly any points of resemblance at all to a lonely, moonlit shrubbery.

The real basis of prejudice against Negroes is economic and historical, not sexual or psychological. The people who talk about "keeping the niggers in their place" never admit this, because it doesn't show them in an entirely favorable light. Such people prefer to fall back on more melodramatic arguments, usually (a) the honor of their women and (b) the danger of a Negro revolt. Neither of these two arguments stands up very well under close inspection.

Revolt is a troublesome and dangerous occupation. People will put up with an awful lot before they resort to it. If the Negroes ever do rise in the night sometime and murder every white man south of the Mason-Dixon Line, it will be because those white men richly deserved it. But there's one way to make absolutely certain that neither the Negroes nor any other section of our population feel impelled to rebel. That is to see that they have nothing to rebel about. If Negroes have the same education, the same housing, the same jobs, the same opportunities, and the same social treatment as all the other citizens in this country—all of which things we promised them in the Declaration of Independence and again in the Constitution—they will have no more impulse to rise against us than redheads, stamp collectors, and sufferers from stomach ulcer have the impulse to rise against us.

The other argument, about the honor of our women, collapses even faster than the one about revolt. Women—ask the man who owns one—can take care of themselves a good deal better than they ever let on. The way to protect your honor is to be honorable. If white people stood, in the minds of the Negroes, for fair play and justice and real democracy, they wouldn't ever have to worry about either sexual or non-sexual assaults.

The real reason back of the refusal of some of you to mingle with Negroes at the Canteen isn't nearly as romantic and dramatic as you like to think it is. The real reason has nothing to do with rape, seduction, and risings in the night. The real reason can be summed up in two extremely unromantic little words: cheap labor. As long as you treat Negroes as subhumans, you don't have to pay them so much. When you refuse to dance with Negro servicemen at the Canteen, you are neither protecting your honor nor making sure that white Southerners won't have their homes burned down around their ears. All you are doing is making it possible for employers all over the country to get Negroes to work for them for less money than those employers would have to pay you.

Do you find that romantic?

You don't live in a romantic age. You live in a machine age, and it's getting more machinery every day. In the old days large groups of people could live out their entire lives without ever finding out what other large groups of people were doing. That is no longer possible. Unless you can de-invent the airplane and cause it to fall into general disuse, you are going to spend an increasing amount of your time mingling with Negroes, Russians, Chinamen, Patagonians, and all sorts of hitherto-unfamiliar people this side of accredited lepers. You might as well get used to it here and now, on Sunday nights at the Canteen. It will save you a lot of trouble later on.

In our world we have radios, telephones, bathtubs, air-cooling, vitamin pills, and sulfa drugs, but we no longer have any group privacy. We can no longer wrap ourselves up in the comforting notion that we are better than other sorts of people. Our own inventions drop these other sorts of people right into our laps, and we either have to get along with them or watch our inventions—along with a lot of other things we hold dear—go crashing into the dust in a series of obliterating wars. There's only one possible basis for getting along with other sorts of people, and that basis is equality. Real, genuine, three-ply, copper-bottomed equality. If we have any secret yearning to think of ourselves as a Master Race, we have only to pick up a newspaper to see that nobody is giving odds on Master Races these days.

One word of warning before I close. Don't be surprised if you find some of the Negro servicemen sullen and unresponsive and some of them aggressive and too responsive. The war has put the Negroes in a hell of a spot. We need them in the war effort, so we've been forced to give them more equality than we were ever willing to concede before. They aren't used to it, and neither are we. There are bound to be awkwardnesses and mistakes on both sides. If there are, remember that they are inevitable and take them in your stride.

Try to be a little imaginative and put yourself in the Negro's place. When you go into the Canteen, nothing worse can happen to you than getting tired or being bored. When a Negro goes into the Canteen, he has no reason to suppose he won't be snubbed by one of the girls on our shift or openly insulted by a Southern soldier whose "superiority" has not been noticeably enhanced by rye with beer chasers. Naturally the Negroes are nervous and very possibly may not behave with Chesterfieldian calm. You wouldn't either, under the same circumstances.

The main thing to remember is this: The Negroes aren't under any obligation to behave better than we do. They didn't come to this country because they wanted to. We brought them here in chains. They didn't write the Declaration of Independence or the Constitution. We wrote those documents, and if we now wave them in the Negroes' faces and say, "Ha-ha! Practical joke!", we must expect to meet the customary fate of practical jokers. We kept the Negroes in official slavery until 1864, and we've kept them in unofficial slavery ever since. If you meet a Negro serviceman at the Canteen whose conduct doesn't come up to your delicate and exacting standards of behavior, just don't forget this one thing —whatever he is, you made him that way.

As a matter of fact, you meet plenty of white servicemen whose conduct fails to enthrall. Few outsiders realize, but all of us know, that being a Junior Hostess and entertaining unselected strangers for three and a half hours is difficult at best. You only make it more difficult when you artificially set aside a portion of these strangers as targets for unreasonable, unscientific, and undemocratic emotion. If you'd just relax and keep your pores open, there wouldn't be any "Negro problem."

DEMOCRACY IS FOR THE UNAFRAID

Chester B. Himes

Chester B. Himes, who was brought up in Cleveland, has written numerous short stories. He worked in Los Angeles war plants gathering material for a novel to be published in the fall, called If He Hollers Let Him Go.

WHAT FRIGHTENS ME MOST today is not the recurring race riots, the economic pressures on "minorities," the internment of Americans of darker-skinned ancestry whose loyalty to the ideology of white supremacy is doubted, nor even the whole scope and viciousness of the recent growth of race hatreds and the insidious beginning of propagandism for a white alliance for "self-protection"—not these so much as the white man's sudden consciousness of his own fear of other races, of which these are but manifestations. I can see no hope for any "minority" group, nor even for democracy itself, in the existence of this fear.

People who are afraid are cruel, vicious, furtive, dangerous; they are dishonest, malicious, vindictive; they destroy the things of which they are afraid, or are destroyed by them. The host who is afraid, hearing a noise in his kitchen, tiptoes down the back stairs and blows out the brains of an icebox raiding guest whom he thinks is a burglar; the policeman who is afraid shoots the manacled prisoner who bends to tie his shoelace; the industrialist who is afraid hires thugs and murderers to fight unionists; the capitalist who is afraid sabotages public welfare; the politician who is afraid attacks leaders of weakly supported causes to hide his own compromises; the statesman who is afraid endeavors to isolate his nation; and the government head who is afraid fails in the execution of laws, both national and international.

A race that is afraid bands in mobs to lynch, murder, intimidate, and destroy members of other races. Long ago we realized the Nazis did not hate the Jewish people so much as fear them. Members of the Ku Klux Klan, Silvershirts, Bundists, and other similar American organizations whose aims are the destruction and intimidation of certain racial and religious groups are cowards from the word *go;* they are as representative of cowardly people as the storm troopers are of Nazism. Only cowards seek to destroy "minority" groups; courageous people are not afraid of them. In themselves such people are not dangerous. In themselves the cowardly are never dangerous, never more dangerous than Hitler in 1930. But when they become representative of the majority race within a nation, when they infect the entire body with their own cowardice, then a complete breakdown of law and decency follows, and all persons not contained in that race suffer the most cruel oppression.

This is what I fear is happening in America today—the cowardice of a relatively small percentage of white Americans is seeping into the consciousness of the majority and making them all afraid of the darker races. No thinking person, especially no thinking Negro, wants this to happen, for such fear, he knows, will drive them first to destroy the Negro in America.

Perhaps because the white man has always realized how greatly he is outnumbered by the dark peoples of the world, he has always had fear of them tucked away in his subconsciousness. Today shortened horizons are bringing white and colored abruptly face to face, and the fear is breaking out. We find it in the insidious advocacy of a white alliance which would perhaps include Germany after the Hitler regime has been overthrown. We find it in a Jim Crow Army that sends unarmed Negro soldiers into a hostile South to be booted and lynched by white civilians. We find it in a question which keeps coming back to mind—are we seeking the defeat of our "Aryan" enemies or the winning of them?

Fear may easily become the greatest tragedy of this historic period. For the eventual peace of the world and the continuation of progress depend upon the white man's ability to live in equality, integrity, and courage in a civilization where he is outnumbered by peoples of other races. *It is imperative that he be unafraid.* For if, because of his fear, he finds himself unable to live as a neighbor and equal competitor with other races, there will be no peace and little progress.

What concerns me more at the present is that, if the white man is not unafraid, the United States will never attain democracy.

Dictatorship is not so much a government *for* the weak and the afraid, but *of* the weak and the afraid. With even one dictatorship remaining in the world after the war, there will soon be another struggle. The fear of dictators is an evil and tremendous thing; they are afraid of everything that does not agree with them and of most things that do. Because of this, driven by it, struggling desperately to overcome it, dictators will always try to enslave the world. They have to; they cannot otherwise exist. Many of us have yet to understand this. We have also to understand that in the growing weakness of the white race in America, as demonstrated by its present fear-driven actions, dictatorship may come to the United States before we know what true democracy is like.

For democracy is for the unafraid. It sprang from the minds of people who were unafraid and was intended for them. Had our forefathers been cowardly, we would have had no Declaration of Independence. (Can you imagine our present congressmen saying, and meaning: "Give me democracy or give me death!" or our capitalists posing this question: "Is white supremacy so false and white leadership so precarious as to be upheld by lies, hate, and violence?") No, we would not even have our semblance of democracy; we would have no Constitution, no history and heritage of pride. The decision our colonial forefathers had to make in 1776, of rejecting England's tyranny, was a decision harder than today's, of granting all of America's varying ethnic groups full participation in democracy. The price they had to pay in human blood and sacrifice was a price greater by far than even the most rabid Southerner predicts, should Negroes be granted their democratic rights now.

In the winter of 1777–78, when the Army of Independence hovered at Valley Forge, hungry, ragged, and dispirited, a single thread of fear would have lost for us our nation. The very structure and existence of democracy depends upon the courage of its people; upon their ability to impart fairness, exact justice, and correct evils. It exists only in the premise that its adherents are not afraid to accept the fundamental fact of mankind's equality, to guarantee that it shall be preserved in all the circumstances of life.

Any Negro family could live in happiness and accord in a neighborhood of white Southerners—if the white families were unafraid. With confidence in the execution and administration of their laws, the whites could not be afraid that Negroes would slit their throats, rape their daughters, or burn their homes. With confidence in their schools, which Negroes would of course attend, they could have no fear of Negroes' lack of sanitation, convention, decency, and quietness—which they would learn along with whites. With confidence in their own sagacity and intelligence, they could have no fear of Negroes ruining their business by competition or fleecing them out of their wealth by cunning. With confidence in their own democratic ideology, the thought could never occur to them that Negroes are not ready for democracy; it would be part of their unchangeable convictions that since the signing of the Declaration of Independence the simple fact of being born within the boundaries of the territory of the United States is all that insures any person—white or colored—his democratic rights and privileges. Nor could the thought occur that the presence of a Negro family in their community would bring them disgrace or shame: they would feel the Negro family not only had a right to live in the community, but was part of it. With confidence in their own children, were they all agreed that Negroes were atypical or socially distasteful, they could have no fear that their sons or daughters would marry into the Negro family. What kind of logic is it, incidentally, that makes people cry over "black mammies" who, they admit, raised them and taught them the fundamentals of virtue, religion, and decency, and then lynch their "black mammies'" sons?

When the white man banishes his fear, he will banish with it all the bugaboos of race; and he himself will for the first time be free. For people who nurture race hatreds and dedicate their lives to the proposition that they are superior are never free; their thoughts, efforts, and aims are always limited and hindered by the necessity of proving it.

I once heard a rich and famous white man relate how he freed his mind of all thoughts of race and color and looked upon all peoples as equal in an effort to learn, if possible, whether there was any fundamental and distinguishable difference in peoples of different races. He realized that, having been brought up in a tradition of white superiority, this would be impossible as long as he could identify people. So he pretended an eye infection and for a month went about with his eyes bandaged.

For the first time in his life as a rich, famous, white American he felt free. He was relieved of the necessity of pretending superiority, of hating people because of their color, of despising people because of their race; he did not every moment have to be aware of his reactions; he did not have to feel affronted, disgraced, humiliated, tolerant, condescending, or philanthropic because of another person's physical attributes or identifiable religious beliefs; his mind was free from all the psychoses of race antagonisms.

War is teaching this lesson of equality to many of our youths in uniform. Coming upon the bodies of two soldiers lying face downward in the muck of a distant battlefield, both having died for the preservation of the same ideal, under the same flag, in the same uniform, they are learning the ridiculousness of thinking: "This man, being white, is superior to that man, who is black." They have learned that in a week's time the color which made one "better" than the other will have gone from both.

Here at home white Americans must learn courage, too. They must learn that Negroes and members of other races working and living side by side with them in a community of interests do not detract from their prestige but add to it; that equal participation by all peoples in the benefits of democracy is not a thing to bring disgrace but a thing to inspire praise and create pride. They must learn that bravery does not consist in persecuting the few and the weak (for then all our enemies would be the bravest of nations) but of protecting them.

The white race has attained leadership in the world of today. Although people of other races have played a magnificent part, the white race is largely responsible for the creation of our present civilization. So far much of the white race's talent, its ingenuity, creative genius, and ability to organize, produce, and conquer have been employed to subdue and exploit the other races of the world. While the mechanics of this civilization may continue for many centuries to come, its character is bound to change, for the other races of the world have reached the point where they will no longer be exploited or subdued.

Now this is the question: Is the white race courageous enough to accept the inevitable, to accept the fact that exploitation and oppression of other races is no longer physically or materially possible, and to continue its leadership in integrity and equality, competing with other races in fairness while respecting their rights of self-determination, meeting with them and negotiating justice and equity for all, dealing with them in culture and commerce? Or is it afraid of ultimate extermination or subjugation?

No thinking Negro prays for black supremacy; he does not want any kind of supremacy—black, white, or indifferent. He prays the white race will have sufficient strength and courage to be unafraid of democracy. For he knows there are much greater things to fear than racial equality—the historic tragedy of Nazism, for instance, or the unutterable chaos of a race war.

ADDRESSED TO WHITE LIBERALS

Lillian Smith

Lillian Smith is the author of Strange Fruit *and comes from a Southern background. She lives in Georgia, where, with Paula Snelling, she publishes the liberal magazine* South Today.

WE ARE FACING a serious racial crisis in our American life today, a crisis that cannot be met in the old way or with the old answers if we are to avoid tragedy. The hopeless believe this tragedy is unavoidable. But those of us who believe in the power of the creative mind cannot accept such defeatism. We know there is a way out if we can but find it. Many of us are searching for that way, though some still refuse to leave the old path, retracing their steps again and again in circles, as all lost men tend to do.

I believe we can find the way if we are willing to look in a new direction for the source of our trouble. We have looked at the "Negro problem" long enough. Now the time has come for us to right-about-face and study the problem of the white man: the deep-rooted needs that have caused him to seek those strange, regressive satisfactions that are derived from worshiping his own skin color. The white man himself is one of the world's most urgent problems today; not the Negro, not other colored races. We whites must learn to confess this.

There are many among us who think of segregation as merely a Southern tradition, a Southern "custom" that grew out of poverty, out of certain economic patterns, out of certain racial dilemmas, when in reality segregation is an ancient psychological mechanism used by men the world over whenever they want to shut themselves away from problems which they fear and do not feel they have the strength to solve. When men get into trouble they tend to put barriers between themselves and their difficulties. We white people got into deep trouble long ago when we attempted to enslave other human beings. A trouble we have never faced and never tried with all our strength to solve. Instead, to shut our troubles from us, we have used a mechanism so destructive that it, in itself, has become a menace to the health of our culture and our individual souls. For segregation as a way of life—or shall we say *a way of death*—is cultural schizophrenia, bearing a curious resemblance to the schizophrenia of individual personality. It is chilling to note the paranoid symptoms of those among us who cling to segregation: their violence, their sensitiveness to criticism, their stereotyped defenses, their inability to identify their overesteem of themselves with the emotional needs of others, their reluctance to reach out and accept new ideas, their profound desire to withdraw from everything hard to face, everything that requires of their personalities further growth.

Those who believe in this philosophy of segregation have chosen the schizophrenic way: withdrawing from reality; and this withdrawal has profoundly affected their minds and emotions.

It is the *effect of segregation* upon the human beings who segregate as well as upon those who are segregated that should concern us all. For we cannot consider racial segregation (and its counterparts, political and economic isolationism) apart from man's whole personality, apart from his whole culture. We cannot separate men's specific needs from the destructive effects of a *way of life* that attempts to withdraw from reality; nor can we meet these specific ends, one by one, first, and then hope that somehow in the shuffle this schizophrenic philosophy of death will change into a philosophy of creative living.

Hard as it is to acknowledge, the simple truth is that the South's and the nation's racial problems cannot be solved by putting a loaf of bread, a book, and a ballot in everyone's hand. I am not unsympathetic to those among us who are trying to believe that the loaf, the book, the ballot are all the Negro needs—or wants. I understand the desperate fear that causes certain Negroes to deny their hunger for things that make men human. I understand also the fear in the white man's heart that makes him more willing to work for specific, short-range goals, such as the vote, better schools, better jobs for Negroes, than to change his own attitude about himself and his white race.

These fears, these emotional hungers, need to be faced and understood by all of us, though it will not be easy for white or black to face them.

A first step is to acknowledge that man is not an economic or political unit. To pretend that he is, is to ignore personality and cheapen the human spirit. And by ignoring man's psychological needs, by pretending to ourselves that his economic or political status is more important than his personality status, we oversimplify a complex, subtle, tragically profound problem and fail miserably in our efforts to solve it. As we have been failing for almost a century.

We whites cling desperately to the belief that the problem of race relations is the "Negro problem," that it is a matter of economics, that it will take a long time to "educate the Negro." Why? Because we dare not face the fact that race prejudice and the cultural and psychological patterns of segregation which have grown out of the white man's complex feelings about skin color profoundly affect us and our children on every level of our life and culture. We dare not acknowledge and meet in a creative way those emotional needs within our own families that, in a white-supremacy culture, we have been permitted to project upon the Negro, making him our scapegoat, using him as our psychological safety valve. Upon whom can we turn our hate if we no longer can turn it upon him? To whom can we feel superior, if we bring the Negro up to us on a level of human equality? We say it will "take a long time" for the Negro to "get to the place where he is worthy of democracy." Some of us, I fear, hope it will take a long time—*because we do not know what we shall do* with our own fears and hates when we can no longer take them out on the Negro or on some other scapegoat. We hope "it will be a long time" before we have to change our own selves, our attitudes toward sex, our family patterns; before we have to find new outlets for old frustrations, not only economic frustrations but those deeper hungers of our emotional lives that in our culture are too often left unsatisfied. These are complex, difficult problems which must be probed more deeply before we shall fully understand them, and before we can confess their implications for our personal lives.

It is easier, however, to see the immediate effects of racial segregation upon children. We know a child's personality cannot grow and mature without self-esteem, without feelings of security, without faith in the world's willingness to make room for him to live as a human being. Self-esteem and emotional security are to character what vitamins are to the body. No colored child in our country, however protected within the family, is being given today what his personality needs in order to grow and mature fully and richly. No white child, under the segregation pattern, North or South, can be free of arrogance, hardness of heart, blindness to human needs. The bitter and inescapable fact is that our children, white and colored, are growing distorted, twisted personalities within the crippling frame of segregation which we have imposed upon them.

I personally would prefer that my own child do without shoes than that he do without the esteem of his fellows, and I would prefer that he never look into a book than that he look down upon another human being. Of course I want him to know what is in books, but I want him much more to know what is in men's hearts. This he can never learn unless he looks at them with level eyes. Shoes are important for both white and colored feet—who would deny this! But a child can go barefooted without great harm; he cannot go one day unesteemed by his fellows without deep injury to his personality. Our children, Negro and white, need all of these things, but will probably have little of them as long as we refuse to acknowledge them as human beings in *need of that which makes men human.*

Believing this, I cannot endure the idea so many liberals hold that segregation must change slowly. I believe it can change as rapidly as each of us can change his own heart. I believe it will never change until we look at what it is doing to the personality and character of every child, every grownup, white and colored, in the South today—and to a less bitter degree throughout the country. Segregation is spiritual lynching. The lynched and the lynchers are our own people, ourselves, *our children.*

These are grave matters, troubling matters, which I feel must be faced, analyzed. For problems must be enunciated before we can know clearly what they are. We who do not believe in segregation as a way of life must say so. We must break the conspiracy of silence which has held us in a grip so strong that it has become a taboo. We must say why segregation is unendurable to the human spirit. We must somehow find the courage to say it aloud. For, however we rationalize our silence, it is fear that is holding our tongues today. A widespread denial of a belief in segregation and all that it implies will shake this way of life to its roots. Each of us in his heart knows this. In the beginning was the Word, and today the Word is powerful. To remain silent while the demagogues, the Negro haters, the racists, the mentally ill, loudly reaffirm their faith in segregation and the spiritual lynching which their way of life inflicts is to be traitorous to everything that is good and creative and sane in human values. I believe the time has come when we must take our stand.

THE TOUCHIN' CASE OF MR. AND MRS. MASSA

St. Clair McKelway

As S. M., St. Clair McKelway is a well-known contributor to the New Yorker. *He is a lieutenant colonel in the Army and when last heard from was somewhere in India.*

Oh, let's fix us a julep and kick us a houn'
(Sing "Yassah! Yassah! Yassah!")
And let's dig a place in de col', col' groun'
For Mr. and Mrs. Massa!

[*Boogie-woogie*]

Oh, this Mr. and Mrs. Massa have always lived in old Virginia and old North Carolina and old South Carolina and old Alabama and old Kentucky and old So Forth and old So On and nobody has ever understood the colored people the way they do because down in old So Forth and old So On is where the white folks understand the colored folks like no other white folks on earth understand colored folks. Yassah, Massa! Yassah!

[*Boogie-woogie*]

Oh, before the war and for some time afterward Mr. and Mrs. Massa understood the colored folks so well that they had a washerwoman they paid $1.50 a week and a cook they paid $1.75 a week and a butler they paid $2.25 a week and it was mighty lucky for these colored folks that the washerwoman was the cook's mother and the butler was the cook's husband because this enabled the three of them to live cozily in the fifth one-room shack from the left on the other side of the railroad tracks and thus pay $0.85 less a week for rent than the total of their combined salaries.

[*Boogie-woogie*]

Oh, and over and above the total of their combined salaries Mrs. Massa every other week gave the cook a ham bone outright and Mr. Massa every other month gave the butler a whole quarter of a dollar extra right out of a clear sky. It was manna, Mammy! Manna!

[*Boogie-woogie*]

Oh, but after the war had been going along for a while the butler, whose name was Charles F. Parker, came to Mr. Massa and told him he was going to quit because he had been offered a job as a counterman in the cafeteria of a defense plant at a salary of $15 a week plus three meals a day and Mr. Massa understood the colored folks so well he told Charles F. Parker that up to then he (Mr. Massa) had been able through influence to persuade the local draft board not to draft him (Charles F. Parker) but that if he (Charles F. Parker) quit his job as butler he (Mr. Massa) would have to persuade the draft board to go ahead and draft him (Charles F. Parker). Swing low, sweet Lincoln!

[*Boogie-woogie*]

Oh, but then Charles F. Parker told Mr. Massa that as he (Charles F. Parker) understood the situation after conversations with the draft board he (Charles F. Parker) had already been classed as 4-F owing to a number of physical disabilities, including chronic hoecake poisoning, and that therefore he thought he would take the job at the defense-plant cafeteria but with all due respect to Mr. Massa, etc. and etc. Hit that hoecake, boys! Hit it!

[*Boogie-woogie*]

Oh, so Mr. and Mrs. Massa saw the straws in the wind, saw which way the wind was blowing, and also recognized the trend of the time, so they took another tack, changed face, turned over new leaves, and each gave Charles F. Parker fifteen cents as a bonus and wished him success in his new job and raised the washerwoman (Esther G. Henderson) from $1.50 a week to $1.75 a week and raised the cook (Mrs. Charles F. Parker) from $1.75 a week to $1.85 a week with the understanding that Mrs. Esther G. Henderson would help out Mrs. Charles F. Parker in the kitchen and that Mrs. Charles F. Parker would wait on the table. Pass the hominy grits, boys! Pass it!

[*Boogie-woogie*]

Oh, but at the end of the first week under the new arrangement Mrs. Charles F. Parker came to Mrs. Massa and said she was going to quit because she had been offered a job as cook at the defense-plant cafeteria at a salary of $22.50 per week plus three meals a day and Mrs. Massa jus' had to cry. Weep some mo', my lady, oh, weep some mo'!

[*Boogie-woogie*]

Oh, and then the washerwoman (Esther G. Henderson) came to Mrs. Massa and said she was going to quit because she was eighty-two years old and her back ached and her daughter and son-in-law were going to support her for nothing, and Mrs. Massa jus' had to cry some mo'!

[*Boogie-woogie*]

Oh, and then one day a week after that Mr. and Mrs. Massa were walking back home after a dinner at the Old Southern Greek Chophouse and they saw Charles F. Parker and Mrs. Charles F. Parker and Esther G. Henderson coming out of the colored section of a movie house after having seen a Technicolored feature featuring Jack Benny and Mr. and Mrs. Massa noticed that Charles F. Parker had on a new suit and looked happy and that Mrs. Charles F. Parker had on a new dress and looked happy and that Esther G. Henderson had on a new shawl and looked happy and moreover was still laughing at the jokes Jack Benny had made inside the movie house and Mr. and Mrs. Massa saw the three of them go into a three-room stucco bungalow where Esther G. Henderson had a room all to herself and Mr. and Mrs. Charles F. Parker had a room all to themselves and then Mr. and Mrs. Massa looked at each other understandingly and tears came into the eyes of Mrs. Massa and Mr. Massa put his hand on her shoulder and said to her softly, "Nevah you mind, there'll be a reckonin' one of these days!"

[*Boogie-woogie*]

Oh, and so Mr. and Mrs. Massa finally closed up the house in old So Forth and old So On and came to New York and leased a suite at the Savoy-Plaza and the Savoy-Netherlands and the Savoy-So Forth and the Savoy-So On and any time you want to listen day or night as well as any time you don't want to listen day or night they will tell you for hours without stopping how they understand the colored people like no other white folks on earth understand colored folks and how the war and high wages are jus' ruinin' everything down in old So Forth and old So On and how never you mind there's goin' to be a reckonin' one of these days. Reckon twice and hit it again, boys! Hit it!

[*Boogie-woogie*]

Oh, and the bones of Mr. and Mrs. Massa are not growing cold and their heads are not bending low and no angel voices are calling to them and if nobody will carry them back to old So Forth and old So On, oh, then . . .

[*Boogie-woogie*]

Let's fix us a julep and kick as a houn'
(Sing "Yassah! Yassah! Yassah!")
And let's dig a place in de col', col' groun'
For Mr. and Mrs. Massa!